PERSONALITY AND THE BEHAVIOR DISORDERS

—

IN TWO VOLUMES

Edith O. Mercer.

PERSONALITY

and the

BEHAVIOR DISORDERS

A HANDBOOK BASED ON EXPERIMENTAL
AND CLINICAL RESEARCH

Edited by

J. McV. HUNT

DIRECTOR, INSTITUTE OF WELFARE RESEARCH, COMMUNITY SERVICE
SOCIETY OF NEW YORK. FORMERLY, ASSOCIATE PROFESSOR OF
PSYCHOLOGY, BROWN UNIVERSITY

VOLUME II

THE RONALD PRESS COMPANY ⋅ NEW YORK

CONTENTS

VOLUME II

PART V

DETERMINANTS OF PERSONALITY—EXPERIENTIAL AND SOCIOLOGICAL

PART VI

SOME OUTSTANDING PATTERNS OF BEHAVIOR DISORDER

PART VII

SOME INVESTIGATED CORRELATES OF BEHAVIOR DISORDER

CONTENTS

CONTENTS

By DONALD B. LINDSLEY, PH.D., Associate Professor of Psychology, Brown University; Director of Neurophysiology, Laboratory and Psychology Department, The Emma Pendleton Bradley Home

PART VIII

THERAPY AND THE PREVENTION OF BEHAVIOR DISORDERS

By KENNETH E. APPEL, M.D., Lecturer in Psychiatry, University of Pennsylvania; and a Psychiatrist, The Pennsylvania Hospital

By GEORGE S. STEVENSON, M.D., Medical Director, Inc., National Committee for Mental Hygiene

PART V

DETERMINANTS OF PERSONALITY— EXPERIENTIAL AND SOCIOLOGICAL

Chapter 20

INFANTILE EXPERIENCE IN RELATION TO PERSONALITY DEVELOPMENT

By MARGARET A. RIBBLE, M.D.

INFANTILE EXPERIENCE as an important dynamic factor in the determination of adult personality has received little attention outside the field of psychoanalysis until recent years. The first edition of Murchison's (1931) *Handbook of Child Psychology* carried no chapter on the neonate, and Pratt's (1933) chapter in the second edition contains no discussion of the effects of the newborn's experience on his later development. The most detailed studies of infancy which we now have, those of Gesell at Yale (see: Gesell, 1929; Gesell and Thompson, 1934; Gesell and Amatruda, 1941) and those of C. Bühler (1930) in Vienna, deal for the most part with the ontogenetic patterning of behavior and with the responses which may be elicited at the various ages. We have in American psychology no longitudinal observations concerning the effect on the progress of this patterning of such highly personal factors as difficulty in the organization of primary body functions, or of the influence of differing kinds of mothering which may be skilful and tender, meager and inconsistent, or actually damaging because of fixed emotional attitudes or actual neurosis in the mother.

It appears to have been the general opinion of both psychologists and pediatricians that if an infant is properly fed and protected against cold and infection, his abilities and personality will develop as fully as his heredity and native endowment warrant. It seems to have been assumed that his emotional and social characteristics are essentially predetermined by genetic control.

Yet it is reasonable enough to suppose that the sensitive organism of the human infant would register the effects of experiences related to body security and well-being or to insecurity and lack of personal care.[1] Once registered, these experiences of security or insecurity would be expected to foster responses of positive groping on the one hand, or of negative resistance or withdrawal on the other. These early mechanisms of

---

[1] It is known in this connection that conditioned responses can be established in the newborn (Marquis, 1931) and that their activity cycle can be altered by variations in their feeding schedule (Marquis, 1941). (Editor)

reaction might then readily gain momentum so as to alter or even to distort the succeeding phases of personality development.

Indeed, the establishment of the biogenetic or developmental approach to the problems of personality makes it unnecessary to do much supposing. Our knowledge of infancy and its biopsychological significance is growing rapidly. We know well that personality is a consequence not only of an evolution from within but also of the effects of repeated experiences through which a relationship is established with the mother and with the immediate environment, particularly with that part of it which satisfies the needs of life. Contributions from the fields of prenatal development (Minkowski, 1921; Snyder and Rosenfeld, 1937a, 1937b, 1938), neuroembryology (Coghill, 1929; Detweiler, 1936; Grinker, 1937, Ch. 1) have clarified our thinking about the evolution of awareness. In the field of experimental biology, Levy (1934, 1938) and Hunt (1941) have added further information with experimental control of the life histories of animals. It is gradually becoming evident that the psychological care of the infant is fully as important for his emotional, intellectual, and social development as is careful feeding for adequate nutrition and good digestive functioning.

Freud's Theory of Psychosexual Development [2]

A remarkable and stimulating contribution to our conception of personality development has been made by Sigmund Freud. Through the technique of psychoanalysis, which includes free association (see Freud, 1910; Chapter 7 by French; Chapter 6 by White), dream analysis (Freud, 1900), and the technique of analyzing and utilizing the transference situation (Freud, 1904a, 1912), Freud was enabled to probe deeply into the unconscious layers of the personalities of adult patients and to reconstruct their developmental histories. A rich clinical experience in the study and treatment of neurotic individuals revealed consistently that their sufferings derived from a struggle to repress or to disguise infantile pleasure strivings connected with basic bodily functions. Of the nature of this struggle, these neurotic individuals were unaware; they perceived only such superficial effects as their symptoms and their sufferings (Breuer and Freud, 1893; Freud, 1895, 1896, and see also his other papers of this period). Once uncovered, however, these strivings or desires appeared closely related to the sexual perversions (Freud, 1905). They had been pushed out of awareness because they were thus unacceptable to conscious social and personal standards; they had been repressed (Freud, 1915a). The symptoms appeared to exist in these neurotic individuals because their infantile drives had been improperly guided in early life (Freud, 1906, 1915b, 1916). Because of either over-

---

[2] In the interests of brevity and breadth of coverage, the editor has revised the text of this section and added references. For any changes in emphasis or in intended meaning, he must take the responsibility. (Editor)

indulgence or excessive frustration, which had interfered with the natural processes of maturation and sublimation, these unacceptable drives had become intensified. Because the early conflicts remained unsolved under conditions of stress in adult life they appeared as symptoms (Freud, 1906, 1910).

Freud's (1905) study of instinctual drives in the human being led him to broaden the concept of sexuality to include far more than the genital or mating activity of normal adults. In its biologically undifferentiated form, he considered it as a primary creative and adaptive striving which is present in the infant at birth. Psychologically, the satisfaction of these strivings connected with basic body functions is expressed in feelings of pleasure. In this sense, sexuality contributes to the primary orientations of the organism and to the infant's first awareness of himself and of his body security and of his well-being. This is the core of the libido theory (see also Freud, 1911). A polymorphous pleasure striving exists in every activity of the baby. Remnants of these primitive auto-erotic pleasure strivings are found in our nightly dreams (Freud, 1900), in our daydreaming (Freud, 1908b), and in other waking activities which serve to free us from painful impressions. Furthermore, Freud's (1904b) study of primitive customs, ceremonies, and myths indicated that these also have their basis in conflict over the primitive pleasure strivings.

In Freud's theory, libido is comparable to the appetite in the nutritional system. It may be conceived as the force working within the organism to bring about a pleasurable and satisfying state of affairs both within itself and concerning its relation to the outside world (Freud, 1905, 1911). This pleasure striving appears to have a manifest relation to adult sexuality after about the fourth year of life, when it blossoms briefly into easily recognizable manifestations of what will be a mature form of genital activity at adolescence. Both psychoanalytic findings and direct observation of human infants indicate that these pleasure strivings exist from the beginning of extrauterine life.

The Infantile Stages of Psychosexual Organization.—In the psychological development of the individual, Freud (1911) found a close dynamic relationship between the drives of the instinctual life and higher psychic activity. Because of this relationship, the development during the formative years when the organism is most plastic and the processes of maturation are most rapid is of great importance. The constant balancing and guiding of the sexual or pleasure strivings is the true aim of both child training and therapeutic endeavor. Freud described various mechanisms (see Chapter 7 by French and Chapter 9 by Sears) arising from both overindulgence and repeated frustration of pleasure striving in young children. He also described the manner in which these factors may damage their educability and their capacity for mature and controlled sex behavior after adolescence (see Freud, 1915b, 1916, and his many case reports).

During the pregenital period before about the fourth or fifth year, the child's pleasure striving becomes organized in relation to the satisfaction or frustration of his most prominent biological needs, and these change as he matures (Freud, 1915b). The oral, anal, and urethral regions, where the skin blends with the mucous membranes lining the body orifices, are the predominant pleasure-getting (erogenous) zones of early infancy (see also Jones, 1916a, 1916b). The skin, the general body musculature, and the sense organs also play their role in pleasure-getting. During this pregenital period, the child goes through three overlapping stages of libidinal organization.

THE ORAL STAGE.—The newborn infant's first and most intense pleasure-getting derives from sucking and swallowing. At this stage pleasure-getting is not yet separated from food ingestion. The baby makes no distinction between incorporation and contact. In thumb-sucking one can observe the differentiation between food ingestion and sucking *per se*. It is difficult to grasp the significance of fusion and diffusion in these early impulses from direct observation. The various factors in early oral organization become evident when disturbances occur in the orderly course of development. Later, as a consequence of maturation and of the frustrations of weaning, pleasure in sucking and swallowing changes to pleasure in biting, and still later to pleasure in vocalization and speech. From the fantasies of neurotic and psychotic patients, and from study of the customs of certain primitive races, the term *cannibalistic* has been applied to the pleasures from biting and incorporating (see Freud, 1915b, 1915c, 1917; Abraham, 1916, 1924a). From observation of the personality differences among primitive peoples who treat their infants differently during this nursing stage, it appears that the effects of this period carry over into adult behavior (Róheim, 1934; Money-Kyrle, 1939).[3]

THE ANAL STAGE.—The second phase of the pregenital organization is known as the anal sadistic stage (Freud, 1916). Very early in his life the child appears to become aware of and to derive pleasure from expelling faeces and urine. With his growing awareness in general (ego development), the child also discerns the distaste of parents for excrement. These observations coupled with the alternately tender and stern treatment connected with his elimination tend to establish an ambivalent attitude toward the parents. In this stage, too, the duality of the sexual life is beginning to develop, but it cannot yet be designated as masculine and feminine. It is merely relatively active or relatively passive (Freud,

---

[3] After a survey of some of this anthropological evidence, Money-Kyrle concludes as follows:

"It is impossible not to be struck by this juxtaposition of facts. Free feeding and late weaning would seem to promote generosity and optimism. Oral deprivation and early weaning would seem to promote stinginess and greed. To say more would be to over-simplify the generalization." (1939, p. 126)

1916). The active element is supplied by the body musculature which in infancy may play an important role in the expulsion of faeces. The passive feeling element comes from the sensitivity of the mucous membrane around the anus.

This expulsive phase gradually gives way to the retentive phase wherein the child comes to get pleasure from retaining and controlling his faeces. He usually learns that by judiciously presenting his excrement like presents, he can gain attention and rewards from parents, or by presenting them at inappropriate times, or even by smearing them, he can cause his parents real distress. From such experience he gains a sense of power and some appreciation of social reality. As the pressures from social reality for sphincter control continue to increase, however, and as the child begins to identify himself with his powerful parents and to take over (introject) their standards, these pleasures derived from the control of elimination for his own (narcissistic) uses are gradually relinquished.

Normal continuations of the anal expulsive phase manifest themselves in the prevalent concern for daily bowel movements and in interest in anal humor. Such plastic arts as painting are sometimes seen as sublimations of tendencies fixated at the expulsive phase (Jones, 1918). For the carry-over from fixations at the anal retentive phase, Freud (1908, 1916) has summarized the characteristic traits as parsimony, pedantry, and petulance (see also Abraham, 1921). The hoarding of money is sometimes seen as a sublimation of the retentive tendency (Ferenczi, 1914).

THE PHALLIC PHASE OF THE GENITAL STAGE.—In the period between the second and the fourth years of life the pleasure-getting of the child comes to be definitely related for a short time to the genital organs (Freud, 1923b). The first aspect of this phase appears to be connected with getting control of the urinary function which probably provides the occasion for the child's discovery of his genitalia. Overt sexual activity may be noticed, usually in the form of masturbation or an urge toward physical contact with the parent of the opposite sex (Oedipus complex) or in exhibiting the genitalia. These early genital pleasures are still self-centered (narcissistic), but self-awareness, emotional reactions, and inquisitiveness especially are developing, and these can provide pleasures. Several factors operate to bring about the repression of these early genital strivings. Shame and disgust are actively inculcated by the parents. Corporal punishment is common, and it may occur in the form of threats to damage the genitalia (castration complex). Furthermore, with the child's growing awareness of his own weakness in relation to the powerfulness of his parents, he strives to be like them (identification). In this striving, the child tends to take over (introject) the moral values of his parents, and thus he adds guilt to the various unpleasant consequences of his genital activities (Freud, 1923a, 1924). Gradually, as the unpleasantness and anxieties connected with these activities become greater than the pleasures to be derived from them, the child relinquishes sexual activities until adolescence when the maturation of the sex glands increases their urgency and reactivates the infantile conflicts (see Freud, 1910).

Like the previous stages of psychosexual development, this phallic stage has its effects on later personal characteristics. The self-centered (narcissistic) aspect of the pleasure-getting involved is a trend likely to continue unless the child's strivings are successfully sublimated. This self-centeredness may appear in an unreasonable need to be loved, as opposed to the tendency to give love and to form mutual social relationships.

The Latency Period.—The gradual repression of sexual activity just described initiates what Freud called the "latency period." In this period, the most active sublimation of pleasure striving into intellectual curiosity and social strivings takes place. The child's patterns of self-control are influenced by both parents, but particularly by the father (see Freud, 1923b; also Flügel, 1935). The impressions and standards taken over from these first models (identification) constitute the nucleus of what Freud has termed the *super-ego,* i.e., the conscience. This important aspect of the personality is kept active by the child's love for the parents and by fear either of losing their love or of corporal punishment (castration) (see Freud, 1923a).

Symptoms and Anxiety.—The child who has overintense or misdirected pleasure strivings from either overindulgence or excessive frustration in infancy, is potentially neurotic. In either case he is prone to develop pathological anxiety. Because of the weakness of the ego during childhood, he cannot control the id strivings so strengthened, and they are likely to break through precociously during the latency period. This interferes with normal sublimation. Furthermore, physical immaturity makes precocious sexual activity painful and exhausting. In consequence, the child may regress to earlier forms of pleasure-getting, or, if his parents will not permit these, he may develop symptoms of infantile neurosis (Freud, 1910).

Anxiety is a phylogenetic inheritance which may be intensified. The anxieties of early infancy, Freud (1917) believed to be due to the frustrations of prolonged or sudden separation from the mother (see also Greenacre, 1942). The first example of this is birth itself. Otto Rank (1929) has elaborated this theory. Anxiety also has intricate biological roots connected with the protracted period of psychic helplessness and dependency of the infant, hence, the intensification of environmental dangers because of this inner unreadiness to make independent adjustments, hence also, the overvaluation of the mother who is the natural protector against these dangers. This elemental need for love, from which the human being never escapes, arises directly out of the factors connected with the maintenance of life itself during the period of infancy. Still another factor predisposing the human being to anxiety, Freud considered to be a tension within the organism created by sexual repression, and this, too, he considered to be a part of man's phylogenetic inheritance (Freud, 1926, pp. 130–132).

The general principles in Freud's theory of development are well established. They have received confirmation from the study of primitive peoples (Freud, 1904b; Róheim, 1934; M. Mead, 1935; Money-Kyrle, 1939). They have also received confirmation from the psychoanalytic study of children (see A. Freud, 1928, 1937; Klein, 1932), and they are gradually being incorporated as part of the working conception of personality development by those outside psychoanalytic circles (see Chapter 3 by Mowrer and Kluckhohn). These findings of Freud and his followers suggest a new approach to the study of development in early infancy from the standpoint of direct observation.

Evidence of the Effects of Infantile Experience on Personality Development from Direct Observation

It has been the privilege of the writer to make clinical observations on a large group of infants, 600 in number, for a long period of time. These studies are not yet completed and the work has not yet been published.[3] However, some of the findings which have a bearing on the problem of this chapter are presented in the material which follows.

The original purpose of this study was to observe reactions in the baby which might be related to later personality disorders. We have watched particularly for regressive or withdrawn tendencies, for negativism, and for exaggerated reaction to frustration or to a change of routine. We have attempted to determine whether such reactions were present to a pathological degree at birth, or were developed as a result of adverse experiences. Moreover, we have studied in detail how the primary relationship of the infant to his mother is built up, and we have examined the significance of this relationship for the development of later emotional and social life.

Our method has consisted in the observation of sequences in the development of the infant-mother relationship over long periods rather than in the study of immediate reactions to any artificial situation. Our records consist chiefly of moving pictures and of case notes. The newborn infants were studied in three different maternity hospitals which varied somewhat in their methods of infant care. We have also studied infants born at home. Personality studies of a small group of cooperative parents were made both before and after the birth of the child in an

---

[3] This study was financed through the National Committee for Mental Hygiene with funds granted by the Committee on Research in Dementia Praecox founded by the Supreme Council, 33rd Degree Scottish Rite, Northern Masonic Jurisdiction, U. S. A.

attempt to get some light on the "emotional environment" which might affect the infant. So far as the mothers were concerned in this part of our study, we investigated their childhood, their emotional satisfaction in marriage, and their willingness to accept the feminine role as determined by their life activities, each so far as possible. With fathers, the same general factors were investigated, and, in addition, his indirect relationship to the child through the emotional support he gave the mother during the pregnancy and the early months of the child's life was considered.

In our studies we have given particular emphasis to the anxiety or tensional states of the infant. We considered that these might be due to disturbances of metabolic economy related to the rapid development of the brain in the first months and to the inadequate distribution of the blood stream which, in turn, is due to delay in the obliteration of the foetal system of circulation. We took the development of awareness as our primary object of study. We watched for evidences of security and insecurity—observed in terms of respiratory changes and of turgescence of the skin—of pleasure-getting, and of the manner in which the tactile and kinaesthetic senses participate in the child's primary orientation and contribute to the sense of reality. Our results indicate that all of these are related to an innate need for contact with the mother, and that the mother who supplies this contact unstintingly fosters her child's development.

Characteristics of the Newborn Infant

Psychological Characteristics.—Complete helplessness is the outstanding psychological characteristic of the newborn baby. There is little evidence of voluntary activity except that in connection with sucking until between the second and third month following birth. During this period, the human infant is practically a precerebrate organism, for the forebrain is incomplete (Tilney and Kubie, 1931). Histologically, we know that the cerebrum is incomplete, and many of the nerve tracts are unmyelinated (Peiper, 1932; Langworthy, 1933; Conel, 1939, 1941). The development of the forebrain during the first year of life is a tremendous feat in view of the phylogenetic history of this organ. Largely because of the undeveloped state of this organ, during this early period, the human infant is presumably concerned only with his own inner tensions of growth and development. Furthermore, brain circulation is not yet well established (Peiper, 1928), and the capillary system is inadequate for its function in these first months. Even functional activities like sucking, breathing, and eliminating are not yet well established in many infants for some time after birth. Fifty per cent of the 600 babies in our own study were definitely not "self-starters" in sucking. This fact, we believe, has not been sufficiently stressed heretofore. And finally, the persistence of a high mortality rate during this first few months of extra-uterine life also bears witness to the newborn's helplessness and vulnerability. All these psychological characteristics, with their organic bases, point to the child's need for mothering.

Behavioral Characteristics.—Direct observation shows that the behavior of the infant is periodic random activity which consists in twisting, flexion and extension of the torso, kicking, arm waving, and head turning. This "mass activity" (Coghill, 1929) is repeated at varying intervals, and the rhythm is more or less individual (see also Pratt, 1933). It begins gradually, increases in violence, and usually culminates in crying, sucking, or eliminating. It is followed by a sleeplike condition lasting two or three hours, during which time the muscles may be tense and small movements may frequently be seen.

These tensional states have a physiological basis, and to the writer, they appear to be concerned with the maintenance of the circulation of oxygen and nutritional substances to the head during the period before the foetal channels are obliterated and the heart has definitely assumed its postnatal function. In cases of the persistence of foetal circulatory mechanisms, this behavior is shown in extreme form, and it persists longer than in the average well-organized child. Thus, this primary spontaneous activity of the newborn apparently functions to relieve the inner tensions connected with hunger and asphyxia by aiding circulatory distribution of oxygen and nutritional substances. It would thus appear to be closely related to the establishment of tissue metabolism in rapidly developing organs, of which the brain is foremost, and it doubtless tends to produce feelings of inner satisfaction.

Although the stimuli for this primary spontaneous activity and tension appear to be internal and very little concerned with the environment, external conditions may influence the activity and tension considerably. A generalized state of observable muscular tension existed and readily became exaggerated in about 30% of the 600 newborn babies in my study. This tension disappeared when the child sucked or when it was put in close contact with the body of the mother. It was also relieved by stroking the head and face, by general rhythmic movement such as rocking, by a warm bath, by maintaining the child in a secure position either by holding it in arms or by supporting it well with wrappings and pillows, and by lowering the head and dimming the light. Such mothering definitely fosters functional integration. From my own observations I have found that infants who do not get this sort of mothering show increasing and persistent muscular tension, and this increasing tension is accompanied by inadequate breathing. Furthermore, in such cases the tension usually persists long past the period when it may be regarded as purely physiological. It becomes a kind of primitive anxiety.

Physiological Characteristics.—The most striking and consistent characteristic of the infant during the first three months of extrauterine life is the tendency toward functional disorganization. Breathing is shallow, rapid, and frequently irregular (Brock, 1932, Vol. 2, Ch. 6). It would appear that the integration between external respiration and the tissue needs for oxygen, particularly the metabolism of the central nervous system, becomes established gradually. The progress of this integration may be inferred from changes in muscle tone. Furthermore, the circulation of the child is unstable, and the gastrointestinal functions are easily disturbed as is shown by the frequency of regurgitation, hiccups, and diarrhea.

The organization of these physiological processes progresses gradually, probably, with the maturation of the autonomic nervous system, but it is also clear that the progress of this organization can be affected considerably by external factors. The emotionally healthy mother or nurse can maintain balance in the body activities of the newborn child with amazing ease unless actual disease or defect is present. But the most trivial irregularities in the personal care and handling of any baby, such as too little contact with the mother, too little handling, or changes of nurses or in general routine, frequently result in such disturbances as pallor, irregular breathing, and feeding disturbances. In infants who are constitutionally sensitive or poorly organized, these disturbances, if they are too frequent, may permanently alter the organic and psychic development, and not infrequently they threaten life itself. This characteristic instability, so marked in the first three months of life before the cerebral integrative functions are in evidence and the nervous system is more complete, continues in a lesser degree until well into the second year when speech and locomotion are becoming established.

Direct observation thus confirms Freud's (1926) theory of the innate predisposition of the human infant to anxiety. The infant is, by its very incompleteness of brain and nervous system, continuously in potential danger of functional disorganization. Outwardly the danger is that of sudden separation from the mother who either intuitively or knowingly must sustain this functional balance. Actual neglect or lack of love may be equally disastrous. Inwardly the danger appears to be the mounting of tension from biological needs and the inability of the organism to maintain its inner energy or metabolic equilibrium and reflex excitability. The *need for oxygen* may become acute because the young infant's breathing mechanisms are not well enough developed to work adequately, with the increasing inner demand caused by rapid forebrain development. The need for contact with the mother is urgent in order to keep the reflex mechanisms connected with breathing in operation as well as to bring the sensory nervous system into functional activity. This *need to feel* in the baby which is gratified best through personal stimulation is remarkably similar to hunger for food.

Besides these dangers deriving from the possibility of interference with the function of the organ systems themselves, the child is predisposed to the danger of forming strong negative emotional reactions which later will be difficult to extinguish. At six months an inadequately mothered infant's first dawning awareness may be that life is constantly threatened; at a year such a child tends to feel itself unloved.

Establishing the Child's Emotional Attachment to the Mother

Much of the quality and the cohesiveness of a child's personality depends upon an emotional attachment to the mother. This attachment or, to use the psychoanalytic term, cathexis for the mother grows gradually out of the satisfactions it derives from her.[4] We have studied the nature of this developing attachment which is so elusive yet so essential in considerable detail. Three types of sensory experience, namely, tactile, kinaesthetic, or the sense of body position, and sound, contribute primarily to its formation. The development of these sensory capacities has been mentioned by nearly all observers of infantile behavior (Pratt, 1933), but their particular importance for the personal relation between mother and child has not been emphasized. The sense of touch is relatively acute about the head and face at birth, but it is stimulation around the mouth that brings forth the most vigorous reactions in the small infant. Minkowski (1921) has shown that oral sensitivity and the beginnings of the sucking response already are present in the foetus of three months. The first definite evidence of satisfaction, the disappearance of activity and muscular tension, appears in the newborn after vigorous sucking. More than hunger satisfaction appears to be involved, for relief of tension appears even when an insignificant amount of food, as determined in a breast-fed baby by weighing before and after nursing, has been ingested. The sucking itself appears to be pleasurable. From the fact that these phenomena appear during the first days of life it is clear that the newborn infant must derive his first pleasurable orientation to the outside world through the mouth *by way of his own sucking*. It is common hospital practice to separate the infant from the mother immediately after birth and to maintain this separation during the two weeks of the lying-in period except for brief feeding or "visiting" periods. From the observations of the writer, such early experience definitely interrupts the formation of the child's emotional attachment for the mother and the initial sense of security that should replace the chemical union through the placenta. Furthermore, such early experience predisposes these sensitive infants to anxiety.

The newborn child gets kinaesthetic satisfaction from being held, moved about, and fondled by the mother. The satisfaction derived from these forms of stimulation are registered in improved breathing, and when observation can be made over a prolonged period, it shows in improved digestion. Infants who do not suck vigorously seldom breathe deeply and regularly. Those who are not held in the arms sufficiently, particularly if they are bottle-fed babies, also develop gastro-intestinal disorders. They become air swallowers and frequently develop what is popularly known as colic. They may have trouble with defecation, or they may vomit frequently. It appears that the reflex tone of the gastro-

---

[4] For a description of this process in terms of dynamic learning theory, see Chapter 3 by Mowrer and Kluckhohn. (Editor)

intestinal tract as well as of the breathing mechanism in this early period depends in some special way upon stimulation from the periphery. Freud has held that libidinal pleasure is involved and that libidinal energy is distributed in these functions. Thus the touch of the mother (or her substitute) has a definite biological implication in the regulation of the reflexes connected with breathing and nutritive functions.[5]

The sense of body position is acute in the infant at birth. It constitutes a second aspect of kinaesthetic experience that is important in establishing the affective tie between mother and child. The change from a liquid to an air environment at birth has to be compensated for gradually by the organism. If the body of the newborn infant is not well supported by wrappings or if the child is picked up suddenly or moved about rapidly or violently, it reacts immediately with a startle. This innate sensitivity, or fear of falling as it has been called (Moro, 1918), tends normally to be overcome through gentle motion or rocking. The old-fashioned cradle and rocking chair have considerable value in the first months of life and they could well be returned to modern nurseries, although the baby carriage may also supply this need.

In our follow-up study of some of these babies during the early months, we have found that many of those who did not get this form of mothering frequently substituted it themselves with head rolling, body rolling, or other hyperkinetic manifestations, during periods of stress. We found also that a large group of babies who cried persistently at night so that they had to be walked about were cured by rocking them at regular intervals during the day. It seems clear that the nervous system of the infant needs some sort of "stimulus feeding" or rhythmic vibratory movement to facilitate its development.

A third sensory factor which comes into this elementary child-mother attachment is the sound of the mother's voice. The majority of newborn babies show a violent startle-reaction to loud or sudden noises. After the first week of life it soon becomes evident that the human voice begins to exert a peculiarly soothing effect upon the child. We found that mothers who make a practice of speaking softly or singing to their infants while holding them have a much better relationship to the child. The innate sensitivity to sudden loud noise appears to be counteracted in this way. These children, as they grow older, can be soothed readily by the mother's voice. Sensitivity to noise tends to disappear much more rapidly from infants who are rocked and sung to judiciously at regular intervals than in those who are left in the isolated seclusion of the modern nursery.

It is rarely recognized, even among experts in child development, that these early mothering activities are a vitally important factor in bringing about nervous integration, in conserving energy for mental growth, and in making possible the sublimation of pleasure-getting, or what Freud

---

[5] Interesting in this connection is the story of the taming of the wolf child by means of massage (Gesell, 1941, p. 32).

has called sexual activities, in the interest of socially approved emotional and later intellectual development. We found that emotionally disturbed women and those who either consciously or unconsciously reject the child are as unable to "mother" it as they are to secrete milk.

Reactions to Inadequate "Mothering."—Young babies who have not been "mothered," or those who have had adequate care and then suddenly lose it, commonly develop one of two general types of reaction. They may develop a form of negativistic excitement or a form of regressive quiescence.

NEGATIVISM.—The negativistic reaction may show itself locally in the oral zone as a refusal to suck. With this goes what appears to be a complete loss of appetite and, perhaps even more serious, a failure to assimilate food. Accompanying this negativistic reaction to sucking, close observation will reveal more or less hypertension or rigidity of all the body muscles. Arms and legs resist extension. The torso is arched slightly backward. The muscles of the back and the back of the neck are particularly tense. This extensor reaction, or hypertonic reaction as it is sometimes called, is also at times accompanied by vomiting and by frequent periods of violent screaming during which it is extremely difficult to quiet the child. Still other common accompaniments are breath-holding, shallow breathing, and constipation. Apparently the tension is present in both the striped muscles and in the smooth visceral muscles.

REGRESSION.—The second type of reaction to lack of or loss of mothering, and to insufficient sucking activity, is a form of depressive and regressive quiescence. This form of reaction has even more sinister implications than the negativistic one. When such infants are put to the breast or given the bottle, they make a few sucking movements in response to the stimulus situation, then quickly fall into what appears to be sleep. This sleep has more the quality of stupor, however, for the child does not waken for his next feeding. Frequently he can only be aroused by repeated tickling on the soles of the feet, by shaking, by spanking, or by being chucked under the chin. In a few babies who show especially poor functional organization, the sucking reflex may disappear altogether and the child has to be tube fed. Along with this oral lethargy there is a general loss of muscle tone and reflex excitability throughout the body. Such infants gradually develop a marked pallor and what the pediatrician describes as skin turgor is diminished. With this condition are marked gastro-intestinal disturbances with regurgitation of food or diarrhea. Breathing is apt to be irregular with periods of apnoea. Hiccups and yawning are frequent. This regressive reaction shows a marked resemblance to the clinical picture of shock. In the mature individual, however, shock is considered the result of overstimulation which has put the higher nerve centers out of action. This reaction in the infant appears to result from frustration or too little peripheral stimulation, and it appears to consist in a tendency of the organism to function as it did before

birth with a predominance of activity in the splanchnic area. Such privation appears to interfere with the blood supply to the higher centers and
thus interrupts the developmental processes through which these centers
are brought into action.

What has worked empirically in the treatment of this condition tends
to confirm our interpretation. Babies with this regressive reaction are
restored to normal, where this is possible, by supporting the peripheral
circulation with daily subcutaneous injections of saline. Body massage
and raising the foot of the bed to increase cerebral circulation are also
helpful. Artificial stimulation of the sucking reflex must be maintained
persistently for the best results. Traction on the tongue and dilatation
of the rectum may be employed in emergency, as they are for surgical
shock, to stimulate respiration.

This regressive reaction, which may develop acutely in young infants,
is strongly similar to, or is perhaps identical with, a chronic disease
known as *marasmus*. The name comes from a Greek word meaning
"wasting away." The affliction was well known to physicians of an
earlier time (Holt, 1918, pp. 221–226). It affects particularly children
in the first year of life, and less than three decades ago, under the name
of "debility" or "infantile atrophy," it used to be responsible for nearly
half the infant mortality rate (Holt, 1918). It was at one time thought
that this illness was due primarily to insufficient or inappropriate food,
but many of the older pediatricians connected the disease with lack of
individual care and with the institutionalization of young children. Some
related it to sudden weaning and to radical changes in routine. The
present indications are that this malady was not due primarily to inappropriate feeding or digestive disturbance, nor, as some investigators
have thought, to some basic biological defect of circulation. It has
instead the nature of a general disorganization of functions and a
deterioration of primary body reflexes due in large measure to lack of
"mothering" or stimulation.

These babies with marasmus develop a peculiar grayish color, as if
there were no blood in the surface of the body. Their skin lies in loose
folds over the underlying muscles which gradually lose their tone and
become flabby. The abdomen protrudes and is swollen in an exaggerated
way due to the distention of the intestines with gas and also at times
to passive congestion of the liver. We were able to study in great detail
the reactions of several marasmic infants in the nutrition ward of a large
city hospital. The experimental introduction of a "foster mother" to
give personal care and massage to these infants brought dramatic results in restoring appetite, alertness, and reflex excitability. The greater
part of the food given them, which they sometimes take quite eagerly,
goes through them with little change and is unabsorbed (Abt and Abt,
1924, pp. 263–276).

Marasmus is now becoming a rare disease, probably due to the fact
that a series of medical and social investigations have shown that an
infant, even in poor hygienic surroundings, usually thrives if it has

good mothering, whereas the finest institution equipped to give the most expert scientific care frequently could not supply the subtle personal factor necessary to maintain healthy development. In consequence, young infants are now kept in hospitals only for short periods when acute illness demands it, and in cases where a baby has not suitable care at home, it is sent to a supervised foster home.

It seems clear from these reactions that inadequate mothering is an actual privation which may result in biological, as well as psychological, damage to the infant's organism. It is in no sense a casual matter of sentiment.

If we may be allowed to speculate as to the meaning of this damage, it seems most probable that we are dealing with a defective blood supply to the brain during the developmental shift from placental to post-natal circulation, resulting in anoxemia or starvation to the rapidly developing nerve cells. "Physiological shock" is potential for all babies and the prophylaxis against this or the treatment for it is consistent mothering. Rhythmic functioning of the body reflexes and of the muscles appears to be necessary to maintain growth in the nervous system. It would appear that the gross extensor reaction of the body serves to bring blood or spinal fluid into the cerebral circulation, as happens in the familiar stretching and yawning of adults, and to maintain reflex tone.[6] The transition from the vegetative life of the foetus to the independent and reactive life of the infant requires a longer time in man than it does in other mammals, and consistent mothering is required if the human infant is to pass this transition unscarred.

Early Breathing Experiences.—Because of recent indications that mental disease may be related to deficient oxygen consumption by the brain cells, we have made special investigations of breathing in our infants. One of the most important findings has been that the breathing of the neonate is precarious not only during the first days of life but up to the time that regular vocalization begins, which is usually around the third month. Crying during this period appears in all probability to be a form of emergency reaction stimulated by partial suffocation. For this reason the advice to "leave the child alone to cry it out" is dangerous for probably the first six months of life. The crying infant needs assistance with his breathing at least until vocalization is well established. The vital importance of adequate respiratory function during this period is its relation to the metabolism of developing brain tissue. Studies of cerebral metabolism in the living tissue of lower animals as well as of man indicate a tremendously high relative rate of oxygen consumption by brain cells. "Gray matter uses more oxygen than white, and the younger the animal, the higher the oxygen consumption of the brain"

---

[6] The first expression of this extensor reaction is probably that which brings about birth. It also appears in temper tantrums (see below). Peiper (1928, p. 50) suggests that it may also be responsible for the transverse positions of the foetus that make deliveries so difficult. He speaks of it as a "*Zwangshaltung.*"

(Grinker, 1937, pp. 72–73; see also Wortis, 1941, and Peiper, 1932, p. 115).

Ten per cent of the 600 newborn babies studied needed considerable stimulation in order to bring their breathing activity into momentum. The respiration of these infants during the first two weeks of life was extremely shallow, rapid, irregular, and disturbed by every readjustment. The majority of infants who did not show birth asphyxia were also found to have unstable respiration, and such experiences as handling by inexperienced nurses or mothers as well as no handling at times brought about a pathological degree of irregularity.

Recent research on foetal respiration both in lower mammals and in man has thrown some light on the reason for this breathing inadequacy. It has been shown that definite breathing movements occur in the foetus (Barcroft, 1936; Snyder and Rosenfeld, 1937a and 1937b). These movements are related to the muscle of the diaphragm which in the foetus arches high into the chest cavity over the large liver like a suction cup. It is thought that in all probability its action is to suck oxygenated blood toward the heart and chest generally from the region of the placenta. After birth when air is inspired into the lungs, this action becomes reversed. However, until the foetal circulation is obliterated and the innervations of the diaphragm are well developed, it appears possible for the organism to revert to the prenatal form of breathing activity. This possibility appears to be due to the anatomical conformation of the infant's chest and the large size of the liver (Peiper, 1932, p. 114). As a consequence of the undeveloped state of the central nervous system, this prenatal or splanchnic orientation of the infant may persist, and in all probability it is the biological basis for the tendency toward regression and acute inanition. The fact that a baby can feed and also breathe for a time from the supplies of his own liver and body tissues may be the biological basis of these depressive processes.

We have definite chemical evidence from the study of prenatal blood chemistry that a low margin of oxygen is present in the general circulation of the foetus (Haselhorst and Stromberger, 1930). This physiological anoxemia makes the birth process dangerous (see Chapter 19 by Shock). In all probability this deepening of the oxygen privation provides the stimulus for the extensor reaction which starts birth and assists the delivery. This extensor reaction appears as a sort of primitive migratory activity, and it appears to be the first major protective adjustment of the organism against privation. The process of birth must further reduce the oxygen content of the infant's blood, particularly of the cerebral supply, so that when delivery is unduly prolonged or when anaesthesia is used freely, damage may occur to the delicate brain cells from oxygen privation as well as from the more familiar mechanical trauma.

The discovery of Snyder and Rosenfeld (1938) that the respiration is not regulated primarily by the percentage of carbon dioxide in the blood in either the foetus or the newborn is also of great importance in connection with the child's need for mothering. Since the newborn infant does not get the same respiratory stimulus from this source as does the adult, stimulus from appropriate handling is necessary in the majority of babies to keep them breathing adequately.

Oral Experience

Modern infant culture has emphasized primarily the nutritional needs of the infant, has limited sucking to periods of food intake, and has largely ignored the dynamic developmental aspects and the psychological implications of this activity. We have already mentioned the importance of the newborn infant's first sucking activities in fostering his emotional attachment for the mother. From my observation of 600 infants during their stay in the lying-in hospital, of many through the first year of life, and of a few, who received divergent forms of treatment, over a period of five years, I am thoroughly convinced that a favorable sucking experience for the first three months contributes considerably to the development of several aspects of structure and of behavior. The evidence indicates that sucking experience is important for the structural development of the face and jaws, for digestion, for the general well-being of the child, for the development of alertness toward factors outside the child's own body, for the age at which speech appears, and for the facility of the speech function. Furthermore, I have found oral stimulation also closely associated with breathing. Active sucking reflexly stimulates respiration.

The importance of sucking for the structural development of the face and jaws depends upon the role it plays in both stimulating circulation in the oral areas and in pleasure-getting. Brock (1932, Vol. 1, p. 165), in his summary of the biological development of the mouth cavity, describes two structures which show erectile capacity. These are the longitudinal swellings on the inside of the infant's lips and the so-called magotot membrane along the lateral margin of the gums. I have been able to see these erectile structures immediately after *breast* feeding in many of the infants studied, but in bottle-fed babies they were rarely to be seen. These structures tend to disappear after the second or third month of extrauterine life. These findings and the fact that babies whose sucking experience is favorable show a distinctly pleased expression lead me to believe that sucking plays an important part in the structural development of the face and jaws and of the sections of the brain connected with facial expression.

Of the 600 babies I observed in maternity hospitals, 10% showed exaggerated sucking activity at birth. They sucked their own fingers, their lips, and their tongues. Excessive tension in the musculature of the entire body was also usually apparent in these infants. Interference with this sucking by tying the hands away from the mouth, which is common hospital practice, led in the majority of cases to severe reactions. Muscular tension increased; irregular breathing appeared, and frequently periods of prolonged spasmodic crying occurred. In others of this subgroup, the restriction of sucking was followed, after a brief struggle, by a deep stuporous state from which the child was aroused with difficulty for the following feedings. A more successful way of reducing this exaggerated oral activity was to soothe the child by gently stroking the head or by holding the infant in the arms for short periods at regular intervals and rocking him with a gentle rhythmic motion. These procedures reduced both the excessive sucking and the body tension in all except a few particularly exaggerated cases. Lowering the child's head at regular intervals and lowering the head of the bed during sleep were also effective. We consider this further evidence that cerebral anoxemia is a factor in the tension manifested in this exaggerated sucking activity.

These procedures did not produce "spoiling" as was usually feared by the mother or the nurse in charge. On the contrary, this soothing care could be gradually diminished as the child's functions became stabilized.

It was also interesting to note that these infants with exaggerated oral drive, when assisted in this way, subsequently showed an unusual degree of alertness. They proved precocious in the development of visual and auditory recognition, and even later in the development of speech. When properly handled, it appeared that this early oral drive was associated with general alertness later.

Fifty per cent of our 600 infants had to have considerable assistance from the nurse or mother in order to get vigorous sucking activity established. The sucking response appeared to be either undeveloped or inhibited in these children. If their primary sucking was not made easy and satisfying, their sucking activities gradually diminished, and they became either stuporous or resistive. Conditions in the mother tending to produce this result were inverted nipples which were difficult to grasp, unskilful holding so that apposition to the breast was not attained, and holding the infant's head too high. Conscious or unconscious hostility was apparently communicated to the child in some way, for a poor sucking response appeared invariably in the unwanted infant. Frequent feedings proved to be an efficient way of establishing a strong sucking activity in the majority of this subgroup. Frequent repetition gave the activity the necessary momentum. With these infants it was particularly important that the nursing periods be left completely free and uninterrupted. Moreover, when they were fed only every 4 hours, these babies tended to become pathologically quiet and lethargic and had to be awakened for feedings.

The average sucking time required during the first weeks of life for our whole group of infants was approximately 2.5 hours of the 24. After the first month, this average was reduced to about 2 hours. At this latter age, 20 minutes every 3 hours was the optimum schedule for the average healthy child, and this schedule corresponds well with feeding needs. Infants allowed complete freedom of sucking activity at the breast, or bottle babies whose opportunity for sucking was supplemented with a pacifier, rarely exceeded 2.5 hours of sucking a day after the first month. In no baby allowed such freedom of sucking, did marked thumb-sucking occur, except when illness interfered, or the child had insufficient mothering of other sorts.

Favorable Effects of Unrestricted Sucking.—Several physiological functions are fostered by unrestricted sucking. The breathing of the young infant which is characteristically shallow and irregular was definitely deepened and made more regular by satisfactory sucking experience. Well-being was increased as is shown by the fact that the first prolonged and generalized relaxation and the first quiet and relaxed sleep occurred after periods of unrestricted sucking. Digestion, gastro-intestinal function, and elimination were consistently better and more regular in babies who were allowed to suck freely at frequent intervals.

Psychological functions are also fostered by unrestricted sucking. Those babies in our group who had no difficulty with sucking and were unrestricted focused their eyes considerably earlier on the average than did those whose sucking was interrupted at the end of a specified time. The unrestricted babies grasped for objects earlier. They generally manifested a higher degree of alertness. And finally, with other factors of mothering held equal, they began vocalizing earlier, and they began speaking earlier. Presumably the fostering of these early developed skills by unrestricted feeding should provide an advantage in making later adjustments.

Effects of Restricted Sucking.—Besides delaying development of the functions just described, nursing privations produced two other types of clearly unfortunate reactions. The first consisted of excessive restlessness and periods of exaggerated crying, sometimes with general hypertension, and sometimes with muscular rigidity and extension of the neck. Sudden changes of routine which forced a reduction in sucking activity frequently resulted in excessive thumb sucking. A few of these infants who reacted with excitement and restlessness developed constipation following more or less sudden limitations of sucking activity. A second type of reaction, almost diametrically opposed to this restlessness, appeared in a large group of infants. In these, limiting sucking time or prolonging the interval between meals diminished the impulse to nurse and sometimes even produced a stuporous condition. In a few of these infants, the sucking response disappeared completely so that they had to be tube-fed. Such infants became generally lethargic, and all the body muscles became lax. They frequently developed diarrhea which in a few cases was accompanied by profuse discharges of mucous and blood. It appears that the entire organism may be affected by sucking frustration in these early months. Possibly these two types of reaction, excessive restlessness and excessive lethargy, are prototypes of the primary mood swings which become differentiated later in the course of development.

Weaning.—Our observations indicate that the old-fashioned practice of weaning at some given age is unnecessary, and it is an unfortunate procedure for the majority of infants. In this practice the individual child's stage of development and his latent readiness for new experiences are ignored. The individual differences in rate of development are not sufficiently recognized, and neither are the effects of frustrating situations on this development. We found definitely that the sucking impulse spontaneously wanes as new oral activities become differentiated and are brought into momentum around the fourth month of life. Moreover, other avenues of pleasure-getting are appearing. Vocalizing and biting begin to supplement the primary sucking activity. The development of hearing and seeing, as it is guided by the child's tactual contacts with the pleasure-giving mother, enable him to be satisfied by the sound or sight of her. When this stage has been reached with skilful handling and with a minimum of privation of the primary mothering, the child gives up sucking activity spontaneously, and weaning is not necessary. When children have been frustrated in their earlier sucking and in primary mothering, they give up sucking later and less spontaneously (see also Levy, 1928 and 1934).

Halverson (1938) has described important experiments in which muscle tension, air pressure, and other mechanical aspects of the sucking response were carefully registered, and in which associations between infantile sucking and tensional behavior were demonstrated. He does not, however, consider the pleasure-getting aspect of sucking, nor does he consider the relationship of sucking satisfaction to such other oral functions as speech and to brain development. In another paper, I (Ribble, 1939) have taken up the developmental role of sucking in connection with the prenatal maturation of the tongue and its close embryological relationship to the heart and diaphragm.

Experiences Connected with Elimination

The reactions of the infant to elimination are particularly hard to study for many obvious reasons, and the evidence available is neither so clear nor so plentiful as that connected with oral activities. In our own study, a few definite facts were clearly observed.

During the first four or five weeks bowel movements occur shortly after feeding in a more or less automatic fashion. At this time, little general reaction to faecal elimination is apparent in the child, and no reaction to urination is apparent unless the wetting is accompanied by chilling, or unless skin abrasions are present. After the first month or so, however, close observation reveals such reactions to the passage of the stool as breathing changes, reddening of the face, and changes in the tension of the lower limbs. From an interesting study by Dennis (1932), it appears that a muscular coordination between the diaphragm and the abdominal and anal muscles is gradually developing at about this time. This developing coordination is soon accompanied by a tension in the lower limbs which may be related to preparation for sitting and for standing. This developmental stage is important in relation to breathing, to standing and locomotion, and also to later vocalization. The first "grunt" is, I believe, a significant aspect of the development that brings speech. In babies who are neglected or unloved, for instance, and particularly in unmothered foundlings, the concern and excitement connected with elimination appears to be exaggerated, and it is correlated with a delay or unsteadiness in vocalization. Furthermore, breathing is shallow in these infants. At a later stage, stimulation of the anus by the passage of the stool may develop a tension which leads to retention of faeces. In these unloved babies an exaggeration of anal tension almost invariably develops, and they become constipated. In institutional practice, this constipation is usually treated with enemas and suppositories which, as would be expected from the conditions which appear to create this condition, only result in increasing the tendency to constipation. Furthermore, this treatment brings these activities into the social sphere and tends to fix the child's attention on them. In a small group of foundlings which I studied, the difficulty with constipation disappeared spontaneously when they were taken from the institution at an early age and adopted into homes where they got an adequate amount of affection and of general physical care. The "mothering" activity appears to have been an important factor in reducing the general nervous tension of these children, and in so doing, it removed the constipation. We have been led to believe that such mothering is the most appropriate treatment for early infantile constipation.[7]

Toilet Training.—Just as is true in the case of weaning, a child's individual stage of development should be taken into consideration in connection with toilet training. Our investigations indicate that attempting to demand cleanliness of an infant before he is able to sit alone securely, before he has acquired at least a definite sign language, and before he has a strong positive emotional attitude toward the mother paves the way for later incontinence, and for later emotional and behavior disorders. Moreover, the functions of elimination may easily become overerotized when early and excessive concern is shown by the mother for eliminational regularity or cleanliness. In many babies, too frequent diapering or insistent attempts to get the child to evacuate on a "pottie" appeared to serve as a sort of sexual seduction, and it was

---

[7] In this connection, a personal communication from the late Dr. Charles Stockard told of thoroughbred pups which could not eliminate when they were taken from the mother at birth so that she had no opportunity to lick them. Many valuable dogs were lost because the keepers continued to separate pups from mothers soon after birth and did not discover for a long time the necessity in the pup for this "dog mothering." Thus, even in dogs mothering appears to be a factor in the tension level and in elimination.

followed by evidences of excessive nervous tension which in turn appears to have been a factor conducive to excessive masturbation. Because of the mother's cleanliness demands, bathing and diapering form, in many infants, a large part of the child's early social experience. Where this is true, the subsequent desocializing of these activities is apt to constitute a frustration quite as severe as weaning. With emotionally sound mothers and nurses who take care to watch the behavioral signs in the children under their care, elimination need be no problem. It can remain in a purely physiological role.

Treating Constipation in Older Babies.—In connection with direct observation of a group of so-called "constipated babies," we found that the condition was relieved definitely within a period of two or three weeks by substituting some form of pleasure or interest of a social nature which tended to make the child feel secure and well loved. Most effective was the instituting of frequent periods of directed play in which singing or some form of motor activity appropriate for the age and individuality of the child is provided. Such play periods should also precede feeding and sleeping in the child's routine. Allowing the constipation to go on over a period of several days until "nature took its course" caused no damage, but obviously this does not apply to any baby who has fever, rash, or other evidence of physical illness. Moreover, careful observation over a fairly long period is required to determine the toilet needs of any individual child.

We found that suppositories and cathartics resulted only in increasing the tendency to difficult bowel function. The results of these procedures, particularly of repeated enemas, were not evident at once. Only later it was observed that those children who had been subjected to these artificial measures reacted later on, when they were disappointed or when they felt themselves displaced by a new sibling, with constipation, incontinence, or diarrhea. These symptoms appeared clearly related to getting maternal attention, and even punishment appeared to be preferred to no maternal concern. In particularly sensitive or seriously frustrated children, overt smearing, dirt eating, and anal masturbation were occasionally seen. These symptoms, and excessive nervous restlessness which may be developed when these symptoms are severely punished, are seen in great profusion in foundling homes. They can also be found, however, in the sterilized, but often loveless, homes of cultured and professional people who have no time to show consistent love and understanding to an infant. They can best be corrected by substituting more suitable forms of pleasure-getting, just as thumb-sucking is cured by bringing the infant into a more complete emotional security.

Effects on Later Personality Development.—The feelings connected with elimination, and the treatment the child receives in connection with toilet training and constipation, appear particularly important later for self-regulation and control. The triad of traits—parsimony, pedantry, and petulance—were consistently shown in the course of personal histories by Freud (1915c) and it was revealed in the course of analytic study, that such patients had had periods of mishaps in connection with bowel function recurring long past the time when this training was supposed to be completed. Following this many sorts of unusual behavior were said to have been noticed by parents or siblings in these persons in connection with their elimination, and they retained a persisting interest in eliminational functions. Although we have traced our children at most for only five years, it appears that those who exhibit the more severe anal symptoms are likely to continue to be personality problems.

Experiences Related to Affectional Needs

By approximately the third month, in cases where no undue amount of frustration has occurred in connection with a child's early cathexis of the mother, the mother-child relationship takes on a distinctly new coloring. By this time, the organic activities of breathing, of digesting, and of circulating blood have begun to show considerable stability, indicating that the autonomic nervous system has taken over its specific functions. We know from anatomical studies that the foetal system of circulation is usually obliterated by this time (Brock, 1932, Vol. 1, Ch. 3). At about this time, typical adult patterns of brain waves begin to appear in the electroencephalogram (see Chapter 33 by Lindsley), and they probably indicate a more mature form of cerebral activity. Outbursts of emotional reaction, not always well differentiated but obviously expressing positive or negative direction, are seen to involve the entire motor system (Gesell and Thompson, 1934). Furthermore, and most important perhaps for the relation between mother and child, the distance receptors have matured to the point where they can function, and the psychological activities have begun to develop rapidly.

With the distance receptors the child develops the ability to orientate himself more and more through sight and sound. The eyes focus well and can follow the mother about, the ears function well and can differentiate the sounds she makes. Sound of her or sight of her produces the positive emotional responses formerly obtained only from contact, and consist of appropriate smiling and even genuine outbursts of joy. From this time on actual physical contact is no longer necessary for fairly prolonged periods just so long as the child can hear the mother's voice or see her while he is awake. Actual contact with the mother is necessary at frequent intervals, however, and it is important that the child be active in the separations which occur instead of the mother simply going away. Frustrations of the sight and sound of mother easily produce fearfulness and restlessness. When the mother arbitrarily, from the child's point of view, comes and goes about her business and social duties, or when a continuous shifting of nurses occurs, anxiousness is the common result. The much dreaded emotional dependency begins to develop in this period. And it may appear as a response to either too much mothering or too little mothering.

In this new phase of psychological development, the reactions of the child to frustration, i.e., of not seeing or hearing the mother enough, are considerably changed. The most conspicuous negative emotional reaction during this phase is the temper tantrum. It appears to develop from and to represent an exaggerated form of the extensor reaction of early infancy. It appears to be a basic defense mechanism which is closely related to many early aspects of developmental behavior.

Let us trace this response from its beginnings. We found this extensor reaction important in initiating the birth process where it represents a primitive postural adjustment well known to the obstetrician. Next we found it as a reaction to frustration, i.e., inadequate sucking and mothering, during the early weeks of extrauterine life. It has appeared to have something to do with maintaining the internal chemical and fluid equilibrium of the body, and perhaps with the circulation of blood, the pressure of spinal fluid, and even with the distribution of nervous energy. It appears normally in the yawning and stretching reaction. It is undoubtedly related to the opisthotonus seen in pathological conditions where cerebral pressure is developing (meningitis, tumor of the brain, or tuberculosis) and interfering with the blood supply to the brain. It would appear to have survival value connected with the relief of tensions in the head. Its danger lies, however, in the fact that it may become the main avenue of nervous discharge, and thus assume exaggerated importance. The results then may appear as marked interference with sensory-motor coordination, seen first as the late appearance of coordinated grasping behavior, and later as a tendency to drop objects, and still later as a tendency to fall easily. It is highly important that this response not be allowed to become too well established early in life. Tantrums, like early crying, cannot be ignored until the child has gained considerable degree of ego-development and is capable of choosing mechanisms of expression which are to his advantage.

In the field of early emotional development we are still grossly ignorant. Occasions for the study of such intimate social and relational processes are over long periods of time seldom available except in the psychoanalysis of very young children (see A. Freud, 1937; and Klein, 1932). In the psychoanalytic transference relationship, adults frequently relieve these reactions, and, at the present time, this is the approach from which most of our information about the development of emotional relationships comes. Direct observation lies now only in the hands of emotionally free and psychologically well-oriented parents.

Animal Studies

Within the last decade two investigators have attacked the problem of the effects of infantile nursing and feeding experiences by way of experiments on animals. These investigators have been interested, not in generalizing the specific consequences of various kinds of infantile experiences in animals to human beings, but in the general principles by which the effects of infantile experience may be understood.

Assuming a separate need for an adequate amount of sucking, Levy (1934) took four puppies from a litter of six and put them on controlled bottle feeding. For 20 days all conditions except the time devoted to sucking were kept as constant as possible. One pair, the "long-time-feeders," sucked from nipples in which the holes were small, and these two were also given supplementary opportunities for sucking. The other pair, the "short-time-feeders," were fed from nipples with large holes. In test situations these latter "short-time-feeders" showed a tendency to prolonged sucking of all kinds of objects between meals. Levy argued that thumb-sucking in human infants could be similarly explained by their having had inadequate opportunities to satiate the sucking impulse. Later Levy (1938) did a similar study with chickens. Again he assumed a pecking instinct that would require satiation. He found that chicks raised on wire mesh that limited the amount of pecking to a minimum were more restless, had a lower average weight, showed more preening behavior, more pecking at droppings and at the wall than did chicks of the same stock which were raised under conditions similar except that the floor of their pen was earth. An interesting additional observation was the prevalence of feather pecking in the former. The chicks raised on the wire floor virtually denuded their less aggressive pen mates.

Hunt (1941) has recently attempted to get controlled evidence concerning whether the traces of infantile experiences actually endure to adulthood, and to determine the importance of age at which the same experience, quantitatively measured, occurs. Using split litters to control heredity, he submitted halves of two litters to a controlled feeding schedule of 15 days beginning at the twenty-fourth day of life, and halves of another two litters to the same schedule beginning at the thirty-second day of life. Control animals from all litters were allowed free feeding. Then after five months during which both experimental and control animals were allowed free feeding, he measured the amount of food hoarded after the adult animals had been allowed only one feeding a day for five days. The infantile frustrates in the 24-day group hoarded approximately two and one half times as many pellets as their litter-mate controls. The infantile frustrates in the 32-day group hoarded approximately the same as their litter-mate controls. Thus, the traces of the infantile experience did endure to adulthood in that group frustrated at the early stage. Hunt explained these results in terms of learning theory. He argued that the hunger aroused in the adult feeding frustration served as a conditioned stimulus that set off hunger-anxiety in those animals that had suffered sufficiently severe hunger in infancy so that the total excitation aroused by this adult experience was greater than that in the control animals. He argued that the traces failed to endure in the 32-day group because, being older and better developed, the same feeding schedule that was effective for the 24-day group was sufficiently less severe for them so that it failed to fix the traces of the infantile experience.

Such animal studies can be of considerable value for uncovering the basic principles of adaptation and of the effects of infantile experience. They are not, in our judgment, well adapted for investigation of the detailed information that can be derived from clinical observations concerning the consequences of frustrating human instinctual drives in infancy on adult human personality. There are at least two reasons why such animal studies are ill adapted for this latter purpose. First, in the human infant the instincts are more diffuse, or less well channeled, than they are in the lower animals. Secondly, the human capacity to generalize its experience from one situation to others is much greater than is that of lower animals.

General Discussion

Precise and controlled evidence as to the permanence of the effects of these early infantile experiences in human beings is not yet available from direct observation. In such a complicated phase of life, where physiological as well as psychological factors are so deeply concerned, more extensive observations are necessary than we have been able to make. In general, however, it may be said that the younger the organism the more serious and widespread is the effect of frustration. However, the very extreme plasticity of early infancy prevents the irreversibility of most pathological reactions, and in general, if they are recognized and appropriately readjusted within a short enough time, no disabling damage is done. The most important factors are the stage of development at which the adverse experiences come and how long the widespread effects of frustration, characteristic at an early age, are allowed to continue.

A radical change of attitude toward the instinctual life of the human infant is necessary if overindulgence and frustration, the latter of which is the more common, are to be avoided, and we are to substitute sound emotional direction in their stead. The oral impulses that are implicit in the first sucking can readily be regulated to foster better breathing, eating, and digesting during the first six months of the child's life, and to foster the development of vocalization and good socialization during the second six months. Toilet training should be left until body equilibrium, sitting, and standing and adequate language responses are developed. It is the individual child's stage of development that should serve as the guide in these matters and not some arbitrary age.

One fact is reasonably clear, and that is that too little or inconsistent "psychological mothering" predisposes the infant to the hazard of anxiety and exaggerated autoerotism which may be recognized most readily in prolonged or excessive thumb-sucking, in constipation, and in early and excessive masturbation. Punishing these activities only increases the anxiety, but by providing consistent and healthy emotional satisfactions and security in the child's relationship to its parents, these practices and serious exaggeration of the primary anxiety states are avoided. Moreover, consistent security lays the foundation for the natural sublimation of the instinctual drives in the interest of better emotional, intellectual, social, and ethical development.

The human baby appears to have already at birth some innate tendency for associating sense impressions from other sorts of personal contact with the mother with his feelings of oral satisfaction. Suckling forms the nucleus to which the concomitant stimuli of warmth and pressure are associated, and to which the stimuli of taste, of smell, and then of sight and of sound are still later associated. These gradually come to form an ever-widening nucleus of awareness. Into this nucleus the early emotional and social reactions of both positive and negative tendency are integrated. In close relation to these early emotional experiences, the concept of father and mother arise, and with them the basic interpersonal reaction tendencies, which are so important for defining the later personality, are formed.

Our findings from direct clinical observation of babies tend to confirm orthodox psychoanalytical theory. The pleasure got from primary body functions appears to be an important factor in the early stabilization and integration of the various biological activities as they are differentiated in the course of maturation and in bringing them to full functional capacity. The role of the mother in maintaining an orderly rhythm in sucking, in eliminating, in general bodily movement and comfort, and in the basic feelings of orientation and security, all of which comes from adequate handling and fondling, is fundamental for emotional and social development as well as for physiological control. Ruthless repression of the pleasure-getting impulses of the baby results regularly in disorganization and in anxiety or tensional states with the resulting formation of such habits as thumb-sucking, persistent crying, repetitive activities, masturbation, all of which apparently serve to relieve this anxiety or tension to some degree.

A Few General "Psychological Rules" for Handling Young Babies.—1. The newborn child urgently needs a long and uninterrupted period of consistent and skilful psychological mothering, and this should be given by a single individual where the mother herself is not available. Such personal relationship during the early months is a necessary psychological supplement to the period of intrauterine protection. It counteracts biological anxiety and maintains body integration while the nervous system is maturing. It is also basic for the socialization of the child. This first dependency relationship appears to be analogous to what the biologist calls *symbiosis* wherein two organisms with essentially different needs profit by a relationship. The mother gets the satisfaction of completing the psychological creation of the child, and the infant not only receives food and affection but gets a primary form of orientation which helps to bring the development of the emotional, the sensory and perceptive processes into functional momentum.

2. Freedom of sucking activity is a necessity during the first months of life. Unrestricted sucking means in no sense a lack of direction of oral activity on the part of the parent. Instead, it means the gradual establishment of rhythmic regularity in providing for sucking, preferably in connection with feeding, and a careful balancing and integrating with it of other experiences like active and passive body movement, tactile experience, and ear and eye stimulation. We have found frequent, uninterrupted periods of feeding to be most beneficial. The intervals between feedings should be carefully regulated to the individual needs of the child. Such provision for sucking exercise serves definitely to prevent anxiety.

3. The transition from sucking to biting and vocalizing is a crucial phase of personality differentiation. The growing association of mouth grasping with hand grasping and of sensory intake through eyes and ears with these activities leads to emotional satisfaction and fosters perceptive capacity. During this stage of development, provision should be made for biting; stimulus for vocalizing should be given, and the process of grasping and carrying a cup to the mouth should be encouraged long before withdrawal of the breast, the nursing bottle, or the pacifier is attempted. The progression to the new and the abandonment of old forms of satisfaction must be brought about gradually. Moreover, a parent should be extremely tolerant of incidents where a child slips backward in the behavioral progression in order to avoid anxiety.

4. Attempts at toilet training before the infant sits comfortably alone and has a definite sign language with which to make known his wants should be avoided. They predispose the child to excessive anal eroticism. The adult should not confuse problems of laundry or individual standards of fastidiousness with questions of biological organization. The needs of the adult should not interfere with the child's satisfying his biological need or with his emerging feelings of self-direction. Toilet training is a process wherein the adult point of view should be abandoned, and the practices of the nursery should be governed by the laws of physiological and psychological development. Our studies show that if the small child is well loved and secure, and is simply given the opportunity and the time, he will automatically train himself in the control of these basic body functions as do many of the lower animals. This comes about as a result of the child's identifying with the wishes of a loved parent, and it is the first sign of loving cooperation and educability in the baby. Early forced or rigid training paves the way for disturbances in the primary integration between physiological, emotional, and locomotor activities.

BIBLIOGRAPHY

ABRAHAM, K. 1916. The first pregenital stage of the libido. In *Selected papers*. (Trans. and ed. by C. A. D. Bryan & A. Strachy.) London: Hogarth, 1927.
—— 1921. Contributions to the theory of anal character. In *Selected papers*. London: Hogarth, 1927.
—— 1924a. The influence of oral erotism on character formation. In *Selected papers*. London: Hogarth, 1927.
—— 1924b. Character formation on the genital level of libido development. In *Selected papers*. London: Hogarth, 1927.

ABT, I. A., & ABT, A. F. 1924. Pediatrics. Vol. 3. Philadelphia: Saunders.
BARCROFT, J., & BARRON, D. H. 1937. The genesis of respiratory movements in the foetus of the sheep. *J. Physiol., 88,* 56–61.
BERNFELD, S. 1929. The psychology of the infant. London: Kegan, Paul.
BREUER, J., & FREUD, S. 1893. The psychic mechanism of hysterical phenomena. In *Collected papers.* Vol. 1. London: International Psychoanalytical Press, 1924.
BROCK, J. 1932. Biologische Daten für den Kinderarzt. (2 Vols.) Berlin: Springer.
BÜHLER, C. 1930. The first year of life. New York: John Day.
COGHILL, G. E. 1929. Anatomy and the problem of behavior. New York: Macmillan.
—— 1933a. The biological basis of conflict in behavior. *Psychoanal. Rev., 20,* 1–4.
—— 1933b. The neuro-embryologic study of behavior. *Science, 78,* 131.
CONEL, J. L. 1939. The postnatal development of the human cerebral cortex. Vol. 1: The cortex of the newborn. Cambridge: Harvard University Press.
—— 1941. Development of the human cortex in the first month of life. *Arch. Neurol. Psychiat., Chicago, 45,* 387–389.
DENNIS, W. 1932. The new responses in infants. *Child Develpm., 3,* 362–363.
DETWILER, S. R. 1936. Neuroembryology. New York: Macmillan.
FERENCZI, S. 1914. The origin of the interest in money. In *Contributions to psychoanalysis* by Sandor Ferenczi. (Trans. by E. Jones.) Boston: Badger, 1916.
FLÜGEL, J. C. 1935. The psychoanalytic study of the family. London: Hogarth.
FREUD, A. 1928. Introduction to the technique of child analysis. *Nerv. ment. Dis. Monogr.,* No. 48.
—— 1937. The ego and mechanisms of defense. New York: Stechert.
FREUD, S. 1895. On the right to separate from neurasthenia a definite symptom-complex as "anxiety neurosis." In *Collected papers.* Vol. 1. London: International Psychoanalytical Press, 1924.
—— 1896. The aetiology of hysteria. In *Collected papers.* Vol. 1. London: Psychoanalytical Press, 1924.
—— 1900. The interpretation of dreams. In *The basic writings of Sigmund Freud.* (Trans. and ed. by A. A. Brill.) New York: Modern Library, 1938.
—— 1904a. Freud's psychoanalytic method. In *Collected papers.* Vol. 1. London: International Psychoanalytical Press, 1924.
—— 1904b. Totem and taboo. In *The basic writings of Sigmund Freud.* New York: Modern Library, 1938.
—— 1905. Three contributions to the theory of sexuality. In *The basic writings of Sigmund Freud.* New York: Modern Library, 1938.
—— 1906. My views on the role of sexuality in the aetiology of the neuroses. In *Collected papers.* Vol. 1. London: International Psychoanalytical Press, 1924.
—— 1908a. Character and anal eroticism. In *Collected papers.* Vol. 2. London: Hogarth, 1924.
—— 1908b. The relation of the poet to day dreaming. In *Collected papers.* Vol. 4. London: Hogarth, 1925.
—— 1910. The origin and development of psychoanalysis. *Amer. J. Psychol., 21,* 181–218.
—— 1911. Formulations regarding the two principles in psychic functioning. In *Collected papers.* Vol. 4. London: Hogarth, 1925.
—— 1912. The dynamics of the transference. In *Collected papers.* Vol. 2. London: Hogarth, 1924.
—— 1915a. Repression. In *Collected papers.* Vol. 4. London: Hogarth, 1925.
—— 1915b. Instincts and their vicissitudes. In *Collected papers.* Vol. 4. London: Hogarth, 1925.
—— 1915c. Some character types met with in psychoanalytic work. In *Collected papers.* Vol. 4. London: Hogarth, 1925.
—— 1916. On the transformation of instincts with special reference to anal eroticism. In *Collected papers.* Vol. 2. London: Hogarth, 1924.
—— 1917. Mourning and melancholia. In *Collected papers.* Vol. 4. London: Hogarth, 1925.
—— 1923a. The ego and the id. (Trans. by J. Riviere.) London: Institute of Psycho-Analysis and Hogarth Press, 1927.

FREUD, S. 1923b. The infantile genital organization of the libido. In *Collected papers.* Vol. 2. London: Hogarth, 1924.
—— 1924. The passing of the Oedipus Complex. In *Collected papers.* Vol. 2. London: Hogarth, 1924.
—— 1926. The problem of anxiety. (Trans. by H. A. Bunker.) New York: Norton, 1936.
GESELL, A. 1929. Infancy and human growth. New York: Macmillan.
—— 1941. Wolf child and human child. New York: Harper.
GESELL, A., & AMATRUDA, C. S. 1941. Development diagnosis: normal and abnormal child development. New York: Hoeber.
GESELL, A., & THOMPSON, H. 1934. Infant behavior, its genesis and growth. New York: McGraw-Hill.
GREENACRE, P. 1942. The predisposition to anxiety. *Psychoanal. Quart., 10,* 66–94.
GRINKER, R. 1937. Neurology. Springfield, Ill.: C. Thomas.
HALVERSON, H. M. 1938. Infant sucking and tensional behavior. *J. genet. Psychol., 53,* 365–430.
HASELHORST, G., & STROMBERGER, K. 1930–1932. Über den Gasgehalt des Nabelschnurblutes vor und nach der Geburt des Kindes und über den Gasaustausch in der Plazenṭa. *Z. Geburtshilfe, 98,* 49–79, and *100,* 48–70.
HOLT, L. E. 1918. The diseases of infancy and childhood. (7th ed.) New York: Appleton-Century.
HUNT, J. McV. 1941. The effects of infant feeding frustration upon adult hoarding in the albino rat. *J. abnorm. soc. Psychol., 36,* 338–360.
JONES, E. 1916a. The unconscious life of the child. In *Psychoanalysis.* (2nd ed.) New York: Wm. Wood, 1918.
—— 1916b. The child's unconscious. In *Psychoanalysis.* (2nd ed.) New York: Wm. Wood, 1918.
—— 1918. Anal-erotic traits. *J. abnorm. Psychol., 13,* 261–284.
KLEIN, M. 1932. Psychoanalysis of children. New York: Norton.
LANGWORTHY, O. R. 1933. Development of behavior patterns and the myelination of the nervous system in the human infant. *Publ. Carnegie Instn.,* No. 433.
LEVY, D. M. 1928. Finger sucking and accessory movements in early infancy. *Amer. J. Psychiat., 7,* 881–918.
—— 1934. Experiments on the sucking reflex and social behavior in dogs. *Amer. J. Orthopsychiat., 4,* 203–224.
—— 1938. Instinct satiation, an experiment on the pecking behavior of chickens. *J. gen. Psychol., 18,* 327–348.
MARQUIS, D. P. 1931. Can conditioned responses be established in the newborn infant? *J. genet. Psychol., 39,* 479–492.
—— 1941. Learning in the neonate: the modification of behavior under three feeding schedules. *J. exp. Psychol., 29,* 263–282.
MEAD, M. 1935. Sex and temperament in three primitive societies. New York: Morrow.
MINKOWSKI, M. 1921. Sur les mouvements, les réflexes, et les réactions musculaires du foetus humain de 2 à 5 mois. *Rev. Neurol.,* Paris.
MONEY-KYRLE, R. 1939. Superstition and society. London: Hogarth.
MORO, E. 1918. Das erste Trimen. *Münch. med. Wschr., 65,* 947.
MURCHISON, C. 1931. A handbook of child psychology. (1st ed.) Worcester, Mass.: Clark University Press.
PEIPER, A. 1928. Hirntätigkeit des Säuglins. Berlin: Springer.
—— 1932. Aufbau und Zerfall des Atemzentrum. In Brock, J., *Biologische Däten für den Kinderarzt.* Vol. 2. Berlin: Springer.
PRATT, K. C. 1933. The neonate. In Murchison, C., *A handbook of child psychology.* (2nd ed.) Worcester, Mass.: Clark University Press.
RANK, O. 1929. The trauma of birth. New York: Harcourt, Brace.
RIBBLE, M. 1939. Significance of infantile sucking for psychic development. *J. nerv. ment. Dis., 90,* 455–463.
RÓHEIM, G. 1934. The riddle of the Sphinx. London: Hogarth.
SNYDER, F. F., & ROSENFELD, M. 1937a. Direct observation of intrauterine respiratory movements in the foetus and the role of CO_2 and O_2 in their regulation. *Amer. J. Physiol., 119,* 153–166.
—— 1937b. Intrauterine respiratory movements of the human foetus. *J. Amer. med. Assn., 108,* 1946–1948.

SNYDER, F. F., & ROSENFELD, M. 1938. Stages of the development of respiratory regulation and the changes occurring at birth. *Amer. J. Physiol., 121,* 242–249.

TILNEY, F., & KUBIE, L. S. 1931. Behavior in its relation to the development of the brain. *Bull. Neurol. Inst., N. Y., 1,* 229–313.

WORTIS, H. 1941. Some nutritional aspects of brain metabolism. *Psychiat. Quart., 15,* 693–714.

Chapter 21

CHILDHOOD EXPERIENCE IN RELATION TO PERSONALITY DEVELOPMENT

By Lois Barclay Murphy, Ph.D.

STUDIES OF CHILDREN between the ages of weaning and of adolescence have been directed by a group of rather independent trends:[1] (a) interest in what the child communicated verbally, which has provided the material for work, like that of G. Stanley Hall, Stern, and Piaget, on the child's ideas, imagination, moral attitudes, etc.; (b) interest in the child's behavior as observed, with varying degrees of willingness to ask what lay back of the contacts, conflicts, approaches, nervous habits, etc., which were being counted;[2] (c) interest in the child's emotional development, chiefly as this has grown out of the analysis of adult patients whose early sex experience and relationships with parents were found to be of crucial importance for subsequent development.[3]

The relation between early experience and later personality structure has until recently been largely the concern only of this third group, the analysts. Most of the concepts which they used have continued to come from work upon adults, and those analysts who have worked with children (see e.g., A. Freud, 1928, 1937, and Klein, 1937) have tended to take their direction from this earlier work upon adults. This is certainly not without good reason, since the child's interest in sex differences and other experiences connected with the genitals (observation of which is believed to be the basis for the castration complex or fear of loss of the penis or even loss of love) and the child's intense love relation to parents in the preschool period (which becomes involved in the "Oedipus complex"), together with the prevalence of self-comfort patterns (thumb-

---

[1] The reader who is particularly interested in the field covered by this chapter should familiarize himself with the detailed discussion of this area in H. A. Murray's chapter "The genetical investigation of personality: childhood events" in his *Explorations in Personality*. The present chapter makes no attempt to duplicate this much more extensive presentation, but is based primarily on the bibliography presented at the end of this chapter, research at the Sarah Lawrence College Nursery School, and unpublished records of the Institute of Child Welfare in Berkeley, and the Cooperative School in New York.

[2] I refer to studies from about 1928 to 1932 by or under the direction of D. S. Thomas, F. L. Goodenough, W. C. Olson. Bibliographies for and a discussion of these can be found in Murphy, Murphy, and Newcomb (1937).

[3] In the last ten years, this has been supplanted by a growing body of insights based on analytic work with children by Anna Freud, Susan Isaacs, David Levy, E. H Erikson, and others.

sucking and masturbation, see Levy, 1928) have not been successfully challenged.

The time has come, however, to look at childhood experience from a broader perspective than that which revealed these points of reference. The Oedipus complex is primarily a way of describing one aspect of the child's relation with his parents; and there are many other aspects. The relation between sibling rivalry (D. Levy, 1936b) and the Oedipus picture is now seen to be quite as important as the relations with parents. The castration complex is one way of describing some of the small child's feelings about his discovery of sex differences, and the things he can relate to this discovery. The child makes many other discoveries. The development of the Super-ego (Freud, 1923) implies many problems in the kinds of authority experienced by the child, some of which are now being made explicit (Fromm, 1936). The Ego undoubtedly formulates a certain direction for itself, and is caught between the urgings of the Id, or impulse-life, and the pressure of Super-ego, or conscience (see Chapter 3 by Mowrer and Kluckhohn); but what these urgings are may differ so enormously from one child to another as to deserve attention, and they may differ for the same child at different points in his physical development. We can accept the basic point of view which underlies these concepts; that is, that the earliest authority, love, and competitive relationships of the child to his parents, and to his brothers and sisters, are of the greatest importance for his personality development. But we want to look at these emotional relationships in a wider context.

Growth and the Organism-Environment Field.—Growth brings new functions, activities, and awarenesses into the child's experience as he moves from one developmental stage to another. Individual differences of a constitutional sort will determine areas of interest, or susceptibility to the environment, and differences in the meaning of these growth stages, all of which need to be understood in connection with the basic child-adult emotional patterns. Erikson (1940a), Macfarlane (1939), and Fries and Lewi (1938), among others, have contributed major features of this pattern.

Furthermore, both the approach developed in the writing of Goldstein (1939) on the organism and the field-theory of Lewin and his associates (1939) indicate the need for more serious consideration of child-in-total-field. An immediate illustration appears in the personality development of three small boys, each with dominating mothers: one defiant rebellious boy is cared for solely by the mother in a family in which he is the only child and there are no servants. The second, a withdrawn, pseudo-retarded boy, is being cared for by a restricting nurse, while the mother's attention is chiefly given to her career. The third, a disorganized, emotional, aggressive, and lovable boy, is cared for partly by two irritable grandparents, partly by an inefficient maid, partly by the mother when she is not working. The impact of a dominating mother differs, depending on whether it constitutes the chief or a less important aspect of his experience and how it is aggravated or offset by other relationships. Although it is true that in each case the boy had difficulties in achieving a clear identification with a masculine role, the three boys presented strikingly different personality structures. This problem of child-in-total-field is directly related to the problem of variations in experience with the subculture and specific family group, including such patterns as those described in this volume by Bateson (Chapter 23), those described in Bender's (1940) discussion of children whose parents belong to Father Divine's group, and Bühler's (1939) records of differing educational attitudes of parent toward child.

This necessity of looking at Oedipus patterns (in the sense of love relations between parent and child) in the broadest setting and in relation to the total context of parent-child relations is implied in Champney's (1941) analysis of characteristics of the parents in the longitudinal studies of the Fels Research Institute. The character of contact with the child is considered in terms of intensity of contact, duration of contact, and child-centeredness of the home. In a given instance, we may assume, various aspects of the relation between parent and child can be seen in relation to one another, as a step toward understanding the experience for the child which results from the balance of various factors reinforcing or offsetting one another. An intensely affectionate, erotically stimulating mother whose emotions are centered upon her child will give him a different experience from that which an equally intense mother with varied outlets will give her child. Authority-love balances will differ in meaning for the child, as they are experienced in different contexts of great or little time with the mother, general discord or harmony in the home, and the explicitness of love-pleasure responses to the child as compared with those of an authoritarian character. Detailed reports on these patterns may be expected from the Fels Research Institute.

The basic point of view which emerges from consideration of contemporary work on the development of the child is as follows: personality development during the childhood period can be understood completely only when we consider the basic experiences of the child in relation not only to his particular parents, and to universal discoveries of sex differences, but to his individual pattern of physical and mental growth, the specific range of constitutional tendencies (abilities and affective responses), and to the total field (family and neighborhood in a given subculture) in which he is growing up. In the rest of the chapter we shall discuss data and illustrations of specific problems within this basic frame of reference.

Developmental Experiences Vary in Different Subcultures

The experiences of children during infancy, as at other periods, vary strikingly with differences in the particular subculture group in which the child is growing up. This fact has been demonstrated vividly by the

analyses of personality and culture relationships in the writings of
Kardiner, DuBois, Mead, Erikson, Bateson, and the Henrys (see
Chapter 23 by Bateson). The contrast between Tennessee hill-country
families described by Claudia Lewis (1943) and those of metropolitan
areas is not limited to the contrast between the infant who is nursed for
months and the infant who is fed by the bottle method on a rigid schedule. Toilet training is different when there are no toilets. The hill-
country child accompanies his mother on every sort of activity, shopping,
to funerals, and even births, at the age of two to four, while metropolitan
children are usually limited to a relatively restricted area, and generally
accompany mothers only to places like the grocery store and the parks.

The effects of these differences are not trivial. Wayne Dennis
(1940a) has, to be sure, shown that the "minimal attention" type of
handling which has some points in common with the more extremely
routinized methods of handling infants, does not inhibit the basic pattern
of maturation of motor and social skills. But I have not seen any reports
that tell us what "minimal attention" does to the child's personality. We
have seen in the preceding chapter by Dr. Ribble that the trend of
opinion from the clinical side emphasizes the need for emotional warmth
and gratification during the first year of life, as well as attention to
physical needs, if the child is to develop normally (see also Aldrich,
1939). Our longitudinal studies of children from "superior" homes in
Westchester County, New York, include several cases of severe difficulties (including a type of retardation that often yields quickly to warm
attention) resulting from excessive confinement to a nursery until the age
of two or longer, and lack of affectionate contact when a child was being
raised "scientifically." David Levy's (1937) discussion of "affect-hunger"
is concerned with this problem in detail. The emphasis on the child's
need for love and gratification, as well as physical care, illustrated by
Frank's (1938) article, has provided a much-needed corrective to the
trend toward early routine training, and excessive demands for independence.

But it may be questioned whether the present trend is not likely to
lead to overoptimism about the long-time effects of favorable experiences of the first twelve months. The first experiences of frustration
may indeed sometimes traumatize the child, as "Alec" was traumatized,
so that he may never have a completely normal orientation to reality;
or the first experiences of gratification may satisfy the child so deeply
that they truly lay the foundation that determines a healthy direction for
all subsequent personality development. But studies of normal children
who are observed over a period of years indicate that the many extremely
important experiences of the next five years, including those originating
in the child himself (Shirley, 1941), may have great importance. They
may go far toward counterbalancing the ill effects of an unsatisfactory
infancy, or to undermine the first security that has resulted from satisfying experiences. It is hard to find in our culture as dramatic an
illustration of this as Bateson and Mead's (1942) account of Bali

infants who are tenderly nursed and gratified through the first months but emotionally frustrated in the second and third years and later, with resulting emotional indifference to personal relations as adults. The experiences of infancy may determine to a large extent the child's expectations and the attitudes with which he approaches subsequent experiences. Examination of our case records provides instances, however, where extreme gratification has made later frustrations harder to accept, but more attention is being given, doubtless rightfully, to extreme frustration during infancy which often sensitizes the child to further frustration. Specific interests in bottles, or lights, or wheels, which result from frustrations or isolated gratifications, may or may not direct the subsequent development of interests, depending upon release opportunities which may appear during the preschool period to free the child from a premature fixation of interest. Especially striking among our longitudinal records of 90 children are several instances of pseudo-retarded children severely deprived emotionally during infancy, very constrained as a result, whose intelligence quotients increased by 20 to 30 points during one to three years in nursery school (see also Kephart and Strauss, 1940; Skeels, *et al.*, 1938; Wellman, 1940). Just as important as the increase in IQ was the general expansion and broadening of response to children and materials, accompanied by release from the preoccupations that absorbed their attention during the constrained period. The assumption of flexibility of personality and the possibility of release underlies all therapy, of course. The point here is that accidental therapy provided by changes in the environment or parents' security may operate as effectively as planned therapy to change the total balance of childhood experience and that the child's resilience sometimes provides its own therapy as Shirley (1941) indicates.

Three years ago, approximately 150 nursery school teachers chiefly from W.P.A. nursery schools sent in reports of characteristic patterns among families in their communities, which included mill and factory towns from the middle west, migratory camps in California, Chinese-American communities and others. It was clear from these reports (Murphy, 1940) that some of the incompletely Americanized groups, such as those which were predominantly Bulgarian or Italian, were giving children more of the kind of warmth and consistent mothering which psychiatry and pediatrics have recently come to consider desirable than were the more completely Americanized groups (J. P. Anderson, 1940, Baruch, 1937). The unspoiled maternal attitude has much to counteract, however, when it confronts the instability of depression years for children migrating from the Dust-bowl to tents in California where "we ain't got nothing for keeps," or sudden changes of the Defense areas, which move families unexpectedly out of their village life. Changes of longer trend are also bringing into existence new configurations of child-adult relationships, as the proportion of children to adults changes and the number of old people increases. In the various subculture groups, we find then different combinations of *gratification and frustration*; a satisfying infancy does not necessarily compensate for economic deprivation in the next ten years, and there is increasing evidence that later gratification may go far toward offsetting the effects of early frustration.

Maturation and the Socialization of New Functions in the Preschool Period

The appearance of walking and talking brings a period of active socialization for nearly all middle-class children. In families where property is particularly important, manipulatory activities, exploration, keeping out of dirt, and not messing around may be major issues (Lerner and Murphy, 1941). An impressionable child may recoil from manipulating things and become inhibited in manual activities as a result of this training; or he may become so preoccupied with orderliness that he does not play freely with toys. If he is more spirited and stubborn, he may persist in handling things his own way; or he may learn when, where, and how to handle things. The patterns of inhibition or spontaneity developed in this way are reflected in the structures that are created in his handling of toys and plastics. The anxiety which arises from excessive constraint or guilt about manipulation both of objects and of himself, may become generalized so that it is also expressed in social attitudes and in bodily posture. Our records also show instances where a general anxiety acts as a general inhibitor on both manipulatory and locomotor activities, and sometimes speech as well.

Locomotion—that is, walking, climbing, jumping, sliding, and all other leg-activities that become possible when coordination of legs improves—may have similar possibilities; encouragement may lead to the development of security in getting around the world of space and objects; interference, anxiety, or punishment from adults for locomoting into, onto, down from, or up on the wrong places, may block the use and enjoyment of new coordinations. Or these frustrations may lead to compulsive concern with substitute activities such as unhooking, unscrewing, unlocking, i.e., opening the closed or forbidden places. Children in apartments are very often exposed to a great deal of inhibition of locomotion; if you dance, jump, hop, or skip, the neighbors on the floor below may protest. When compensatory outlets are afforded by all-day nursery schools or playgrounds, the child may be able to structure his activity in terms of areas of freedom and areas of control. But without such compensatory outlets he may become inhibited, or confused and anxious about motor activity.

Even language, which does not damage property, may become a source of new rapport with adults who are delighted with the increasing companionship that comes with the child's ability to communicate his thoughts. or it may have a nuisance-value for the parent who is irritated by two- and three-year-old chatter. We have instances of children who, blocked by adult restraint of manipulation or locomotion, compulsively use language as a substitute.

Manipulation, locomotion, and language are then three obvious developmental experiences which, because of what they stimulate the child to do, and how they are treated in the child's family and broader culture-group, acquire valences and meanings which become deeply embedded in the child's personality.

Interaction of Mother's Personality with Growth-Needs of the Young Child.—As these and other new capacities emerge, our records indicate that the influence of the mother and others in the family largely determine what these new capacities for experience will mean to the child, what new securities they may bring, and what new threats they may present. Probably no family succeeds in making maximal use of each developmental stage for the child's personality development. In infancy, the protective mother may give the child a great deal of satisfaction if she is the kind who is protective because she is fond of babies and gets a great deal of satisfaction from them. But at the stage of expanding locomotion and exploration, the overprotective mother becomes an inhibitor and deprives the child of opportunities which he needs to use his new abilities (see also Levy, 1939a). This deprivation may be even more disturbing to the child who has earlier been handled permissively than to the child who has made some kind of adjustment to early deprivations.

The excessively scientific mother, or rejecting mother, or other type of mother who deprives the child of emotional satisfaction at the infancy level, may by contrast give the child more approval and emotional satisfaction at the locomotor period, because she is pleased by the new signs of independence. This may be releasing to the child, or he may overreact so that he becomes compulsive about the new activities which gain so much approval; this may then lead to a kind of forced spontaneity or exploratory activity which we see not uncommonly among children from homes which give little affection and much encouragement to motor activity.

On the other hand, mothers who are unable to accept the child's increasing explorativeness, may virtually imprison him, keeping him "out of the way" or "safe" in crib, playpen, playroom, or fenced-in yard, so as to minimize his nuisance-value, and thus add this deprivation of the exploratory stage to the basic emotional deprivation of the earlier stages. Or the child may not feel deprived, but may accept the place-confinement with subsequent fear of new places and dependence upon some definite home-base.

The experience which the child has at each new stage depends then partly on how this new stage is interpreted and accepted by those who surround him, and the values they place upon it. The values of individual mothers even in a limited culture-area may vary considerably. Dan's mother accepts *boisterous activity, but not dirt*; her son remarked, "There isn't any place to dig in my garden, there isn't any place for myself." Another mother accepts boisterousness and dirt but gets explosive when things are *broken*. Another mother does not mind any consequences of vigorous exploratory activity, but gets very anxious *when the child regresses* to earlier phases, such as thumb-sucking or bed-wetting. In each case the mother has some criterion for success; she feels successful when her child is clean, or well-behaved, or has good habits; she feels that she is a failure when he is not.[4]

This discussion of universal experiences of growth in the early pre-school period has illustrated the variations in the meaning of these experiences to the child, as these variations are related to parental handling and attitudes toward these growth experiences. Parental handling and attitudes cannot be completely separated from the question of individual differences in the original values of locomotion, manipulation, and language to the child himself.

The child with more active sensory interests and less skilful coordination, described by Shirley (1939), may often be more responsive to sensory stimuli and less interested in social experiences or in experiences involving skilled coordination. If, as in the case of several children in the writer's social behavior study (Murphy, 1937), the child wants music, dancing, or the enjoyment of fascinating objects like cars, for the sake of the enjoyment, not for the sake of constructive activity, his experience will vary with the mother's or teacher's willingness to encourage, or compulsion to frustrate, the child's preferred response. In our culture, children whose own interests lead them to longer periods of appreciation rather than to "constructive" activity are less likely to receive approval than those who build with blocks, and ride tricycles early. In some groups construction is virtually a criterion of good adjustment.

Authority Patterns Experienced by the Child

Variations in the methods of exercising authority must be seen in relation to the total pattern of the parents' personalities and of the home life, as well as variations in the children's sensitivity to different kinds of treatment. Regardless of the mother's concern and the mother's interests, and regardless of particular patterns of child-adult companionships in any community, the methods of enforcing authority and attitudes with which socialization is done are also of importance for the child's personality (Fromm, 1934). Fromm-Reichmann (1940) and

---

[4] Oddly enough, recent reports on the Sioux (Erikson, 1939), the Hopi (Dennis, 1940b), the Navaho (Kluckhohn, 1942), and other Indian groups in this country are giving us a more complete conception of the rearing of infants and young children in these cultures than we have for a comparable variety of white or of Negro children. We actually know rather little about the variations in gratification, frustration balance, or the specific experiences of preschool children outside of a few university centers.

others point out that in this country the processes of socialization and personality development of the child are complicated by the fact that both discipline and love are to so large a degree centered in the mother, in contrast to the European pattern of family life where the father has been predominantly the giver of discipline, and the mother the giver of love. Where this is true, it must affect the development of identification with the parents, though it must result in a somewhat different form of the Oedipus pattern, since the daughter is confronted with the necessity to identify with the person who is frustrating her as well as loving her, and the son may not feel the father as "strong" since he does not figure so vigorously in discipline situations, and may therefore sometimes find it difficult to switch his identification from mother to father (see also Mowrer and Kluckhohn, Chapter 3).

Related to this is the problem of the balance of love, protection, and attention with discipline and control. The literature (see Symonds, 1939) is full of admonitions to mothers to avoid the pitfalls of over-protecting, overloving, underloving, overdisciplining and giving too little discipline, giving too little attention and companionship or too much, identifying too closely or too little with the child. With all of the discussion of these pitfalls and their undesirable results, there is little recognition of the relative rather than the absolute nature of these excesses and deficiencies. Each mother is herself, and has not been selected by any omniscient agency as parent to her particular child. What is overprotection for one child is underprotection for another; an amount of affection which fails to satisfy one child's craving stifles another; an amount and kind of discipline that is inconsequential for one child is very inhibiting to a more timid one. In an unpublished study, Anna Hartoch points out that the child's longings, capacities to resist, to accept, to evade, to build his own world for himself will to a large extent determine what a given parent's balance of love, discipline, attention, and protection will do to him or for him.

Whatever these experiences have been, of being loved, disciplined, protected, and attended to (too little or too much for him) they become deeply a part of his affective and mental development, so that his behavior, the words he uses (Despert, 1938a, 1940), the games he makes up (Lowenfield, 1939), the way he responds to a Rorschach test (Amen, 1940), or to free play with miniature toys (Erikson, 1940b), and a host of other everyday behavior, betray these experiences, the way in which they have furnished his life-space, and the balance of inhibition and spontaneous satisfaction which they permit him (Lerner and Murphy, 1941).

The Child's Life-Space.—These authority-love relations with his parents are, however, only a part of the picture; the environment they create for him, the rhythm of life which emerges from the pattern of their activities, also shapes his life-space and is assimilated into the structure of his personality. The home which is rigidly organized and proper, the home which is chaotic, the home which has certain areas of clear organization with other areas of freedom, the home which is specially concerned with eating or sleeping, or with new furnishings and decorations, or with much company coming and going—each of these has been spontaneously depicted by a three- or four-year-old child who has been given the opportunity to describe his life-space in free play with toys, without knowing that this is what he is doing (Lerner and Murphy, 1941). The way in which he organizes objects, however, is not the only record of this home experience; his organization of objects is often related to his pattern of inhibitions or freedom of bodily movements, conversation, and emotional expression. What he does with paint is not independent, unrelated to his play with toys, or with other children, but usually reflects the same underlying attitudes of freedom to experience new situations, a need to create a protective structure before he can be free, or a need to compensate for pressures and restraints against which he rebels (Schmidl-Waehner, 1943). These illustrations describe only a few of the possible patterns which observation of the child's expression will give; the specific structure and content of any child's expression will be his own.

Eating, and washing, and going to bed makes a routine pattern which seems to form the basis of one child's life, which he contrasts with the spontaneity of animals in the woods; another organizes life within the house in a mechanical way, but carries on outside of the home exciting activities such as boat and train rides, horse and dog shows, which correspond accurately to the pattern of his own life. These experiences of fun, excitement, and participation contribute to the whole texture of life as the young child experiences it, and form the backdrop against which experiences of discipline or deprivation or love seem more or less important. A family that is in many ways rigid and overcontrolled may stimulate spontaneity in a child by having an active dog or kitten in the house; or by allowing freedom for play with neighborhood children; or by providing experience at a releasing nursery school. The total balance of hours spent and satisfaction gained on the side of release as compared with the inhibition side may determine not only the thematic content of the child's consciousness, but whether or not he needs to rely on actions of obstinacy, overcompliance, or evasive detachment, and whether he carries along anxiety and irritation regarding authority and the grownups. If his experience with parents has been satisfactory, the identification with them which results may, according to Zucker (1943), be one of the most important deterrents to delinquent behavior.

Individual Susceptibilities in Response to Social Experience

We must now return to the question of the *individual way in which each child experiences the events and attitudes to which he is exposed.* Burgum's recent article (1940) on some positive results of rejection must imply just what we have been saying: that a given experience will mean different things to different children depending on the child's needs and resources. The children who showed severe personality reactions to experiences of emotional malnutrition in our studies were by no means children from families which were unique. They came from families that were not spontaneous and warm, to be sure; but their families in all likelihood would be no more lacking emotionally than those of a number of other children who had survived without showing neurotic or prepsychotic signs of any sort. Similarly, children who show strong resistance to authority are not merely those who have had excessive authority. Discipline which rolls off the back of one child will keep another child awake at night. This seems obvious enough when put this way, but it is often left out of account when discussing parental patterns in relation to the experience of the child. Often we discuss the child's behavior in terms of what the parent has done and fail to ask what the child was like to start with and how his sensitivities and resources have affected his response to the parent. Reports of the mature personalities of twins reared apart under grossly differing conditions, such as extreme rejection for one twin and great security for the other, indicate how powerful the inherent pattern of personality development is (Burks, 1942). Only slightly less startling are the data on differences in the personality structure of twins reared together (Troup, 1938; see also Chapter 16 by Penrose).

What are some of the possible innate factors that may affect a child's response to the amount of love and discipline that he gets? An infant's satisfaction in contact and cuddling or social experiences (Washburn, 1929) is one item; the thresholds of one child are lower for these experiences than are those of another child. A child's sensitivity to sounds, loud noises, and to physical pain will play a part in determining how painful the scoldings and spankings actually are. His thresholds for reactions to sudden experiences, to changes in atmosphere, will also be important in relation to his response to the variability of a parent's mood.

Or we may take, as another example, comparable situations of family structure, which again point up how the child selects from the situation what he will react to and make use of, thereby creating his experience. In a pair of families there are two active parents in each case, with an active and vigorous older brother and a younger sister. In one case the sister is an artistic, independent youngster who does not identify with the rest of the family intensely, but has built up a sturdy world of her own. In the other case the younger sister "insists on her rights" and tries to keep up with older brother at every point. More consistently included in the group of older members of the family, she has probably more conflict about her role than the other sister who has accepted a more independent relation to the family, although she is more isolated. When we look at older sisters with young brother, we find different relations also, depending on the resources of the two children, their energy and growth patterns. One older sister is dominant, preferred, secure, indifferent to her younger brother. Another feels dispossessed, unable to cope with the greater energy, physical vigor, even size of her younger brother, and retreats into a shell. It is doubtless because of these many variations, obvious or subtle, in the capacities and feelings of children that it has been so hard to get a clear formula for the personality consequences of a given sibling constellation. In a broad statistical sense there probably are some character-trends associated with family position (Murphy, Murphy, and Newcomb, 1937, pp. 348–363), but the trends are often overwhelmed by individual factors. The child chooses, not consciously, but nevertheless significantly, what his particular family constellation is going to do to him, and of course we may add, what he is going to do to it.

The discussion so far has repeatedly implied that constitutional differences in the child must be taken into account in evaluating the actual experience which results from exposure to any pattern of parent attitudes or handling, or indeed any pattern offered by the culture at all. These differences include not only the measured and recorded differences of physical dimensions, of performance on intelligence tests, and of sensory and motor functions such as pitch discrimination and muscular strength; they include the thousands of other differences, such as those of sensitivity to pain, of response to color, to sound, of readiness for motor or manual coordinations, which are familiar to teachers acquainted with many children. Psychiatrists, well aware of the conditioning influences of all parental attitudes, have been inclined to put the burden of proof on the person who pointed out possible innate differences as responsible for such difficulties as inability to spell, do arithmetic, draw, or act. They found it easy to point to cogent evidence that Mary T. obviously had reading difficulties because of her emotional tension over her sister's superiority; and that Billy D. had been put under so much pressure from his father that his difficulties were largely due to resistance to his father's authority pattern. This type of thinking has contributed a great deal to our understanding of a child's development in so far as emotional conflicts actually are responsible for specific competences or difficulties. But it has also helped to postpone the day when we would arrive at a more complete picture of the two-way passage of interaction between child and parent which underlies the child's personality as we see it. Horace English some years ago (1929) pointed out that even such an obvious hypothesis as Watson's statement about loud sounds as a cause of fear needed to be revised with some attention to individual differences. He cited the behavior of a small girl who, sitting in a high chair, heard the violent sound of a two-pound hammer striking an iron spring behind her chair, without giving any evidence of fear at all. Jean Macfarlane (1939), with a background of both clinical experience and training in experimental psychology, has been following the evidences of consistent patterns of adjustment of infants and children. Her data suggest that instead of confining our notions of variability in human beings to whatever cortical functions underlie differences as they are measured in studies of intelligence and physique, we might better think of each infant *as an individual organism* with its own pattern of thresholds or readiness for stimulation or responsiveness.

R. W. Washburn's early reports (1929) of striking individual differences in readiness for laughter, and the more recently published reports of Gesell and his associates (1940) noting important differences in perceptiveness or awareness of infants, as well as the differences in perceptual and manipulative abilities, contribute further support to this approach. Shirley's (1939) study of about 200 premature children indicates that these children show greater responsiveness to sensory stimuli, such as colors, sounds, tones, textures; greater emotional responsiveness; but less skilful motor coordinations. These factors may combine to give a "syndrome" of "sensitiveness" which makes the personality development of these children similar despite their genetic differences.

Margaret Fries, who has been especially interested in the way in which infants respond to frustration rather than in the skills studied by Gesell or the patterns of responsiveness noted by Shirley, observes (Fries and Lewi, 1938) that among the children she has watched from birth, clear differences may be seen between those who adjust to frustration in passive ways and those who are more active (see also Ribble, Chapter 20, who notes these reaction types in the newborn). It would be interesting to relate these differences both to the pattern of abilities and to the interests of the child, especially in the light of those differences in sensory and motor skills or responsiveness which Shirley discussed. This difference in activity-level in response to frustration may be related to the difference between infants who show *overt* as compared with *internal* evidences of emotional response as described by H. E. Jones (1935). But we do not yet have a study which combines behavior observation, physiological measures and the equivalent of a Rorschach for infants, to show us the relation between these differences and their meaning for the personality structure of individual children. (In this connection, recall also the "inhibited" and "excited" dogs of Pavlov; see Chapter 12 by Liddell.)

Macfarlane (1939) summarizes her own analyses of longitudinal studies of several hundred children in terms which integrate all of the findings referred to above. She sees the individual child as sharing common needs, response patterns, and susceptibility to stimulation with other children; but he also possesses individual characteristics "which make for differing susceptibilities to stimulation, differing needs and differing response patterns." She comments:

> Whether these differences are in large part a function of heredity and maturational processes, or in large part a function of modification of basic structure by health, special experiences or differing environmental pressures and assaults, they exist and must be inspected along with common structure in terms of their meaning to the adjustive process. . . . Differences exist in morphology, size and rate of growth, muscular equipment, nervous reactivity, sensory acuity,

energy level, achievements, tensional states (directly organic, and produced by conflicting reaction patterns). Not only are there specific
differences, but differences in configurations of equipment occur
which have differing influences both upon susceptibility to stimulation
and upon response patternings. The child who is at either end of the
distribution curve has not only different organic stresses to contend
with than the child in the middle of the distribution—a fact which
may influence behavior appreciably—but he may also develop totally
different attitudes and reactions toward himself through continuous
comparisons with the group. And additionally, because certain
behavior is precluded or fostered for him by these facts of equipment, he may receive differential treatment by the social environment
and an even larger discrepancy in behavior may appear than these
structural differences (in and of themselves) would produce. (1939,
pp. 4–5)

Constitutional differences are at least indirectly involved also in differences between three four-year-old boys who use aggressive behavior in
different situations: one is aggressive only when blocked or frustrated
or interfered with; another is aggressive when he is afraid; another is
aggressive as a way of enhancing his sense of bigness.

Probably innate differences in sensitivity to form and structure are
important in contributing to one child's extreme sensitiveness to adult
patterns (with resulting strong Super-ego development), while another
child faced with similar standards but possessing less sensitivity to form
is not so strict with himself (see Sheldon, Chapter 17). Differences in
the extent to which individual children resort to thumb-sucking and
masturbation are not only the result of the amount of frustration or need
for comfort, but are related to the strength of these satisfactions in comparison with others.

Growth Spurts Create Sensitivities.—Erikson's analysis (1940a)
of the importance of growth nodes for experience thresholds is important both for groups and for individual children. He emphasized the
importance of "proper rate" and "normal sequence" of development in
the successive manifestations of personality, on the analogy of the pattern
of sequences which must take place in its preordained order if the embryo
is to emerge with normal equipment for physiological functioning. *Each
new phase of post-natal development* brings its own opportunities for
satisfaction in functioning, and its own need for adequate satisfaction at
each level. *Interruption* of sucking, manipulation, motor activity, or
speech may not only have important consequences for this function but
for a wide range of personality and behavior traits related to it. *Traumas*
during early childhood are likely to find a response at that point which,
through recency of maturation, is most vulnerable, and most easily apt
to become disorganized. Thus, a child who has been walking six or eight
months with considerable security but only recently talking, will not be
so likely to show disturbance of general motor coordination as of speech,

if shocked by a traumatic experience at that point. Here again, we may say that the *point of lowest thresholds will determine the way in which a given external event will be experienced by the child.*

The child's experiences of his own growth pattern may also be intensified *when spurts of growth do not coincide with those of most of his friends:* unpublished records from the Jones longitudinal studies of children from ten to sixteen at Berkeley include instances of children who gain additional security from the consciousness of early physical maturing, and also records of other children who, though secure in leadership at ten, become unhappy when other children spurt ahead of them, or when others develop masculine and feminine interests of adolescence for which they themselves are not ready.

The Child's Experience of Self

The child's own sense of himself, or experience of self-hood, probably overlaps only partially with the self that we ascribe to him when we make a complete inventory of the characteristics of his individuality. For his experience of self is built partly out of the reactions of other people to his individuality: what his height-weight ratio means to them in relation to that of other children, or their ideal, or his parents' expectations. Partly it is built out of his own comparisons of himself with others. The child, as Schilder (1935) points out, perceives his own movements with an experience of ease and pleasure or of effort, and also has the experience of keeping up, or not keeping up, with the movements of others. He experiences his face as one which evokes smiles, or withdrawal, or sympathy from others; he also experiences it, sooner or later, as one which "doesn't fit my personality"—as one nine-year-old would-be boxing expert commented—or one which does fit, or *is* his personality. So with his abilities: intelligence, talents, capacities for social communication, leadership, and simple things like size and strength. Defects and diseases not only produce physical sequelae which are important for the personality as seen by others; they produce patterns of desire, will, aspiration-levels, and estimations of self that make up the child's feeling of himself. The vigorous, spastic child described by Gesell (1939), who succeeded in getting his friends to help him through a tunnel in which they had been crawling, had a different conception of self from that of a more passive child.

This process of self-evaluation is not dependent solely upon social responses to the physical differences we have discussed. It may be subtly bound up with the child's affective responses to the external world. Thus a child who is small and who also has a tendency to perceive and enjoy and use fine detail may find in himself a likeness to those objective qualities in the outside world which are satisfying. Such a child may be less likely to show marked compensatory behavior directed at overcoming his experience of small size than a child of the same build whose affective and perceptual patterns are the reverse. If a child who is small enjoys larger units in the objective world, and the activity that goes with them, he may be stimulated to attempt them even though his size places him at a disadvantage. Thus we see small individuals whose whole life seems dominated by a quality of fine or dainty or detailed activity which appears to be both a part of themselves and a response to the external world. Similarly we may find large children whose whole life is an expression of largeness, being large, responding to large activities, and enjoying it, while others are uncomfortable with their size because their perceptual-affective responses ask for different values. Another example is that of the child whose sensitivity to tactual and texture experiences leads her to enjoy soft materials and objects, and who may identify her own soft hair, skin, dresses with this pleasant experience, while another child with the same perceptual and affective responses does not find these satisfactions in herself. Patterns of self-loving, or of dependence upon the outside world, or of conflict between inner and outer values may be rooted in this type of experience, as Schilder (1939) has suggested, granted that socialization processes augment or frustrate the spontaneous pattern.

Macfarlane (1939) summarizes the social aspects of the child's adjustive pattern and of the value he places upon himself, with the illustration of the small boy whose experience will differ, depending upon whether his father was a football hero and expects his son to be one, or a college professor with a desire that his son follow that tradition. Similarly, she observes, this boy has a very different adjustive picture if his brothers are larger and more athletic than he has if they are like himself. "His size, then, takes on meaning in terms of (1) the other aspects of his structural equipment; (2) in terms of the size of people with whom he is closely associated; (3) in terms of family and social expectancies and values connected with size or achievement dependent on size . . .; (4) in terms of the adequacy of other family and social supports; and (5) in terms of the success of direct or compensatory achievements which do not depend on size." In addition, "His vulnerability may vary in a fast-growing or slow-growing period because of physiological changes, or new adjustments to learn . . . or because of new attitudes and pressures from outside to which he must adjust" (p. 5).

Up to this point we have tried to illustrate in different ways the general principle that the young child's experience, and the personality it produces, varies both with the particular events, attitudes, patterns of objects, and people to which he is exposed, and with the pattern of thresholds for response to, or needs for, different types of stimulation inherent in both the relatively stable and the rapidly changing aspects of his own organic structure at the time the experience occurs. (For some behavioral correlates of various types of structure, see Chapter 17 by Sheldon.)

Changing Status in Early Childhood

All children are exposed to the shifting attitudes of parents, of siblings, and of other persons in immediate contact with the child—attitudes which shift as the changing behavior, appearance, interests, and activities of the growing child fit into or conflict with the parents' style of life, or image of what is desirable in a child. Most children show some periods when they are either an ego-asset or an ego-hazard to their parents. If, as an infant, the child is beautiful, brilliant, cute, or in other ways fulfils the parents' expectations of what a baby should be, he obtains rapport easily. If he appears ugly, or possessed of the undesirable traits of "the other side of the family," or seems dull, or unresponsive, the parent may be frustrated and cannot help but give the child a different response: either compensatory pity, defensive love, or unconscious or conscious coolness or rejection. If the child changes as he grows, and becomes definitely more, or definitely less, beautiful, well-behaved, physically adequate, or conforming to the conventional pattern for his age, the parents' attitudes may change, depending on how fluid the parents' own attitudes are. In particular, if an originally "good" child becomes, in response to frustrations too great for him to deal with easily, a "bad" child, the parents' irritation and anxiety are likely to add to the frustration and set up a circle which is hard to penetrate. However, neither painful treatment nor excessive attention from adults brings a uniform response from every child; one child may develop a protective wall or mask to defend himself against the very attention that another child has come to crave. In each case, however, the interactions with people have contributed to the personality structure of the child, the narcistic wounds or ego-inflation, and his defenses against further hurt or his expectations of further adulation.

Nursery School Experience.—Experiences in nursery school are also different for different children. Some children, frustrated in non-child-oriented homes and inhibited by their experience, may respond quickly to the permissive and warm atmosphere of a good nursery school. The mother discovers that the child who "never smiled" and who seemed unappealing has now become lovable, and is herself warmed into responsiveness. The reverse, unfortunately, may also happen. A child who has grown up in a protected home, where he has been gay and serene in the warm atmosphere of parental affection, goes to nursery school, and may find himself bewildered by the presence of many children who seem to be competitors. Such previous experience is unlikely to give him techniques for dealing with the combination of aggressive, exploratory, playful overtures which he may receive from other children.

Reports from many groups make clear the great amount of conflict which the nursery school child experiences, although this varies with the space, equipment, and age-range of the children in different groups, as well as with the authority patterns of teachers (Fite, 1940; Murphy,

1937; Jersild and Markey, 1937; Roff and Roff, 1940). Protection from and cooperation with others of one's own age are other aspects of participation in a large group, and this rich experience may bring dramatic changes in the expressions of personality, whether or not it touches the basic structure set by earlier experience in the family.

The vivid experience of moving from the group of little ones to the big ones affords many children at the age of four considerable compensation for the inevitable sense of littleness in relation to the adults at home. This sense of bigness in the nursery group is sometimes accompanied by an aggressive and dominating expression of the ego-enhancement to which it gives rise, only to be followed by deflation as the child goes to the still larger group of kindergarten in a school where he is once again among the littlest. In our culture where the educational system is divided into a sequence of schools—elementary school, junior high school, high school, and college or technical school—the child has a sequence of inflating experiences in being among the oldest in each group, which are followed by deflation as he becomes one of the youngest in the next school.

Ego development during the preschool period is not only enhanced by the promotion experiences during that period; it is furthered by the conscious philosophy of many schools which regards the cardinal points of the curriculum to be the encouragement of the child in his explorations and experiments with materials and people. Children have more space, often, than they could have at home, are greeted with more tolerance, and are treated to a more consistent response from calmer adult authority. Anxiety arising from the confusion of Oedipus and authority problems at home can be relieved by the clarity of areas of permissiveness and areas of tabu at school. The anxieties related to sex, which may be heightened by an intense sibling rivalry situation at home, may also be diluted by participation in a larger group which permits the expression and restructuring of hostilities and fears toward other children, and the development of security with them.

In the nursery school period, differentiation in patterns of personal interaction develops rapidly. Isaacs (1933) analyzes aspects of aggression rooted in rivalry and possessiveness, while the writer (Murphy, 1937) finds that sympathetic behavior takes a variety of forms, including solicitude, helping, defending, comforting. From a statistical point of view, not all varieties of personal interaction patterns are equally characteristic of all children. On the contrary, in the writer's study of sympathy some children used many patterns of behavior while others used only one or two. Even among children with high frequency of responses to other children, and a varied repertoire, one pattern such as defense of another child, or comforting another child, or helping another child, or warning another child would be especially characteristic of certain children. This seems to suggest the early formation of a personality structure in which each type of social response to a specific situation (sympathetic or aggressive) is channeled by a pervasive need (to be active, emotional, anxious, dominating) which determines the way in which the child will express sympathy and aggression, or other social responses.

Typical Patterns of Personality Change

We have indicated that even during the first three or four years of the preschool period a child's "personality" may change owing to the rapidly changing character of his physique, his abilities, and his needs, and to the response of others to him at one time and to his changes. The frequency of such changes or variability is implicit in a number of statistical analyses of children's behavior reviewed in *The Influence of Social Situations on the Behavior of Children* (Murphy and Murphy, 1935). Some of the important patterns of development may be discussed now.

Perhaps the simplest pattern whereby experience becomes structured is based on this principle: the child obtains a satisfaction, wants more of the same, gets it, and builds a pattern of wanting, getting, and expecting a certain type of satisfaction. Early interest in food, physical romping play, music, smearing, painting, may become established through this simple mechanism (see principles of learning in Chapter 3).

The experience, however, may be repeated not only because the child finds it satisfying and spontaneously demands it. It may be repeated for the good reasons of the adults who may consciously or unconsciously find it useful to instrumentalize the child's experience for their own purposes. Oral satisfaction is thus encouraged to "quiet the child" when he is given a soother. Humor, or music in the form of soothing songs or the radio or victrola, may be used to distract him or comfort him or keep him quiet.

If this instrumentalizing has been successful, the child may continue the use of these soothers, oral, auditory, or whatever, for himself when he is older and able to dose himself with comics, swing or Beethoven, life-savers, or a pipe. The question whether this adjustive function of the experience continues uninterrupted may depend upon the subsequent attitudes of the culture, i.e., other children and adults whom he meets. The pattern may be reinforced by approval: "Isn't it fine that he likes Beethoven?" Or it may be punished by disapproval: "Isn't it dreadful that he still sucks his thumb at the age of six?" This cultural reinforcement or conflict then determines in the end whether the simple adience and instrumentalizing of experience has its way, or whether the child sustains his early satisfaction with a burden of conflict and guilt, or gives it up under pressure.

But suppose the desire is interfered with after initial satisfaction, as through weaning, or other deprivations. Depending upon the strength of the organic tension underlying the need, the desire may be repressed with the help of some defense against feeling it, or may give rise to continued demands for satisfaction, or for substitutes, or for retaliation upon the depriver.

Instrumental values may also facilitate some spontaneous psychosomatic patterns of adjustment in the case of many children. The attention value of a stomach-upset, the frustration-to-adult value of constipation, are familiar enough. Similar functions also appear for temper tantrums and perhaps for compulsive questioning or demands for gifts. But this principle must not be carried too far, and in the case of nightmares, phobias, hyperactivity, and vague or confused reality orientation we need to look at more primary forces. Here the distinction of Fries and Lewi (1938) between those who respond passively and those who respond actively to experiences of frustration may need more elaboration. One type of passive child may handle his problems with a rich fantasy development, while another may withdraw more deeply into himself and fail to use the reality world even in fantasy or dreams. One active child may remain normal in every respect except for the development of very restricted phobias, while another becomes scattered or "wild." There is no evidence that such differences are instrumental in origin. On the contrary, it is likely that they point to the fact that each organism has its own thresholds for breakdown, and its own pattern of breakdown when it comes, just as it has its own thresholds for positive response to the array of experience to which it is exposed.

Within limitations set by the amount of fixation to which such processes have led, personality is still relatively flexible in the preschool period. Jersild and Fite (1939) showed how the child's adjustment to nursery school may vary with the relation which he has to his group, particularly with the presence or absence of a friend or child with whom he feels secure: the writer pointed out how relatively impersonal aspects of group structure could make the difference between an outgoing, active social child and a child who scored low on social traits; Jack (1934) and Page (1942) demonstrated experimentally how a child's rating on shyness could be changed by special training in skills in which he competed with other children; Keister and Updegraff (1937) showed experimentally how a child's attitude toward failure could be changed with understanding training. Most of these same points regarding the flexibility of personality and the child's capacity to change in his attitudes toward experience could be made also in reference to the elementary school period (Lowenstein and Svendsen, 1938). Here we have as evidence chiefly the demonstrations of Lewin, Lippitt, and White (1939) that differences in aggressive behavior may result from a shift from a democratic to an autocratic pattern of adult authority.

Changes in release, in amounts of gratification or frustration, may "make a different child out of" almost any youngster at the age of four. I have often quoted the story of the little boy who was removed from one nursery school for kicking, spitting, distractible behavior, temper tantrums. He was also biting his finger nails very badly. He was brought to another nursery school where, when he started to spit at children, the teacher said with amusement, "You can spit in the toilet if you want to, but not here." Feeling his need for attention and response she handled him affectionately. All of the extreme behavior for which he had been punished in the other nursery school vanished immediately and within three weeks he had also stopped biting his finger nails. His comment to his mother after the first day was, "My teacher smiled at me all day long, I like this nursery school."

There are, however, individual differences in flexibility and rigidity of response to experience which may account for some of the variations in success of such efforts to help a child's adjustment. Lerner found a wide range of such patterns in his studies of ego-blocking, and they also appear in my studies of records of free play with miniature toys. (Lerner and Murphy, 1941). Tentatively we may say that rigid and artificially imposed habit-training is apt to beget rigidity in other aspects of a child's response to experience. The report on the later development of twins *T* and *C* (Gesell and Thompson, 1941) gives an important confirmation of some of the expectations which we have come to have regarding the effects of rigid training. The twin, for example, who received some hundreds of hours of special, formal training writes a systematic, colorless, constrained story-account of graduation, while the untrained twin writes a personal, enthusiastic, spontaneous account. The trained twin draws in straight-line and angular patterns, where the untrained twin uses curving lines. The trained twin has fewer movement responses on the Rorschach (indication of inner fantasy and imaginative life) than the untrained twin. Cause and effect are of course not conclusively proven. More longitudinal studies of individual children are needed to give us enough data for the construction of sound principles of type-formation in personality development in childhood.

Granting that many children still show considerable flexibility in their response to new experience, we find some who show definite patterns of change which are not necessarily related to changes in group-structure or atmosphere. We have records of children who appeared to be extremely passive during their third or fourth year, but who became very active a year later, often showing marked aggression, or leadership. We also have records of children who begin their contacts with a new group very actively and later become shy or constrained. Their direct outgoing methods have not been adequate, perhaps, to cope with the complexity of the situations with which they have had to deal, and they must go through a belated taking-in period to get more oriented. These changes in extraversion and introversion are more familiar at the adolescent level where we have come to expect them as a normal part of the adjustment to the deeply significant changes in the biology of the child and his relations with his group and with adults.

Many research studies point to approximately the third year as a peak time for resistance or negativism (Murphy, Murphy, and Newcomb, 1937). If we see this in relation to the child's experience at that time it seems inevitable that this should be so. Just at the time that the child gets some sense of security in locomotion and large-muscle activities so that he begins to feel some power over objects in his world, he also acquires some competence in speech. His increasing competence carries along its own urge for opportunity to use his skills, to get around his world independently, and to enjoy his new sense of self. But the adults must teach him when, how, what, where, he can be allowed to do the things he wants so much to do. They have a great many ideas about things they want him to do, just when he is so full of ideas himself which he has not had time to follow up. The result is resistance, and often an increase in egocentric behavior. During the next year or so he grows clearer about things; he accepts some of the definitions as to when, where, what, and how he may use his legs and hands, and enjoys freedom within limits. By the time he is five he has usually accepted adult authority within limits and has a clearer ego-pattern or conception of himself in relation to that authority. This sequence varies, of course, with different children and the different authority patterns of adults. In some progressive circles of the vaguer sort, children sometimes do not get a clear pattern of authority and its limits, and may as a result have more conflict and anxiety about authority than children who have been handled with more simplicity. Variations on this pattern of shift from resistance to acceptance of authority are associated with varying ego-patterns of children such as those analyzed by Lerner and Murphy (1941).

The patterns of change described so far have been chiefly those which are an expression of development of one kind or another in the child's relation to himself and people around him. More confusing to parents and teachers are those changes which have some regressive or repetitive origin; for example, a child goes to nursery school for three years during which he develops from a shy, quiet child to an active participant in all the school activities. Then he goes to kindergarten and appears to have "lost all that he gained" during his three years of preschool experience. He seems to "start all over again." Actually he is repeating his earlier experience, in the sense that he is responding to the newness of the situation just as he did three years earlier. Often the sequence of adjustments the child goes through before he again becomes adjusted as an active participant is more rapid and the period of initial shyness does not last so long. In other cases the child "picks up where he left off" in the preceding school, and growth seems more obviously cumulative. Underlying these individual differences in tendency to repeat earlier adjustment-sequences as against building on current achievement may be patterns of personality structure especially related to the child's dependence upon his relations with his external environment.

Common Experiences Producing Aggressive and Friendly Personality.—In metropolitan nursery-school groups the period from three to five enjoys increased activity, more contacts with other children, the development of friendships, of competitive and cooperative play, and also of conflicts and aggression, all part of the enriched social experience which comes after the initial period of experience with objects (see studies reviewed in Murphy, Murphy, and Newcomb, 1937). With great individual differences related to the way in which different children handle this social debut, they learn somehow to deal with the need for defense in relation to their fellows. Most nursery schools have their own culture, with its patterns of taking turns, respecting the rights of the child who had it first, letting the other child have a share, etc., which are introduced by the teachers, adopted gradually by some children and evaded or resisted by others (Jersild and Markey, 1935; Fite, 1940). Physical aggression has been observed to increase even through kindergarten in the sense that more children fight their way through a conflict when it arises. It must always be added, however, in *that kind* of kindergarten. For this generalization cannot be applied to kindergartens other than the types studied, and it is to be doubted whether the same thing would be true of those with a more authoritarian regime, where aggressive behavior is successfully repressed in many children. What happens to the child who does not have this opportunity for release of hostile feelings, and who does not develop the ability to defend himself against his competitors or attackers, has then to be described by the clinicians. One assumption is that those children who have learned to deal aggressively with conflict situations by kindergarten age are less likely to suffer the effects of repressed conflicts and hostility, less likely to be neurotic than those who do not have this opportunity. There is considerable justification for this assumption in Charlotte Bühler's unpublished data on English children, who, more socialized than Austrian children, show many more psychosomatic difficulties of the enuresis and gastric-disturbance type than do children in the groups with more social difficulties.

Along with the increase of active aggression, especially among boys, there is an increase at about the age of five in verbal expressions of an aggressive nature as well as competitive ones: "stinky," "skunk," "you big fool," etc., offer outlets not available ordinarily to the three-year-old, and are sometimes particularly consoling to the five-year-old who for whatever reason does not have success with physical measures.

A number of developments are taking place about this same time. Sex differences in behavior have been relatively inconspicuous among three-year-olds. Play groups are often mixed, and games of mother and baby, or fireman and policeman, are shared by girls and boys alike (Hattwick, 1937; Murphy, 1937). Boys in our culture are still largely identified with mothers, and are not ordinarily very conscious of sex roles. The he-boy is apt to make his role and his consciousness of it felt by the age of four or five. This is stimulated doubtless by observation of boys just a little older who are beginning to play ball and to ape still older boys; by adults who comment on what a big boy you are; by clothes more differentiated from girls' clothes. At any rate, boys who have been playing happily with miniature life toys reject them violently about this age, while girls continue to accept them (Lerner and Murphy, 1941). Bravado, swashbuckling, bullying behavior may become part of the picture as an expression of the boy's new realization of who he is, and that he is he. About the same time, costumes, jewelry, and dress-up testify to some girls' increasing consciousness of femininity. All of these aspects of the task of clarification of sex role, which takes place in the fifth and sixth years, are tied up with the shift in the child's identification with parents, referred to earlier.

Experience Expands with Expanding Imagination.—Reality experiences do not have time to mellow before the child begins to expand his range of experience through fantasy, pretense, imaginative games, stories, and conversation. At first reality and fantasy may not be clearly distinguished; at the age of four, a child may be very anxious about a wolf in Red Riding Hood, a witch in Snow White, which is delightful a couple of years later. The period between four and six, then, is a period of clarification of the distinction between reality and fantasy experiences. The child is experimenting with his own fantasy and can take a certain amount of fantasy from adults provided it is not too strong for his digestion at that time. Oddly enough, the fantasy which he creates at this time is apt to be meat that is too strong for many adults. The child seems to be less sensitive to the idea of chopping off heads, when it is his idea. The adult can stand a fairy story with violent elements, but may be shocked by the violence of the child's own fantasy. The interaction of child and adult feelings about aggression and violence in fantasy thus contributes to the child's ability to assimilate, or to his anxiety about the meaning of the experiences related to the fantasy. When let alone, his own fantasy may help him to digest painful experiences in the world (Bender, 1941). Exposed to adult anxieties, he may have to repress what he might otherwise have been able to deal with himself.

The development of fantasy has other implications for the development of the child's personality also. One of these relates to the way in which fear is assimilated by the child. Macfarlane (1939) points out that her data appear to justify a contrast between children who adjust inwardly, with both fantasy and physiological reaction as indications of inward adaptive patterns, and other children who react outwardly, with temper tantrums, aggressive efforts, and peripheral physiological responses like eczema, in her group of outward adjustive patterns. On the basis of our own data, I would like to offer the hypothesis that the child who up to the age of three has been assimilating fear and other stress experiences inwardly, perhaps with an accompaniment of considerable nonverbal fantasy, may, after the development of language and verbalized fantasy, become more overt in reactions precisely through the releasing influences of communicable and objectified fantasy. Nursery rhymes and fairy stories are, from this point of view, a traditional and culturally accepted method of stimulating this externalization of formerly internal reactions in the child. Differences in the child's opportunity to relate his own internal and personal fantasy to the objective or universal fantasies of the culture may be important in the formation of personality during this period, especially in relation to the degree of "extraversion" which the child is able to achieve. Perhaps the most important value of play groups and nursery schools is the opportunity which they provide at this stage to externalize and thus socialize the fantasy life of the child. When this socialization is completely and satisfyingly experienced, it may constitute a deep source of security for the child which might be likened to the sense of security that is achieved in adult life through work, friendship and sexual and parental fulfilment.

When fears are elaborated and assimilated through fantasy with the result that thresholds for reactivity to fear stimuli in the reality-world are raised, we may consider that the fantasy experience has had a therapeutic effect. Sometimes, however, the fantasy and the emotion going with it becomes stereotyped and cumulative, as in the case of phobias or obsessions and the opportunity for objectified or social fantasy as such does not help the child.

The meaning of this period of fantasy varies not only with the child's opportunity to objectify his fantasy, but also with the unsolved problems which feed his fantasy. Different subculture areas vary considerably at this point. If you are a hill-country child who is taken to funerals, and to the home of a new baby shortly after it is born, basic experiences of birth and death are much closer to the world of reality than they are for the usual metropolitan child who wonders where people come from and what it is like when they die. This may account in part for the fact that observers like Claudia Lewis (1943) find less imaginative activity among the Tennessee children than among protected Westchester nursery school children, who will spend hours in play sessions centered on symbolic dramatization of "how babies get in," and "how they get out."

The basic features of the child's social experience up to six, then, have usually included:

1. Experience with parents and other adults, some adjustment to adult authority, and some patterns in relation to the kinds of satisfactions expected from adults.
2. Experience with other children, awareness of sex differences and sex roles, exposure to patterns of aggression and friendliness, and the varying social techniques of different children.
3. Experience of himself, his body, its competences, the reactions it gets from other people, the satisfactions it gives, the difficulties it presents.
4. Experience of fantasy, both emerging spontaneously in the child's mind, and fed by the stories of adults and other children.

All these aspects of experience, assimilated by an organism with its own thresholds for adjustment and tension in different areas, produces the personality structure that we confront when we come to know any six-year-old. By this time each child usually has his characteristic themes for fantasy: bigness, mountains, or towers; dominating or punishing adult, policeman, or parent; ideal adult, princess, Lone Ranger; threats from nature, creatures of prey, death, fire, whirlpool; cultural demands, baths, shampoos, bedtime, keeping clean; primitive experiences, eating, defecating, messing, sucking, drinking, or masturbating. When he draws or paints he is likely to produce patterns clearly characteristic of these fantasy themes and the free or constrained space-world in which he lives: he starts with a boundary line or he approaches his paper more freely; he tightly fills up space or he leaves it open; he draws in squares or curves with rigid forms or free and lively ones; his figures may be a child alone or in a group; he paints with sensuous abandon or with great control. Thus he reveals the dramatic content of life and his way of handling it.

Elementary School Experience.—Even at six, we often find that children have clearly defined personalities: an artist, an architect, a mechanic, a little mother, a scientific observer, a verbalist, or a social butterfly. What, then, can the next six or seven years do, and what does their experience mean to the child? This depends upon the personality. Some personalities, which have already decided to vote on the side of the Tories, convention, the priests, and "the right" are likely to continue in the path laid down by the social structure, provided no major obstacles to this path present themselves. Others, at *another*, not *the* other extreme, are so traumatized that their relation with their fellows will always be a deviant one. Some six-year-old rebels may remain rebels for the rest of their lives; others become rebels later for other reasons.

Within a wider group, basic personality structure, ways of perceiving and experiencing, remain consistent. A child with oral and narcistic structure, at three does not usually change to a compulsive or a narrowly constricted type at eight. But this underlying personality structure may find expression in many different ways, and a delinquent career may be made or prevented by the experience which the child has between six and fourteen, granted the underlying personality remains consistent. That is, a given set of needs and attitudes may find ways of satisfying and expressing themselves that are acceptable to the culture, or ways that are considered taboo. Recent studies of prevention of delinquency have given clear evidence of this (R. J. Levy, 1941).

Whether neurosis can be prevented with equal effectiveness is an open question; I know of no comparable studies which attempt to deal with paired groups, giving treatment to one group and not to the other. The outcome might be harder to judge, since neurosis is often handled by the individual skilfully enough to prevent detection by mere observation of behavior.

The large group of normal children, whose personality structure maintains a certain recognizable consistency beneath striking differences in behavior, share a variety of significant experiences during the elementary school period (Biber, *et al.*, 1942). First, perhaps, is the new experience of participation in a more structured group, a larger group, with a more teacher-directed experience. This is true not only of the majority of traditional schools where children sit at desks in a row, hands folded, to recite when told to. It is also true to a lesser extent of progressive schools where school-desks are moved about, materials are adapted to the individual child and decisions are often made by vote. In either case, *the child has a more complicated group situation*, and has to meet the expectation that he will conform to certain behavior patterns as a member of this larger group. Children experience this change in different ways, depending on their previous experience and ways of handling authority. Children who have accepted clear authority from parents usually are ready for school, while children who have had a great deal of freedom either through permissiveness or through neglect are apt to find the new situation more demanding. In the progressive atmosphere in which Biber and her associates studied seven-year-olds, open complaints that "grownups are too bossy" were frequent. This is a different response, with different meanings for the children who show it, from the surreptitious spitball-throwing defiance shown by rebellious minorities in autocratic schools. Children with a great deal of inner life and capacity to keep their thoughts to themselves may conform outwardly, with inner reservations. Children with very open, outgoing patterns of responding may grumble and complain a great deal at this new state of affairs. The former will of course appear more adjusted, and sometimes they are.

Going to school often means more independence, going around town, shopping for the family, going to the movies, playing with a group of children in the neighborhood, and joining clubs or other extra-home groups. All of this means exposure to a wider cultural field, and this may present new reinforcement of old experiences, or new conflicts. These have been described by Hartshorne, *et al.* (1930), who pointed out that for some children the conflict between home and school grows more acute and cumulative through the elementary school.

Larger groups mean new structures and organization, in the form of rules, first of a simple sort like those in hide and seek where each child takes the role of "it," pursuer at times and pursued at other times. Later, as J. E. Anderson (1939) has pointed out, roles become more differentiated, as in baseball and football, and the structure of the game is tightened up. We find little analysis of the relation of personality structure to capacity for adaptation to these new types of organization, to supplement Piaget's (1932) delineation of stages in the child's relation to rules.

Observation of seven-year-olds indicates that it is easier for some children than others to enjoy this type of experience; some children prefer through the elementary school years the more loosely structured activities which allow room for fantasy, such as cops and robbers or dramatic play. In other words, the new experiences of this age level also mean very different things to different kinds of children. Similarly the more defined "manners" expected of children in this period may mean an opportunity for adult approval to some children, or an interference with "my own ideas" to other children.

Along with increasingly differentiated structure in group activity, there is considerable pressure toward greater objectivity: the curriculum is usually directed toward the achievement of basic skills and the expansion of information about the world of nature, city life, communication systems, local and national geography (Biber, *et al.*, 1942). Both this trend and the opportunity to explore the environment with greater freedom and independence doubtless contribute to whatever lessening of interest in organic functions and biological experiences we find in the so-called "latency period." Actually, the spontaneous needs of the child, stimulus from movies, from observation of people around him and of animals, keeps sex interest more vigorous than adults often admit. Other interests in masculine and feminine role, in babies, their care and development, might well get more attention in the curriculum than they usually do.

The increasing rigidity of sex differentiation is itself a stimulus (Moreno, 1934). Most nursery schools allow children to use common open toilets, in order to encourage children to get accustomed to sex differences in anatomy. At school, toilets are separated, closed, and privacy emphasized. Clothes are different, and games are increasingly distinct, as boys grow into the rougher games like football, and form gangs which exclude girls. Sometimes considerable competition accompanies this differentiation and is expressed in verbal hostility, teasing, etc. This seems less conspicuous in a progressive school where there is less pressure from adults to differentiate sex roles than it does in more traditional groups.

Along with the new emphasis on objective interests encouraged by the school curriculum, there is an equally important emphasis upon objective achievement, with its sources of new stimulus and new anxiety. Plant (1937) urges that school and home recognize their respective areas of security—the school's job being to develop the "whatness" side of the child's personality, while the job of the family is to give the child security in "who" he is. Biber and her co-authors (1942) give extended consideration to the meaning of their findings that seven-year-old children appear to be especially conscious of work-standards, and typically run down or depreciate their own work; it is suggested that this is part of the process of assimilating and adjusting to the new standards of work which school brings them.

It was to meet the problems indicated by the frequency with which this institutionalized emphasis upon adequacy of accomplishment, and the competition that went along with it, produce anxiety and personality problems in children, that the progressive education movement has urged the elimination of marks, stars, and other trappings of status and achievement, substituting less honorific methods of encouraging the child and correcting mistakes. However, progressive methods in reading have not eliminated "reading problems," and the effect of failure with its consequent insecurity for the child is dramatically discussed by Dr. Preston (1940) and other observers of elementary school children.

The point that failure in reading may not be due solely to the failure of either modern or older methods is implicit in Dr. Liss' discussion (1940) of mechanisms involved in learning. If we follow his approach to its logical conclusion, we may say that the whole school and learning experience itself means something different to each child, depending upon the pattern of his identification with the achievement values and successes of parents; and with the emotional connections which are made between the school situation as a whole—teachers, children, materials, and tasks—and the pattern of values and resistances or anxieties which the child brings to school.

The increased structuring of activity and direction by adults doubtless creates certain new tensions, which may be related to the new patterns of withdrawal: having secrets, secret clubs, and secret activities. Comics include stories concerned with child-adult authority problems, of which the Katzenjammers is still perennial and not the only one of its kind. Authority conflicts are also sublimated in drawing, writing skits, or just in extra-curricular crabbing, depending again on the resources of the individual child.

Against this general background of experiences provided by elementary school culture, we find individual children who fit with greater, and with less, success into the demands which the culture is imposing on children at this age. The problem of sex differentiation is confused and difficult for the artistic boy who is not physically vigorous (less or no problem if he is physically vigorous) and the aggressive girl or the large fat girl. Depending on the rigidity or flexibility of the specific subculture group, the presence or absence of bullies, sympathetic teachers, understanding parents, these deviations from the demands of the culture may lead to serious traumas or to a sturdy individuality.

Experiences of Children in Minority Groups.—Up to this point we have discussed the experiences of children against a general background of research and observation of average children in middle class homes in metropolitan areas. This is necessary because of the lack of adequate material on other culture groups, especially rural children, or children in the highest economic brackets, who go through private schools where psychologists do not do research.

Just a few notes on the experience of children in special groups may be added, however. The increase of intelligence of Negro children in proportion to the length of their exposure to the relatively stimulating experience of town schools, reported by Klineberg (1935), and the corresponding improvement of children in the Iowa studies, are probably paralleled by other changes. Personality development would probably respond even more dramatically to a shift from an environment that was emotionally malnourishing to one which had adequate emotional vitamins.

E. and R. Horowitz (1939) have described the process with which parents inculcate race consciousness in children, but no studies have been made of the processes by which some children in minority groups develop socialized personalities as compared with those who become aggressive in an antisocial way, or merely socially unpleasant.

Subculture conflicts experienced by children of different racial, national, and religious backgrounds, and children's ways of dealing with these conflicts deserve more attention than they have received. Subtler conflicts between families in a neighborhood where some parents are strict and some are permissive may be illustrated by the plight of the seven-year-old girl who ran to her mother weeping and asked, "You are too 'strict enough,' aren't you, mommy?" Ego-threats of 30% of our children who belong to minority groups (Negro, Jew, Oriental, etc.) originate in experiences of exclusion or jeering, and are either offset by intra-family love and security or aggravated by conflict within the family, lack of attention from working parents, anxiety about economic security, or awareness of race conflicts increased by war.

"Problem Children"

Deviations in the personality development of children, or "problem" children, are being looked at from a variety of points of view, since child psychiatry and even the field of child development are so new that a stable orientation has not emerged. An extreme emphasis upon symptoms appears to be characteristic of some approaches such as that in Kanner's *Child Psychiatry* and of many of the studies of nervous habits, and of the frequency of "problems"; however, in action the child guidance movement is eclectic and usually dynamic rather than atomistic in approach, and attempts to deal with the total picture of difficulties, both organic and psychogenic in origin, presented by a child. D. Levy's (1939) work on maternal overprotection deals with something deeper than a collection of symptoms: it is concerned with the total pattern of kinds of behavior rooted in a basic attitude of the mother, and with the total pattern of behavior of the child rooted in the child's response to the overprotective attitude of the mother. This tendency to approach symptoms (aggressiveness, dependence, rebelliousness, etc.) as part of a structure of parent-child interaction is characteristic of considerable recent work, both research and clinical (Fromm-Reichmann, 1940; Symonds, 1939).

At the same time there is increasing interest in better understanding of types of behavior for themselves; behavior in children which is like schizophrenic behavior in adults has attracted especial attention (Despert, 1938, 1942; Bradley, 1941; Isaacs, 1939). In our own records of nearly 100 normal children, miniature samples of several different kinds of behavior that resemble adult breakdown behavior are to be found: "catatonic" behavior, "schizophrenic" language, "compulsive characters," and the like. In some of these cases, the behavior has appeared during the preschool phase of adjustment to the first outside group and being emotionally weaned from the parents, and has disappeared by the time the child reached first or second grade. In other cases this change did not occur. There is some evidence from the family histories that these patterns of response to periods of unsatisfactory adjustment may have organic bases, but only a small per cent of schizophrenic children have psychotic parents.

The patterns of adjustment of some children are weighted by physiological factors rather than by environmental ones; with others the opposite is true according to Macfarlane (1939). Examples of physiological weighting would be persistent low energy level and mucous membrane irritability (e.g., gastro-intestinal irritability). In the early periods these are heavily weighted factors in internalized and withdrawn trends of response. Conversely, high energy levels and peripheral irritability (e.g., skin allergies) are important factors in externalized patterning. An adequate discussion of psychosomatic aspects of personality development in children would require a chapter in itself. The reader will find leads in the bibliographical listings in a paper by Bruch and Touraine (1940), in the paper of Chobat, et al. (1939) on allergic children, in Hall's (1940) work on asthma, in Harrower-Erickson's (1940) study of the effects of brain lesions in children, and in the study of behavioral effects of testosterone injections in young boys by Bize and Moricard (1937). Stone and Barker's (1939) study revealing differences in interests between post- and premenarcheal girls of the same age points to another evidence of the influence of biochemical factors upon responses to the environment.

Situational weighting is illustrated by Macfarlane (1939) in the following examples: response patterns associated with intimate personal contacts of the early periods of physical dependence, affectional, hostile, tearful, etc., are critical ones for psychosexual adjustments at maturity. Unconscious ambivalent drives in parent-child relationships and strained marital adjustments are associated with anxiety trends and compulsive or explosive behavior in children; Baruch (1937) finds similar results in her study of the relation between marital relationships and children's problems. Being an older child in a pair is conducive to a different patterning from being a younger child. For examples, the older of a pair of boys two or three years apart is more apt to be insecure in social relationships, the younger insecure about his intellectual ability.

For some time the statistical studies of children's problems, such as those of Tilson, Hattwick, or Olson (summarized by Murphy, Murphy, and Newcomb, 1937), have indicated that problems do not come singly but in bunches, as any clinician would expect who approaches behavior not segmentally or phenotypically, to use Lewin's term, but in terms of genotypic forces. Macfarlane's approach takes hold of both horns of what for a time was a scientific dilemma, showing how the particular symptoms in which an adjustment (or anxiety) problem is expressed will be an expression of organic thresholds as well as conditioned patterns of the individual child's personality (see also Ribble's approach in Chapter 20).

Partly because of the fact that many of the multitudinous "problems" of the preschool period evaporate or are translated into subtler and more socialized behavior during the elementary school period, our picture is very incomplete when we look at it longitudinally. Except for the discussions of schizophrenic behavior in childhood referred to above, there is as yet no adequate longitudinal study of the processes of character-formation, either starting from the hypotheses intrinsic in the oral, anal, genital type theory of Freud and Abraham, or any other framework oriented to the question of the integrated personality as a whole. The case-studies presented in Stuart's (1939) growth-studies are the nearest approach, but we shall have to wait for results of research now under way and to be planned before we have an empirical demonstration based on actual research data of the process of formation of basic personality structure in different subgroups in our culture. Such a demonstration will have to look at growing personalities in terms of the individual pattern of susceptibilities for response to the particular parental, sibling, school, and neighborhood experiences to which they are exposed, and will have to take into account the continuing dynamic interaction of the partly crystallized aspects of the personality, and the more flexible ones, with the new stimuli, pressures and satisfactions which each developmental stage provides from within and from without the child.

Summary

Childhood experiences which contribute to the formation of personality may be conveniently looked at from the side of growth and that of expanding social relationships. Growth experiences after the weaning period include the experience of *increasing manipulative skill*, making possible self-feeding, self-dressing, organization of objects such as that of building and dramatic use of objects; *locomotor or large-muscle skills*, making possible the experiences of climbing, jumping, swinging, bicycle riding, as well as running to and away from places and objects feared or of interest; *language*, with its possibilities of expression of wants, observations, feelings; *fantasy*, with its new world of reconstruction and dramatic reliving of experiences actual, feared, desired; increasing clarity of *form-perception*, as an aspect of clearer grasp of objective realities, and making possible both analytic and creative manipulation of reality; increasing grasp of *concepts of space, time, object-relationships, and human relationships*, making possible adjustments through substitution, postponement, construction, submission to standards; grasp of *complex sequences*, making possible participation in complex games and social structures, and maintaining roles of different sorts at different times.

Changing *social experiences* include changing areas and patterns of expression of *parental authority, companionship, and love*, in response or reaction to the changing status of the child resulting from the growth patterns just summarized; stimulation, rivalry and love in *relationships between siblings*; sequential changes in relation to members of the neighborhood or preschool *play group*, in which a common but not universal pattern is the sequence from isolated to parallel to cooperative to group play; exposure to a wider *environment*, which in metropolitan culture includes doctors, police, firemen, grocers, and other commercial persons, and in some rural sections may include participation in funerals, celebrations of births; later membership in a *gang*, and in the more *regimented structures of school life*. In metropolitan culture, exposure to radio and movies provides certain types of experiences not included in the other categories.

Variations in the content and meaning of these experiences rooted in variations in the child's own pattern of growth, and the variations in the pattern of expanding social relationships in different subcultures and different families go far toward determining the basic structure of the child's personality and provide the background against which his reaction to his individual experience of puberty must be understood.

BIBLIOGRAPHY

STANDARD SECONDARY REFERENCES IN CHILD PSYCHOLOGY

BURKS, B. S., & JONES, M. C. 1936. Personality development in childhood. *Monogr. Soc. Res. Child Develpm.*, No. 4.
JERSILD, A. T. 1940. Child psychology. New York: Prentice-Hall.
MURCHISON, C. (Ed.) 1931. A handbook of child psychology. Worcester, Mass.: Clark University Press.
MURPHY, G., MURPHY, L. B., & NEWCOMB, T. 1937. Experimental social psychology. (2nd ed.) New York: Harper.
MURPHY, L. B. 1941. Social and emotional development. *Rev. educ. Res., 11,* 479–501.
SKINNER, C. E., & HARRIMAN, P. L. (Eds.) 1941. Child psychology: child development and modern education. New York: Macmillan.

SPECIFIC REFERENCES FOR CHAPTER

ACKERMAN, N. W. 1938. Constructive and destructive tendencies in children: an experimental study. *Amer. J. Orthopsychiat., 8,* 265–285.
ALDRICH, C. A. 1939. The role of gratification in early development. *Proc. 3rd Bienn. Mtg. Soc. Res. Child Develpm.* 1–2. Abstract.
ALPERT, A. 1941a. Education as therapy. *Psychoanal. Quart., 10,* 469–474.
—— 1941b. The latency period. *Amer. J. Orthopsychiat., 11,* 126–133.
AMEN, E. W. 1941. Individual differences in apperceptive reaction: a study of the response of preschool children to pictures. *Genet. Psychol. Monogr., 23,* 319–385.
ANDERSON, H. H. 1937. Children in the family. New York: Appleton-Century.
—— 1939a. Domination and social integration in the behavior of kindergarten children and teachers. *Genet. Psychol. Monogr., 21,* 287–385.
—— 1939b. The measurement of domination and of socially integrative behavior in teachers' contacts with children. *Child Develpm., 10,* 73–89.
ANDERSON, J. E. 1939. The development of social behavior. *Amer. J. Sociol., 44,* 839–857.
ANDERSON, J. P. 1940. The relationship between parental affection and dominance and the behavior of children. *Psychol. Bull., 37,* 505.
[ANON.] 1941. War strain in evacuated children. *Brit. med. J.,* Part I, 128–129.
BARRETT, W. G. 1937. A childhood anxiety. *Psychoanal. Quart., 6,* 530–535.
BARUCH, D. W. 1937. A study of reported tension in interparental relationships

as co-existent with behavior adjustment in young children. *J. exp. Educ., 6,* 187–204.

BATESON, G., & MEAD, M. 1942. Balinese culture, a photographanalysis. New York: N. Y. Academy of Science.

BENDER, L. 1939. Behavior problems in negro children. *Psychiatry, 2,* 213–228.

BENDER, L., & LOURIE, R. S. 1941. The effect of comic books on the ideology of children. *Amer. J. Orthopsychiat., 11,* 540–551.

BENDER, L., & SPALDING, M. A. 1940. Behavior problems in children from the homes of followers of Father Divine. *J. nerv. ment. Dis., 91,* 460–472.

BENDER, L., & VOGEL, F. 1941. Imaginary companions of children. *Amer. J. Orthopsychiat., 11,* 56–66.

BERKMAN, M., RAPPAPORT, E., & SULZBERGER, B. 1939. Therapeutic effects of an authoritative situation in children's court. *Amer. J. Orthopsychiat., 9,* 347–355.

BIBER, B., MURPHY, L. B., WOODCOCK, L. P., & BLACK, I. S. 1942. Children in school: a study of a seven-year-old group. New York: Dutton.

BIZE, P. R., & MORICARD, R. 1937. Psychic changes following injection of testosterone in young boys. *Bull. Soc. Pédiat. Paris, 35,* 38.

BLATZ, W. D., MILLICHAMP, D. A., & HARRIS, A. L. 1937. Routine training of the Dionne quintuplets (sleeping, eating, elimination, routine, washing, dressing, etc.). *Univ. Toronto Stud. Child Develpm. Ser.* No. 15.

BRADLEY, C. 1941. Schizophrenia in childhood. New York: Macmillan.

BRANDER, T. 1941. [Psychiatric observations of children during the war in Finland 1939–40.] *Z. Kinderpsychiat., 7,* 177–187.

BROWN, G. D. 1938. The development of diabetic children, with special reference to mental and personality comparison. *Child Develpm., 9,* 175–184.

BRUCH, H., & TOURAINE, G. 1940. Obesity in childhood: V. The family frame of obese children. *Psychosom. Med., 2,* 141–206.

BÜHLER, C. 1933. The social behavior of children. In Murchison, C., *Handbook of child psychology.* Worcester, Mass.: Clark Univ. Press. Pp. 374–416.

—— 1939. The child and his family. New York: Harper.

—— 1940. Clinical studies of mother-child relationships. *Psychol. Bull., 37,* 586.

BURGUM, M. 1940. Constructive values associated with rejection. *Amer. J. Orthopsychiat., 10,* 312–326.

BURKS, B. S. 1942. A study of identical twins reared apart under differing types of family relationships. In McNemar, Q., & Merrill, M. A., *Studies in personality.* Stanford University: Stanford University Press. Pp. 35–70.

BURT, C. 1940. The incidence of neurotic symptoms among evacuated school children. *Brit. J. educ. Psychol., 10,* 8–15.

CABOT, P. S. DE Q. 1940. A long term study of children: the Cambridge-Somerville youth study. *Child Develpm., 11,* 143–151.

CAMERON, W. J. 1938. A study of early adolescent personality. *Progr. Educ., 15,* 552–563.

CAMPBELL, E. H. 1939. The social-sex development of children. *Genet. Psychol. Monogr., 21,* 461–552.

CARPENTER, J., & EISENBERG, P. 1938. Some relations between family background and personality. *J. Psychol., 6,* 115–136.

CHAMPNEY, H. 1941. The measurement of parent behavior. *Child Develpm., 12,* 131–166.

CHAVE, E. J. 1937. Personality development in children. Chicago: University Chicago Press.

CHILD STUDY ASSOCIATION OF AMERICA. 1939–40. Psychotherapy in childhood. *Child Study, 17,* 42–45.

CHOBAT, R., SPADAVECCHIA, R., & DE SANCTIS, R. M. 1939. Intelligence rating and emotional patterns of allergic children. *Amer. J. Dis. Child., 57,* 831–837.

CLOTHIER, F. 1939. Some aspects of the problem of adoption. *Amer. J. Orthopsychiat., 9,* 598–615.

CONN, J. H. 1940. Children's reactions to the discovery of genital differences. *Amer. J. Orthopsychiat., 10,* 747–754.

COWAN, E. A., & STOUT, E. 1939. A comparative study of the adjustment made by foster children after complete and partial breaks in continuity of home environment. *Amer. J. Orthopsychiat., 9,* 330–338.

DARLING, R. P. 1940. Autonomic action in relation to personality traits of children. *J. abnorm. soc. Psychol., 14,* 111–115.

DAVIS, K. 1940. Extreme social isolation of a child. *Amer. J. Sociol., 45,* 554–565.

DENNIS, W. 1940a. Does culture appreciably affect patterns of infant behavior? *J. soc. Psychol., 12*, 305–317.
—— 1940b. The Hopi child. New York: Appleton-Century.
DESPERT, J. L. 1938a. Emotional problems in children. Utica, N. Y.: State Hospitals Press.
—— 1938b. Schizophrenia in children. *Psychiat. Quart., 12*, 366–371.
—— 1940. A comparative study of thinking in schizophrenic children and in children of preschool age. *Amer. J. Psychiat., 97*, 189–213.
DOLL, E. A. 1938. Social maturation. *Proc. 5th Inst. except. Child., Child Res. Clin.*, 31–36.
DuBOIS, C. 1937. Some anthropological perspectives on psychoanalysis. *Psychoanal. Rev., 24*, 246–263.
DUREA, M. A. 1939. A survey of the adjustment of school children. *Child Develpm., 10*, 107–114.
—— 1941. Personality characteristics and degree of delinquency: I. An empirical analysis of blameworthy circumstances and anxiety states. *J. soc. Psychol., 13*, 329–339.
ENGLISH, H. B. 1929. Three cases of the "conditioned fear response." *J. abnorm. soc. Psychol., 24*, 221–225.
ERIKSON, E. H. 1939. Observations on Sioux education. *J. Psychol., 7*, 101–156.
—— 1940a. Problems of infancy and early childhood. In *Cyclopedia of medicine, surgery and specialties.* Philadelphia: Davis. Pp. 715–730.
—— 1940b. Studies in the interpretation of play: I. Clinical observation of play disruption in young children. *Genet. Psychol. Monogr., 22*, 557–671.
FARNSWORTH, P. R. 1938. The measure of emotional maturity. *J. soc. Psychol., 9*, 235–237.
FAUQUIER, W. 1940. The attitudes of aggressive and submissive boys towards athletics. *Child Develpm., 11*, 115–126.
FIELD, M. 1940. Maternal attitudes found in twenty-five cases of children with behavior primary disorders. *Amer. J. Orthopsychiat., 10*, 293–311.
FITE, M. D. 1940. Aggressive behavior in young children and children's attitudes toward aggression. *Genet. Psychol. Monogr., 22*, 151–319.
FLÜGEL, J. C. 1929. The psychoanalytic study of the family. London: International Psychoanalytical Press.
FORD, F. R. 1937. Diseases of the nervous system in infancy, childhood and adolescence. Springfield, Ill.: Thomas.
FOSTER, S. 1927. A study of the personality make-up and social setting of fifty jealous children. *Ment. Hyg., N. Y., 2*, 53–77.
FRANK, L. K. 1938. The fundamental needs of the child. *Ment. Hyg., N. Y., 22*, 353–379.
—— 1939a. Cultural coercion and individual distortion. *Psychiatry, 2*, 11–27.
—— 1939b. Projective methods for the study of personality. *J. Psychol., 8*, 389–413.
FREUD, A. 1928. Introduction to the technique of child analysis. *Nerv. ment. Dis. Monogr.*, No. 48.
—— 1937. The ego and mechanisms of defense. New York: G. E. Stechert.
FREUD, S. 1923. The ego and the id. London: Hogarth, 1927.
FRIES, M. E., & LEWI, B. 1938. Interrelated factors in development: a study of pregnancy, labor, delivery, lying-in period and childhood. *Amer. J. Orthopsychiat., 8*, 726–752.
FROMM, E. 1936. The psychological dynamics of submission to authority. In Horkheimer, M., *Studien über Autorität und Familie. Schr. Inst. SozForsch., 5.*
—— 1941. Escape from freedom. New York: Farrar & Rinehart.
FROMM-REICHMANN, F. 1940. Notes on the mother role in the family group. *Bull. Menninger Clin., 4*, 132–148.
GERLACH, M. 1939. A study of the relationship between psychometric patterns and personality types. *Child Develpm., 10*, 269–278.
GESELL, A., CASTNER, B. M., THOMPSON, H., & AMATRUDA, C. S. 1939. Biographies of child development. New York: Hoeber.
GESELL, A., HAVERSON, H. M., THOMPSON, H., ILG, F. L., CASTNER, B. M., AMES, L. B., & AMATRUDA, C. S. 1940. The first five years of life: a guide to the study of the preschool child. New York: Harper.
GESELL, A., & THOMPSON, H. 1941. Twins T and C from infancy to adolescence: a biogenetic study of individual differences by the method of co-twin control. *Genet. Psychol. Monogr., 24*, 3–121.

GILL, S. E. 1940. Nocturnal enuresis: experiences with evacuated children. *Brit. med. J.*, Part II, 199–200.

GITELSON, M., ROSS, H., HOMBERGER, E., ALLEN, F., BLANCHARD, P., LIPPMAN, H. S., GERARD, M., & LOWREY, L. G. 1938. Section of "Play Therapy." *Amer. J. Orthopsychiat., 8*, 499–524.

GOLDSTEIN, K. 1939. The organism. New York: American Book.

GREENACRE, P. 1941. The predisposition to anxiety. *Psychoanal. Quart., 10*, 66–94.

GREIG, A. B. 1937. Learning disability in intelligent children. *Med. Ann. Dist. Columbia, 6*, 9.

—— 1941. A child analysis. *Psychoanal. Quart., 10*, 395–430.

GUTTERIDGE, M. V. 1939. A study of motor achievements of young children. *Arch. Psychol., N. Y.*, No. 244.

GUTTMAN, E., & CREAK, M. 1940. A follow-up study of hyperkinetic children. *J. ment. Sci., 86*, 624–631.

HALL, C. S. 1938. The inheritance of emotionality. *Sigma Xi Quart., 26*, 17–27.

HALL, G. S., & BROWNE, C. E. 1903. Children's ideas of fire, heat, frost, cold. *Pedag. Seminary, 10*, 27–35.

HALL, M. B. 1940. Asthma in childhood; a discussion of the psychological aspect. *Brit. med. J.*, Part II, 110–113.

HARROWER-ERICKSON, M. R., & MIALE, F. R. 1940. Personality changes accompanying organic brain lesions: pre- and post-operative study of two pre-adolescent children. *Rorschach Res. Exch., 4*, 8–25.

HARTSHORNE, H., MAY, M. A., MALLER, J. B., & SHUTTLEWORTH, F. K. 1930. Studies in the nature of character. (3 Vols.) New York: Macmillan.

HATTWICK, L. A. 1937. Sex differences in behavior of nursery school children. *Child Develpm., 8*, 343–355.

HENRY, J. 1940. Some cultural determinants of hostility in Pilaga Indian children. *Amer. J. Orthopsychiat., 10*, 111–122.

HILDRETH, G. 1938. Characteristics of young gifted children. *J. genet. Psychol., 53*, 287–311.

HILL, J. M. 1941. Unwanted—unloved children; a study of nervous parent-child relationships. *Dis. nerv. Syst., 2*, 135–139.

HOROWITZ, E. L. 1941. Some aspects of the development of patriotism in children. *Sociometry, 3*, 329–341.

HOROWITZ, R. 1939. Racial aspects of self-identification in nursery school children. *J. Psychol., 7*, 91–99.

HOROWITZ, R., & MURPHY, L. B. 1938. Projective methods in the psychological study of children. *J. exp. Educ., 7*, 133–140.

HUNT, W. A. 1941. Recent developments in the field of emotion. *Psychol. Bull., 38*, 249–276.

ISAACS, S. 1933. Social development in young children. New York: Harcourt, Brace.

—— 1939. A special mechanism in a schizoid boy. *Int. J. Psycho-Anal., 20*, 333–339.

JACK, L. M. 1934. An experimental study of ascendant behavior in preschool children. *Univ. Ia. Stud. Child Welf., 1938, 15*, No. 4.

JERSILD, A. T., & FITE, M. D. 1939. The influence of nursery school experience on children's social adjustment. *Child Develpm. Monogr.*, No. 25.

JERSILD, A. T., & MARKEY, F. V. 1935. Conflicts between preschool children. *Child Develpm. Monogr.*, No. 21.

JONES, H. E. 1935. The galvanic skin reflex as related to overt emotional expression. *Amer. J. Psychol., 47*, 241–251.

JONES, M. C., & BURKS, B. S. 1936. Personality development in childhood. *Monogr. Soc. Res. Child Develpm., 1*, No. 4.

JOST, H. 1941. Some physiological changes during frustration. *Child Develpm., 12*, 9–15.

KANNER, L. 1935. Child psychiatry. Springfield, Ill.: Thomas.

KARDINER, A. K. 1939. The individual and his society. New York: Columbia University Press.

KEISTER, M. E., & UPDEGRAFF, R. 1937. A study of children's reactions to failure and an experimental attempt to modify them. *Child Develpm., 8*, 241–248.

KEPHART, N. C., & STRAUSS, A. A. 1940. A clinical factor influencing variations in I.Q. *Amer. J. Orthopsychiat., 10*, 343–350.

KLEIN, M. 1937. The psychoanalysis of children. London: Hogarth.

KLINEBERG, O. 1935. Negro intelligence and selective migration. New York: Columbia University Press.

KLOPFER, B., & MARGULIES, H. 1941. Rorschach reactions in early childhood. *Rorschach Res. Exch., 5,* 1–23.

KNIGHT, R. P. 1941. Some problems involved in selecting and rearing adopted children. *Bull. Menninger Clin., 5,* 65–74.

KUBIE, L. S. 1937. The fantasy of dirt. *Psychoanal. Quart., 6,* 388–425.

LAYMAN, J. W. 1940. A clinical study of children under foster care. *J. Psychol., 10,* 107–120.

LERNER, E., & MURPHY, L. B. (Eds.) 1941. Methods for the study of personality in young children. *Monogr. Soc. Res. Child Develpm., 6,* No. 4, Serial No. 30.

LEVY, D. M. 1937. Primary affect hunger. *Amer. J. Psychiat., 94,* 643–652.

—— 1939a. Maternal overprotection. *Psychiatry, 2,* 99–128.

—— 1939b. Sibling rivalry studies in children of primitive groups. *Amer. J. Orthopsychiat., 9,* 205–214.

—— 1940. "Control-situation" studies of children's responses to the difference in genitalia. *Amer. J. Orthopsychiat., 10,* 755–763.

LEVY, R. J. 1941. Reductions in recidivism through therapy. New York: Thomas Seltzer.

LEWIN, K. 1933. Environmental forces. In Murchison, C., *Handbook of child psychology.* (2nd ed.) Worcester, Mass.: Clark University Press. Pp. 590–625.

LEWIN, K., LIPPITT, R., & WHITE, R. K. 1939. Patterns of aggressive behavior in experimentally created "social climates." *J. soc. Psychol., 10,* 271–299.

LEWIS, C. 1944. Observations of rural children in Tennessee. (Unpublished)

LISS, E. 1940. Learning: its sadistic and masochistic manifestations. *Amer. J. Orthopsychiat., 10,* 123–128.

LOWENFELD, M. 1939. The world pictures of children. A method of recording and studying them. *Brit. J. med. Psychol., 18,* 65–101.

LOWENSTEIN, P., & SVENDSEN, M. 1938. Experimental modification of the behavior of a selected group of shy and withdrawn children. *Amer. J. Orthopsychiat., 8,* 639–653.

LOWREY, L. G. 1938. Problems of aggression and hostility in the exceptional child. *Proc. 5th Inst. except. Child., Child Res. Clin.* 22–30.

—— 1940. Personality distortion and early institutional care. *Amer. J. Orthopsychiat., 10,* 576–586.

MACFARLANE, J. W. 1939. The guidance study. *Sociometry, 2,* No. 3, 1–23.

MACKINNON, D. W. 1937. Trends in the study of personality. *Character & Pers., 6,* 150–155.

McCAY, J. G., & FOWLER, M. G. 1941. Some sex differences observed in a group of nursery school children. *Child Develpm., 12,* 75–79.

McCORMICK, H. W. (Ed.) 1941. Physically handicapped children in New York City. New York: Report of the Committee for the Study of Physically Handicapped Children.

McFARLAND, M. B. 1937. Relationships between young sisters as revealed in their overt responses. *J. exp. Educ., 6,* 173–179.

McGRAW, M. G. 1939. Later development of children specially trained during infancy. Johnny and Jimmy at school age. *Child Develpm., 10,* 1–19.

MELBO, I. R. 1940. A review of the literature on children's interests. *Yearb. Calif. elem. Sch. Prin. Assn., 12,* 6–22.

MICHAELS, J. J., & GOODMAN, S. E. 1939. The incidence of enuresis and age of cessation in one thousand neuropsychiatric patients: with a discussion of the relationship between enuresis and delinquency. *Amer. J. Orthopsychiat., 9,* 59–71.

MOHR, G. J. 1940. The influence of mothers' attitudes on mental health. *J. Pediat., 16,* 641–646.

MORENO, J. L. 1934. Who shall survive? *Nerv. ment. Dis. Monogr.,* No. 58.

MORGAN, J. J. B., & BANKER, M. H. 1938. The relation of mental stamina to parental protection. *J. genet. Psychol., 52,* 347–360.

MURPHY, G., MURPHY, L. B., & NEWCOMB, T. 1937. Experimental social psychology. (Rev. ed.) New York: Harper.

MURPHY, L. B. 1937. Social behavior and child personality. New York: Columbia University Press.

MURPHY, L. B. 1940. The nursery school contributes to emotional development. *Childh. Educ., 16,* 404–407.

MURPHY, L. B., & MURPHY, G. 1935. The influence of social situations upon the behavior of children. In Murchison, C., *A handbook of social psychology.* Worcester: Clark University Press.

MURPHY, M. 1938. The social adjustment of the exceptional child of borderline mentality. *J. consult. Psychol., 2,* 169–175.

OLDHAM, H. W. 1940. Child expression in colour and form. London: John Lane.

PAGE, R. M. 1942. Aggression and withdrawal in relation to possible frustrating factors in the lives of children. In *Summ. doct. Diss. Northw. Univ., 9.*

PAULSEN, A. 1941. Rorschachs of school beginners. *Rorschach Res. Exch., 5,* 24–29.

PEARSON, G. H. 1939. The chronically aggressive child. *Psychoanal. Rev., 26,* 485–525.

PIAGET, J. 1932. The moral judgment of the child. New York: Harcourt, Brace.

PLANT, J. S. 1937. Personality and the cultural pattern. New York: Commonwealth Fund.

POWELL, M. 1940. The Fels child behavior ratings: initial report. *Psychol. Bull., 37,* 572.

PRESTON, M. I. 1940. Reading failure and the child's security. *Amer. J. Orthopsychiat., 10,* 239–252.

REICHENBERG, W. 1939. An experimental investigation on the effect of gratification upon effort and orientation to reality. *Amer. J. Orthopsychiat., 9,* 186–205.

RICHARDS, T. W. 1940. Factors in the personality of nursery school children. *J. exp. Educ., 9,* 152–153.

RIEMER, M. D. 1940. Runaway children. *Amer. J. Orthopsychiat., 10,* 522–527.

RIESS, B. R., & DeCILLIS, O. A. 1940. Personality differences in allergic and non-allergic children. *J. abnorm. soc. Psychol., 35,* 104–113.

ROFF, M., & ROFF, L. 1940. An analysis of the variance of conflict behavior in preschool children. *Child Develpm., 11,* 43–60.

SCHACHTEL, E. 1941. The dynamic perception and the symbolism of form; with special reference to the Rorschach Test. *Psychiatry, 4,* 79–96.

SCHILDER, P. 1938. The child and the symbol. *Scientia, Milano, 64,* 21–26.

SCHILDER, P., & BENDER, L. 1940. Impulsions: specific disorder of the behavior of children. *Arch. Neurol. Psychiat., Chicago, 43,* 990–1008.

SCHMIDL-WAEHNER, T. 1944. Personality studies through children's paintings. In Murphy, L. B., *Personality development in ten children.* (To be published)

SHERMAN, M. 1939a. Emotional disturbances and reading disability. In *Recent trends in reading.* Chicago: University Chicago Press. Pp. 126–134.

—— 1939b. The interpretation of schizophrenic-like behavior in children. *Child Develpm., 10,* 35–42.

SHIRLEY, M. 1933. The first two years: III. Personality manifestations. Minneapolis: University Minnesota Press.

—— 1939. A behavior syndrome characterizing prematurely-born children. *Child Develpm., 10,* 115–128.

—— 1941. The impact of the mother's personality on the young child. *Smith Coll. Stud. soc. Work, 12,* No. 1, 15–64.

SHUTTLEWORTH, F. K. 1938. Sexual maturation and the skeletal growth of girls age six to sixteen. *Monogr. Soc. Res. Child Develpm., 3,* No. 5.

SKEELS, H. M., UPDEGRAFF, R., WELLMAN, B. L., & WILLIAMS, H. M. 1938. A study of environmental stimulation: an orphanage preschool project. *Univ. Ia Stud. Child Welf., 15,* No. 4.

SOLLENBERGER, R. T. 1940. Some relationships between the urinary excretion of male hormone by maturing boys and their expressed interests and attitudes. *J. Psychol., 9,* 179–189.

STERN, W. 1930. Psychology of early childhood. New York: Holt.

STONE, C. P., & BARKER, R. G. 1939. The attitudes and interests of pre-menarcheal and post-menarcheal. *J. genet. Psychol., 54,* 27–71.

STUART, H. C., & staff. 1939. Studies from the Center for Research in Child Health and Development, School of Public Health, Harvard Univ., The Center, the group under observation, sources of information, and studies in progress. *Monogr. Soc. Res. Child Develpm., 4,* No. 1.

SYMONDS, P. M. 1939. The psychology of parent-child relationships. New York: Appleton-Century.

TROUP, E. 1938. A comparative study by means of the Rorschach method of personality development in twenty pairs of twins. *Genet. Psychol. Monogr., 20,* 461–556.

WASHBURN, R. W. 1929. A study of the smiling and laughing of infants in the first year of life. *Genet. Psychol. Monogr., 6,* 397–537.

WELLMAN, B. L. 1940. Iowa studies on the effects of schooling. *Yearb. nat. Soc. Stud. Educ., 39,* Part II, 377–399.

WITMER, H. L., LEACH, J., McKEE, L., SEIBEL, M., STENINER, V., & RICHMAN, E. 1938. The outcome of treatment of children rejected by their mothers. *Smith Coll. Stud. soc. Work, 8,* 187–234.

WITTY, P. 1940. A genetic study of fifty gifted children. *Yearb. nat. Soc. Stud. Educ., 39,* Part II, 401–409.

ZUCKER, H. 1943. The emotional attachment of children to their parents as related to standards of behavior and delinquency. *J. Psychol., 15,* 31–40.

Chapter 22

ADOLESCENT EXPERIENCE IN RELATION TO PERSONALITY AND BEHAVIOR

By Phyllis Blanchard, Ph.D.

It is not easy to evaluate adolescent experience as a determinant in the development of personality and behavior, for the relevant material comes from studies of adolescence oriented from such different viewpoints as the psychological, psychoanalytic and sociological and varied in methodology from controlled experimental research, questionnaire returns and statistical reports to clinical and general observations. Moreover, there is a continuity in the personality development from birth to adult life, with intimate relationships between the experiences of infancy, childhood and adolescence, so that it is often difficult to state with certainty that phenomena observed during or after adolescence are to be ascribed to adolescent experience alone.

In order to reduce these difficulties, we shall exclude two groups of adolescent individuals, in whom definite physical pathology or mental deficiency complicates the picture, and confine our discussion to adolescence when uncomplicated by either of these conditions. In clinical diagnosis and treatment, it is important to take into account any physical or intellectual handicaps that exist in a particular case. But in this chapter, our concern is less with individual problems and more with general theoretical formulations. Hence we are justified in excluding, so far as possible, gross physical or mental pathology, for the purpose of facilitating the task of relating adolescent experience to personality and behavior.

General Psychological Literature

The pioneer work on adolescence in this country was G. Stanley Hall's two volume treatise (1904), which encompassed the biological aspects of adolescence, its normal and abnormal emotional phenomena, its psychology and psychopathology. It was Hall who first described the emotional instability of adolescence but at the same time noted the enrichment of the emotional life at puberty; his description of adolescent anger (pp. 367–370, Vol. 2) is full of keen observations concerning efforts to conceal and suppress it, revengeful phantasies, etc.; his discussion of youthful suicide or suicidal phantasies includes such motivations as grief over loss of love, wishes to be revenged upon parents or a loved one who does not respond, disappointment in self- and self-disillusion-

691

ment (pp. 374–384, Vol. 1). It was Hall, too, who first collected from many sources and brought together data on the physical growth and physiological changes at puberty and indicated the relationship between biological changes in the adolescent organism and the psychological phenomena observed at that period of life.

Later writings by psychologists have stressed the necessity for considering the physiology of adolescence in order to understand its psychology. Luella Cole (1936) has given an excellent summary of the usual adolescent bodily changes, such as the acceleration of physical growth, the unequal rates of growth in different parts and organs of the body, complex glandular changes, maturation of the reproductive organs and functions, development of the secondary sexual characteristics, etc. She considers that during adolescence the organism is in a state of disequilibrium, due to the unevenly developing organs and functions, and therefore can be thrown into a state of emotional disturbance very readily. Hence, the adolescent tends to respond emotionally to comparatively slight stimuli. Most other authors also mention considerable emotional instability as characteristic of adolescence.

There is general agreement among authors that another cause of seemingly exaggerated emotional responses during adolescence is the strain produced by the necessity of making readjustments to the self and to others. This necessity is imposed by the adolescent's own drives and desires as well as by the expectations of the social group in which he lives. Jones (1938) states that the adolescent must become able to direct his own behavior with increasing independence of parental guidance or control, must develop satisfactory relationships with the opposite sex, and must achieve integration of his own personality. Hollingworth (1928) mentioned four major adjustments during adolescence: "psychological weaning" from the family, vocational choice and preparation, establishment of heterosexuality, and organization of the self. A long list of authors could be quoted in agreement on the viewpoint that successful adjustments in these fields during adolescence are of fundamental importance for personality and behavior in adult life.

There is further agreement that childhood experiences and parental attitudes may favor these adolescent adjustments or interfere with them, causing them to be delayed or in extreme instances not accomplished adequately at all. Parental efforts to prolong childish dependence or to continue strict control, parental restrictions of the adolescent in social relationships with the opposite sex, parental demands for vocational choices out of harmony with the adolescent's own interests or abilities, all are frequently mentioned as leading to difficulties in adolescent efforts at readjustment. They are also productive of increased conflicts between the adolescent and parental or other adult authority—an aspect of adolescence which has been stressed by many writers on the subject. These family conflicts do not break out suddenly at adolescence as frequently as might be assumed, however. In clinical experience with adolescents and their parents, an increase of conflict previously present in the parent-child relationships is seen more often than friction that begins de novo at adolescence.

Experimental and Statistical Research

While the physiological changes during adolescence have been regarded as contributing to emotional instability, it has also been assumed that the physiological maturation at puberty is accompanied by tendencies toward psychological maturity and by the reinforcement of sexual and other drives, so that inner forces impel the adolescent toward heterosexuality and toward new interests and adjustments. Experimental research on adolescence is not extensive but the data from such investigations as have been made seem to confirm this hypothesis.

Stone and Barker (1937) gave the Pressey Interest-Attitude Test and the Sullivan Test for Developmental Age to 175 post-menarcheal girls (girls who had menstruated) and to 175 premenarcheal girls (who had not yet begun to menstruate). The post- and premenarcheal girls were paired for age and there were no important differences in the social-economic status of their families. Analysis of responses to the items of the Pressey Interest-Attitude Test showed that the post-menarcheal girls gave the mature responses with statistically significant greater frequency than the premenarcheal girls of the same age. On the Sullivan Test, the post-menarcheal girls likewise gave mature responses more frequently than premenarcheal girls of the same age. The post-menarcheal girls were more interested in their physical appearance, reported more heterosexual interests and activities, had more tendency to avoid vigorous physical exertion, indulged in more daydreaming, and were more concerned over conflicts in the family life.

In this study, Stone and Barker noted those groups of items on the Pressey and Sullivan tests which seemed to differentiate better than other items between post-menarcheal and premenarcheal girls. Using these differentiating items and adding new ones, they developed an interest-attitude test which they then gave to a larger number of girls. In this second study (1939), in order to exclude the influence of the factors of chronological age and social-economic status, two groups of 564 post-menarcheal and 387 premenarcheal girls were subdivided into smaller groups, matched for age (within five to fifteen days) and also matched for similarity of social-economic status of the families. Racial influences were excluded by limiting the study to American-born girls of middle and north European stock; none of Hebrew, Negro, Mexican, Oriental or south European stock was included. As in the preceding study, this investigation with a larger number of subjects showed that post-menarcheal girls gave mature responses on the interest-attitude test in larger proportion than premenarcheal girls of approximately the same age, social-economic background and racial stock; heterosexual interests and activities were indicated for more post-menarcheal than premenarcheal girls, regardless of chronological age; concern with personal adornment, disinclination for vigorous physical exercise and daydreaming were much more characteristic for the post-menarcheal than for the premenarcheal girls.

Sollenberger's study (1940) of sexually mature adolescent boys compared with boys less mature sexually was made with only a small number of subjects, but nevertheless should be mentioned. Sexual maturity or immaturity was determined by analysis of the urine: if the urine contained a high content of male sex hormone, the boy was regarded as more sexually mature; if the male sex hormone content was low, the boy was considered less mature sexually. A preliminary trial of three different tests led to the selection of the Furfey Test of Developmental Age, which was then given to ten boys whose urine had a high male sex hormone content and to thirteen boys with low male sex hormone content in their urine. Analysis of the test responses revealed that the more sexually mature boys (those whose urine had high hormone content) had greater interest in personal adornment, heterosexual activities and strenuous competitive sports than the less sexually mature boys (those whose urine had low hormone content).

Garrison (1940) and Partridge (1939) have summarized several studies of the interests and activities of children and adolescents, but in these investigations the comparison was made on a chronological age basis, not on such evidence of adolescent maturation as the establishment of menstruation in the girls or increased secretion of male sex hormone in the boys. However, it can be inferred that a large proportion of junior and senior high school students would be adolescents and that lower grade pupils seldom would be adolescents. Hence it is worth noting that studies of the interests and activities of these age groups for the most part indicate a trend toward more mature and more heterosexual inclinations among high school students. This is in harmony with the findings of the more carefully controlled experimental investigations previously mentioned.

Willoughby (1937) summarized data on sexuality during the second decade of life, quoting from studies made by a large number of investigators. Many of the studies employed questionnaire or interview methods, used with adult subjects, so that much of the material depended upon conscious memories of adults with reference to their sexual experiences during childhood and adolescence. A large proportion of individuals remembered striking impressions about sex received before puberty; the sources of these impressions were varied, but information about sex was obtained from reading, from companions outside the home, or from other sources outside the family, a little more often than from parents. Adolescent attitudes toward the phenomena of sexual maturation differed greatly: some adolescents reacted with pleasure or sexual excitation but many felt shame, disgust, or other negative attitudes. Frankly erotic dreams were common for boys, rare for girls; an adolescent period of masturbation was more characteristic for boys than for girls. Data on homosexual tendencies suggested more individuals were homosexually inclined than is usually considered probable, but for the most part their homosexuality seemed due to restrictions of the environment upon opportunities for heterosexual companionship and in only small measure a deeply ingrained aspect of personality development. From all the data, which were reviewed in much more detail than the selected high lights given above might imply, Willoughby drew certain general conclusions to the following effect. Interest and curiosity about sex begins in early childhood; during the second decade of life the glandular changes at puberty greatly reinforce sexual drives and desires, and these probably are increasingly intensified up to a point somewhat beyond the end of the second decade. Inhibiting influences on sexual drives may be exerted by negative attitudes, or moral and ethical ideals and conflicts between sexual drives and these inhibiting forces may be severe enough to produce neurotic symptoms or to turn the individual away from heterosexuality to substitute forms of sexual gratification, such as prolonged masturbation or homosexuality.

Stott's recent researches (1940a, b) are of interest to our discussion in so far as they seek to test the theory that personality integration during adolescence may be fostered or hindered by parental relationships. Stott found that serious criticisms of parental behavior by adolescents tended to coincide somewhat with low personality scores obtained by averaging the ratings on several personality tests. Parental behavior, particularly of the mother, appeared to be most significantly related to the personality development of adolescent boys living in city homes; parental conduct seemed less important for the personality development of boys living on farms or in small towns and for the personality development of girls in all three types of environments. Punishment (scolding, slapping, whipping, being made to stay at home) correlated slightly with low scores on the personality tests, particularly in items relating to self-reliance. Boys and girls living on farms apparently were not punished as frequently as those living in cities or towns and were less affected by punishment when they did receive it.

Partridge (1939), in a chapter on young people in the family, has summarized statistical studies on the relationships between parents and adolescent boys and girls, which lead to the following conclusions: Intimate and confidential relationships with parents, particularly with the mother, are definitely connected with good adjustment during adolescence; maladjustment is much greater among the boys and girls who do not have harmonious, confidential relationships with parents. Poor marital relations between the parents and very severe parental discipline of children contribute heavily to adolescent and adult maladjustments.

Cultural Studies

In some primitive cultures, for instance among the Trobriand Islanders as described by Malinowski (1929), adolescence is a period in which considerable freedom for prenuptial sexual relationships is permitted, in contrast to our own culture, in which premarital sexual relationships are out of keeping with the mores and a period of sexual abstinence conventionally is expected during adolescence in spite of the individual's biological sexual maturity. Cultural viewpoints emphasize this disharmony between biology and culture, in our society, as a contributory factor in the emotional instability of adolescence and in the emotional conflicts at that age. Mead (1930) supports this conclusion by citing examples of primitive cultures characterized by considerable adolescent freedom in contrast to others where adolescent sexual behavior is subject to very strict taboos. She states that little adolescent instability and conflict is to be found when the culture imposes few restraints but that adolescent instability and maladjustments are evident in cultures imposing severe restrictions on behavior or fostering inhibiting attitudes toward sex.

The cultural approach suggests that not only adolescent instability but also friction and conflict with parents during adolescence result largely from cultural influences. According to the authors of *Frustration and Aggression* (1939), the adolescent is an adult physiologically but socially is still regarded very much as a child and surrounded by many of the restrictions of childhood. Both sexual activities and personal independence are denied to the adolescent in our American culture, so that he is frustrated in securing satisfaction for both sexual drives and desires for personal independence and responsibility. The adolescent naturally reacts aggressively to this situation of frustration, so that rebellion against adult authority and conflicts with parents are seen as expressions of aggression toward the frustrating agents. These authors further suggest that the adolescent, through a trial and error process, has to attempt to find substitute satisfactions for the sexual and self-assertive strivings that cannot be directly gratified. As he succeeds in finding substitute satisfactions, he feels less frustrated and therefore his aggression diminishes. Thus the rebelliousness of early adolescence tends to be followed by a period of decreasing rebellion and lessening of family conflicts.

It should be noted that cultural influences do not operate upon the adolescent merely as restrictions imposed by external social authority. The individual has been exposed to the culture in which he lives from the time of birth and by adolescence has absorbed much of this culture into himself in the form of ethical ideals and standards of behavior. This way in which the culture affects the adolescent may be even more important than the demands of the culture as imposed upon the adolescent by parents and other adults acting as its agents, as we shall see in the following section on psychoanalytic theories.

Freudian Theories of Adolescent Development

In order to outline some of the Freudian viewpoints on adolescence, it is necessary to start from the background of these psychoanalytic theories of childhood psychosexual development and the structure of the personality. The Freudian literature describes three principal stages of preadult sexual development: the period of infantile sexuality, the latency period and adolescence (see Chapter 20 by Ribble). The erotic phenomena of early infancy are called pregenital, because they are connected with other parts and functions of the body than genital ones. By the age of four or five, however, the genitals become the chief erogenous organs and there is pleasure in masturbatory manipulations of the genitals. Coincidentally, the phenomenon known as the Oedipus complex may be observed in childish fantasies about sexual relationships and birth which often center around having babies with the parent of the opposite sex to the child.

By the age of six or seven, both the Oedipus complex and the period of infantile sexual development normally have come to an end. The child has begun to substitute other interests and activities for sexual curiosity and sexually colored fantasies; in other words, he has repressed and sublimated his sexual interests and entered the so-called latency period, which normally will not terminate until shortly before puberty. As the young child turns away from the Oedipus complex, the normal tendency is also to identify more strongly than before with the parent of the same sex and thus to begin more differentiation along masculine or feminine lines.

The psychoanalytic concept of personality structure includes three chief aspects—called the id, the ego, and the super-ego. The id is used as a collective term to include all the instinctive and emotional drives of the human organism, such as the sexual and aggressive drives. By super-ego is meant that part of the personality which is built up through identifications with parents and others and in response to cultural pressures. It is suggested that at first the child accepts adult standards and conforms to them in his behavior because conformity brings love and approval while nonconformity is disapproved or punished. The young child therefore yields to the requirements of the adults who care for him in order to have the affectionate relationships with them which he wants and needs. Very soon, however, because of his love and admiration for parents or other adults and also because it is pleasanter to direct and control his own behavior than to have constant instruction and control from others, the child takes many of the standards and requirements of his intimate adult world into himself and makes them his personal ideals and standards of conduct. His conformity then becomes necessary in order to preserve his own self-respect and to avoid self-criticism and feelings of guilt. Thus, by the time the child enters the latency period, his own super-ego is partly formed and operates to control many of his id-drives. Super-ego development continues through the latency period and adolescence, probably even through the young adult years of life, being modified somewhat from family patterns through the ever broadening social relationships outside the family circle.

The ego is best described in terms of its functions. One of its functions is to act as mediator between incompatible demands arising from the id and the super-ego and to find ways of action that provide some satisfaction of the id-drives without behaving too much in opposition to the ideals and standards of the super-ego. Another ego function is the evaluation of reality situations and the adaptation of behavior to them.

Nunberg (1931) has given an excellent presentation of the Freudian theories of personality development during infancy, childhood, and adolescence. At puberty, he states, there usually is a brief revival of early infantile sexual interests and a reactivation of the Oedipus complex but the reinforcement of the physiological sexual drives at puberty furnishes a strong impetus away from pregenital sexual interests to genital ones and away from the Oedipus complex to love relationships with persons of the opposite sex outside the family circle. In other words, adolescence normally brings with it tendencies toward genital and heterosexual interests and activities. There is also a tendency to reinforce masculine identifications for the boy and feminine ones for the girl. If the parent of the same sex has been lost or is unsatisfactory for such purposes, the adolescent tends to find some other person in his environment with whom to identify in establishing masculinity or femininity.

If the adolescent's environment is too unfavorable, or if there were too many difficulties in his earlier development during childhood, the normal tendency to establish heterosexuality and make suitable masculine or feminine identifications may be defeated. Then the adolescent may have to fall back on homosexuality or other infantile sexual satisfactions. Nunberg also speaks of the adolescent conflict between the reinforced sexual drives and the super-ego's standards of behavior and sees the outcome of this conflict within the personality as important for the establishment of a well integrated personality or of neurotic patterns.

Anna Freud (1937) has elaborated this last point considerably. She agrees with Nunberg that genital drives tend to predominate in adolescence but she believes that the sexual drives are not the only ones to be greatly reinforced at puberty. The aggressive impulses and all the other id-drives are also strengthened and intensified, in her opinion. The increase in quantity and quality of the id-drives threatens the ego with being overwhelmed by their strength and becoming unable to continue its function of mediating between the instinctive impulses and the super-ego's demands based upon moral and ethical standards. For normal development, the adolescent must find a new balance between these parts of the personality, the ego must preserve its function of modifying both the id-drives and the super-ego's demands for acceptable conduct without sacrificing completely either satisfactions for emotional and instinctive needs or all ethical ideals. If the ego surrenders to the id, allowing the id-drives to obtain complete domination, the outcome would be uninhibited efforts to satisfy sexual and other drives; presumably this uncontrolled attempt at direct gratification of impulses might go far enough so that it would end in delinquency. If, on the contrary, the ego yields entirely to the demands of the super-ego and strictly inhibits or represses all instinctive and emotional drives, rigidity of the personality would result, with a loss of the flexibility necessary for suitable adaptations to continually changing reality situations. Zilboorg (1937) speaks of youthful suicide as another possible outcome of these adolescent personality conflicts.

Anna Freud also discusses adolescent asceticism and intellectualization as frequent reactions to the personality conflicts arising during this period of development. Asceticism is utilized as one of the defenses against the instinctive and emotional drives, in her opinion. Adolescent intellectualization may be observed in the tendency to debate various abstract subjects, such as free love versus marriage, revolution versus support of existing political forms of government, atheism versus religious faith, etc. These intellectual interests reflect the conflicts between the id-drives and the super-ego, but Anna Freud points out that they are also an effort to work through those conflicts and to obtain mastery over the instinctive and emotional drives without either completely yielding to them or denying them entirely. Hendrick (1938) suggests that adolescent intellectualization may serve still another purpose by giving intellectual practice which later can be utilized by the ego in its function of evaluating reality.

Perhaps this summarization of Freudian theories has given too much of an "either-or" implication regarding the chances for favorable or unfavorable outcomes for adolescent personality development. If so, this would be too great an oversimplification, for asceticism, neurotic symptoms, "wild" behavior, etc., may be only transitory reactions, followed by a better balance and integration within the personality when the peak of the conflict between id, ego, and super-ego has been passed. Certainly Anna Freud, Nunberg, Hendrick, and others writing from the Freudian viewpoint have stressed the normative impetus furnished by biological maturation at puberty, as well as seeing adolescence as one of the critical periods in personality development.

Freudian theory has always given due consideration to the sublimation of the instinctive and emotional drives as a normal aspect of personality development and it seems important to mention the significance of sublimation for adolescence, as well as for the latency period of childhood. Many observers have noted that an increase of creative activities is often characteristic of adolescence; an adolescent phase of interest in literary or artistic productions followed by a gradual decrease in such interest, is a fairly common phenomenon. Adolescent stories, poems, drawings, and paintings very often reflect personality conflicts and are an attempt to work through those conflicts or master intensified emotional drives, in a manner similar to that described by Anna Freud in discussing adolescent intellectualizations. Moreover, as Hendrick said of the intellectual activities of adolescence, so we may also say of adolescent creativeness, that the practice it offers in sublimation may be important for later adjustment, for our culture ordinarily requires individuals to live at more or less sublimated levels and does not always permit direct and full gratification of instinctive and emotional drives even in adult life.

Adolescence from the Rankian Viewpoint

In a paper read at the National Conference of Social Work (1941), Hankins has discussed adolescent development from her own experience and from a background of Rankian theory. This theory starts from an assumption that the unborn child is part of a physical whole but loses this wholeness at birth, when he becomes a separate biological organism instead of a part of the mother's organism, as was the case during embryonic life. But after the biological differentiation that occurs at birth, the infant is so dependent upon the mother that psychologically he still is very largely undifferentiated from her and has little awareness of a self apart from hers. The infant soon begins to become aware of the fact that he and his mother are two separate individuals, however, and this brings a sense of loss of the wholeness previously experienced in relation to the mother as embryo and helpless newborn baby. In very early childhood, therefore, the individual begins efforts to regain a sense of wholeness or "totality" but the only way this now can be achieved is through totality in and for himself, by gaining a sense of a self distinct and different from other persons. First by identification with the mother and then with other persons, the child takes into himself the material with which to build up an individual self, but gradually he becomes able to differentiate himself from those with whom he was earlier identified. As he becomes less receptive and more self-assertive and self-differentiating, he becomes increasingly aware of his own individuality and acquires a sense of wholeness or totality through the possession of a self which he can feel is all his own.

At the same time that this self-development is taking place, the child also must learn to relate himself to others with parts of the self. For comfortable living, a balance between total action and partial action is necessary. Adolescence brings both opportunity and necessity to find a further balance between maintenance of the sense of totality in the self and relating the self to others, but the latter requires partial action and hence produces fearfulness of sacrificing too much of the individuality and totality that has slowly been achieved. From the Rankian viewpoint, the sexual drives of adolescence appear as generic forces within the individual which offer a threat to his independence and sense of self. The adolescent fears and resists his sexual impulses because they might dominate him and force him to renounce his capacity to act as a total self. In our culture, the reconciliation of the generic sexual drives and individual self-expression lies in a love relationship with another person, but the adolescent often fears to enter into such a relationship since he would have to give up total personal control and to accept partial control from that other person. The adolescent has only just begun to feel some freedom from the domination of parents and other adults and is far from ready to give up this glimpse of personal freedom by yielding to sexual impulses in the form of a love relationship with another individual, for to love another is to yield parts of the self to the loved person and to sacrifice the possibility of independent total action, at least to some extent.

Hankins suggests that the normal outcome for adolescence would be through learning that new experiences and relationships may be enriching to the personality even if they do involve some self-sacrifice. She further suggests that adolescent asceticism is not explained correctly by Anna Freud, but is to be understood as a method of maintaining individuality by denying generic sexual drives or keeping them under strict control. Hankins also sees sexual promiscuity not as an uninhibited effort at instinctual gratification but rather as another attempt to preserve the individual self, since the transitory sexual relationship can be used to dominate another person through his sexual needs while at the same time refusing to yield any part of the self, as would be necessary in a real love relationship.

Mental Disease and Delinquency in Adolescence

With all the emphasis that has been placed upon adolescent instability and the personality conflicts of adolescence, it might be expected that psychoses or delinquency would often have their onset at this period of life. Statistical studies do not confirm this expectation; instead, it would seem from the available statistics that mental diseases (psychoses) usually come into the open during the adult life after adolescence, while delinquency ordinarily begins before adolescence during the childhood years.

Using the 1930 figures for the population of the country and the figures for first admissions to mental hospitals in 1933, Landis and Page (1938) compared the percentage of hospital admissions for certain age decades with the percentage of the general population in the same age decades. In 1930, a greater percentage of the general population was in the age decade from ten to nineteen years than in any age decade above nineteen years, but the smallest percentage of hospital admissions in 1933 was for the age decade ten to nineteen. Only 5% of the mental hospital admissions were in the ten to nineteen-year group, while 19.2% of the general population fell into that age group. Yet for each succeeding age decade, the percentage of state hospital admissions became increasingly larger than the percentage of the population falling into the same age group. In the 20 to 29-year decade, 17.1% of first admissions to hospitals compared with 16.9% of the general population; the disproportion of hospital admissions to population increased with each decade thereafter.

While these figures indicate that psychoses are not the immediate outcome of adolescent personality conflicts, they do not negate the opinion of many psychiatrists that functional mental diseases, such as dementia praecox (schizophrenia) and the manic-depressive psychoses have their etiology in childhood and adolescent experiences and development. In this connection, it should be noted that these two types of psychoses, according to both Landis and Page, and Malzberg (1935), account for most of the state hospital admissions during adolescence and young adult life. Moreover, studies based on age of admission to state hospitals undoubtedly tend to underestimate the number of individuals developing psychoses during adolescence. In clinical experience, when we see adolescents suffering from a beginning psychosis, we find that parents are often reluctant to consider hospital care and that hospitalization is postponed until it becomes inevitable when the psychotic condition is further advanced.

Hunt (1938) has described a neighborhood group of boys who engaged in sexual perversions and also went through experiences of religious conversion at revival meetings. A few boys in the same neighborhood attended the revivals but did not engage in the sexual practices; a few participated in the latter but not the former. The boys who took part in both the sexual and religious experiences developed mental disease later in life, while those sharing in one experience only, did not become psychotic. Thus, only those members of the neighborhood group who developed conflicts during adolescence because of the incompatibility between their sexual behavior and their religious ideals, and carried those conflicts on into adult life, became mentally ill. The age of onset for their mental illnesses differed considerably and Hunt suggests that the differences in age at which they became psychotic probably indicate variations in their capacity to endure and tolerate conflict before reaching a breaking point. This suggestion is pertinent to the present discussion, for the statistics on age of admission for patients in mental hospitals may mean that psychosis is not an immediate outcome for adolescent personality conflicts in any great number of cases, but do not necessarily mean that it is not a delayed outcome. Probably a great many persons have enough capacity to bear conflict so that the conflicts begun during childhood and adolescence do not take their full toll in the form of mental illness until some time afterward in young adult life or even in later adult years.

Many studies of delinquents have indicated that the childhood environment is a large factor in the etiology of this behavior; we only need to refer in passing to such findings as the large proportion of broken homes or other extremely unfavorable family situations, neighborhood conditions producing so-called delinquency areas, etc., for these sociological findings are reported in the chapter on ecology, by Faris. In this chapter, therefore, it is only necessary to include the statistical evidence that for the most part delinquency has its beginnings in childhood, before adolescent experiences can become a determinant.

Investigating the histories of 500 offenders sentenced to a reformatory, the Gluecks (1930) found that 51 had been in conflict with social authority by the age of ten or younger; 137 by the age of fourteen or younger; 393 by the age of sixteen or younger. In the same 500 cases, 45 had their first known arrest by the time they were ten years old; 121 by the age of twelve or earlier; 214 by the age of fourteen or earlier;

297 by the age of sixteen or earlier. Cole (1936) has interpreted data reported by the Gluecks for 1,000 juvenile court cases, in relation to adolescence; 31.6% had been brought into court before adolescence; 83.7% had manifested delinquent tendencies before adolescence, even if not brought to court; at least 35.7% could have been recognized as delinquent by the end of the second grade in school. Less than one-fifth of these 1,000 children became delinquent during adolescence; more than four-fifths were delinquent before adolescence and continued delinquent behavior after becoming adolescent. Healy and Bronner (1936) report that in 153 intensively studied cases, the first known delinquency occurred at eight years or earlier in 48% and after twelve years in only 22%.

Clinical Material

Many of the statistical studies based on clinical cases indicate that the parent-child relationship is important for personality and behavior development, since a large amount of unfavorable parental relationships appears in the cases of personality and behavior difficulties coming to clinics. Most of these reports include a larger proportion of children than of adolescents and probably should not be referred to in this chapter limited to a discussion of adolescence, except to remark that unfavorable relationships between parents and children usually will be carried on into the adolescent years and increase adolescent difficulties of personality development.

There is one clinical statistical study concerned entirely with high school students, which should be mentioned in more detail. McBee (1935) classified the problems of 328 students seen at a high school mental hygiene clinic. Since the delinquent and truant groups were small, the findings with respect to them may be omitted, as may be also the findings for the groups with problems of scholastic failure and problems associated with physical handicaps or organic illnesses. The material on 102 students with personality problems is most relevant to the purposes of the present chapter, and may be summarized as follows:

Nearly all the 102 students with personality maladjustments were of average or above average intelligence; in this respect they did not differ greatly from the total student body. McBee considered it significant, however, that 57% of the mothers and 40% of the fathers were foreign born, in the 102 cases of personality problems, while only about 30% of the parents of the total student body were foreign born. There seems to be some inconsistency in the figures given in two of McBee's tables—one on home situation and another on broken homes—but if the lowest figures are taken, it appears that at least 40% of the 102 students with personality difficulties were not living in homes with both parents but in homes broken by the death of one parent or by separation of the parents. These findings suggest that one factor in the adolescent personality maladjustments was the friction in the family due to disharmony between the old-world standards of foreign-born parents and the new-world standards of the Americanized adolescent sons and daughters. They also suggest that emotional disturbances over the loss of a parent who has died or over marital difficulties and separation of parents were other factors contributing to adolescent difficulties in personality adjustments.

Howard (1941) classified the problems presented by 117 college girls, attempting to distinguish between those which represented a continuance of adolescent conflicts and maladjustments and other types of problems. The continuing adolescent difficulties were described as follows: 24 cases in which interfering family ties were prominent; 23 cases of anxiety; 11 cases of neurotic depression; 8 cases of adolescent asceticism and intellectualism; 7 cases of adolescent rebellion against work and routine; 7 cases of masculine identification. Among the 79 girls thus described, 41 also complained of difficulties in adjusting to sexual drives.

In most other reports on the adjustment and personality problems of college students, no differentiation has been made between problems of adolescence carried over into young adult life and other types of problems. Hence the data from other studies of college students cannot be so definitely related to a discussion of adolescence.

Individual Case Studies

In actual clinical work, the chief interest is in the adolescent as an individual, with his own particular personal problems, and in helping him with his efforts to make adjustments and to achieve a better personality organization. Case reports illustrating a wide variety of adolescent problems are to be found in many of the books and papers included in the bibliography for this chapter. Other case material is relevant to the purposes of this chapter in so far as it can be related to the general and theoretical material previously summarized and can be utilized to clarify certain points in the preceding discussion.

The tendency toward a change of interests and attitudes at puberty, indicated by the Stone and Barker studies of premenarcheal and postmenarcheal girls, may be illustrated by the case of a girl in whom menstruation was established during the time when she was having regular interviews with the psychologist. The purpose of these interviews was to help the girl with emotional conflicts over the loss of her parents and the necessity of living at a boarding school. This aspect of the case, however, has little bearing on the present discussion. The material of special interest is the striking change observed in the girl's interests and activities as soon as she began to menstruate.

She was first seen at the age of eleven and a half and weekly interviews with her continued until she was nearly twelve and a half. For some time in these interviews, she spoke of playing with dolls and taking them to bed with her and liked to play with dolls or cut out paper dolls while talking to the psychologist. At the school, she played active outdoor games as well as playing with her dolls. She displayed little interest in her personal appearance or dress and was careless about wearing soiled or torn clothing. She never talked of any plans as to what she might do when she was through school and must take care of herself.

At the age of twelve she menstruated for the first time. In the next three months, although no effort was made to redirect her interests and activities either by the psychologist or by her teachers at school, the following changes occurred. The girl mentioned that she had given away her dolls and no longer wanted to play with the dolls in the psychologist's office or to cut out paper dolls during her interviews. At the school she read romantic fiction in her leisure time instead of continuing to play active outdoor games. She became very particular about her personal appearance and the neatness of her clothing; began to curl her hair and to use face powder and nail polish. She made herself a dress in sewing class at school although she had previously expressed some distaste for sewing. She became very much concerned over plans for vocational preparation and began to worry over what high school course to select, although choice of a high school course was not required until ninth grade and she was still in seventh grade.

The case of a fourteen-year-old boy offers an illustration of adolescent efforts to adjust to the reinforced sexual drives of puberty and to establish masculinity.

The boy was seen just after he had written a note to a young woman, making definite sexual advances. In his first interviews he talked almost continuously about sexual questions, expressing intense curiosity about anatomical differences between the two sexes and wanting to know how babies were conceived and born. It is difficult to believe that any fourteen-year-old-boy actually could be as uninformed as this boy seemed when he advanced various theories that might answer his questions; the possibility that babies came out of the breast or navel of a woman is a sample of his attempts to elucidate the mysteries of sex and birth. His questions and his explanations were those usually characteristic of a five-year-old and suggest the revival of early childhood curiosity and fantasies about sex and birth, mentioned in psychoanalytic theories as a common manifestation at adolescence.

After partially exhausting these sexual interests, the boy began to talk about his relationship with his father, who had died a few years previously. He told of the satisfying companionship with his father and how much he had missed him since his death. A little later, he described his activities with a gang of boys slightly older than himself. In the year of his association with these boys, he had heard many stories about sexual relationships between men and women and had experimented considerably with masturbation. These boys had talked about the young woman to whom he had sent the note, describing her as sexually promiscuous, and had suggested his writing to her, inviting her to have sexual relationships with him.

The boy showed guilty feelings over his sexual activities in the gang when he became anxious about the possibility that masturbation might have injured him either physically or mentally and when he said that if his father had still been living, he would never have allowed him to go with such bad boys. On the other hand, he doubted whether he would have started to go with the gang if he had not been so lonely after his father died. At this point he was able to see that in joining the gang of boys he was not only attracted by their conversation about sex but also was seeking some masculine companionship to replace that lost through the death of his father.

Shortly afterward, the boy began to talk admiringly of a man who was his teacher in Sunday school. He became very friendly with this man and told of going on fishing trips with him as he once had done with his own father. This man also helped him to make model airplanes, and lent him books about animal breeding. To a casual question about his gang, the boy answered that he had not seen much of those boys recently and added that going around with them had only gotten him into trouble. A little later, he said that he had a girl friend at school, mentioned inviting her to go to the movies and reported that she had accepted.

It seemed evident that the boy had now begun to sublimate his sexual interests first through his studies of animal breeding and then through social activities with a girl friend. In the Sunday school teacher, he had found a suitable substitute for the father whom he had lost and had been able to identify with this father substitute in establishing his own masculine interests.

The extent to which parental attitudes can interfere with adolescent personality development is shown very clearly in such an extreme case as that of a seventeen-year-old girl whose teachers were concerned because she had no friends of her own age and took no part in the school social functions. Although well developed physically for her age, the girl appeared for her interviews dressed in a childish style. Her conversation readily explained her attitude toward her classmates and their social activities.

She said that she would not go around with the other girls because they used cosmetics and were crazy about boys. Her mother had told her that she was not to use rouge and lipstick and make herself look like a prostitute. Her mother had also told her what dirty beasts men and boys were. She hated boys and men and couldn't stand the other girls' silly talk about their boy friends. She would not go to school social affairs because if she did she would be supposed to talk with the boys, as well as with the other girls. She had never learned to dance and did not wish to learn to dance. It was only because they liked to be with boys that the other girls had learned.

The girl saw no reason for her teachers wanting her to see a psychologist. Her mother also did not consider it necessary. Indeed, her mother made it quite clear that she resented the teachers wishing the girl to make friends and attend social functions at the school. She spoke disapprovingly of her daughter's classmates and said that she had brought up her daughter so that she would not be boy crazy. If the teachers were going to encourage girls to be boy crazy, she would take her daughter out of school.

Besides illustrating the influence of parental attitudes upon adolescent development, this case might also be used to illustrate strict super-ego control and denial of normal instinctive drives, resulting in a rigidity of personality—one of the possibilities for outcome of adolescent development described by Anna Freud. The Rankian viewpoint probably would stress still another aspect of the girl's development and would see her as having failed to achieve any differentiation from her mother and to establish any independent self of her own.

An illustration of adolescent literary productions as efforts to work through conflict rather than expressions of unusual literary talent, appears in the following poems written by a sixteen-year-old girl after the termination of an extra-marital sexual relationship. They show very clearly her effort to forget her lover and her remorse and guilt over having gone counter to the dictates of her moral ideals, with momentary thoughts of suicide as a way out of conflict and grief over lost love.

FORGETTING

I thought that I had forgotten
All the sorrow caused by you.
I hoped that I could forget—
'Tis the only thing for me to do.
Oh, I hoped that I had forgotten
The man who broke my heart,
But a song, a song that you sang,
Tears my very soul apart;
The tears fill my eyes, I remember
Your voice as you sang it to me;
Oh, I long for you wildly, my dearest,
My darling, please come back to me.

THE REACTION OF CONVENTIONS

Buried in the secret heart
Is an unknown, bitter dread
Of things that one is forced to do
Though longing to do the opposite instead.
Remorsefulness turns into hate,
At last wild rage breaks forth;
The things we once were forced to do,
We'll always hate, of course.

MY TROPICAL ISLE

Lost on a tropical island
In a lonely expanse of sea,
To some might be a misfortune,
But I wish it could happen to me.
I could sleep 'neath the southern moonlight,
Undisturbed 'till I chose to awake.
Should I choose to sleep on forever
What difference would it make?
Should I choose to sleep on forever
What would there be to fear?
In death I might find peace
With no one to interfere.

The last illustration is the case of a girl who was finally able to achieve a healthy integration of personality after first resorting to neurotic illness and asceticism as transitory attempts to solve her adolescent conflicts. She was first seen at the age of fifteen, shortly after she had begun to complain of inability to recite, because of choking sensations in her throat, when called upon in the classroom. Repeated medical examinations were negative, indicating that her symptoms were of a neurotic nature. Menstruation had been established at least a year before the onset of the difficulty in reciting.

Although the girl appeared to talk very freely in her first interviews, there was nothing in what she said that seemed to have any bearing upon the development of her symptoms. She never complained of the choking sensations or was unable to talk when with the psychologist. After several interviews had thrown no light on her difficulty in reciting, a conference with the school principal and school nurse was requested, in the hope that further information from them might be of help. They confirmed their previous reports of the girl's superior rating on intelligence tests and good standing in her school work. They could think of nothing unusual in the girl's school situation prior to the onset of the symptoms except that one of her friends had withdrawn from school because she was about to have an illegitimate child.

In the next interview with the girl, she was asked about this friend. When she saw that the psychologist knew what had happened, she felt free to tell how her friend had confided in her, but had exacted a promise that the confidence be kept a secret. The girl had not thought about this secret when talking with the psychologist, she said, but at school she often thought of it, wondered if any of the other girls knew why her friend had left school, but could not ask them because of her promise. When asked whether she might have feared to talk in class, lest somehow she break her promise and betray her friend's confidence, she answered, "Well, it won't be a secret much longer; the baby will be here in another week or two." The friend's baby was born within that time. The girl then began to recite in class and no longer had choking sensations in her throat that prevented her from doing so.

However, it seemed that these symptoms had been replaced by another set, for apparently the girl began to withdraw from social contacts with the other girls and boys at school. She spoke of this in her interviews. She had been wondering how her friend got into trouble, she said, and thought her friend must have been too much interested in boys. But the other girls were just the same, always flirting with the boys. So she had decided to keep away from them and not get into their bad habits. She had wondered which boy had induced her friend to "go too far"; her friend had refused to tell her the boy's name. Since she didn't know which boys at school could be trusted, she thought it best to keep away from all of them.

This girl's mother had died when the girl was about thirteen years old. She said that she knew how her mother would have felt if anything should happen to her such as had happened to her friend. She quoted her mother's dying words to her—"Be a good girl"—and her own promise, "I will, mother." Her mother had always liked to have her go to church, sing hymns, and study hard so as to get good school reports. Since thinking so much about her mother recently, she did not feel like singing popular songs but only hymns. She had decided to spend her time on her school work, keep away from the boys and girls at school, and stay out of trouble. She also had decided to become a school teacher, so she had to work hard on that account, too.

It was some time before she dared to admit that, like the other girls, she had formerly been interested in boys and wanted dates with them. Once she was able to recall these attitudes, she could say that there was no need for her to be so worried, it was no sign that she would get into trouble just because her friend had done so. Shortly afterward, it was reported that she had resumed her usual social relationships with the other students at school. The case was closed with the girl seeming free from neurotic symptoms and anxiety, enjoying ordinary social contacts with girls and boys at school, but not making dates with boys and still planning to be a teacher.

About a year later, she came for a visit, to let the psychologist know that she had not had any recurrence of illness symptoms. At this time, she announced that she had a "steady" boy friend who was eighteen years old and had secured a good job since he graduated from high school. He wanted her to marry him as soon as she was through high school, she said, and she was planning to do so. She would be eighteen when she finished high school and she thought that would be old enough to marry, for her mother had married her father just before she was eighteen. Since she was no longer planning to teach, she had dropped some of her college preparatory courses and replaced them by domestic science courses which would help her to become a good wife and mother.

It is not difficult to interpret this case in terms of Anna Freud's description of the adolescent personality conflict. Probably the girl's knowledge of her friend's behavior precipitated a severe inner conflict, since it may have stimulated her own curiosity and desires while at the same time emphasizing the dangers of heterosexual interests. In talking of the possibility that she, like her friend, might "go too far" with boys she was expressing her fear of her own impulses and of becoming too free in behavior. When she recalled her mother's teachings and dying admonition, she may well have been seeking a support that would help her to feel secure in her ability to control her sexual impulses. The memory of a promise to a dying person would be an especially powerful reinforcement for her own moral ideals because the tendency to regard such promises as sacred invests them with some of the qualities of a magical protective charm.

To have discussed her friend's trouble would have required talking about sex matters, as well as betraying the friend's confidence. Presumably she was fearful of conversation along this line as well as tempted to initiate it and this conflict was disguised in the symptoms that kept her from reciting in class. In giving up these symptoms, she mobilized the memories of her dead mother's moral standards to reinforce her own ideals of conduct. But she overdid this for a time, carrying it to the extent of asceticism and extreme absorption in intellectual interests. The asceticism could be partly relaxed when she realized that her friend's behavior need not influence her own conduct and could be entirely discarded when the prospect of an early marriage promised a satisfying emotional life in harmony with her ethical ideals and with the realities of social conventions.

Conclusion

From whatever viewpoint adolescence is regarded, it seems to be agreed, with but few exceptions, that the changes in the physiological organism that take place at puberty result in reinforcement of heterosexual drives and of strivings for independence and personal responsibility. These drives have been in existence during the earlier years of childhood but become much stronger than ever before at adolescence. Whether aggression is also reinforced at puberty or only increases then in reaction to a cultural environment which is frustrating to the adolescent's desires for satisfaction of heterosexual drives and drives toward personal independence seems to be a question on which there is somewhat less agreement.

While there is plenty of evidence indicating that parent-child relationships may be favorable or unfavorable to personality development, it seems doubtful that this situation is peculiar to adolescent development, for favorable or unfavorable parent-child relationships are more likely to begin early and continue into adolescence, rather than first making their appearance only at this age. Perhaps we should say that the background of family relationships may bring the child to adolescence either well prepared to continue previously good development or badly prepared to meet the necessities for individual and social readjustments that arise at puberty.

There have been two differing viewpoints concerning adolescent conflicts. One sees the adolescent as in conflict with social authority vested in parents or other adults. The other viewpoint on adolescent conflicts emphasizes those within the individual's own personality and sees the external family and social influences as favorable or unfavorable for a healthy outcome of these inner personality conflicts.

Experimental investigations seem to confirm the psychoanalytic theory that the normal growth and maturation processes of adolescence exert their force on the side of a better integration of the personality and the establishment of heterosexuality and may even be strong enough to overcome previous childhood developmental difficulties or environmental obstacles to heterosexual adjustments and personality organization. But in spite of the impetus toward normal personality development, there may be less desirable outcomes for adolescent personality conflicts. There is the possibility of the adolescent's renouncing the drives toward more mature emotional satisfactions with such personality losses as damage to the capacity for flexible adjustments to reality. There are also the possibilities of such outcomes of adolescent experience as delinquency, neurosis, psychosis, or even suicide.

Aichhorn (1935) has distinguished between two types of delinquency, one developing over a long period of time, the other manifested as a sudden outbreak in a previously nondelinquent individual. Statistical studies in this country suggest that the latter type is more rare than the former, for these statistics indicate that delinquent conduct begins in childhood much more frequently than during adolescence. Perhaps we may conclude that while delinquency may be an outcome of adolescent conflicts, even if it has not been characteristic of the individual in childhood, it is a more probable outcome if it has previously been the reaction to earlier childhood conflicts or other childhood experiences.

While the facts regarding psychosis as an outcome for adolescent development are somewhat less clear, it seems likely that they may be almost the opposite of those with respect to delinquency. Instead of a childhood or adolescent onset of psychosis, there probably is more apt to be a prolongation of severe emotional conflicts arising in these earlier stages of development, resulting in an onset of psychosis later on in adult life, when the limit of the individual's capacity to tolerate conflict has been reached. If, as Hunt (1938) suggests, there may be considerable variation in the capacity for toleration of conflict, a large proportion of the mental illness having its onset in adult years is actually a delayed outcome for childhood and adolescent experience and development. Many psychiatrists have stressed childhood and adolescent experience as significant in the etiology of the functional psychoses. Psychoanalytic work with neurotic patients has shown that most of the neurotic illness which appears in adult patients had its etiology in childhood and adolescent experience and represents a delayed outcome for childhood and adolescent personality conflicts even when it has not been openly evident as the immediate outcome during or directly after adolescence. Suicide as a way out of conflict often is postponed until the individual's capacity to endure conflict is exhausted, rather than being to any great extent an immediate outcome for adolescent conflicts.

Hall once spoke of adolescence as a kind of rebirth experience. Perhaps this is a figurative way of saying that the impetus toward psychological maturity furnished by the intensified emotional and instinctive drives at puberty normally is powerful enough to so modify and enrich the personality that an individual often seems like a different person after adolescence than he was ever before. But it also is true that the experiences of infancy and childhood or unfortunate environmental influences sometimes may be as strong or even stronger determinants for personality and behavior, may prevent psychological maturation from following upon biological maturation, and may interfere with the adolescent's utilization of the opportunity for modification and enrichment of the personality.

BIBLIOGRAPHY

ACKERLY, S. 1933. Rebellion and its relation to delinquency and neurosis in sixty adolescents. *Amer. J. Orthopsychiat., 3,* 147–160.

AICHHORN, A. 1935. Wayward youth. New York: Viking, 1938.

BERNFELD, S. 1938. Types of adolescence. *Psychoanal. Quart., 7,* 243–253.

BLANCHARD, P. 1920. The adolescent girl. New York: Dodd, Mead.

—— 1939. Problems of the adolescent girl. In *Cyclopedia of Medicine.* Philadelphia: F. A. Davis. Pp. 772–782.

COLE, L. 1936. Psychology of adolescence. New York: Farrar & Rinehart.

DOLLARD, J., *et al.* 1939. Frustration and aggression. New Haven: Yale University Press. Ch. 5.

ELLIOTT, G. L. 1930. Understanding the adolescent girl. New York: Holt.

FREUD, ANNA. 1937. The ego and the mechanisms of defense. London: Hogarth. Chs. 11, 12.

GARRISON, K. C. 1940. Psychology of adolescence. (Rev. ed.) New York: Prentice-Hall.

GLUECK, S., & GLUECK, E. 1930. 500 criminal careers. New York: Knopf. Ch. 8.

HALL, G. S. 1904. Adolescence. (2 Vols.) New York: Appleton.

HANKINS, D. 1943. The psychology and direct treatment of adolescents. *Ment. Hyg., 27,* 238–247.

HEALY, W., & BRONNER, A. 1936. New light on delinquency and its treatment. New Haven: Yale University Press.

HENDRICK, I. 1938. The ego and the defense mechanisms: a review and discussion. *Psychoanal. Rev., 25,* 476–497.

HOLLINGWORTH, L. S. 1928. The psychology of the adolescent. New York: Appleton-Century.

HORNEY, K. 1935. Personality changes in female adolescents. *Amer. J. Orthopsychiat., 5,* 19–26.

HOWARD, E. McC. 1941. An analysis of adolescent personality problems. *Ment. Hyg., N. Y., 25,* 363–391.

HUNT, J. McV. 1938. An instance of the social origin of conflict resulting in psychosis. *Amer. J. Orthopsychiat., 8,* 158–164.

JONES, M. C. 1938. Guiding the adolescent. *Progr. Educ., 15,* 605–609.

LANDIS, C., & PAGE, J. D. 1938. Modern society and mental disease. New York: Farrar & Rinehart. Ch. 4.

MALINOWSKI, B. 1929. The sexual life of savages in north-western Melanesia. (Vol. 1) New York: Liveright. Ch. 3.

MALZBERG, B. 1935. A statistical study of age in relation to mental disease. *Ment. Hyg., N. Y., 19,* 449–476.

McBEE, M. 1935. A mental hygiene clinic in a high school. *Ment. Hyg., N. Y., 19,* 238–280.

MEAD, M. 1930. Adolescence in primitive and modern society. In Calverton, F. V., & Schmalhausen, S. D., *The new generation: a symposium.* New York: Macaulay. Pp. 169–188.

MURRAY, J. M. The conscience during adolescence. *Ment. Hyg., N. Y., 22,* 400–408.

PARTRIDGE, E. DeA. 1939. Social psychology of adolescence. New York: Prentice-Hall.

NUNBERG, H. 1931. Allgemeine Neurosenlehre auf psychoanalytischer Grundlage. Bern: Hans Huber. Ch. 3.

RICHMOND, W. 1933. The adolescent boy. New York: Farrar & Rinehart.

—— 1925. The adolescent girl. New York: Macmillan.

ROSS, H. 1941. The case worker and the adolescent. *Family, 22,* 231–238.

SOLLENBERGER, R. T. 1940. Some relationships between the urinary excretion of male hormone by maturing boys and their expressed interests and attitudes. *J. Psychol., 9,* 179–190.

STAGNER, R. 1938. The role of parents in developing emotional instability. *Amer. J. Orthopsychiat., 8,* 122–129.

STONE, C. P., & BARKER, R. G. 1937. Aspects of personality and intelligence in post-menarcheal and premenarcheal girls of the same chronological ages. *J. comp. Psychol., 23,* 439–455.

—— 1939. The attitudes and interests of premenarcheal and post-menarcheal girls. *J. genet. Psychol., 57,* 393–414.

STOTT, L. H. 1938. The relation of certain factors in farm family life to personality development in adolescents. Lincoln, Nebraska: *Res. Bull. Univ. Neb. agric. Exp. Sta.*, No. 106.
—— 1940a. Adolescent's dislikes regarding parental behavior and their significance. *J. genet. Psychol.*, 57, 393–414.
—— 1940b. Home punishment of adolescents. *J. genet. Psychol.*, 57, 415–428.
WILLOUGHBY, R. R. 1937. Sexuality in the second decade. *Monogr. Soc. Res. Child Develpm.*, 2, No. 3.
ZACHRY, C. B. 1940. Emotion and conduct in adolescence. New York: Appleton-Century.
ZILBOORG, G. 1937. Considerations on suicide with particular reference to that of the young. *Amer. J. Orthopsychiat.*, 7, 15–31.

Stott, L. H., 1938. The relation of bragging to certain family life conditions of adolescents. *Adolescence*, Jersild, ed. *Teach. Coll. Bull.*, Vol. __, __, __.

—— 1940. Adjustment analysis revealing personal balance and mental hygiene. *Adolescence*, Home, personal and social adjustment. __, __.

Whatesmith, M. K., 1937. The psychology of adolescence. *Monogr. Soc. Res. Child Development*, __, __.

Zachry, C. B., 1940. Emotion and conduct in adolescence. *New York: Appleton*.

—— the young, __. *Adolescence*, Outlines boys, __, __, __.

Chapter 23

CULTURAL DETERMINANTS OF PERSONALITY

By Gregory Bateson, M.A.

WHEN WE THINK OF THE MULTITUDINOUS VARIETY of the special cases of human behavior, when we watch a native of New Guinea doing this, a native of New York doing that, a native of Samoa doing something else, we are faced, as scientists, with a very serious difficulty—the difficulty of trying to imagine what order of general statement will cover these very diverse phenomena, and many different scientific approaches have been devised in the effort to solve this problem. In this book we have, for example, the theories which have been devised by physiologists and neurologists, and other theories devised by those who studied the phenomena of experimental learning; other theories, again, devised by those who studied mental pathology, and so on. The basic presumption of such a symposium as this is that these various theories, no matter how diverse, are not necessarily mutually contradictory; that there is a possibility of translating, in the end, from the theories devised by psychoanalysts into terms of the theories derived from physiology; and those again into terms derived from experimental learning.

In spite of this great hope of ultimate translation, we have the fact that the theories have originated among workers using different kinds of data. This chapter is intended to give some general statement of the theories which have been reached by those who worked with a very curious kind of data, namely, observations upon preliterate people, and we shall endeavor to build up this picture inductively, starting from the various different threads in cultural anthropological work. But before we do this, it is necessary to make one negative statement about "cultural determinism," which needs to be kept clearly in the mind of the reader. We do *not* suggest that culture fully "determines" anything. The phrase "economic determinism" has, unfortunately, become a slogan of those who believe that economic "factors" are more "basic" than, perhaps, any others. In the opinion of the writer, this view is disastrous, and I should like to see substituted for it the notion that, at best, an economic approach to human behavior is rewarding, perhaps very rewarding, for the insight which it gives. This is a very different position, and implies that economics is something that scientists do, not something that exists in the world as a determinative or "basic" cause. Similarly, we shall use the phrase "cultural determinism" to imply that "culture" is an abstraction—a ready label for a point of view built up by a number of scientists—a point of view from which those scientists have achieved some insight.

Origin of the Concept of Cultural Determinism

The early days of anthropology were concerned chiefly with the business of description, and especially the early anthropologists were struck by outstanding bizarre features of the cultures which they studied. In their attempts to generalize, they were concerned chiefly to find identities or close similarities between phenomena in one place and phenomena in another. This is perhaps always the first step in a new science—the search, not for an abstract regularity, but for a concrete, episodic similarity between what occurs here and what occurs elsewhere; or between something which occurs now and something which occurs at some other time. Correspondingly, the theories of these early anthropologists were chiefly oriented to explaining such similarities, and naturally, since the similarities searched for were episodic, the type of theory which was devised was episodic or historical theory. Controversy raged, for example, between those who believed that resemblance between far-separated cultures ought to be accounted for in terms of similar evolutionary process and those others who believed that all such resemblance could only be accounted for by processes of cultural contact and diffusion. In the latter half of the nineteenth century and the beginning of the twentieth, cultural anthropologists were very seriously influenced by ways of thinking which they believed were in line with the Darwinian theory of evolution, and indeed it is perhaps fair to blame upon Darwin some of the errors of this period in anthropology. The Darwinian theory, in the form in which it was popularized, gave great emphasis to problems of origin. It was assumed that the way to account for some biological phenomenon—especially for some anatomical detail—was to seek for the philogenic origin of that anatomical detail. Similarly, the anthropologists concerned themselves with looking for cultural philogenies, and their controversies were parochial squabbles within the general assumption that philogeny was the answer.

In the biological field, the ways of thought have changed very much since 1900. Biologists have focused more and more upon the *processes* of evolutionary change and less and less upon the actual history or philogenic "tree" of any given species. In place of philogeny, biologists nowadays talk about genetics and growth. The same change has been taking place in the field of cultural anthropology. We may have lagged a bit behind the biologists, but the direction of change in our ways of thinking has been the same. Nowadays, in place of arguing points of cultural philogeny, we discuss the fine details of cultural change, and still more the fine details of internal organization within a culture at a given time. We have developed a sort of cultural "physiology" in place of the former groping after isolated details of cultural anatomy, and a sort of cultural "genetics" in place of the former cultural philogeny. It is this sort of cultural "genetics" and cultural "physiology" which I have tried to sum up with the phrase "cultural determinism."

The basic shift in our ways of thinking, from this episodic-historical approach which looks for similarities toward a more orthodox scientific approach which looks for *regularities* in human behavior, has taken place gradually over the last 20 years, and those who contributed most to the shift often scarcely realized what order of contribution they were making. The shift from one approach to another means that, in place of investigating one set of variables, we turn to another set, and the first step was, perhaps, the establishment by Boas (1938) of the concept of "culture area," which enabled us to dismiss one set of variables and to start paying attention to others. According to this theory, it is possible to delimit areas within which so much contact has occurred between the various cultures that every one of the cultures in the area can be presumed to have had access by contact to every one of the principal cultural motifs which occur in the area. The delimitation of these areas is done by a careful study of the *resemblances* between the neighboring cultures and is oriented to testing the bare fact of their relationship rather than to any sort of speculative reconstruction of their history. This theory, when it appeared, was regarded as a historical approach to culture, and the preliminary inspection of the cultures in order to determine whether they constituted such a "culture area" and to determine the limits of the area was, in fact, historical. The theory was safe against historical attack because of this preliminary spade work, but the implicit rider—that we could say of any given culture: "this culture or this community has had access, by way of diffusion, to all the main motifs current in this area" —set us free to think about differences between cultures within such a cultural area. We could dismiss the problem of diffusion within a general "other things being equal" clause and proceed to investigate the cultures in terms of variables other than the episodic-historical details of diffusion and contact.[1]

When we looked at two neighboring cultures, say the Zuñi pueblos and the Indians of the Southwest, we could stop asking "What similarities are there which show that these two cultures are related?"—because this question had been answered by the preliminary spade work with a general affirmative—"Yes, the two cultures are related." And we could go on to ask: "Why, then, is the one so very different from the other?" and we could try to reduce these differences to generalizations, e.g., by showing that the internal emphases of Zuñi imply so much dislike of loss of self-control that, no matter how much contact that culture might have with neighboring tribes who base religious cults on the use of the peyote drug or with Europeans who base conviviality on the use of alcohol, the

---

[1] In this connection, there is an interesting polemic book (Radin, 1933) in which the author attacks Boas for not being a historian, without realizing the implications for further and more scientific development of anthropological theory which are implicit in Boas' break-away from conventional historical thinking. See also Kroeber (1939).

Zuñi will at most only adopt extremely denatured versions of these cultural traits.

A second trend in modern anthropological thinking, almost as important as the escape from the episodic and historical, has been the gradual recognition of the fallacy of "misplaced concreteness" (Whitehead, 1920), and this recognition came, not from epistemology, but from careful factual demonstration that theories which ascribed causal effectiveness to "religion," "geography," "language," and the like, would not fit the facts. Boas (1938) again was a leader in this discovery. He showed that the family of language which a people has does not determine other aspects of their culture; that the geographic circumstances under which they live similarly do not determine the other aspects of their culture, and so on. In fact, Boas first freed us from examining two unprofitable sets of variables, and then went on to demonstrate that certain other variables were not profitable subjects of inquiry.

Overlapping with the main period of Boas' work, there were other anthropologists similarly engaged in developing a nonhistorical and abstract approach to the phenomena of culture. Malinowski (1927a), with a team of well-trained, careful field workers, showed that the behavior patterns in any community formed an interlocking, interdependent unity; that the "culture" of any people is not to be seen as a set of parts, each separately investigable, but rather that we should see the whole mass of behavior and artifacts and geographical circumstances as an interlocking functional system, such that, if we started from, say, the food-getting behavior—the system of agriculture, hunting, fishing, and the rest—and examined that system carefully, we should find that the functioning—the effective, continual working of the agricultural system—interlocks at every step with the religion of the people, with their language, with their magic, with the geographic circumstances of their life, etc., and, similarly, that their religion interlocks with all other phases of their behavior; their economics likewise; and their kinship likewise. Malinowski, in fact, laid a basis for an organismic approach to cultural phenomena. While Boas had demonstrated that language is not a cause of religion or magic, Malinowski demonstrated that everything in a cultural system was, if not a cause, at any rate a necessary condition for everything else. He showed that, in describing a culture, it was possible to start with any institutional category of behavior and from that to work outwards in ever-widening circles of relevance, until the whole cultural system appears as relevant background for the particular set of data from which we started.

While Malinowski and his fellow workers were engaged in demonstrating the enormous complexity and mutual interdependence of all the parts of a culture, working out, like a fine patch-work quilt, the continuity and ramifications of all these relationships, Radcliffe-Brown (1931, 1940) approached the problem from a different angle. He accepted, as a matter of course, this enormous interdependence within a culture and regarded the system of behavior in any community as organic in this sense. Then he went on to ask: "What is the bony structure, what are the salient features of this fine, intricate design?" And his answer was what he called "social structure." Running through the whole variety of serious anthropological field work from the time of Morgan (1871) to that of Radcliffe-Brown, there was a very strong emphasis upon the study of the kinship systems of preliterate peoples, and these very profound and conspicuous differences between one cultural system and another had stimulated a very wide variety of speculation. The data were then interpreted in evolutionary terms. The peculiarities of differentiation between mother's brother and father's brother were regarded as symptoms of a former matriarchy. The same peculiarities of preliterate cultures have also been interpreted by diffusion theories. When Radcliffe-Brown was working, the central theme, the central problem of ethnography, was kinship. Thus, Radcliffe-Brown's work developed as a study of the interrelationship between kinship structure and what he called "social structure." By "social structure" he meant the system of subgroups—clans, moieties, age-grades, factions, classes, castes, and the like, in the community. Radcliffe-Brown's classical work was done on the Australian tribes, and he succeeded in demonstrating the functional interplay between the totemic system and the highly complex system of behavior roles towards various kin. The totemic system is unilateral and "closed," which meant that the position of any given relative—say, a mother's brother, or a father's sister's husband—in the totemic system, is fixed relative to ego, so that all ego's brothers-in-law are necessarily of the same generation and the same totemic group. There is not space to go into the fine details of the Australian system. Basically, if we consider only two exogamous divisions of the community, e.g., Eagle Hawk and Crow, with membership determined either by matrilineal or patrilineal descent, it is clear that if everybody obeys the rule of exogamy, every Eagle Hawk man will have relations-in-law in the Crow group and, even before his marriage, he might logically classify all Crow people together as "potential relatives-in-law." Australian systems have carried this principle much further by superposing more dichotomous divisions which define generations, as well as lineal descent, until it is possible for every individual to classify all the other people in the community by equating subgroup membership with potential kinship to himself.

Such a system could be analyzed as working on two levels of abstraction. We have first the enjoined behavior patterns between kin, e.g., between wife's brother in Eagle Hawk and sister's husband in Crow; and, second, the whole symbolism of myth and ceremony which defines the major group relationship between Eagle Hawk and Crow.

Radcliffe-Brown was concerned to show that the psychological presumptions within the family—the patterns of behavior between man and wife, between parent and child—were related to the whole pattern of this totemic system, which also governs the pattern of behavior of clan members.

The clans and other subdivisions of an Australian tribe are parts of a very complex system of opposition and allegiance. The ambivalent tensions which are culturally induced between affinal relatives are expressed again in the relationship between groups which are potentially related by affinal ties, and the whole functioning of the society depends upon these ambivalences and the nice balance between positive and negative components of hostility and love (just as our own society depends, in a *laissez-faire* period, upon nice balance between competition and cooperation, production and consumption, etc.). Thus, Radcliffe-Brown's work led, finally, to some general notion of how opposition and allegiance can be balanced against each other in a stable community, and this work of Radcliffe-Brown's was perhaps the first push which deflected the study of culture and society towards a study of psychology.[2] He did not himself regard his work as psychological, but implicit in it were assumptions about the human personality, about the psychological nature of maleness and femaleness, parenthood and childhood, opposition and allegiance, love and hate, which were a first step towards that later development in cultural anthropology which has diverted more and more attention to the tracing of the characterological aspects of human behavior.[3]

In Radcliffe-Brown's work there is still an assumption that peoples are psychologically alike, that there are certain basic psychological traits within individuals. The task of the anthropologist was to ask about the structure and the functioning of human society, "other things being equal"; and within this phrase "other things being equal" was a presumption that human personality is, in some measure, constant.

The next great change in anthropological approach came with the attempt to explore yet other variables. It was demonstrated that human personality is *not* constant, and this was accomplished largely under the influence of Boas' students, Ruth Benedict (1934a) and Margaret Mead (1928a). The latter went to Samoa to study the phenomena of adolescence at the behavioral level. It had been tacitly assumed that the psychological impact of puberty "naturally" caused behavior to be intense and erratic during the period of adjustment to the new physiological equilibrium. It followed from this assumption that, if human character and human physiology were essentially alike the world over, we ought to expect a similar period of maladjustment to occur in all cultures. Margaret Mead showed, however (1928a), that this was not true of Samoa, and, further, that the smooth, easy adjustment of the Samoan adolescent could be referred to peculiarities of the Samoan family organization. Whereas in Western cultures family organization is such that very intense ties are established between the child and one or two adults, in Samoa the ties of affection are slighter and are diffused over a large num-

---

[2] It is difficult, in this connection, to estimate the contributions of Radcliffe-Brown's teacher, W. H. R. Rivers. Rivers was originally a psychologist and physiologist, but later became a historically-minded anthropologist. (1923)

[3] For further development of Radcliffe-Brown's approach, see Warner (1941), and Dollard (1937).

ber of adults and child nurses. The capacity for intense emotional behavior is, in fact, a variable which depends on the cultural milieu.

Since that time, cultural anthropology has devoted itself more and more to unravelling the very complex problems which arise when we regard as variable not only the whole structure of social groupings, the whole system of behavior, but also, as equally variable, the human individual who exhibits these various forms of behavior.

This research into problems of culture and human behavior has developed along many different lines, all of them ultimately contributing one to another, but as yet imperfectly synthesized together. And since this synthesis is still not achieved, it will be necessary for us to consider each one of these lines separately.

Typology and Psychiatric Syndromes

For all anthropologists who regard personality as a variable which must be taken into account, the crucial technical problem is that of *describing* the personality. It is no use to recognize a variable until salt can be put upon its tail. The problem of handling a new variable, or rather such a complex of variables as is denoted by the word "personality," at once forces us to try to find either numerical statements—dimensions which can be measured—in terms of which personality can be evaluated, or failing such a quantitative approach, we must develop adjectives which will describe personality. It is natural, therefore, that anthropology has turned to psychology, and especially to those schools of psychology which have tried to define or to discriminate different *types* of personality. The earliest work on these lines was done by Seligman (1931), who used the typology suggested by Jung, of "introvert" and "extravert" types of personality. Seligman attempted to describe cultures according to whether they produced, in the individuals, a more introvert or a more extravert personality structure.

Seligman's work was very little followed up by other psychologists, and the next major attempt to describe culture in terms of personality types was made by Ruth Benedict (1934a). Benedict was stimulated, not by Jung, but rather by the Dilthey and Spengler school of historians. She attempted to apply the "Apollonian" and "Dionysian" dichotomy [4]

---

[4] Benedict does not follow Nietzsche in the finer details of his description of this typology. The sense in which she uses the terms "Appolonian" and "Dionysian" can best be conveyed in her words: "The Dionysian pursues them (the values of existence) through the 'annihilation of the ordinary bounds and limits of existence; he seeks to attain in his most valued moments escape from the boundaries imposed upon him by his five senses, to break through into another order of experience. The desire of the Dionysian, in personal experience or in ritual, is to press through it toward a certain psychological state, to achieve excess. . . . The Apollonian distrusts all this, and has often very little idea of the nature of such experiences. He finds means to outlaw them from his conscious life. He 'knows but one law, measure in the Hellenic sense.' He keeps the middle of the road, stays within the known map, does not meddle with disruptive psychological states. In Nietzsche's fine phrase, even in the exaltation of the dance he 'remains what he is, and retains his civic name.'"

to the contrast between the Zuñi, a quiet Apollonian group in the southwest pueblo, and two groups of violently Dionysian people, the Plains Indians and the Mexican Penitentes, with whom the Zuñi were in contact. It is significant that this technique of describing cultural contrast was most successful in Benedict's hands, when applied to cultures which were actually in contact. She was able to show, for example, that a very high valuation was placed upon various forms of dissociated excitement by the Plains Indians and the Penitentes. The Plains Indians achieve mystic experience when seeking for a vision either through drastic self-torture or self-repression; or they may achieve it by the use of drugs. Among the Zuñi all these things were either absent, or—more significantly—if present, were practiced in such a way that they no longer had any Dionysiac quality. Where the Plains Indians use peyote, a drug, for the achievement of a high degree of disassociation, the Zuñi, with the same drug, living close to the area where peyote is obtained, have never accepted the peyote cult as part of their religious practices, with the exception of one, small, deviant group. Similarly, the Zuñi have resisted alcohol, to which every other group of American Indians has, to some extent, succumbed. In general, where the Plains Indians seek for ecstasy, for the extremes of religious experience, the Zuñi practice their religion with decorum and precision. Their dancing is exact, a following of a careful pattern; it is not ecstatic. Benedict was able to follow this contrast through the whole gamut of Zuñi and Plains Indian cultures, and to show that these cultures had consistently specialized in these particular forms of expression in all their fields and institutions.

In addition to using this dichotomy, Benedict (1934a) also used concepts derived from psychiatry. She analyzed two cultures, that of Dobu in the Western Pacific, and that of the Kwakiutl in the Northwest of America, and showed how paranoidal suspicion runs through Dobuan culture, while a more megalomaniac paranoidal tendency is characteristic of the Northwest.

This use of terminology derived from psychiatry raises at once certain problems and difficulties. We, in Western civilization, regard paranoidal trends as pathological, and our picture of the paranoiac is of a deviant living among other people who are not compelled strongly by paranoia. Benedict's picture of Dobu or of the Northwest is of a community in which paranoidal trends are normally developed in all, or in a great majority of individuals. The norms of these cultures are only understandable if we suppose that these trends are either present in all individuals or in so many individuals that the trends appear as the normal stuff of social life. In such a community, the paranoidal constructs, instead of being the illusions of a few, become the knowledge and vision—the correct assumptions—of the many. The paranoidal suspicion which every Dobuan has for every other Dobuan is not an unreal figment; it is a legitimate generalization from his experience that the other Dobuan is out to do him in, to beat him in one way or another—to sorcerize him or to steal his yams by magical attack on his garden.

So that while, to us, the term "paranoid" is descriptive of a relationship to other nonparanoid individuals, the term as applied to the Dobuans refers to relationships *between* paranoid individuals.

This raises in very serious form the problem of cultural deviance, and Benedict's (1934b) contribution to this problem is to point out that deviance is a culturally relative phenomenon—that a character structure which is normal among us may be deviant among the Kwakiutl or the Dobuans, while a structure which is normal and highly respected among them would be looked on as dangerous and disruptive in our community.

This typological approach to cultures has been criticized on the lines that, presuming some degree of standardization, it makes no allowance for deviance. To this type of criticism, the reply is, first, that the term "deviance" implies standardization; and, second, that deviance *is* allowed for and expected to occur in all cultures, though it is not expected that deviance will occur in the same directions in all cultures. Indeed, if similar distribution of *sorts* and frequency of deviance in all cultures could be demonstrated, the whole theoretical approach would have to be abandoned. Such demonstration has, however, not been achieved. Some work has gone into statistical study of the frequency of various forms of psychopathology in different parts of the world, but as yet this work has given only very inconclusive results. The methods of diagnosis and especially the methods of selecting deviants for commitment to institutions vary so widely from country to country and function so irregularly in those parts of the world where European medicine is in contact with preliterate peoples, that none of the statistical data is fit for comparative study.

There is, however, some indirect evidence to show that, in fact, the forms and frequencies of deviance do depend upon cultural circumstances. This evidence is derived from our communities. We find, for example, that considerable changes in frequency of psychosomatic and other psychopathological deviance occur from one period to another. One of the most striking of these demonstrations concerns the sex-distribution of perforated peptic ulcer. It has been shown repeatedly (Alstead, 1939; Jennings, 1940; Mittelmann, *et al.*, 1942) that, in the latter half of the nineteenth century this condition affected more females than males, in Western cultures. Mittelmann, *et al.*, give the ratio for New York as six males to seven females for the years 1880 to 1900. The corresponding figures for the years 1932 to 1939 are twelve males to one female. In the same paper, the authors examine the case histories of a number of recent New York cases and show that perforated peptic ulcer follows a definite type of psychological history and character formation; that this background is at least as much a cause as it is an effect of the ulceration; and that the cultural changes in sex roles in the last 50 years have been such as would fit the striking change in sex distribution.

It may be argued that the differences between New York of 1900 and New York of 1935 are, at most, only of "subcultural" order. But from this we would predict that, *a fortiori*, still greater differences in form and frequency of psychosomatic deviance ought to occur between basically different cultural milieux.

Another reply which might be made to those who criticize the typological and psychiatric approach for its handling of the problem of deviance would be based on the notion of configuration. The theories are built upon a gestalt level of abstraction, rather than upon notions of simple cause and effect. They presume that the human individual is endlessly simplifying and generalizing his own view of his own environment; that he constantly imposes upon this environment his own constructions and meanings; and that it is these constructions and meanings which are regarded as characteristic of one culture, as over against another. This means that, when we approach a context of extreme deviance —when we look, for example, at the melting-pot communities of our own culture—we must be willing to see that heterogeneity itself may be a positive standardizing factor.

Granted that, in such a community, individual experience is infinitely various, and that each individual in New York City is, in this sense, a unique product, we can still say that all individuals are alike in so far as all have experienced the heterogeneity of the city; and, in terms of this common experience, we may look forward to finding certain psychological resemblances among them. We can even find these resemblances institutionalized in the cultures of such communities. Such poems as John Latouche's *Ballad for Americans*, which rejoices in the richness of a heterogeneous background, the quiz programs of the radio, and the infinite disconnected variousness of Ripley's *Believe It or Not*, are all symptomatic of this standardization due to heterogeneity. Even in the institutionalized curricula of higher education we can trace the analogous tendencies towards the dissection of knowledge into separate bits. We find that high value is placed upon factual information and that the student's progress is judged largely by the percentage of disconnected factual questions which he is able to answer correctly. He is, in fact, being fitted to live in a heterogeneous world in which generalizations are hard to apply, and he is being taught a way of thinking suited to such a world.

In fact, if we are willing to think at a rather high gestalt level, the phenomena of deviance fall into place very simply, and support, rather than conflict with, notions of cultural standardization. Extreme heterogeneity becomes a factor of standardization, and the isolated accident of a single individual's upbringing equally falls into place. Human individuals do not live in a cultural vacuum, and the isolated accidental deviant is faced with the problem of either accepting the norms of his culture, or reacting against them. Moreover, to react against one norm can usually only be done by accepting many of the premises upon which the norm is based. The individual who resists a hierarchical structure usually does so by attempting to rise in that structure; he accepts the major premise that human life in his cultural milieu is structured in hierarchical terms. So far as his character is concerned, it is molded to fit the cultural emphases, even though he fight against those emphases.

In this sense, and at this level of abstraction, the attempt to describe cultures in terms of the types of individuals which they foster is, I believe, sound; but a greater difficulty in the way of such an approach is that the typologies upon which it is based are still very unclear.

The syndromes of introversion, extraversion, Apollonian and Dionysian character, paranoia, etc., have not been critically and operationally defined. This criticism, of course, is not one which the anthropologist can be expected to answer. We have only taken the terms from other disciplines and adopted them as a convenient tool, and it is not for us, in this chapter, to examine the validity of these typologies. We may, however, express an opinion that the general notion of syndromes of personality is sound even though the study of these syndromes is not yet sufficiently advanced for us, in another science, to use them as tools. Since various other methods of approach are available to us, we need not delay our investigations because one descriptive technique is not completely satisfactory. Our solution is to supplement this technique with others.

Description of Personality in Terms of the Socialization Process

Since the description of syndromes of character is still in a somewhat unsatisfactory condition, we have to proceed to use other descriptive methods of relating character to the cultural milieu in which it occurs. Of these, the most rewarding is the study of the socialization process by which the child is educated to become a typical member of the community into which he was born. This method is, in a sense, historical, rather than scientific. It assumes that a description of personality can be arrived at in terms of the experiences through which the individual has lived. The method accepts the fact that we have virtually no vocabulary for describing what people *are* like, and substitutes for such description statements about their past.

The great pioneer of this method was, of course, Sigmund Freud, whose methods and hypotheses have been discussed elsewhere in this volume. For the present chapter, it is sufficient only to note certain peculiarities of the classical approach. First and foremost, Freud was a therapist, and his contribution was a science and technique of therapy. For this purpose, what we have noted as a conceptual failing in the method, namely, the indirect description of the present through the invocation of the past, was a positive advantage. The therapeutic procedure was based upon communication between the therapist and the patient, and for such communication an enormous new vocabulary of technical terms descriptive of present personality would have been exceedingly inconvenient. All that was necessary was that the patient should understand *himself*; it was not necessary that he should understand a general science of personality structure; and this understanding of himself could best be conveyed in a language provided by the patient himself. The incidents in the patient's anamnesic material provided such a rich variety of illustrative and immediately relevant material that a more precise terminology was unnecessary. In these circumstances, a whole massive science of human behavior and character has been built up around less than a hundred technical terms, and these, for the most part, are imperfectly defined.[5]

When we try to examine Freud's contribution to our understanding of culture, we very soon find that the preoccupation with therapy and the resulting poverty of critical terminology makes it almost impossible to arrive at any clear picture of Freud's opinions about the role of culture, or his opinions as to whether human personality should be regarded as fundamentally "the same" all over the world. That he believed that similar processes (e.g., repression, displacement, introjection, projection, etc.) operated to produce human character in all communities is clear, but it is not clear whether Freud believed that the *products* were everywhere comparable or that the various processes have the same relative importance in all cultures.

"Totem and Taboo" (Freud, 1904) is an attempt to dissect the products of these processes in Central Australia. Freud shows, for example, that the whole gamut of Central Australian ritual dealing with the animal, which is regarded as a clan ancestor or totem, can be seen as an expression of ambivalent attitudes towards the father, and this analysis satisfactorily covers both the general taboo on killing the totem and the special ritual occasions on which the totem is killed, eaten, and mourned for.

Freud, however, goes further than this and constructs a tentative picture of the original patricidal act, by way of illustrating his hypothesis. He suggests that the young men freed themselves from the tyranny of a father, and even says: "Perhaps some advance in culture, like the use of a new weapon, had given them the feeling of superiority." [6]

This early attempt on the part of Freud to account for cultural phenomena in terms of the psychological past raises, in dramatic form, the problems of method and meaning upon which subsequent work has been focused. Broadly, we may classify the various subsequent attempts to use the incidents of the past as a descriptive vocabulary into three groups, according to the sources for data upon past events.

---

[5] The much younger science of stimulus-response psychology, dealing with a very much simpler gamut of phenomena, has already between 100 and 200 technical terms, many of them carefully defined.

[6] In a footnote to another part of the same paragraph, Freud gives an extract from Atkinson's "Primal Law," in which, long before Freud, Atkinson says of the young men: "A horde as yet weak in their impubescence they are, but they would, when strength was gained with time, inevitably wrench by combined attacks renewed again and again, both wife and life from the paternal tyrant." (Atkinson, J. J., 1903, pp. 220–221) Freud does not comment on the parallel between pubescence and the "new weapon."

For the practicing psychoanalyst, the principal source of information about the past is the patient's anamnesic material, the picture which he is now able to give us what he thinks happened at some past time. This picture is, no doubt, a doubly distorted version of the real past events, first distorted in terms of the interpretation which the patient put upon the events when they occurred, and distorted again by the patient's mood at the time when he relates them to the analyst. But in spite of this distortion, the anamnesic picture is undoubtedly a true source, in so far as we use its contents solely as a means of describing the patient's character and personality *today* in the consulting room.

Like the analyst, the field anthropologist uses an indirect source for his information about the psychological past. It is not possible for him to record the experience and behavior of the same individual year in and year out, from birth through adolescence to adult life, which, though cumbersome, would perhaps be the ideal genetic approach. Instead of doing this, he argues that the adult natives whom he can observe today presumably had childhood experiences similar to those of the children of today. He therefore endeavors to describe the adults whom he sees in terms of the way the children of today are treated and the way the children behave under that treatment. (For an examination of this method, see Lasswell, 1937.)

To those who are familiar only with rapidly changing communities, where the cultural norms vary from year to year and a craze for putting babies on schedules may rise and fall in a decade, the basic presumption that a native culture may be stable for over thirty years may seem incredible. In general, however, it is justified. Before contact with the white man, the cultures of preliterate peoples were changing much more slowly than European cultures and their norms were much more clearly defined than ours; and further, it is not difficult for the ethnologist in the field to form an estimate of the degree of disruption which the culture has suffered since contact began.

Using this method, we have come to a new evaluation of the role of culture in shaping the personality and character of the individual. The original Freudian position, which gives maximal importance to the family constellation, still stands unchallenged; and there is no doubt that it will continue to stand. We have, however, come to realize that the family constellations—the behavior patterns between the members of the family and the attitudes which underlie these patterns—differ very profoundly from culture to culture. At the physiological level, we can, of course, refer to the processes of sex and reproduction as universal, but when we come to use these terms as counters in psychological discussion, we find that they may mean very different things in different cultural systems. Sexual initiative may come typically either from the male or from the female (as among the Iatmul of New Guinea), and the sexual act may be conceived of as aggressive (as among the Mundugumor); or as affectionate (as among the Arapesh). The relationship between man and wife may be predominantly tinged with dominance-submission, or with succoring-dependence, or with exhibitionism-spectatorship, or with any of the many variants of competition or cooperation; and these characteristics may be relatively standardized in the most varied ways in different communities.

This means that the constellation into which the child is born, the Oedipus situation which he encounters, varies profoundly from culture to culture. When the child is added to a previously existing relationship involving the two parents, the behavior of the latter towards the child will inevitably be a function of their relationship to each other.[7] Their relationship to each other was in large measure shaped in terms of the conventions of their culture, and where it deviated from those norms the parents were, consciously or unconsciously, influenced by the fact of deviation. Similarly, their behavior towards the child is in large measure conventionalized, and both they and the child, when they deviate from the conventions, deviate not in a vacuum but with conscious or unconscious recognition of deviation.

Thus, in healthy cultures, we find that a very high degree of uniformity of character is passed on from generation to generation, and in unhealthy cultures we find sometimes no less uniformity. Among the Mundugumor (Mead, 1935) we find that deviance and the guilt of deviance are passed on, rather than simple conformity. The marriage system of these people is so complex and so demanding that, as a matter of fact, no marriages at the present time follow the native convention. In spite of this, all are alike in suffering from their deviation from the cultural standard.

So far, we have considered only what might be called the "content" of character and personality, and we have noted that very profound differences occur in what patterns of behavior are passed on to the child. If we go on from this to ask *how* these patterns are passed on, we find that here again differences occur from culture to culture. It is common in Western cultures to find that the growing child builds up a set of intra-psychic habits of self-approval and self-disapproval. This super-ego is modeled upon the child's impressions of the character of one or the other parent. This valuational system may or may not be consistent with other intra-psychic systems in the same individual, and where discrepancies occur we observe the phenomena of guilt. The super-ego system may even be differentiated to such a point that it can be hallucinated as a scolding voice or the like.

This whole system clearly depends upon a very specific set of circumstances. For the establishment of an organized and more or less personified super-ego, such as we are familiar with in Western cultures: (a) the inculcation of cultural norms must be predominantly reinforced by punishment (including threats of withheld affection under this term);

_____

[7] I understand that Dr. Kurt Lewin has recently initiated studies of such triangular relationships, first observing the patterns of behavior between two children and then adding a third child and observing the readjustments which follow this addition (Unpublished).

(b) the punishing role must be played by some individual adult (a parent or parent substitute); and (c) the behavior of this punishing parent must be such that some species of close affective tie is established between the child and the parent. These three conditions may be varied in many ways, according to local convention. The punishment may be intense or mild, regular or irregular; it may be done in anger or in cold blood; the introjected parent may be male or female (as in Manus); the affective tie may be strong or weak; it may have various characteristics and may be broken in various ways. But, provided these three conditions are somehow fulfilled, we may expect to find some structure in the native personality which we can recognize as a "super-ego."

These three basic conditions for this type of character structure are, however, by no means universal. Indeed, it is probably rather rare to find them all in combination. In a very large number of cultures (Samoa, Lepcha, Bali) the baby spends the greater part of its time in the care of some little girl, so that if any strong affective tie is developed (and in such cases the baby is often treated more as a bundle than as a person), the introjected personality will be, not that of an adult, but rather that of a juvenile.

In other cases, punishment is very rare (Samoa); or it may be carried out by some person *other* than the parents. Among many American Indian tribes, punishment is done by masked dancers. Unknown to the child, the parents call in these punishing agencies. When these dancers arrive, the parents go through an appearance of pleading with them, asking them to spare the child. Or, again, the inculcation of cultural norms may be done by invocation of "what other people will say," establishing a proneness to shame rather than to guilt, and introjecting a vague multitude rather than a single personality. (For a general discussion of these variants, see Mead, 1940b.)

Of special interest are the variants of character structure which depend upon the type of affective tie established between the parent and the child. In English-speaking cultures, this tie, in childhood, contains many complementary components. These are patterns of behavior in which the roles of parent and child are differentiated one from the other and mutually complementary (e.g., dominance-submission, succoring-dependence, exhibitionism-spectatorship, etc.). But the business of growing up consists largely in substituting more symmetrical patterns of behavior. In both England and America, we find strong insistence that the child, as he grows up, shall not react with overt dominance or submission in relationships with people stronger or weaker respectively than himself. But, while in England the remodeling of these ties is often done by drastic separation between parents and child, such as sending the child to boarding school, in America the same function is usually performed by the parents themselves, who respond with admiring spectatorship to any signs of independence and self-sufficiency which the child may exhibit. Thus, in both cultures, we develop a character structure in which symmetrical patterns are superposed on a complementary base. These cultures differ, however, in the relationship between these two layers (see Bateson, 1942a).

In some of the other cultures of the world, there is no reversal of this sort, and we know of still other possibilities:

(a) The behavior of the parents may be such that from the very beginning, symmetrical patterns are emphasized. Among the Iatmul of New Guinea, the mother behaves as if the child were as strong as she (Mead, 1940a). She first resists the child's demands for food, and later gives way to them in response to the child's temper, "the child was too strong." Any sort of punishment is preceded by a chase, and usually the child is "too quick" to be caught.

(b) The behavior of the parents may be such that any tendency which the child may have towards developing close affective ties is discouraged from the very beginning. The Balinese mother (and the child nurse) very much enjoys the responsiveness of her child, and often prompts the child to respond, either by small teasings or by affectionate advances. She was, herself, once a Balinese child and had a Balinese mother, and so she herself is not responsive in the same way as the young child. The child responds to her advances either with affection or temper, but the response falls into a vacuum. In Western cultures, such sequences lead to small climaxes of love or anger, but not so in Bali. At the moment when the child throws its arms around the mother's neck or bursts into tears, the mother's attention wanders (Bateson, 1941).

Thus, by using the details of childhood experience as a vocabulary for describing character structure, and studying the parent-child relationship in various cultures, it is possible to show that the cultural milieu is relevant to character and personality at many different levels. It may contribute to determining the content; the list of behaviors which are passed on from generation to generation is different for every culture. More fundamental than this determination of content, the cultural milieu may, by altering the contexts of learning, contribute to shaping the interpretation which the child habitually places upon his own acts and upon the universe in which he lives. The child who has learned by punishment will see one sort of world, and the child who has learned by reward will see a different world. Finally, at a still more fundamental level, the cultural milieu may determine the manner of organization of the learned behaviors. In some cultures, these are elaborately organized into an image of a parent, but it is clear that other types of intra-psychic organization may occur.

The Study of Interpersonal and Intergroup Attitudes

The strong tendency in science to look for cause has led us to try to describe adult character in terms of childhood experience; and, indeed, this approach has so far proved rewarding. But this is not the only scientific method, and several attempts have been made to use adult behavior itself as a descriptive medium. One can build a systematic *classification* of behaviors rather than a systematic accounting for behaviors.

This method is necessarily very cumbersome and exacting, and progress in it will depend more and more upon the use of strict operational definitions and the techniques of mathematics and symbolic logic. When we put adult behavior beside childhood experience, it is not necessary to be very precise in our description of either set of observations, since some extra clarity is given by the juxtaposition. But when we have only a single set of phenomena and must somehow deal with them in their own terms, a very much greater stringency is necessary, not only in our recording of the phenomena, but also in the formulation of the problems which we hope to solve and the analytic procedures which we apply to our collected data.

We have noted, above all, that all the details of behavior and circumstance which go to make up what we call a culture are interrelated, and very little thought is sufficient to show that various sorts of interrelationship occur in every culture. We have, for example, all the relationships which must be considered if we want to understand the integration of the community at a strictly sociological level, and if this is the sort of problem which we set out to solve, we have to put side by side the details of how the community is subdivided into groups and the factors which make for union or dissension among these groups. This particular type of functional approach will, however, scarcely help us towards a psychological picture of the individual in that society.

For such a psychological picture, there are various possible ways of arranging our data, according to the sort of psychological insight which we are seeking.

View of the World.—The data can be arranged to give us information about such matters as: native orientation in space and time, among objects and among people; native systems of cause and effect, the natives' view of the universe in which they live, the sorts of logic and illogic which they follow. This has not yet been done systematically for any culture, though a real beginning has been made by the gestalt psychologists and especially the topological school, in experimental studies of individuals of European and American background. At the preliterate level, we have not been able to approach this degree of precision, but from the crude survey work which has been done, it is evident that marked differences among cultures can be revealed by this approach. We find, for example, that in some cultures the whole ceremonial life is geared to a calendar, so that the precipitating stimulus for any ceremonial celebration is the date. In other cultures, again, we find that the date is ignored, and ceremonial is precipitated by events at the human level, such as birth and death, victories, harvests, quarrels, etc. Even among calendric cultures we find variation. Our own calendar is a double system, with the week as a simple cyclic motif, while the days and months are built into an endless on-going system. For us, the cyclical motif is comparatively unimportant; we forget the day of the week on which we were born but remember the day of the month, and the serial number attached to the year. In Bali, on the other hand (Bateson and Mead, 1942), the cyclical motif is all-important, and any individual can tell you that he was born "on the third day of the five-day week and the sixth day of the seven-day week," and he will probably be able to tell in which month he was born in the twelve-month sequence. He will *not* be able to tell in what year he was born and is not interested in this question.[8]

Differences of this order are more than mere details of the calendar, and if we examine the rest of the culture, we find that the same type of difference in the perceived pattern goes through the whole of life. Our world is shaped in terms of the notion that the past was different from the present and that the future will be different again. The Balinese world is based on a presumption that the present is only a repetition of the past and the future will continue in the same circular fashion. The two cultures are, however, alike in using spatial metaphors in referring to temporal sequences.

Goal Orientation.—A second method of arranging the data will give us, instead of a cognitive[9] picture, a picture of goal orientation. We noted above that the Balinese child is continually frustrated in the climaxes which should follow his sequences of love and hate behavior, and when we examine the adult behavior we find that there are no sequences of mounting tension in interpersonal relations, no factions, and no oratory. Equally, there is no mounting tension in efforts to deal with impersonal barriers. The Balinese have no word for "to try hard," and their goal orientation is not strengthened by any appreciation of the sequence of contrasts in which mounting tension is followed by release. They do not purposely increase their intra-psychic tensions in order to increase the ultimate satisfaction of release, as we do with *apéritifs* or by deliberate abstemiousness.

Affective and Postural Patterns.—The data may also be arranged to give an "affective" picture of the system of linked responses. At a very simple postural level, we may observe that, in our own culture, people tend to leave their fingers, when at rest, in regular positions. If the fingers are flexed, they will either be all flexed to the same extent, or, if differentially flexed, the differences will follow some regular system of progression, commonly each flexed a little more than its neighbor on the radial side. The Balinese, very much more often, leave their fingers in what appear to us to be distorted positions, as though each finger were

---

[8] There is, in Bali, a system which gives serial numbers to the years, but this is not used except by the most pedantic. The majority of the Balinese scholars are content to date their everlasting manuscripts with the day of the week and the name of the month.

[9] The old terms, cognitive, affective, and conative, are here used to refer not to artificially isolated processes which are supposed to occur in organisms, but to different sorts of generalization which we arrive at by different methods of arranging our data.

a separate entity or a separate sense organ. True, in our culture, it is polite in certain sections to extend the little finger when holding a tea-cup, but in Bali this sort of thing is enormously developed, and photographic records show that the tendency to disharmonic finger postures *increases* in the extreme excitement of rioting over the body at funerals (Bateson and Mead, 1942).

Building further on this picture, we find that in witchcraft the emphasis on discrepancy between body parts reaches its height. We find play with fantasies of one-footed balance, and evil spirits consisting of single body parts, personified legs, arms, heads, and even spirits which have a face at every joint.

With this sort of synthesis we arrive at a culturally limited description of "fear," putting together a study of postures and contexts in which certain postures are exhibited. And there is no doubt that comparative studies of different cultures on these lines will show very profound differences in the organization of emotion.

Interpersonal Behavior.—Lastly, we can arrange our data to give a picture of interpersonal behavior sequences. Here, again, our main difficulty is with the operational definition of our concepts and units, and progress will be delayed until we have clear operational definitions of dominance, submission, dependence, exhibitionism, narcissism, climax, identification, and the like. One very significant attempt, however, has been made by Chapple (1939, 1940). Using a small machine with a recording drum, Chapple obtains a record of the duration of all overt behaviors in a conversation between two or more individuals. He ignores completely the verbal content and "meaning" of the behavior, and concentrates attention entirely on the time properties. This simplification gives him the chance to define "initiative" operationally in terms of time relationships, and his data are such that he can proceed to a statistical study of "initiating behavior," "interruptions," "duration of responses," etc. The results show very marked differences between individuals and especially marked peculiarities in the case of deviant and psychopathic personalities.

We may expect that application of these methods to individuals from cultures other than our own will show marked differences, and that this method will give us useful abstractions for the handling of cultural characteristics.

Conclusion

We may sum up our knowledge of cultural determinants of personality by saying that, while culture is not by any means the only determinant, it is very important. The whole of human behavior as we know it (with the possible exception of some reflexes) is either learned or modified by learning, and learning is, in large measure, an interpersonal process. The contexts in which it occurs vary from culture to culture, as also do the methods of reinforcement. Thus, not only *what* is learned is, in some measure, culturally determined, but also the role of the learned behavior in the psychic life of the individual. Eating may mean nearly the same thing to a starving man in whatever culture, but in the ordinary course of everyday life, apart from the extremes of deprivation, we must expect every one of the simple physiological behaviors, such as eating, defecation, copulation, and even sleep, to have special meaning for the individual, and this meaning will be culturally determined and will vary from culture to culture. Our task, as anthropologists or psychologists, is to recognize and define the regularities in this complex tangle of phenomena.

BIBLIOGRAPHY

ALSTEAD, G. 1939. The changing incidence of peptic ulcer. London: Oxford University Press.

ATKINSON, J. J. 1903. Primal law. Bound with *Lang, A., Social origins*. London: Longmans, Green.

BARTLETT, F. C. 1937. Psychological methods in anthropological problems. *Africa, 10*, 400–429.

BATESON, G. 1935. Culture contact and schismogenesis. *Man, 35*, 178–183.

—— 1936. Naven. London: Cambridge University Press.

—— 1941. The frustration-aggression hypothesis. *Psychol. Rev., 48*, 350–355.

—— 1942a. Regularities and differences in national character. In Watson, G., *Civilian morale*. Boston: Houghton Mifflin.

—— 1942b. Comment on Margaret Mead's "The comparative study of culture and the purposive cultivation of democratic values." In *Science, Philosophy, and Religion, second Symposium*. New York: Country Life Press.

BATESON, G., & MEAD, M. 1942. Balinese culture, a photographic analysis. New York: New York Academy of Sciences.

BENEDICT, R. 1934a. Patterns of culture. Boston: Houghton Mifflin.

—— 1934b. Anthropology and the abnormal. *J. gen. Psychol., 10*, 59–82.

—— 1938. Continuities and discontinuities in cultural conditioning. *Psychiatry, 1*, 161–167.

BOAS, F. 1938. The mind of primitive man. New York: Macmillan.

CHAPPLE, E. D. 1939. Quantitative analysis of the interaction of individuals. *Proc. nat. Acad. Sci., Wash., 25*, 58–67.

—— 1940. "Personality" differences as described by invariant properties of individuals' reactions. *Proc. nat. Acad. Sci., Wash., 26*, 10–16.

DENNIS, W. 1940. The Hopi child. New York: Appleton-Century.

DOLLARD, J. 1937. Caste and class in a southern town. New Haven: Yale University Press.

DUBOIS, C. 1937a. Some anthropological perspectives on psychoanalysis. *Psychoanal. Rev., 24*, 246–273.

—— 1937b. Some psychological objectives and techniques in ethnography. *J. soc. Psychol., 8*, 285–300.

ERIKSON, E. H. 1939. Observations on Sioux education. *J. Psychol., 7*, 101–156.

FORTES, M. 1938. Social and psychological aspects of education in Teleland. *Africa, 11*, Suppl., 4.

FORTUNE, R. F. 1932. Sorcerers of Dobu. London: Routledge.

—— 1935. Manus religion. *Mem. Amer. phil. Soc.*, Vol. 3.

FRANK, L. K. 1931. The concept of inviolability in culture. *Amer. J. Sociol., 36*, 607–615.

—— 1938. Cultural control and physiological autonomy. *Amer. J. Orthopsychiat., 8*, 622–626.

—— 1939. Cultural coercion and individual distortion. *Psychiatry, 2*, 11–27.

FREUD, S. 1904. Totem and taboo. In *The basic writings of Sigmund Freud*. New York: Modern Library, 1938.

FROMM, E. 1932. Die Psychoanalytische Charakterologie und ihre Bedeutung für die Sozialpsychologie. *Z. SozForsch.*

GORER, G. 1938. Himalayan village. London: Michael Joseph.

HAMBLY, W. 1926. Origins of education among primitive peoples: comparative study in racial development. London: Macmillan.

HENRY, J. 1936. The personality of the Kaingang Indian. *Character & Pers., 5,* 113–123.

—— 1940. Some cultural determinants of hostility in Pilaga Indian children. *Amer. J. Orthopsychiat., 10,* 111–112.

HOMBURGER, E. H. 1937. Configurations in play—clinical notes. *Psychoanal. Quart., 6,* 138–214.

HORNEY, K. 1937. The neurotic personality of our time. New York: Norton.

JENNINGS, D. 1940. Perforated peptic ulcer: changes in age-incidence and sex distribution in the last 150 years. *Lancet,* Part 1, 444.

KARDINER, A. 1939. The individual and his society. New York: Columbia University Press.

KLINEBERG, O. 1935. Race differences. New York: Harper.

KLUCKHOHN, C. 1939. Theoretical bases for an empirical method of studying the acquisition of culture by individuals. *Man, 39,* 98–103.

KOHLER, W. 1937. Psychological remarks on some questions of anthropology. *Amer. J. Psychol., 59,* 271–288.

KROEBER, A. L. 1935. History and science in anthropology. *Amer. Anthrop., 37,* 539 ff.

—— 1939. Totem and taboo in retrospect. *Amer. J. Sociol., 45,* 446–451.

LANDES, R. 1938. The Ojibwa woman. New York: Columbia University Press.

LASSWELL, H. D. 1935. Collective autism as a consequence of culture contact. *Z. SozForsch., 4,* 232–247.

—— 1937. The method of interlapping observation in the study of personality and culture. *J. abnorm. soc. Psychol., 32,* 240–243.

—— 1939. Person, personality, group, culture. *Psychiatry, 2,* 533–561.

LEE, D. D. 1940. A primitive system of values. *J. Phil. Sci., N. Y., 7,* 355–378.

LEVY, G. 1939. Sibling rivalry studies in children of primitive groups. *Amer. J. Orthopsychiat., 9,* 203–214.

LINDGREN, E. J. 1935. Field work in social psychology. *Brit. J. Psychol., 26,* 177–182.

MALINOWSKI, B. 1927a. Sex and repression in savage society. New York: Harcourt, Brace.

—— 1927b. The father in primitive psychology. New York: Norton.

—— 1929. Sexual life of savages in northwestern Melanesia. New York: Liveright.

MEAD, M. 1928a. Coming of age in Samoa. New York: Morrow:

—— 1928b. The role of the individual in Samoan culture. *J. R. anthrop. Inst., 53,* 481–495.

—— 1928c. A lapse of animism among a primitive people. *Psyche, 9,* 72–79.

—— 1930a. Adolescence in primitive and modern society. In Calverton, F. V., & Schmalhausen, S. D., *The new generation; symposium.* New York: Macaulay.

—— 1930b. Growing up in New Guinea. New York: Morrow.

—— 1930c. An ethnologist's footnote to "Totem and taboo." *Psychoanal. Rev. 17,* 297–304.

—— 1931. The primitive child. In Murchison, C., *Handbook of child psychology.* Worcester, Mass.: Clark University Press.

—— 1932. Investigation of the thought of primitive children, with special reference to animism. *J. R. anthrop. Inst., 62,* 173–190.

—— 1934. The use of primitive material in the study of personality. *Character & Pers., 3,* 1–16.

—— 1935. Sex and temperament in three primitive societies. New York: Morrow.

—— 1937. Cooperation and competition among primitive people. New York: McGraw-Hill.

—— 1939. Researches in Bali and New Guinea. *Trans., N. Y. Acad. Sci., 2,* 1–8.

—— 1940a. Character formation in two South Seas Societies. *Trans. Amer. neurol. Assn., 66,* 99–103.

—— 1940b. Social change and cultural surrogates. *J. educ. Sociol., 14,* 92–109.

MEKEEL, S. 1936. An anthropologist's observations on American Indian education. *Progr. Educ., 13,* 151–159.

MILLER, N. E., & DOLLARD, J. 1941. Social learning and imitation. New Haven: Yale University Press.

MITTLEMANN, B., WOLFF, H. G., & SCHARF, M. P. 1942. Emotions and gastro-duodenal function: experimental studies on patients with gastritis, duodenitis, and peptic ulcer. *Psychosom. Med., 4,* 5–61.

MORGAN, L. H. 1871. Systems of affinity and consanguinity. Washington: Smithsonian Instn.

NADEL, S. F. 1937a. The typological approach to culture. *Character & Pers., 5,* 267–284.

—— 1937b. Experiments on cultural psychology. *Africa, 10,* 421–435.

—— 1937c. A field experiment in racial psychology. *Brit. J. Psychol., 28,* 195–211.

NISSEN, H. W., MACHOVER, S., & KINDER, E. F. 1935. A study of performance tests given to a group of native African children. *Brit. J. Psychol., 25,* 308–355.

RADCLIFFE-BROWN, A. R. 1931. The social origin of Australian tribes. Melbourne: Macmillan.

—— 1940. On social structure. *J. R. anthrop. Inst., 70,* Part 1, 1–12.

RADIN, P. 1933. The method and theory of ethnology. New York: McGraw-Hill.

RIVERS, W. H. R. 1923. Conflict and dreams. London: International Library of Psychology, Philosophy, and Scientific Method.

RÓHEIM, G. 1934. The riddle of the Sphinx. London: Hogarth.

—— 1939. Racial differences in the neuroses and psychoses. *Psychiatry, 2,* 386 ff.

SAPIR, E. 1934. Emergence of the concept of personality in the study of culture. *J. soc. Psychol., 5,* 408–415.

SCHILDER, P. 1940. Cultural patterns and constructive psychology. *Psychoanal. Rev., 27,* 158–170.

SELIGMAN, C. G. 1931. Japanese temperament and character. *Trans. Japan Soc., Lond., 28,* 124–138.

SPITZ, R. A. 1935. Frühkindliches Erleben und Erwachsenkultur bei den Primitiven. Bemerkungen zu Margaret Mead, "Growing Up in New Guinea." *Imago, Lpz., 21,* 367–387.

WARNER, W. L. 1941. Color and human nature. Washington, D. C.: American Council on Education.

WHITEHEAD, A. N. 1920. The concept of nature. Cambridge: Cambridge University Press.

WHITING, J. W. M. 1941. Becoming a Kwoma. New Haven: Yale University Press.

WHITING, J. W. M., & REED, S. 1938. Kwoma culture. *Oceania, 9,* 197–199.

Chapter 24

ECOLOGICAL FACTORS IN HUMAN BEHAVIOR

By ROBERT E. L. FARIS, Ph.D.

THE ECOLOGICAL ORDER, which emerges from a process of competition, may be distinguished from the cultural order which is based on different processes, even though these orders are never in actual occurrence completely independent. The coherence of the ecological order is based on relations of a symbiotic character, similar to the symbiosis that produces the elaborate and interdependent communities of animals and plants, in that it arises automatically and unintentionally out of the struggle for survival. The component elements cooperate without knowing it, or at least without having to know it (Park, 1939).

Durkheim (1893) has called this an "organic solidarity" because it is based on an organization of complementary differences, in which the individuals are utilities to one another, rather than objects of sentiment and affection. The bonds that hold together the populations of an industrial city are of this type.

The cultural order, based on consensus relations, is found only among human beings, as it requires psychological characteristics not possessed by simpler organisms. It is, in Durkheim's term, a "mechanical solidarity," a cohesion of persons on the basis of their similarities, which are valued on the basis of mutual affection and sentiment. The typical family, friendship group, fraternity, is held together principally by this relationship.

The simplest preliterate societies are maintained on a predominantly consensus basis, but with the development of civilization, and particularly industrialization, the symbiotic element has rearranged relationships and penetrated more and more into social systems. This encroachment has the effect of weakening and destroying much of the consensus unity in society, and is therefore one of the important basic causes of the social disorganization so conspicuous in industrial civilization, and, as shown below, is an underlying condition for much of the abnormality in human behavior of modern time. The most disorganizing ecological influences are those which upset established consensus orders by causing large movements of population. The consequences of such movements are so great that they constitute some of the major social problems of modern civilization.

Migration and Mobility and Their Effects on Culture and Behavior.—The most important movements of masses of people are determined principally by ecological factors. This is the case with much of the immigration to the United States, the flow of population from farms to cities, and the flow of populations from the centers of the cities to the suburban districts. There are, of course, certain types of migrations—such as religious pilgrimages, vacation migrations, refugee migrations, and the like—which are due to other factors, and there are also migrations with mixed causes. The ecological migrations are the movements in the struggle for a better place in the economic order. People desert the less favorable regions when they find opportunities to better themselves in new places, and they move to more desirable places when they find themselves able to support themselves there.

In recent times, due to the industrial revolution and to the settlement of the Western Hemisphere there has been a rapid advance in the general standard of living in the civilized countries (Ogburn and Nimkoff, 1940, Ch. 16). As a consequence there has been a great deal of ecological movement upward in the occupational pyramid, and toward the more favored regions on the earth's surface. Of the available studies of the causes and nature of these movements there is little that is conclusive. The most satisfactory knowledge we have concerns the migration from rural to urban regions in the United States. There are some grounds for holding that the general principles accounting for this migration apply to the others as well.

An issue that receives prominent discussion is the question of the extent to which characteristics of persons initiate these migrations. Can it be said that there are types of persons who are constitutionally inclined to migrate, and will migrate regardless of economic conditions? Or is it that migrations follow from the general competitive forces, regardless of the types of persons concerned? The available research is not conclusive, but the consensus of studies of rural-urban migrations favors the latter alternative. The time of migration, for example, is very largely set by the general condition, that is, by the occurrence of favorable employment opportunities in the areas to which the migrants move, and to a lesser extent by particularly unfavorable conditions in the regions they leave. This has been shown by several different methods in the researches of students of population (Ogburn and Nimkoff, 1940, Ch. 15). These studies indicate that migration varies in amount with industrial activity in the regions to which the migrants travel, and in times of depression not only stop but have a net reversal of movement. When prosperity and depression cycles do not coincide in the regions left and entered, the amount of movement relates more closely to prosperity in the region entered, than to depression in the region left.

There has also been extensive examination of the matter of the selection of types of persons in these migrations. The literature has been summarized by Gist and Halbert (1933) and by D. S. Thomas (1938), and though the results are not as conclusive as might be wished, the data appear to favor the conclusion that there is some selection in the migration, but that it is probably not a selection of a biologically different type. The migrants are, as a rule, discovered to be slightly superior in general ability and health to the nonmigrants, and to come from slightly superior homes. If the findings of Smick and Yoder (1929) are typical, the superiority is due mainly to the better opportunities, since the educational superiority did not manifest itself in the sample studied until some time after the eighth school grade.

The conclusion most harmonious with the above data is that the high rates of various types of defectiveness in populations which have undergone migration is not due to their previous inferiority, since the differences noted are more in the direction of superiority. It is more probable that the migration, which resulted from ecological forces, caused the behavior abnormality by disorganizing the social system.

Migration of the type under examination here has characteristic effects on the behavior of persons; effects which for the most part are in the direction of abnormality. It achieves these by interfering with some of the essential elements of cooperation. One of the essentials to normal and conventional behavior is full membership in primary groups in communities of stability. The migrant is separated from such membership and therefore becomes increasingly individuated as the length of separation increases. This is borne out by studies of such mobile populations as hoboes (Anderson, 1923 and 1940), rooming-house dwellers (Zorbaugh, 1929; Cavan, 1928), and hotel-dwellers (Hayner, 1936). In addition to this individuating effect, migration also has a secularizing effect. The resident of a stable community who knows of no other ways of life takes for granted the customs of his community, and regards as outlandish and abnormal the deviations he hears of only occasionally and distantly. But the migrant sees people living quite naturally in other systems, apparently as contentedly as his own people in their culture. When these alternative ways are seen to be successful his own ways become less sacred and less inevitable, and begin to lose their hold on him. Though it is possible that the ways of the outlanders could be so previously defined that they would not break down the old loyalties, the more usual effect of exposure to a different culture is such a secularization of the attitudes.

The effect on a nonmigrant of residence in an area of high mobility is similar. He has no stable community life, and is exposed to the secularizing influence of a variety of ways of living.

The ecology of behavior abnormality, then, is largely a matter of the consequences of migration. The aspects significant to behavior are not the migration itself, but the individuation and the secularization that are the consequences of it. The material in the following sections has a consistency which is intelligible in this light. High rates of behavior disorders, with certain exceptions to be noted, are found in those areas of social disorganization of the type which results from population migrations.

Behavior Disorders and Regional Variations

Comparison of Preliterate and Civilized Societies.—A major barrier to reliable comparisons between preliterate societies, and between preliterate and civilized societies, is the scarcity of accurate knowledge of the incidence of the various forms of behavior abnormalities in preliterate societies. Certainly it cannot be said that abnormalities do not exist in the simple cultures, as a number of reliable reports establish their existence (Gillen, 1939). But there do exist societies in which crime is so rare that it may be said to be virtually absent. And there are reports of a number of societies in which suicide is unknown (Cavan, 1938, Ch. 4). There is also evidence that in some societies functional mental disorders are rare or absent (Faris, 1934). It may be that variations in culture account for variations in behavior abnormalities in preliterate as well as civilized societies. The difficulty of establishing standards in such a relative matter as abnormality, and the difficulty of getting accurate information, may frustrate the research on this point for some time to come. It may be that the Cross-Cultural Survey which is being built up at Yale University will provide material adequate to a satisfactory analysis of this question.

Racial and National Variations.—Material on racial and national variations is only a little more satisfactory than on preliterate societies. International comparison of crime rates is difficult because of the variations in laws and enforcement mechanisms. Comparison of rates of mental abnormality are prevented by lack of standards of diagnosis, hospitalization, and other factors. Suicide rates would appear to be more comparable, but there are the questions of completeness of reporting, definitions of suicide, and intentional distortion of the records. In spite of these difficulties, the general study of suicide by Halbwachs (1930) is very consistent and convincing. The comparisons point to the relationship between high suicide rates and the degree of industrialization. Material in the studies of Cavan (1928) and others (Frenay, 1926; Dublin, 1933) which relates high suicide rate to urbanization, and to the highly mobile populations of the cities, strengthens this conclusion.

Many comparisons of racial and nationality groups within the United States, with respect to behavior abnormalities, have been made. Where conclusions have been drawn they have been subject to the criticism that the conditions under which these groups live vary so greatly that the statistics may reflect these conditions rather than racial characteristics (Klineberg, 1935). In view of the large variations within racial groups which have been demonstrated (Frazier, 1939), and in view of the narrowing or disappearance of some of the racial differences when conditions approach equality (Klineberg, 1935), it appears likely that most of the variations in abnormality between racial groups is due to differing conditions of life, and very little if any to differences in racial biology. Where the statistics are intelligible at all, they are in harmony with the explanation in terms of social disorganization presented above.

Regional and State Variations within the United States.—The ecological sorting of populations and activities is not so much distribution by states and regions, but rather a nucleated arrangement in smaller areas. Many states, for example, contain large cities as well as farms, foreign-born as well as native-born populations, migrant and stable populations, and so these extremes cancel out to some extent. Thus the contrasts in rates of crime and mental disorder in the major regions of the country are very small in comparison to the contrasts in the different sections of the large cities. In so far as there seems to be any meaning in such regional comparisons, it also is apparent that differences in behavior abnormality are associated with the disorganization of industrial areas. Certain forms of abnormality, however, are not particularly characteristic of industrial regions. Although most forms of professional crimes against property have their highest rates in the industrialized regions of the northern states, some crimes are not so concentrated in their distributions, and others, such as murder, which has its highest rates in the southeastern states, offer a sharp contrast.

Rural-Urban Variations.—In some respects the rural-urban comparisons are more satisfactory for showing contrasts than are regional comparisons, but this method also fails to bring out the most significant differences. Cities are neither adequately nor uniformly defined by their political boundaries, nor are cities uniform in their composition. The industrial cities which have been expanding rapidly have a considerable amount of social disorganization, but it is only a part of the city which is affected. The rates for entire cities fail to bring out the contrasts with rural areas because the extremes within the cities are averaged together. Nevertheless, cities have in general higher rates of abnormal behavior. The rates for the professional types of crime—burglary, robbery, larceny—are higher in the cities than in rural areas (Ogburn and Nimkoff, 1940, p. 534). Suicide has higher rates in urban areas (Cavan, 1928, p. 77; Sorokin and Zimmerman. 1929, p. 173). Mental disorders, all taken together, show higher rates in urban areas but some types of mental disorders show the reverse, and other types show little relationship to urban or rural areas (Sorokin and Zimmerman, 1929, pp. 264–265). The suggestion is made that the incidence of mental disorders might not actually be different in rural and urban areas, but that the apparent difference could be due to the difference in likelihood of noticing and committing persons who are psychotic (Landis and Page, 1938, pp. 53–55; Owen, 1941). Among the 1917 United States Army draftees, however, more urban than rural men were rejected because of mental disorders (Love and Davenport, 1920, pp. 351–352). The harmony of the rural-urban comparisons with the more carefully demonstrated comparisons between areas of the city also confirms that there is a real difference in incidence. This is related to differences in degrees and types of social disorganization (Faris and Dunham, 1939).

Behavior Disorders in Urban Areas

The Urban Ecological Pattern and Its Relation to Mentality, Behavior, and Social Institutions.—By far the most extensive, methodical, and fruitful ecological studies dealing with behavior are those based on comparisons between sections of large industrial cities. Following the analysis of "natural areas" of the city by Burgess (Park and Burgess, 1925), a considerable body of knowledge of urban ecology has been accumulated. It is necessary only to summarize the essentials here. The industrial city grows mainly by adding population through migration of unskilled persons who come from smaller cities and rural areas, and from other countries. These enter the industrial system at the bottom, and reside in the central industrial slum regions. As they become established these populations move upward in the occupational pyramid, and outward in the city toward more desirable residential areas, and their places in the slums are taken by newer arrivals. The principal characteristics of the urban areas, however, remain virtually constant as these streams of population pass through. Some of the behavior characteristics of the people are formed by their experiences in these areas, and change when they leave the areas. These characteristics include many aspects of community life, social institutions, political behavior, and other normal and abnormal behavior. Because these conditions remain with the area rather than with the racial or national group, it can be said that they are ecologically determined. By this it is not meant to imply that human nature is of no significance in the behavior, but that innate variations in human nature do not account for these area variations in such behavior traits as crime, vice, suicide, and other forms of abnormal behavior.

Delinquent and Criminal Behavior.—The most important work on the urban ecology of crime is that done by Shaw and his associates (Shaw and McKay, 1931). The foundation of the study was made in Chicago, and the results were checked against less complete studies in more than twenty other cities. The relationship of the type of delinquency that leads to the career type of crime is very clearly shown to grow out of the disorganization that has its roots in urban ecology.

A fact noted in the studies of all the cities is that the incidence of juvenile delinquency varies markedly according to the section of the city. The slum sections, usually but not always near the central parts of the city, inhabited by low-paid working people, with a high proportion of foreign and Negro populations, have relatively very high rates. The outlying residential sections, inhabited by native-born, business and professional population, have very low rates. In the intervening areas there

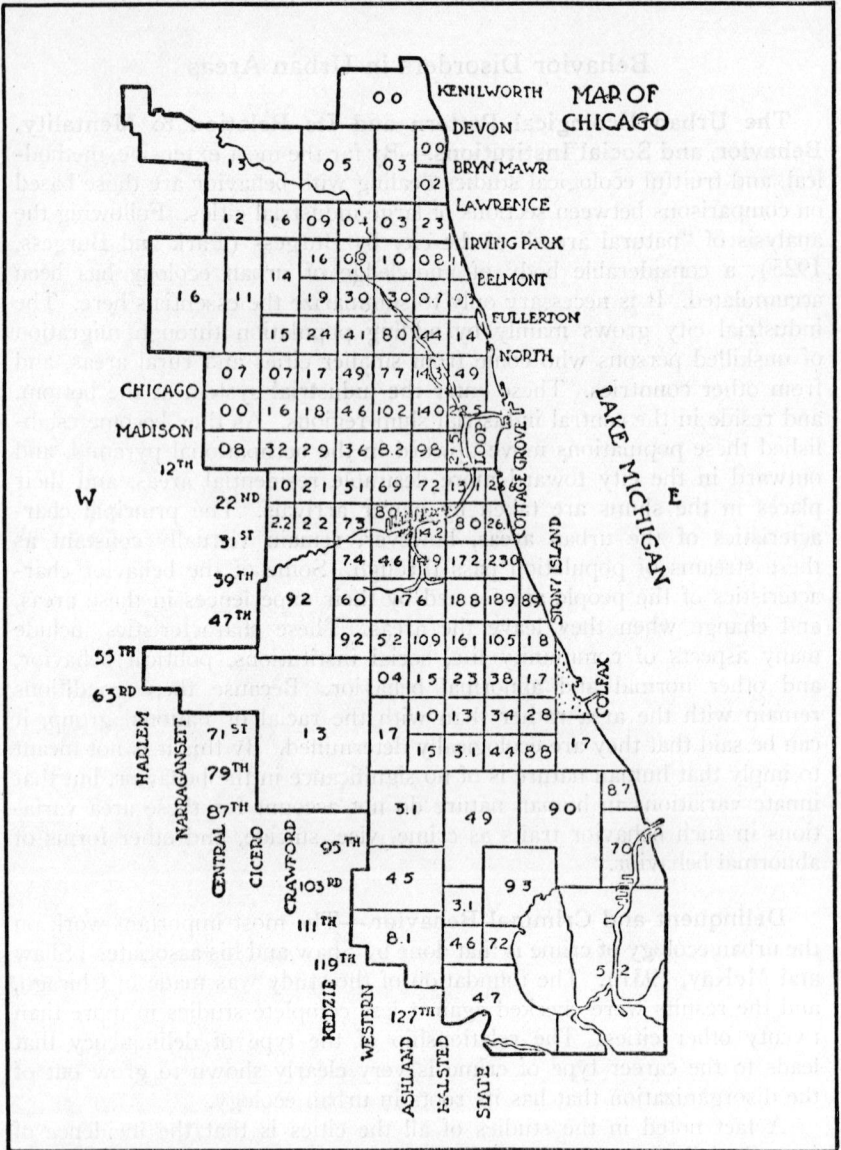

Figure 1

Rates of juvenile delinquents in districts of Chicago, based on 9,243 alleged male juvenile delinquents in the 1921 police court records. (From the *Report on the Causes of Crime,* National Commission on Law Observance and Enforcement, Vol. II, p. 30) is a gradation of rates according to the proximity to the slum areas (see Figure 1). Although the point has been made (Robison, 1936) that rates based on court cases may not necessarily be an accurate index to the amount of delinquency, enough evidence of other kinds converges to establish the point that the rates really do vary in the above manner (Shaw & McKay, 1931).

Taking selected areas in Chicago for special examination Shaw and McKay (1931, pp. 86–98) showed that the rates for the German, Irish, Scandinavian, Italian, Slavic, Negro, and other groups are all high when these groups inhabit the disorganized areas, and that they decrease as these groups move out toward the more stable residential districts. The rates for each racial or national group within the same areas were not identical, but the variation between these groups is much less than the variation between areas.

In a highly methodical and satisfactory fashion the Shaw and McKay study worked out a sociological explanation of the persistence of the high delinquency rates in these disorganized areas. Hypotheses to account for this on the basis of the innate characteristics of the delinquent are too much in conflict with the facts to be acceptable. The explanation of delinquency as due to low mentality, for example, breaks down under the careful and critical examinations of Sutherland (1931) and Tulchin (1939). The delinquent population does not appear to be in fact mentally inferior to the nondelinquent population living in similar conditions, nor does there appear to be any innate inferiority to the law-abiding population in general. Explanations of delinquency based on mental disorder, neuroses, mental conflict, also fail to stand critical examination. That is not to deny that there are delinquents with these forms of mental abnormality, but that such abnormality accounts for any large part of the delinquent behavior in the population. A study by Dunham (1939) of the catatonic schizophrenic cases and the delinquency cases in an area having high rates of both, showed that virtually none of the delinquent boys were in the catatonic group, and none of the catatonics had a record of delinquency. This finding is in harmony with the characterizations by Thrasher (1927), and Shaw and McKay (1931, pp. 222–257) of the members of delinquent boy gangs as normal, sociable, and lively.

There is reported a type of delinquency which is related to mental difficulties—conflict or light neuroses and the like—and which is not necessarily learned from other boys but is devised by individuals. It is expressed in such behavior as petty and useless stealing, and pathological lying. This type of delinquency is different in several respects from the normal gang behavior of the slums. It is not particularly characteristic of low-income classes or disorganized areas. It is not related, as is the gang behavior, to adult professional crime. It is not, so far as is known, related to urban ecology, and is therefore not further examined here, but left to the social psychologist or psychiatrist to explain.

The delinquent gang behavior, on which most adult professional criminal careers are based, grows out of the special social situation characteristic of areas which are disorganized by ecological processes. The most important factor in accounting for the delinquency is the breakdown of the social conditions which maintain normal and conventional behavior in the stable community. It is the integration of families with neighborhood communities that makes possible the type of informal social control that operates in small towns to maintain obedience to the customs and mores. In such a situation each person is known to all the others in his neighborhood and has a reputation to maintain. The supervision of behavior by neighbors and acquaintances is extensive, and the sharing of observations through gossip increases the range of information, so that the person is under virtually constant inspection of others in such a community, and his status is regulated by their judgments. In the normal conditions of community life, this type of control is sufficient to maintain normal and conventional behavior without the aid of such formal agencies as police and courts, and without supernatural sanctions for the control of behavior.

Although the mechanisms of formal enforcement of the laws are far more developed in the large cities than in the small towns, the delinquent behavior is not successfully controlled by them. The ordinarily effective informal control of the family and neighborhood is unable to operate in the disorganized parts of the city. Two important conditions producing the disorganization are the mobility and the heterogeneity of the populations in these areas. Not only is a large proportion new to the city and even to the country itself, but the movements of persons within the area are much more frequent than in the typical small town. This means that most persons live among strangers, who are relatively indifferent to their behavior, and who do not preserve a collective memory of each person and a reputation to guard. The small-town father may appeal with some force to his children by saying, "What will the neighbors think of us when you do that? You might disgrace the whole family." In the mobile parts of the city there are no neighbors in this sense, and so there is much less possibility of disgrace. The heterogeneity of races and nationalities, with their transplanted culture traits from their former countries, produces a variety of standards of behavior which allows for more choice and freedom than does a single moral standard. The experience of living in a community with an assortment of nationalities makes interfamily cooperation in supervising children's behavior much more difficult. Where race prejudice complicates the pattern, hostility toward neighbors further decreases the possibility of informal social control, except in such communities as Chinatown and the Orthodox Jewish Ghetto, where the hostility may be of such strength as to increase the solidarity and the social control within the group.

The result of such neighborhood disorganization is that families have difficulty controlling their children. In some cases the delinquents come from families in which delinquencies are allowed or even encouraged, but this is not the case with the major part of them. Most families try to control the behavior, but fail, due to the circumstances mentioned above. Some homes of delinquent children are incomplete, due to death, divorce, or separation of parents, but this is not in itself a major factor in delinquency. It has been shown that both the broken homes rates and delinquency rates vary according to age groups and according to the section of the city. When the influence of age and area is removed, the difference in broken homes rate between delinquent and non-delinquent children is little or nothing (Shaw and McKay, 1931, pp. 261–284). The more significant factor, then, is neighborhood disorganization rather than family disorganization by itself.

Mere lack of control by family and neighborhood does not in itself determine that children shall become delinquent. There are positive factors at work to maintain the delinquent patterns of behavior in these areas. A tradition of delinquent behavior is maintained by the children and transmitted from generation to generation in the same way legitimate traditions are transmitted. Each boy learns his first delinquency from experienced boys, and in turn transmits the techniques to younger ones. In practically all the cases of this type of urban delinquency, boys are taught their first delinquency in such an apprentice relation. As each boy graduates to more advanced techniques he is taught these also, by those ahead of him in the system. The arrangement is informal, but regular in pattern. The types of delinquency have a sequence, beginning with such simple types as stealing fruit and vegetables from an outdoor stand, stealing milk bottles from back steps, and the like, through such more advanced practices as shoplifting, burglary, auto thefts, and robbery with a gun. Not only the first of each type, but the large majority of all these delinquencies is committed in groups (Shaw and McKay, 1931, pp. 191–199).

In so far as motives can be inferred from observation of this behavior, it appears that hunger or need is not important in the beginning of the process. Even though food is often stolen, it is frequently not eaten, but taken for the excitement involved. A favorite game is to let the proprietor of a fruit stand see the theft of fruit, then as he pursues, to throw some of the fruit on the ground, watching with amusement his conflict between the desire to salvage his property and to catch the thieves. This has the meaning more of a good sociable athletic contest, than of a grim effort to stay hunger. Such a motive as revolt from authority is no more in harmony with the observations. While it is true that older criminals sometimes plan, during incarceration, to take "revenge on society," the boy delinquents appear to be merely following a social code with little thought of its meaning to the nondelinquent community. They realize that their delinquency is disapproved, but consider the law-abiding population somewhat as the opposing side in an athletic contest.

The whole system of prestige in the criminal organization is based on the difficulty and danger of the crimes, so that a boy finds the means of gaining status by learning the more advanced techniques. The older, more experienced men—the "big shots"—are respected and looked up to by the younger boys, who have the ambition to reach the advanced stages themselves in time (Shaw, 1930). When fear causes a faltering spirit in the commission of a dangerous crime, the possibility of disgrace with the members of the gang may prevent withdrawing. In the Shaw study of Sidney Blotzman, who was arrested for committing rape, it is evident that the crime was not due to a sexual craving, but to the desire not to lose caste in the eyes of the gang (Shaw, 1931). In general, the research on the nature of the delinquent gang boy points to the conclusion that he is not innately different from the normal population but that his activity is governed by a separate tradition. His motives for participating in that tradition are similar to the motives of normal persons in a conventional tradition.

The delinquent tradition is also favored by certain other conditions in the cities, such as the corrupt and rewarding alliance between business, politics, and crime, and the existence of "fences" for receiving stolen property, which help to make a career in professional crime profitable.

Organized Vice.—The principal ecological study of vice is that by Reckless (1934). The interpretation is, in general, similar to that of delinquency. Organized vice is made possible by the disorganization of the communities. It is maintained by a business-like organization of persons who do not differ markedly, on the average, from the general population in innate capacities. There are three distinct groups involved: the entrepreneurs, the prostitutes, and the patrons. The entrepreneurs are, for the most part, members of the professional criminal organization described and explained above. The prostitutes have a history similar to that of delinquent boys. A high proportion of them began their sex delinquency as young girls, in the same manner as boys begin their delinquencies (Crook, 1934). The behavior is learned, and motivated more by social motives than by individual sex craving or desperate need to gain a living (Thomas, 1923). After a period of free sex delinquency the career possibilities are recognized, much as the career possibilities of crime emerge after apprenticeship in delinquency.

The patrons are not all members of the criminal group, but come from a wider population, including some from the upper income groups and stable residential districts. But evidence based on examination of the addresses of patrons caught in raids (Reckless, 1934) and on the incidence of venereal diseases (Faris and Dunham, 1939, p. 1931) indicates that the unmarried population of the rooming-house districts furnishes the largest part of this group. Zorbaugh's description of the residents of this area (1929) and Cressey's study of the patrons of the taxi-dance hall (1932) show the relation of the mobility of this population to their disorganization, and to their failure to find adequate sex experience in other than vice resorts.

Suicide.—The most important ecological study of suicide is that made by Cavan (1928), who established that the suicide rates in Chicago vary in orderly fashion in the different parts of the city. A study in Seattle by Schmid (1928) yields similar findings (see Figure 2). The high rate areas are the areas in which there is a high mobility of population—the central business district with a hotel and hobo population, and the rooming-house and hobo areas near the central part of the city. The apartment-house districts, though lower than the rooming-house in suicide incidence, have higher rates than the stable residential districts.

Suicide statistics cluster about three factors: a crisis or failure, a sense of isolation or desertion, and a personality trait which might be called the "quitter attitude." The first of these, the crisis factor, is reflected in the increased incidence of suicides in times of economic depressions, and in the increase during such catastrophes as pogroms (Halbwachs, 1930). The second factor appears to be the one most related to the urban distribution of suicide rates. The rooming-house and hobo areas are inhabited by a highly mobile population. The residents of these districts are for the most part strangers to one another and are socially isolated even though the area is densely settled. The deterring effect on suicide of the knowledge that one will be missed by family and friends, of obligations of various kinds to other persons, are at a minimum here. This isolation factor is also reflected in other statistics. Halbwachs (1930) presents figures on marital status and suicide which indicate that marriage, especially if there are children, is related to a lower suicide incidence. In France the figures indicate that for each additional child up to the sixth, the expectation of suicide of parents becomes less. After the sixth the rate levels off and remains low. Halbwachs suggests also that the decline in rates during wars and extreme political crises may be due to the general increase in social solidarity at such times, and the consequent decrease in the sense of separation from society (1930).

The personality factor in suicide is not primarily a matter for ecological examination. Cavan presents material which suggests that the definition of suicide as the way out of a crisis may be related to personality trends that begin in childhood, and may be seen in such indications as the wish never to have been born (Cavan, 1932). A proportion of suicidal persons, perhaps a third, show signs of mental disorder, and about an equal proportion are addicted to alcohol, which is an indication of a trait of evasion of difficulties (Halbwachs, 1930).

Mental Disorders.—The most intensive ecological study of mental disorders is the analysis of rates in Chicago (Faris and Dunham, 1939). This study includes a check made in Providence, R. I., which though less complete, agrees with the Chicago results as far as it goes. Subsequent to the publication of this study there have been studies carried on in six mid-western cities. The preliminary results, reviewed by

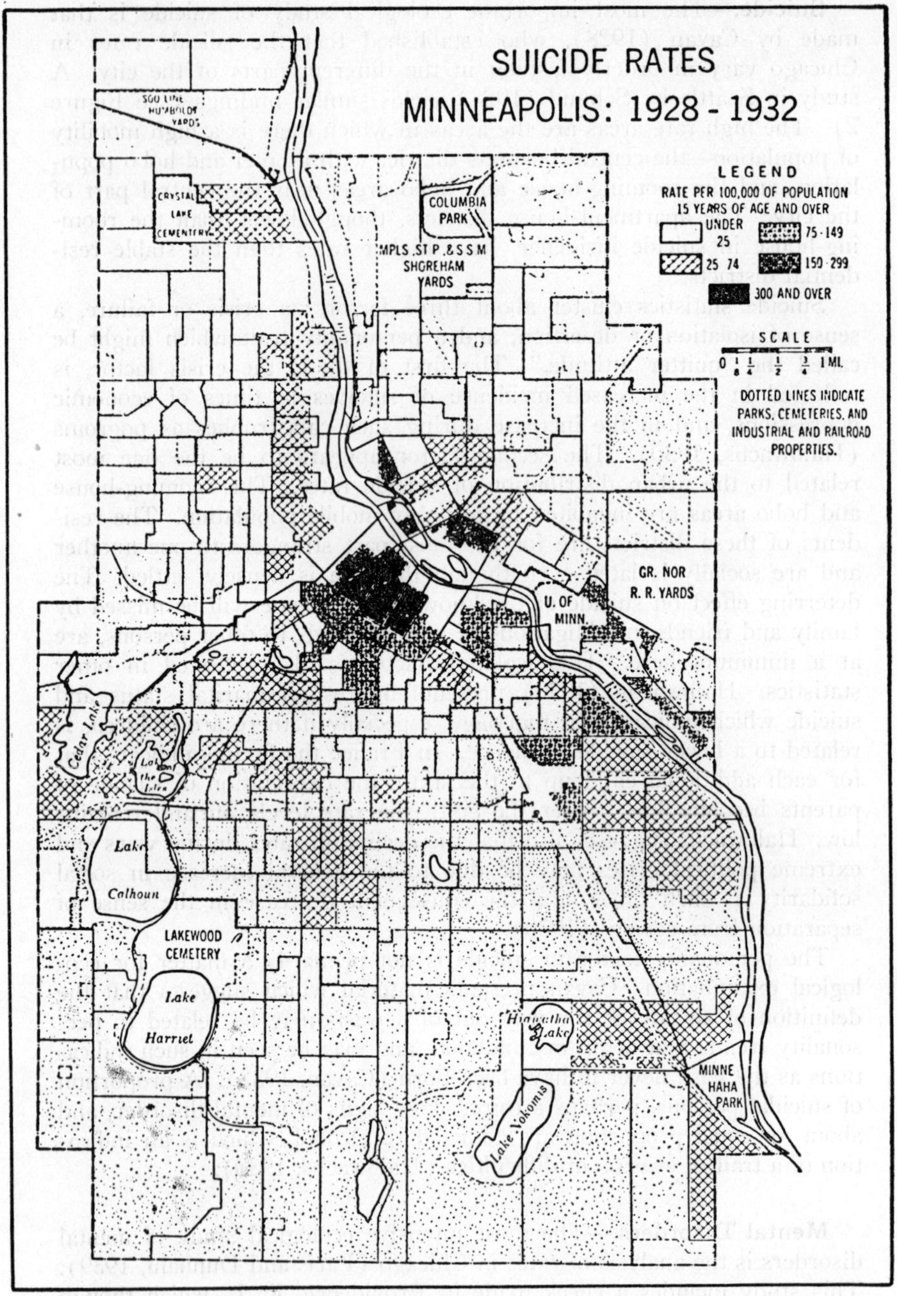

SUICIDE RATES
MINNEAPOLIS: 1928 - 1932

LEGEND
RATE PER 100,000 OF POPULATION
15 YEARS OF AGE AND OVER

UNDER 25	75 - 149
25 - 74	150 - 299
	300 AND OVER

SCALE
0 1/8 1/4 1/2 3/4 1 ML.

DOTTED LINES INDICATE
PARKS, CEMETERIES, AND
INDUSTRIAL AND RAILROAD
PROPERTIES.

Figure 2

Rates of suicide in districts of Minneapolis, 1928–1932. (From Calvin M. Schmid, *Social Saga of Two Cities*. Minneapolis: Minneapolis Council of Social Agencies, Bureau of Social Research, *Monogr. Series* No. 1.)

Queen (1940) are also in harmony with the more elaborate Chicago study.

In Chicago it was found that the rates of first admissions, based on the patients entering all the state hospitals and all the private hospitals in the vicinity, varied in a highly regular fashion. The highest rates are in the central business district; the next highest in the adjacent areas, hobo and rooming-house; and the lowest rates are in the residential areas on the edges of the city. The regularity and extent of this variation is shown by the rates for mile zones in radial segments of the city (see Figure 3). For the segment extending south from the central business district, the zone rates are, in order: 362, 337, 175, 115, 88, 74, and 71. For the segment extending to the northwest, the rates are: 362, 177, 95, 71, 66, and 55. Similar results are found for the three other segments (Faris and Dunham, 1939, p. 36). When the rates are computed by smaller areas, the range is much greater—from 499 to 48. These are average annual first admission rates for the combined years 1922–1934, inclusive, based on 100,000 population of 1930, age fifteen years and over.

This concentration of rates does not in itself prove that the incidence is actually higher in these areas of the city, or that the areas have any direct causal relation to the rates. It is possible that such a result may be explained in other ways. It may be that the incidence is the same throughout the population, and that the higher rates in the central sections represent the higher tendency of low income classes to be hospitalized. It may result from a statistical error due to the differential transiency in the population. That is, if the cases from an area taken during the period of a year are divided by the population taken as of a single day, the rate may be regarded as too high if the population during the year had turned over enough to make a significantly larger population than was present on the one census enumeration day. Another possibility is that the apparent concentration of rates is due to the drift of persons to slum areas as a result of failures due to mental disorder, that is, the concentration does not represent a causal relation of the area to the psychosis but an inevitable drift to such residences by the psychotics. It is also a possibility that the high concentration of races merely measures the racial tendency to mental disorders of the foreign-born and Negro populations that inhabit these areas. None of these hypotheses account for the fact that the patterns of distribution of the various psychoses are markedly different from each other, both in the degree of concentration and in the regions in which the concentrations occur. Further significant, if not conclusive, fragments of evidence on these hypotheses are cited in the Chicago study (Faris and Dunham, 1939, pp. 160–167), making it possible to rule out some of them with certainty, and supporting the conclusion that none of these suggestions is likely to account for the pattern of rates. It seems highly probable that the concentration of rates in the city represents a contribution of these urban living conditions to the causes of mental disorder.

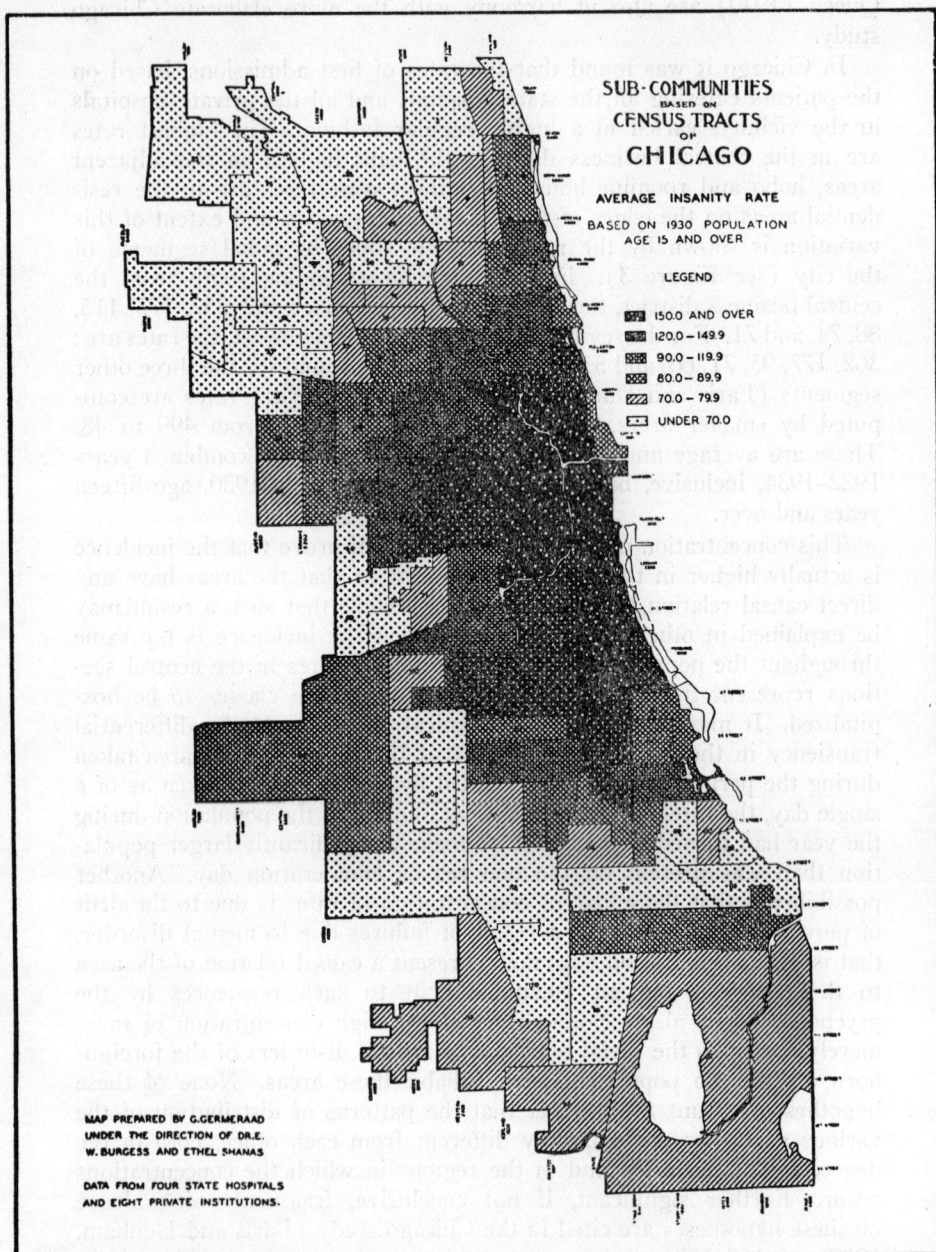

SUB-COMMUNITIES
BASED ON
CENSUS TRACTS
OF
CHICAGO

AVERAGE INSANITY RATE

BASED ON 1930 POPULATION
AGE 15 AND OVER

LEGEND

150.0 AND OVER
120.0 – 149.9
90.0 – 119.9
80.0 – 89.9
70.0 – 79.9
UNDER 70.0

MAP PREPARED BY G.GERMERAAD
UNDER THE DIRECTION OF DR.E.
W. BURGESS AND ETHEL SHANAS

DATA FROM FOUR STATE HOSPITALS
AND EIGHT PRIVATE INSTITUTIONS.

Figure 3

Rates of mental disorders in districts of Chicago, 1922–1934. (From R. E. L.
Faris and H. W. Dunham, *Mental Disorders in Urban Areas*. Chicago: Chicago
University Press.)

The separate examination of the distribution of rates for each type of psychosis reveals that they do not all show the same pattern. Schizophrenia is highly concentrated, much in the same pattern as that of all mental disorders together. General paralysis is concentrated principally in the central hobo and rooming-house areas and in the Negro area. Alcoholic psychosis is concentrated in these areas and in some of the foreign-born slum areas. Manic-depressive psychosis is hardly concentrated at all, but very nearly shows a random pattern of rate distribution. Other distributions of rates for senile psychosis, arteriosclerosis, and drug addiction also reveal characteristic patterns.

The explanation of the pattern of general paralysis rates is not difficult to find. The rooming-house districts contain the bulk of the patrons of vice resorts. Unpublished maps of the distribution of venereal diseases in Chicago show that these diseases have the same distribution as general paralysis. The relation of the rooming-house district to ecological processes has been indicated above.

Alcoholic psychosis has high rates not only in the hobo and rooming-house districts, but also in the foreign-born slum areas. Of all the major types of mental disorder this is the most closely associated with low income. Apart from the common-sense suggestion that addiction to alcohol may be a response to hardships of life, there is not much basis for an interpretation of this pattern. There is a suggestion of a cultural influence, however, in the exceptionally high rates in the communities inhabited by first and second generation Irish, and in the very low rates in Jewish communities.

There is also little basis for interpretation of the pattern of arteriosclerosis and senile psychosis. The patterns resemble that for schizophrenia. This may be coincidental, or may mean that there is some overlapping of these cases with schizophrenia, either in confusion of diagnosis or in the mixture of traits of schizophrenia in these forms of mental disorder. There are other possibilities as well, but at present insufficient data to make possible a reasonable choice between them.

Since the manic-depressive rates are distributed in a nearly random pattern in the city it may be concluded that this psychosis has little relation to any factors involved in urban ecology. This does not rule out factors of experience which do not vary in the different urban areas, but does leave the problem outside of the field of ecology.

The schizophrenia rates, as stated above, varied in about the same pattern as that of all mental disorders combined. But separate examination of types of schizophrenia shows sharp differences in their distribution. The paranoid type is associated with hobo and rooming-house areas, but the catatonic type has very low rates in these areas, and high rates in the foreign-born slum areas. The hebephrenic rates are intermediate, but somewhat closer to the pattern of the paranoid rates. These contrasts are verified by correlation studies of the rates for each type of schizophrenia with indices of conditions in the areas. The paranoid rates, for example, correlate with the percentage of rooming-house and hotel population of the city areas $+.82$, while the catatonic rates correlate negatively with the same index with a coefficient of $-.29$. The hebephrenic rates are intermediate with a $+.57$ coefficient. On the other hand, the catatonic rates show a high relation to the percentage of foreign-born plus Negro percentages, $+.86$; for hebephrenic, $+.40$; and for paranoid, $+.11$. This does not mean that the catatonic cases are necessarily more frequent in the foreign-born or Negro *populations,* but merely more frequent in the same areas where those populations are also frequent.

Owen (1941) attempts to account for the contrast in the schizophrenic and manic-depressive distributions on the basis of a differential probability of being discovered in different parts of the city. In regions in which persons have a large number of primary social contacts it is suggested that the behavior of manic-depressive and of schizophrenics would not be equally conspicuous, and thus the regions would have different rates of commitments, whether or not there are differences of incidence.

Krout (1938) has offered the suggestion that the schizophrenic pattern of rates is the result of the greater tendency of the low-income slum-dwelling populations to produce "frustrations which fixate the schizophrenic make-up" in the stages of birth and early feeding, while the frustrations which produce the manic-depressive pattern occur later, and more frequently in the higher-income populations.

The material gathered in this study, however, fits best with the explanation of the schizophrenia rates in terms of the social disorganization of the areas, which, when combined with certain other factors, isolates persons to a sufficient degree to contribute to their mental abnormality. A study of a large number of life histories of schizophrenia patients committed from the cities involved in this study, reveals typical patterns of experience which appear to bear a causal relation to the mental disorder. In a majority of the cases the early childhood was reported to be normal and without any indications of the schizophrenic symptoms. These symptoms developed after the isolating factors had been at work. In most of the cases the isolating factors, which initiated the process of abnormality, could not be said to be a result of the original nature of the person, but were due to external factors, beyond his control.

The typical process begins with the parental oversolicitude that produces the "spoiled child" type of personality. This is responsible for a certain isolation from all but the intimates within the family, but it does not necessarily result in a seclusive type of personality, or a lack of feeling of sociability for persons outside of the family. The next stage is persecution, discrimination, or exclusion, by children outside the family. This often happens at the time the child begins his schooling. The other children are naturally unwilling to accept the child at the parents' valuation, or at the child's self-valuation which results from the parental treatment. They show their resentment in persecutory treatment. The most usual reaction to this persecution is to feel unhappy, but with no immediate depreciation of establishing friendships. Often the children try for years to make friends, only to fail because of their inadequate personalities, or because of the rigid persistence of their status which received early definition in the community. Eventually there is a resignation—a withdrawal from a hopeless goal. Instead of trying to make friends, they confine their social activity within their own families, or take increased interest in reading, music, art, and other solitary activities. From this time on their interest in sociability declines and they slowly develop the typically seclusive personality that is characteristic of the schizophrenic. The symptoms that are associated with this personality type arise out of the confusion and misunderstanding that is a consequence of their lack of experience in dealing with others. The person who has been isolated for years is deficient in knowledge of human nature, and misunderstands others and is misunderstood by them. He mistakes unintentional slights for active persecution. He interprets his own failures as due to interference by others, since he became so thoroughly convinced by his parents of his own unique superiority that he cannot imagine that his own deficiencies cause the trouble. Not being experienced in intimate personal contacts with a large number of other persons he is deficient in his understanding of the reactions of others, and responds unconventionally and inappropriately to them. If, as is the case with many, his upbringing was of a pious or prudish character, he has missed virtually all knowledge of sex matters, since he was not exposed to the informal education that most children get from conversations with each other during their growing years. His attitudes then are likely to be that anything pertaining to sex is evil and nasty. Since he is exceptionally fine and good, judging from his parents' behavior toward him, his sex feelings could not originate within his own nature, but must result from the attempts of wicked people to poison him, with drugs, gas, electricity, or thought waves. If he should, however, decide that these feelings do stem from his own nature, he may conclude that he is one of the lowest and most depraved persons on earth, and react by hiding in shame, by desperate efforts to save his soul by violent religion, or some equally extreme reaction. Similarly other symptoms which appear fantastic to others can often be shown to be based on misconceptions which could scarcely be avoided by persons so lacking in normal social experience.

It is not suggested here that the process of "spoiling" children takes place more frequently in the disorganized sections of the city. What does vary in the different areas is the reaction of other children to the overprotected child. In the more integrated communities, the relations between adults and children are such as to promote some community cooperation, with the result that sympathy of adults may lead to the lessening of the natural discrimination against the socially deficient child. In the slum areas, however, the lack of this cooperation, the mixture of nationalities, the tradition of "toughness" among the delinquent boys, and such factors, constitute such a barrier to the establishment of social relations that many find it impossible, and are thus turned down the path that leads to the psychosis.

Because it is not clear on what basis the types of schizophrenia were differentiated, it is not possible to make a very satisfactory interpretation of the different distributions. An examination of the cases on which these rates were based showed that the catatonic cases are much younger than the paranoid and hebephrenic at first admission, and that they have a higher proportion of women. The catatonic group also contains a much higher proportion of Negroes, though the proportion of foreign-born is about the same as in the paranoid group. It may be that these characteristics reflect the group which is more likely to have the conflict based on religious prudishness and sex stimulation, and that the older, more mobile paranoid group represents the egocentric failures who cannot accept the blame for their own troubles. Such a suggestion must, of course, await further research before much confidence can be placed in it.

Conclusions

Such research of a scientific character as has dealt with the relation between ecology and behavior has mainly been concerned with social disorganization and the consequent forms of personal disorganization. This disorganization is for the most part a phenomenon of a great transition. With the opening of new continents following the discoveries of the western hemisphere, and with the industrial revolution, there occurred large population movements, which are still going on. Such movements break up the social systems that control and integrate the behavior of persons, so that new, unconventional, and abnormal types of behavior appear. These abnormalities are not essentially aspects of city life, or civilized society, but rather of the populations which are changing from one system to another. There are many successful social systems among the most simple preliterate peoples, and there are established parts of advanced civilized society that have no serious social maladjustments. The trouble occurs in the middle stages of the process of change.

The indices of serious abnormality in behavior, then, show a relationship to this kind of transition. Suicide rates are highest in countries which are becoming industrialized, and particularly in the cities, and most conspicuously in the highly mobile parts of those cities. Professional crime is related to industrial urbanization in much the same way. Mental disorders have such a variety of causes that it is not to be expected that they should all relate to the same processes, but it is shown that certain forms vary spectacularly with the degree of social disorganization.

The focal points of these developments, the large, expanding industrial cities, have a very regular, though unplanned, process of growth, in the course of which certain typical "natural areas" develop. In each of these areas there is a typical social situation which favors the development of the abnormal behavior traits in the ways discussed above. It is likely that much ecological variation of normal behavior will also be demonstrated when more research is applied in the direction to reveal it.

BIBLIOGRAPHY

ANDERSON, N. 1940. Men on the move. Chicago: University Chicago Press.
ANDERSON, N., & LINDEMAN, E. C. 1928. Urban sociology. New York: Knopf.
BLUMER, H. 1937. Social disorganization and individual disorganization. *Amer. J. Sociol., 42, 871–877.*
BOSSARD, J. H. S. 1938. Ecological areas and marriage rates. *Amer. J. Sociol., 44, 70–96.*
BOWERS, R. V. 1939. The ecological patterning of Rochester, New York. *Amer. sociol. Rev., 4, 180–189.*
BURGESS, E. W. (Ed.) 1926. The urban community. Chicago: University Chicago Press.
CARPENTER, N. 1932. The sociology of city life. New York: Longmans, Green.
CAVAN, R. S. 1928. Suicide. Chicago: University Chicago Press.
— 1932. The wish never to have been born. *Amer. J. Sociol., 39, 493–500.*
DAVIE, M. R. 1937. The pattern of urban growth. In Murdock, G. P., *Studies in the science of society.* New Haven: Yale University Press.
DAYTON, N. A. 1940. New facts on mental disorders. Springfield, Ill.: C. C. Thomas.
DEE, W. L. J. 1939. An ecological study of mental disorders in metropolitan St. Louis. St. Louis, Mo.: Thesis, Washington University.
DUBLIN, L. I. 1933. To be or not to be. New York: H. Harrison Smith & Robert Haas.
DUNHAM, H. W. 1932. Urban distributions of schizophrenia. *Coll. Contr. Pap. Elgin St. Hosp.* Pp. 143–146.
— 1937. The ecology of the functional psychoses in Chicago. *Amer. sociol. Rev., 2, 467–479.*
— 1939. The schizophrene and criminal behavior. *Amer. sociol. Rev., 4, 352–361.*
— 1940. Ecological studies of mental disorders: their significance for mental hygiene. *Ment. Hyg., N. Y., 24, 238–249.*
DURKHEIM, E. 1893. De la division du travail social. Paris: Alcan.
FARIS, R. E. L. 1934a. Cultural isolation and the schizophrenic personality. *Amer. J. Sociol., 40, 155–169.*
— 1934b. Some observations on the incidence of schizophrenia in primitive societies. *J. abnorm. soc. Psychol., 29, 30–31.*
— 1938. Demography of urban psychotics with special reference to schizophrenia. *Amer. sociol. Rev., 3, 203–209.*
— 1939. An ecological study of insanity in the city. Chicago: University Chicago Library.
FARIS, R. E. L., & DUNHAM, W. 1939. Mental disorders in urban areas. Chicago: University Chicago Press.
FRAZIER, E. F. 1932. The Negro family in Chicago. Chicago: University Chicago Press.
— 1937. Negro Harlem: an ecological study. *Amer. J. Sociol., 43, 72–88.*
— 1939. The Negro family in the United States. Chicago: University Chicago Press.
FRENAY, A. D. 1926. The suicide problem in the United States. Boston: Chapman & Grimes.
GILLIN, J. 1939. Personality in preliterate societies. *Amer. sociol. Rev., 4, 681–702.*
GIST, N. P., & HALBERT, L. A. 1933. Urban society. New York: Crowell.
HALBWACHS, M. 1930. Les causes du suicide. Paris: Alcan.
HALPERN, I. W. 1934. The slum and crime; a statistical study of the distribution of juvenile delinquents in the boroughs of Manhattan and Brooklyn, New York City. New York: New York City Housing Authority.

HAYNER, N. S. 1933. Delinquency areas in the Puget Sound region. *Amer. J. Sociol., 39,* 314–328.

—— 1936. Hotel life. Chapel Hill: University North Carolina Press.

KLINEBERG, O. 1935. Race differences. New York: Columbia University Press.

KROUT, M. H. 1938. A note on Dunham's contribution to the ecology of functional psychosis. *Amer. sociol. Rev., 3,* 209–212.

LANDIS, C., & PAGE, J. D. 1938. Modern society and mental disease. New York: Farrar & Rinehart.

LEWIN, Y., & LINDESMITH, A. 1937. English ecology and criminology of the past century. *J. crim. Law Criminol., 27,* 801–811.

LIND, A. W. 1930. Some ecological patterns of community disorganization in Honolulu. *Amer. J. Sociol., 36,* 206–220.

LONGMOOR, E., & YOUNG, E. F. 1936. Ecological interrelations of juvenile delinquency, dependency, and population. *Amer. J. Sociol., 41,* 598–610.

LORIMER, F., & OSBORN, F. 1934. Dynamics of population. New York: Macmillan.

LOTTIER, S. 1938a. Distribution of criminal offenses in metropolitan regions. *J. crim. Law Criminol., 29,* 37–50.

—— 1938b. Distribution of criminal offenses in sectional regions. *J. crim. Law Criminol., 29,* 329–344.

—— 1938c. Regions of criminal mobility. *J. crim. Law Criminol., 28,* 657–673.

LOVE, A. G., & DAVENPORT, C. B. 1920. Defects found in drafted men. Washington, D. C.: United States Government Printing Office.

MALLER, J. B. 1934. Delinquent areas in New York City. *Psychol. Bull., 31,* 640–641.

MALZBERG, B. 1941. Social and biological aspects of mental disease. Utica, N. Y.: State Hospitals Press.

McCLENAHAN, B. A. 1929. The changing urban neighborhood; from neighbor to nigh dweller, a sociological study. *Univ. S. Calif. soc. Sci. Ser.,* No. 1.

McKENZIE, R. D. 1921. The neighborhood. *Amer. J. Sociol., 28,* 16–78.

MOWRER, E. R. 1938. The trend and ecology of family disintegration in Chicago. *Amer. sociol. Rev., 3,* 344–353.

—— 1939. Family disorganization. Chicago: University Chicago Press.

NATIONAL RESOURCES COMMITTEE. 1938. Report on the problems of a changing population. Washington, D. C.: United States Government Printing Office.

OGBURN, W. F., & NIMKOFF, M. 1940. Sociology. Cambridge: Houghton Mifflin.

OWEN, M. B. 1941. Alternative hypotheses for the explanation of Faris' and Dunham's results. *Amer. J. Sociol., 47,* 48–52.

PARK, R. E. 1929. Sociology. In Gee, W. P. *Research in the social sciences.* New York: Macmillan.

—— 1936. Human ecology. *Amer. J. Sociol., 42,* 1–15.

—— 1939. Symbiosis and socialization: a frame of reference for the study of society. *Amer. J. Sociol., 45,* 1–25.

PARK, R. E., & BURGESS, E. W. 1925. The city. Chicago: University Chicago Press.

PHLEGER, M., & TAYLOR, E. A. 1932. An ecological study of juvenile delinquency and dependency in Athens County, Ohio. *Publ. Amer. sociol. Soc., 26,* 144–149.

POLLOCK, H. M. 1941. Mental disease and social welfare. Utica, N. Y.: State Hospitals Press.

QUEEN, S. A. 1940. The ecological study of mental disorders. *Amer. sociol. Rev., 5,* 201–209.

QUEEN, S. A., & THOMAS, L. F. 1939. The city: a study of urbanism in the United States. New York: McGraw-Hill.

QUINN, J. A. 1940. Topical summary of current literature on human ecology. *Amer. J. Sociol., 46,* 191–226.

RECKLESS, W. C. 1934. Vice in Chicago. Chicago: University Chicago Press.

—— 1940. Criminal behavior. New York: McGraw-Hill.

RHYNE, J. J. 1934. Delinquency areas in Oklahoma City. *Proc. Okla. Acad. Sci., 14,* 83–84.

ROBISON, S. M. 1936. Can delinquency be measured? New York: Columbia University Press.

SCHMID, C. F. 1928. Suicides in Seattle, 1914–1925: an ecological and behavioristic study. Seattle: University Washington Press.

—— 1937. Social saga of two cities; an ecological and statistical study of social trends in Minneapolis and Saint Paul. Minneapolis: Minneapolis Council of Social Agencies, Bureau of Social Research, *Monogr. Series* No. 1.

SHAW, C. R. 1929. Delinquency areas. Chicago: University Chicago Press.

―― 1930. The jack-roller. Chicago: University Chicago Press.

―― 1931. The natural history of a delinquent career. Chicago: University Chicago Press.

SHAW, C. R., & McKAY, H. D. 1931. Report on the causes of crime. Washington, D. C.: National Commission of Law Observance and Enforcement.

SHERMAN, M., & SHERMAN, I. 1934. Psychotic symptoms and social backgrounds. In Bentley, M., & Cowdrey, E. V., *The problem of mental disorder.* New York: McGraw-Hill.

SMALL, M. H. 1900. On some psychical relations of society and solitude. *Pedag. Sem.,* vol. 8.

SMICK, A. A., & YODER, F. R. 1929. A study of farm migration in selected communities in the State of Washington. *Bull. Wash. St. agric. Exp. Sta.,* No. 233.

SOROKIN, P. A., & ZIMMERMAN, C. C. 1929. Principles of rural-urban sociology. New York: Holt.

SULLENGER, T. E. 1936. Social determinants in juvenile delinquency. New York: Wiley.

SUTHERLAND, E. H. 1931. Mental deficiency and crime. In Young, K., *Social attitudes.* New York: Holt.

―― 1932. Social process in behavior problems. *Publ. Amer. sociol. Soc., 26,* 55–61.

―― 1939. Principles of criminology. New York: Lippincott.

TAFT, D. R. 1933. Testing the selective influences of areas of delinquency. *Amer. J. Sociol., 38,* 699–712.

THOMAS, D. S. 1938. Research memorandum on migration differentials. *Soc. Sci. Res. Coun. Bull.,* No. 30.

THOMAS, W. I. 1923. The unadjusted girl. Boston: Little, Brown.

THOMPSON, W. S. 1935. Population problems. New York: McGraw-Hill.

THRASHER, F. M. 1927. The gang. Chicago: University Chicago Press.

―― 1932. Ecological aspects of the boys' club study. *J. educ. Sociol., 6,* 52–58.

―― 1936. The boys' club and juvenile delinquency. *Amer. J. Sociol., 42,* 66–80.

TÖNNIES, F. 1940. Fundamental concepts of sociology. New York: American Book.

TULCHIN, S. H. 1939. Intelligence and crime. Chicago: University Chicago Press.

WHITE, R. C. 1932. The relation of felonies to environmental factors in Indianapolis. *J. soc. Forces, 10,* 498–509.

WILSON, R. T. 1934. Delinquency areas in San Jose. *Psychol. Bull., 31,* 588–589.

WIRTH, L. 1928. The ghetto. Chicago: University Chicago Press.

ZORBAUGH, H. W. 1929. The Gold Coast and the slum. Chicago: University Chicago Press.

hoods in Minneapolis and Saint Paul. Minneapolis: Minneapolis Council of Social Agencies, Bureau of Social Research, Hennepin County No. 1.

SHAW, C. R., 1929. Delinquency areas. Chicago: University, Chicago Press.

—— 1930. The jack-roller. Chicago: University, Chicago Press.

—— 1931. The natural history of a delinquent career. Chicago: University, Chicago Press.

SHAW, C. R., & MCKAY, H. D., 1931. Report on the causes of crime. Washington, D. C.: National Commission of Law Observance and Enforcement.

SHERMAN, M. & SHERMAN, I., 1923. Periodic symptoms and social backgrounds. In Hanley, M. S. & others, L. V., The problem of mental disorders. New York: McGraw-Hill.

SMITH, M. H., 1900. On some prejudicial relations of poverty and solitude. Polit. Sci. Q., vol. 4.

SMITH, A. A. VOSS, T. R., 1929. A study of large immigration in selected communities in the state of Washington. Burr. High. St. Govt. Rep., No. 73.

SOROKIN, P. A. & ZIMMERMAN, C. C., 1929. Principles of rural-urban sociology. New York: Holt.

SULLENGER, T. E., 1936. Social determinants in juvenile delinquency. New York: Wiley.

SUTHERLAND, E. H., 1931. Mental deficiency and crime. In Young, K., Social attitudes. New York: Holt.

—— 1939. Social factors in behavior problems. Publ. Amer. Sociol. Soc., 27.

—— 1934. Principles of criminology. New York: Lippincott.

TAFT, D. R., 1933. Testing the selective influence of areas of delinquency. Amer. J. Sociol., 38, 699–712.

THOMAS, D. S., 1925. Research memorandum on migration differentials. Soc. Sci. Res. Coun. Bull., No. 43.

THOMAS, W. I., 1923. The unadjusted girl. Boston: Little, Brown.

THOMPSON, W. S., 1935. Population problems. New York: McGraw-Hill.

THRASHER, F. M., 1927. The gang. Chicago: University, Chicago Press.

—— 1936. The boys' club and juvenile delinquency. Amer. J. Sociol., 42, 66–80.

TOWNSEND, P., 1936. Psychiatric approach to social order. New York: American Book.

TUTTLE, S. H., 1924. Intelligence and crime. Chicago: University, Chicago Press.

WHITE, R. C., 1931. The relation of felonies to environmental factors in Indianapolis. Soc. Forces, 10, 498–509.

WOODS, R. T., 1924. Delinquency areas in San Jose. Psychol. Bull., 21, 588–589.

WIRTH, L., 1928. The ghetto. Chicago: University, Chicago Press.

ZORBAUGH, H. W., 1929. The Gold Coast and the slum. Chicago: University, Chicago Press.

PART VI

SOME OUTSTANDING PATTERNS OF BEHAVIOR DISORDER

Chapter 25

BEHAVIOR DISORDERS IN CHILDHOOD

By Leo Kanner, M.D.

IT IS CUSTOMARY TO INCLUDE under the heading of children's behavior disorders a vast range of major and minor deviations from vaguely defined and variously considered norms of general maturation and specific performances. Textbooks and other treatises dealing with the psychopathology of childhood (e.g., Homburger, 1926; Kanner, 1935; Louttit, 1936) are, therefore, of necessity organized collections of a multitude of diverse disturbances of frequent or rare occurrence, variegated or selective symptomatology, and different degrees of modifiability. Just as pediatric literature occupies itself with every known departure from ideal physical health at an early age, so do the discussions of abnormal child psychology comprise every known problem of overt and implicit behavior during the first years of life. These all-embracing data, concerned equally with items as unrelated as fever delirium, nailbiting, stuttering, schizophrenia, and cretinism, are held together by two outstanding factors common to all disorders: the age at which they are observed and the fact that they form the nucleus of a complaint.

The Age Factor.—Bradley (1937; 1941, p. 2) called attention to the confusion which has long existed regarding the concepts of childhood and adolescence. One often finds, indeed, in statistical studies and in presentations of case material, persons in the middle or even toward the end of the second decade of life referred to as "children." On the other hand, persons who have barely emerged from the first decade are sometimes, though less often, treated as preadolescents or adolescents. Potter (1933) stated: "It was found that the term 'children' was used rather loosely and included patients with ages as high as 16 or 17 years." Bradley (1937) offered the following suggestion for the purpose of clarification and uniform recording: "An example which we may well follow in this regard is that of the pediatrician and the children's hospital to whom for classification purposes at least the 'child' is an individual below a definite age level. This age level had best be that which most nearly coincides with the onset of physiological puberty, and both tradition and experience suggest the thirteenth birthday . . . This practice should successfully eliminate the present confusion existing in psychiatric research and in the literature."

Many articles and monographs devoted to children's behavior disorders are compelled by circumstances to exclude from their scope the first two or three years of life. Stevenson and Smith (1934, p. 55) made it clear that most child guidance clinics rarely have an opportunity to become acquainted with small infants, whose problems, therefore, do not figure in reports issuing from those sources. This obvious deficit was remedied by the close collaboration between psychiatry and pediatrics, which was first instituted at the Johns Hopkins Hospital in 1930 and has since then spread to a number of medical teaching centers (Kanner, 1932; Clarke and Jensen, 1941).

The students of normal and educational psychology have realized that "childhood" is a collective term, covering brief life periods of remarkable difference. They investigated the range of performances in successive years, so that at the present time expectations for any given age can be assessed with reasonable accuracy through a variety of tests. These insights have so far not been carried over consistently to behavior deviations. Child psychiatrists have rarely focused their attention on limited sectors of childhood. Psychoanalysis, it is true, assigns to each stage of infantile development a specific state of an hypothecated unconscious but has not succeeded in correlating convincingly the personality difficulties of each age group with the postulated metamorphoses of the unconscious.

The So-Called Period of Resistance.—Toward the end of the second and at the beginning of the third year of life, children acquire normally the meaning and application of negation. This feature has been so commonly observed that many investigators felt justified in speaking of this age as the period of resistance or remonstrance (Levy and Tulchin, 1923; 1925; Reynolds, 1928; Busemann, 1928). Benjamin (1930; 1941) saw in its manifestations and management a most important factor in the development of childhood neuroses. According to Benjamin, the basic disturbance underlying unusually strong or protracted resistance consists of a child's failure of adaptation to his environment, due to insecurity and anxiety. The child's difficulty of adjusting to the task of growing into relationships with other people and accepting the values set by them leads to a state of disorientation, hostile refusals and isolation, with aversion to cleanliness and to the acquisition of functions commensurate with his age. Hence, for example, come the persistence of enuresis and disorders of speech. This failure of adaptation leaves three possible avenues open to the child: developmental standstill, even to the point of regression to a previous stage of existence in which there was a greater feeling of security; introversive turning away from reality to find consolation in thumb-sucking, masturbation, and rhythmic body movements; and spiteful rebellion, resembling the fluttering of a caged bird or the bewildered agitation of an adult in a panic situation. Out of the latter mode of reaction arise feeding problems, vomiting, rebellious wetting and soiling, destructiveness, and temper tantrums. A neurosis is characterized by Benjamin as the unnaturally prolonged duration of the period of resistance and has its origin in a combination of social contact disturbances, partial inhibition of psychic development, inner insecurity, and faulty training. Because of the etiologic significance of the period of resistance as the basis for later neurotic conditions, Benjamin urged early prophylaxis and treatment not of the symptoms alone but of the total person.

Prepubescence and Pubescence.—The termination of "childhood," coinciding with the onset of menstruation in girls, the first seminal emission in boys and the appearance of the so-called secondary sex characteristics in both groups, has sometimes been referred to as a second period of resistance because of simultaneous manifestations of a critical and often resentful attitude toward adults and their standards (Hetzer, 1927; Ruppert, 1931). Progressive emancipation from the home, reaching out into the community, being sucked in by the community, problems of social, sexual, and theologic orientation offer many possibilities for friction and inner conflict. There has been a tendency in psychiatric literature to emphasize similarities between pubescent groping and the essential features of schizophrenia. This trend, expressed most skilfully by Cosack (1933), is part of a habit, now gradually declining, of correlating too readily the thinking of children, "primitives" and schizophrenics. Recent ethnologic studies and an excellent investigation of children by Despert (1940) have sensibly and factually demonstrated that the fundamental differences outweigh the resemblances by far.

On the whole, psychiatric occupation with the age of pubescence has been limited to inquiries into the occurrence of psychotic conditions during this phase. The monographs by Wille (as early as 1898), Klieneberger (1914), and Pappenheim and Gross (1914) are classical examples. There is general agreement that puberty is a critical age from the point of view of personality development and more especially from the point of view of incisive psychopathologic departures.

The Complaint Factor.—Besides age, the complaint factor is the only other common denominator in the consideration of behavior disorders. Its significance has been pointed out by Meyer (1928) and Kanner (1933a; 1941). Acquaintance with any form of behavior difficulty is made possible by the fact that the patient himself, members of his family, neighbors, friends, teachers, employers, physicians, courts, or social workers are sufficiently disturbed to call for expert assistance. The complaint is an entering wedge, a starting point for planned investigation and treatment, the admission ticket to the psychiatrist's office. It is always an indisputable live reality which offers itself for a study of its intrinsic meaning, genetic-dynamic background, relative nuisance-value, diagnostic reformulation and therapeutic management.

THE COMPLAINT AS A BASIS FOR STATISTICAL STUDIES.—All valid statistics in the realm of child psychiatry, with the exception of recorded test results, are derived from indices of the complaints with which children are brought to clinics, juvenile courts, and their equivalents. Attempted statistics of "traits" have proved unyielding because of the inability to come to terms about generally acceptable and unequivocal definitions. This becomes especially evident in the most ambitious and painstaking statistical study of children's behavior disorders by Ackerson (1931), whose exemplary figures regarding complaints contrast sharply with those regarding the far less concrete and more controversial evaluation of traits and attitudes. Enuresis, regardless of all variables of etiology and psychodynamics, can be studied statistically as enuresis, stealing as stealing, and blinking as blinking. But "neurosis," "nervousness," "neuropathy," "aggressiveness" are concepts still too diffuse and open to arbitrariness to lend themselves for clear numerical depositions.

CLINICAL SIGNIFICANCE.—Complaint is not synonymous with symptom. As given to a carefully inquiring and listening examiner, it affords a vivid picture of the disturbing behavior of a specific child and the reporter's attitude concerning the child and his behavior. The complaint thus immediately leads the clinician to an awareness of relationships and life situations which goes far beyond the recording of detached symptoms and directs his curiosity to definite causative and curative possibilities. Expressions, during the recital of the complaint, of parental excuses, feelings of guilt, accusations, hostility, commiseration, and anxiety furnish valuable clues to the understanding of the basic difficulty.

CULTURAL IMPLICATIONS.—Behavior which is undesirable and gives cause for complaint in one culture is not necessarily regarded as disturbing in another culture. There are types of behavior which in our time and civilization create parental anxiety and figure in the current lists of psychopathologic performances, whereas at other times and in other civilizations they either go unnoticed or are even encouraged as signs of normal development. Thumb-sucking is an example of the first category. It was not considered a problem anywhere until late in the nineteenth century, when Lindner (1879) warned against its effects on the formation of the upper jaw and emphasized its hedonic origin. It became the object of much parental worry when the orthodontists declared it to be the main cause of prognathism, hygienists cautioned that it introduced pathogenic germs into the oral cavity, and Freud (1905) spoke of it as the earliest manifestation of oral eroticism. In no other culture is there any objection to thumb-sucking. In our own, a number of medieval artists depicted children and angels with thumbs in their mouths to give them the appearance of serene placidity (Ghirlandajo in *Adoration of the Magi,* Credi, Lippi, Borgognone, della Robbia—see Bragman, 1931).

Heterosexual play among children is dreaded in our culture. Malinowski (1929) reported that it is good-naturedly condoned among the Trobriand Islanders. Masturbation was for nearly two centuries abhorred as injurious to the development of body and mind as a result of the warning by Tissot (1760), Hufeland (1797), and Lallemand (1836). Present-day psychiatry tries to undo the harm done, not by masturbation itself, but mainly by those unfounded scares. Parental admonitions which prophesy insanity for a masturbating child are today considered as much of a "behavior problem" in need of correction as the child's masturbation.

Classification

The manifoldness and complexity of behavior disorders have made systematic grouping extremely difficult. We know today that even Kraepelin's famous classification of adult psychoses has failed to settle matters. We know that the various dichotomies and trichotomies of mankind offered in explanation of tendencies to certain forms of reactions (for example, Jung's personality types, Kretschmer's types of body configuration, Jaensch's types of eidetic imagery) are in the main oversimplifications hardly ever applicable to everyday clinical work. This is especially true of children because personality is still *in statu nascendi* and any cataloging therefore can at best be anticipatory rather than conclusive.

There are, on the one hand, distinct nosologic entitities, such as juvenile paresis or cretinism, which are amenable to a clear-cut, exclusive diagnosis. There are, on the other hand, innumerable problems of behavior in infancy and childhood which cannot be pressed into any categorical system without doing violence to the uniqueness of the constellation in which they occur.

Grouping Based on Complaints or Symptoms.—It is, therefore, not surprising that a classification of the sort applied to most other sciences has never been attempted in child psychiatry. Many clinics and monographic presentations are satisfied to index and sort out leading complaints and bring them under some kind of major headings, such as delinquency, habit disorders, speech difficulties, fear reactions, and many others. But even this cannot be carried out consistently, since other headings, such as feeblemindedness or organic brain disease, rely on the diagnostic reformulation of the complaint rather than on the complaint itself. Brown, Pollock, Potter, and Cohen (1937) offered such a "psychiatric classification of problem children," which has been officially approved by the Committee on Statistics of the New York State Department of Mental Hygiene. This outline distinguishes between ten "principal groups": (1) mental deficiencies; (2) psychoses; (3) psychoneuroses and neuroses; (4) convulsive disorders, including epilepsy; (5) behavior disorders with somatic disease or defect; (6) psychopathic personalities; (7) educational disabilities; (8) primary behavior disorders ("i.e., not secondary to other groups in this classification"); (9) social problems; (10) other problems.

It is evident that such a classification, though doing fair justice to practical needs, is full of inconsistencies, brought about largely by over-lapping, duplication, and a certain degree of arbitrariness which is par-ticularly implied in the subdivision of "primary behavior disorders." The four subheadings are: Habit, personality, neurotic, and conduct dis-orders. Many of the enumerations under each title could be easily inter-changed. A group of experts would be hard put if asked specifically to indicate under which topic fears, day dreaming, disobedience, habit spasms are listed by the authors.

Similar difficulties exist with regard to the grouping which Kanner (1935) has used in his textbook. He divided the material into three main classes: (1) personality disorders forming essential features or sequels of physical illness; (2) personality disorders expressing them-selves in the form of involuntary part-dysfunctions; (3) personality dis-orders expressing themselves clearly as whole-dysfunctions of the indi-vidual. Here, again, definite allocation is sometimes rendered difficult by combinations involving two or even all three of these categories.

Grouping Based on Other Principles.—The use of generic terms has created even greater confusion. There has been a tendency to differentiate between personality problems and behavior problems (Payn-tor and Blanchard, 1929), personality problems and conduct problems (Louttit, 1936), personality problems and conduct problems as sub-species of behavior problems (Ackerson, 1931). Ackerson spoke of con-duct problems as those which are usually socially disturbing, while personality problems are more specifically related to the individual him-self. Louttit, proceeding on a similar principle, had two types of conduct problems ("direct primary behavior problems"): those of limited social significance and those of serious social significance (delinquency). He had also two types of personality problems ("indirect primary behavior problems"): actively aggressive behavior and submissive, withdrawing behavior. All such divisions necessitate artificial definitions. There is, after all, no behavior, problematic or otherwise, which is not intimately linked with what everyone regards as "personality."

Howard and Patry (1935) devised three groups of "reactive dis-orders on the basis of emotional, situational, habit-training and per-sonality maladjustments": (1) habit training problems; (2) aggressive or protest behavior; (3) submissive or recessive behavior. The reasons given for this grouping are inadequate.

The Variety of Disorders Defies Rigid Classification.—This criti-cism is in no way to be construed as directed against the authors who have courageously attempted to present the material in orderly fashion. It is the subject matter itself which, because of its multifariousness, is not accessible to pigeon-holing. If a child bites his nails, day dreams, blinks his eyes and disobeys his parents, he would, according to Howard and Potter (1937), present habit, personality, neurotic, and conduct disorders at the same time. The whole issue then becomes a matter of preferential terminology.

It would be ideal if children, instead of their behavior, could be grouped. But this would lead to complete chaos and leave the door wide open to unscientific name-calling. Who is a neuropath, a psychopath, a neurotic child, a delinquent? Such terms, though applicable at times, have much too often been used as swear words rather than well-founded diagnoses.

Motivation

Not until the beginning of this century did the whence and why of children's behavior disorders become a matter of psychologic and psychiatric curiosity. Unless there was obvious mental deficiency or gross organic disease, undesirable behavior was popularly ascribed to badness, mischievousness, or outright depravity, to be handled, mostly through punitive measures, by the parental and educational disciplinarians. Most psychologists and physicians were, if at all, interested in abnormal child behavior only to the extent of nosologic description. The German textbook of child psychiatry by Ziehen (as late as 1926) and the Italian textbook by De Sanctis (1925) had nothing to say about etiology; De Sanctis went so far as to ridicule the modern direction toward "clinical individualism" and washed his hands of "the intimate investigation of psychodynamics."

However, during the past forty years, the study of motivation has made considerable progress. Two principal trends have developed, which still exist side by side. One might speak of them as monopolistic theories and pluralistic considerations.

Monopolistic Theories.—The monopolistic theories have in common the urge to refer all behavior disorders to one specific set of etiologic factors, to disregard or minimize the importance of all other factors, and to build up "schools" or "systems" on those exclusive premises. One such school, which made dysfunctions of the endocrine glands responsible for all psychopathology of childhood, has never gained wide recognition; discourses about "the glands of destiny" and "the glands regulating personality" have for a time captivated the popular book market but failed to impress the profession. Another school, founded in Germany by the Jaensch brothers and making behavior and misbehavior dependent on eidetic imagery, has never taken root in this country. Beginning with a few factual observations and experiments, most clearly summarized in English by Klüver (1931), E. R. Jaensch, one of the two brothers, became more and more inextricably involved in abstruse philosophic problems of eidetically determined *Weltanschauung* and allowed his "system" to degenerate into a justification of Nazi ideology.

Three monopolistic schools, however, have made considerable inroads on educational and clinical work with children, especially from the point of view of investigative and therapeutic "approaches" to problems of behavior.

PSYCHOANALYSIS.—The psychoanalytic theory has gained a tremendous foothold. It postulates the existence of an unconscious, subdivided into super-ego, ego, and id, the interrelation of which determines personality formation and behavior. Freud (1905) has set down a course of unconscious infantile sexuality, beginning in earliest infancy and spread over the entire period of childhood in successive stages (narcissism, pregenital organization—mainly oral and anal, sex curiosity with development of the castration complex or penis envy, Oedipus or Electra complex, latency period, and pubescent genital organization). Culturally unacceptable impulses are "repressed" by the ego and "sublimated" (diverted into socially useful channels) by the super-ego, the equivalent of "conscience" and the representative of the parent ideal. A child may become caught and "fixated" at any stage, or even "regress" to it at a later time. All psychopathology is viewed as emerging from the failure of smooth, scheduled progression of infantile sexuality.

Psychoanalysis was first applied to children by Freud himself (1909) in the case of a "phobia" of a five-year-old boy. Freud felt that this experiment "fully confirmed" his theories derived from the retrospective analysis of the symptoms and dreams of adults. Since then there have been many contributions to the psychoanalysis of children. Freud's daughter, Anna (1925, 1931), and Melanie Klein (1932) are the best-known representatives. Criticism of the theory of infantile sexuality has arisen not only from nonpsychoanalysts (Sachs, 1926; Kanner, 1939) but also from the ranks of the analysts themselves (Horney, 1939).

INDIVIDUAL PSYCHOLOGY.—Adler, seceding from Freudian psychoanalysis, was led by a study of organ inferiority (1907) to the observation that there seems to be a tendency to compensation or overcompensasation on the part of an inferior organ system. He broadened this observation into the theory that all personality difficulties have their roots in a feeling of inferiority and insecurity derived from physical handicaps, or from clashes with the environment which interferes with a person's need of self-assertion and desire for power. Adler came to view children's behavior disorders as attempts at overcompensation for deficiencies, supplying the child with tools intended to make him the center of attention and to govern the family. Adler's theories have exercised a marked influence in the field of education. Besides Adler himself (1924), Wexberg (1926, 1928) has been their strongest exponent.

BEHAVIORISM.—Watson's behaviorism (1919), leaning strongly on Pavlov's work with the conditioned reflex, was applied to children by Watson himself in his classical observations of infants at the Johns Hopkins Hospital. His system of psychology, disregarding the data of introspection, refusing to have anything to do with the concept of consciousness, reduced all human behavior to an exclusively neurophysiologic relation of stimulus and response. Watson (1928) set forth those principles somewhat radically in a book on child training, which has for several years enjoyed enormous popularity among the laity. However, in clinical work with children's behavior problems, the application of behaviorism has not found a sufficient number of supporters. The very fact that Watson, in his programmatic writings, did not even by implication allude to the intelligence factor, makes his system impracticable in a large portion of psychopathologic disorders.

Pluralistic Considerations.—The monopolistic approaches to the study of personality disorders have undoubtedly made significant contributions. Every one of them has started out with a few novel observations of facts. But these discoveries, valuable in themselves, were allowed to serve as prejudicial motivations.

Other investigators, unwilling to narrow the scope to any one set of facts or theories, have, under the leadership of Adolf Meyer (1929; Kanner, 1933b), kept in closer touch with the plurality of factors and occurrences as they are found to exist in real life. Shying away from preordained simplifications of complexities, they bent their efforts in the direction of deriving their understanding of behavior from the facts and combinations of facts as they present themselves to the observer, instead of forcing realities into any kind of decreed interpretations. This point of view has sometimes been wrongly termed eclectic. Eclecticism denotes a selective nibbling from various systems and schools. Psychologic pluralism does not select but looks for, accepts and includes everything that is factual.

Pluralistic considerations have resulted in the recognition that children's behavior disorders may have their origin, singly or in a variety of mixtures, in different types of factors: physical, intellectual, emotional, situational, and constitutional.

PHYSICAL FACTORS.—Lurie (1935) made an eloquent plea for the physical examination of every child who presents problems of behavior. His analysis of 1,000 cases clearly indicated in approximately 75% the somatic involvement at least as a contributory feature.

Some authors, it is true, gave prominence, sometimes exaggerated, to specific somatic functions in relation to abnormal behavior in general or to circumscribed disorders. A few examples only can be cited here. Orton (1925; 1937) has made a special point of handedness-eyedness conditions in speech pathology, especially stuttering, and reading and writing disabilities, which he ascribed to a confusion in hemispheral dominance; he suggested that changed handedness and split laterality (right-handedness and left-eyedness or vice versa) create a disturbance in the normally one-sided, contralateral cerebral hemisphere lead (left in right-handed and right-eyed people, right in left-handed and left-eyed people). German authors have paid much attention to the patterns of the capillaries around the nailbeds as indicators of immaturity and other abnormalities of personality and behavior (Schiller, 1934). Recently much has been made of electroencephalographic designs found in "problem children" (Jasper, Solomon, and Bradley, 1938); the findings are not conclusive and await comparison with the brain waves of a sufficient number of normal children. There is a tendency, notably in England, to assign particular importance to hypoglycemia (low blood sugar content) in attack disorders, such as fainting spells, night terrors, and migrainous attacks (Henderson and Gillespie, 1932). Studies have been made of correlations between allergic phenomena and behavior deviations (Chobot, Spadavecchia, and De Sanctis, 1939; Forman, 1939).

These experimental studies are supplements to the universal clinical experience that body functioning and behavior cannot be considered separately, since they are fused in any number of ways.

Behavior and personality development can be profoundly affected by organic brain disease or disordered functioning of the glands of internal secretion. Transitory clouding of consciousness with disorientation and hallucinatory episodes occurs in the course of infectious conditions, intoxications and nutritional defects. Many other ailments exercise a direct influence on mood and performance; one need only think of the apathy of the child with cardiac illness, the irritability of the child suffering from eczema, or the stealing of food of a diabetic child on a rigid diet (Shirley and Greer, 1940). Sometimes the behavior is linked intimately with the physical condition as an immediate cause. At other times the illness acts as an abnormal situation to which some children react in an unwholesome manner, often under the impact of injudicious management of the sick child on the part of the parents or the physician. Some authors go so far as to speak of "iatrogenic" (physician-determined) behavior disorders of children (Kanner and Lachman, 1933).

THE INTELLECTUAL FACTOR.—Since the introduction of standardized psychometric rating, it has become increasingly clear that the degree of intellectual endowment constitutes a significant criterion in the evaluation of certain aspects of behavior difficulties. A minus in cognition, expressive capacity, and judgment can be an obstacle to satisfactory adjustment. Severe feeblemindedness of and below the low-grade moron type carries with it invariably a lack of ability to conform to the average standards of training in every existing culture. Adaptation of the higher grades of intellectual inadequacy, often not even recognized as such in simpler societies, depends to quite an extent on the competitive demands made on the children. Such demands come in our society when legal regulations require school attendance and a retarded pupil's scholastic failure creates unhappiness, frustration, and insecurity. Those feelings, in turn, may bring about intense dislike of school, offensive behavior in the classroom, truancy and, in its wake, various forms of delinquent behavior. Reports from juvenile courts are all in agreement about the large contingent of high grade feebleminded and borderline children. Osgood and Trapp (1936), to quote but one example, found among 400 juvenile delinquents only 18% boys and 17% girls of normal intelligence, and 21% boys and 29% girls definitely feebleminded; in other words, as many as 61% boys and 54% girls belonged to the intermediate group. Lurie (1937) found that among 225 children with IQ between 80 and 89, "the intellectual subnormality was directly responsible for the behavior difficulty presented by the child" in 18% of the cases, while of a large group of 1,000 mental defectives the intellectual level was causally related to the behavior disorder in only 3.8%. "For this reason," Lurie concluded, "it is of extreme importance to recognize the rôle that subnormal intelligence may play in the causation of incorrigibility, delinquency, criminality and many other forms of social behavior."

Some psychoanalysts have of late propounded the theory that in many, if not all, instances feeblemindedness, far from being an irreversible deficiency, has its origin primarily in an "emotional blocking" of potentialities possessed by the individual, thwarted by unconscious mechanisms and capable of being released by psychoanalytic procedure. Clark (1933) thus expressed this theory: "The general distribution of libido is such as to restrict the dynamic forces available for intellectual use." At present, the idea of the emotional background of intellectual defect is promulgated largely by the staff of the Southard School at Topeka, Kansas.

THE EMOTIONAL FACTOR.—It is difficult, if not impossible, to study and discuss emotional (affective) happenings without taking into account (1) the individual involved and (2) the situation which gives rise to the happening. We have fortunately got away from the academic armchair method of dealing with emotions as if they were entities existing in their own rights. Emotions are responses to environmental influences and at the same time signs of what goes on in the responding person. The meaning and understanding of any sort of emotional behavior are determined fundamentally by the setting in which it occurs, the manner in which a person is involved or feels that he is involved, his previous experiences with similar situations, his previous reactions to similar situations, phylogenetically determined avenues of response, social conventions and individual peculiarities.

Children's emotional reactions can manifest themselves to the observer (1) through the type of overt behavior; (2) through visceral participation; (3) experimentally, through the method of play investigation.

The general "affective tone" is in the main easily recognized as calmness, pleasure, displeasure, irritability, excitement, or perturbation. Single emotional episodes may be normal, natural, serviceable reactions; thus the realization of danger is almost always connected with fearful avoidance or shrinking, obvious injustice is met with anger in the socialized form of righteous indignation, parental cruelty may encounter reasonable resentment of unreasonable authority. Unusually strong reactions are still to be considered normal if they are commensurate with an unusual situation: marked excitement, differing from the child's usual behavior, before a birthday party or as part of the Christmas anticipations, profound grief following the loss of a parent, or fear of the ragman who has been presented to the child as a dangerous abductor. Abnormal reactions are out of proportion with the situation either in intensity (sweeping, uncontrolled dramatic outbursts, such as breathholding spells, temper tantrums, or panic), in terms of observable relationship (tics or stuttering which have long been detached from the originally responsible setting), or in the sense of bizarre, incongruous behavior which cannot in any way be accounted for situationally (as in schizophrenia).

Visceral participation is a normal concomitant of all emotional responses. One may roughly distinguish between three degrees: (1) physiologic participation, present at all times but usually so unobtrusive that it can be ascertained only through specific methods: (2) near-physiologic participation, still within the limits of normal fluctuation, but often creating discomfort or embarrassment; gastric disturbances with nausea in excitement, marked blushing, the proverbial examination diarrhea are typical examples; (3) pathologic visceral participation makes up a large portion of behavior disorders in which organ dysfunctions play a part. It is responsible for psychogenic palpitation, respiratory disorders, pallor, fainting, anorexia, constipation, vomiting, diarrhea, enuresis, headaches, and some of the hypochondriacal sensations. These somatic manifestations of undesirable behavior may be considered as deriving from normal visceral participation (a) through unusual and habitual intensification (from accelerated pulse rate to rapid heart beat, from gasping to breathholding, from mild gastric discomfort to vomiting); (b) through intentional utilization in order to gain coveted attention; (c) through automatization, when the physiologic concomitants become so frequent and detached from the original emotion that they no longer serve as specific signals in response to circumscribed settings (tics, enuresis).

Until a few years ago, very little could be done to ascertain from children directly how they felt. Their feelings could be deduced only from their performances. Ordinary conversational inquiry did not suffice to elicit a telling account of what went on in the children. New ways had to be found in order to "get at" them. Lowrey (1937) wrote: "Most of us who have been long in children's work began very early to use toys, pictures, drawings and modellings as a means of uncovering children's wishes, fantasies, hostilities, jealousies, and transference." The first systematic efforts to use play as a means of disclosing children's emotional life came from psychoanalysts (Hug-Hellmuth, 1913; A. Freud, 1925; Klein, 1932). The lead has been taken up by many child psychologists and child psychiatrists, who developed three principal methods: standardized, spontaneous, and situational play methods.

The standardized method was introduced by Levy (1936, 1937a), who, setting out to study problems arising from sibling rivalry, tried to "shape the play situations into essentially similar forms by utilizing the same play material and the same stimuli words." Levy confronted the child with an amputation doll, a metal doll which could be dismembered and restored. This doll represented the child's mother; two other dolls, made of celluloid, were identified with the patient himself and his brother or sister being held and "fed" by the mother doll. The child's behavior in this setting (moving toward the dolls, dropping or denting, throwing or hitting, crushing or biting the baby doll, doing something unkind to himself, turning against the examiner, moving away from the group) was interpreted by Levy in a definite, stereotyped fashion.

Despert (1938) studied "aggressiveness" by giving children a knife, locking them in a room, telling them to scrape a piece of cardboard and interviewing them immediately after they had been left unobserved for an hour. Their responses to certain questions were then interpreted as indicating certain emotional attitudes.

"The problem of the child's love relationship with its father and mother and siblings" was studied by Bender and Woltmann (1936) by means of standardized puppet shows on a definitely psychoanalytic basis.

The spontaneous play method ushers the child into a room in which there is a variety of toys, observes his attitudes and actions in relation to the toys and the examiner and draws its conclusions therefrom. As Rogerson (1939) stated, the child "could make as much noise as he liked, say and do what he liked, and in fact do anything except break the windows or lights." Allen (1934, 1937, 1939) stressed the value of this type of play as providing the child with familiar tools to "relate himself" to the examiner: "Into the play he will bring the reactions and feelings common to his relations outside . . . Interpretation then is in terms of the present meaning rather than in terms of the past."

The situational method has been most consistently employed by Conn (1939a, b), who described the "play interviews" as follows:

> It is not a fixed technique but an opportunity for the child to express himself and at the same time to reveal to himself the rôle which he has played in his illness. This is accomplished by providing an opportunity for the child to speak for each of a number of dolls, and simultaneously to view all that is going on while he is actively participating in an intimate discussion of his own attitudes . . . Toy furniture and dolls representing various characters (parents, siblings, teachers, etc.) are used during the play interview, and various scenes are arranged by the physician as upon a miniature stage. In every case the realities of the child's life situation suggest to the physician what play experiments to set up.

The study of the emotional life of children has doubtless been greatly enhanced by the methods of play investigation.

THE SITUATIONAL FACTOR.—Emotions, whether they be normal, near-normal or abnormal, are responses to situations. In child psychology and psychiatry, the motivating values of a child's environment have been recognized from the earliest days. The influences of training and example have been stressed from time immemorial. There is now general consensus that children's personality development and behavior are determined not only by the things that are done to them but also, sometimes directly and sometimes more indirectly, by the personalities and attitudes of the people around them. In fact, the very presence of a child in a home, a play group, or a classroom creates a situation to which the others react in a variety of ways which in turn reflect on the child's own responses. Thus a child's unusual size, obesity, neurologic or orthopedic handicaps, impaired vision or hearing, chronic skin eruptions, or other noticeable physical shortcomings lend themselves to remarks by playmates, need for medical care and parental financial sacrifice and special educational arrangements, all of which cannot help but constitute a situation of incisive importance for the child.

The principal environmental settings which motivate children's behavior and often interact can be roughly divided into three categories: the home, the school and the neighborhood. It is impossible in the scope of this presentation to set forth more than a brief enumeration, with a sampling of the vast literature, of the potentially pathogenic factors referable to a child's environment.

Throughout childhood, the home is the nucleus of a child's social life; there he emerges by degrees from the passivity of the neonatal period to a stage in which he becomes a domesticated member of the household and is gradually prepared for the tasks of communal adjustment. Difficulties may arise from a number of features, none of which is always a breeder of trouble but each of which can alone, or in combination with other factors, play havoc with a child's happiness, security, or adequate habit formation. The effects of emotional problems of parents and of parental dissensions on the development of abnormal behavior patterns of children have been reported by many authors. Myers (1929) has shown how parental suspiciousness and feelings of superiority can be handed on to the offspring. Levy (1932) made a survey of children's problems in overprivileged and underprivileged families; he found in the first group a predominance of temper tantrums, negativism, and "introversion," and in the second group a greater incidence of stealing, lying, and incorrigibility. The consequences of broken homes have been variously evaluated; most investigators ascribe major significance to the dissolution of the home as a motivating or at least contributing force in the origin of behavior disorders; Silverman (1935), in a statistical study, concluded that there is no significant (statistical) relationship between the broken home and the behavior of children coming from such homes.

Of far greater etiological importance is the relationship between parent and child. Levy (1937b) reported a number of illustrative cases which show the untoward results of a lack of maternal affection. He demonstrated three groups of reactions to what he called "affect hunger": one in which there were pathologic residues due to an extreme deficiency in maternal love; one in which the restoration of maternal love had marked therapeutic effect; and one in which specialized difficulties in social relationships were found to be "derivatives of a primary affect hunger." This lack of affection, sometimes overcompensated by over-solicitude, was found by several authors to be based on rejection of the child by his matrimonially frustrated mother (Newell, 1934). Case material from child guidance clinics and juvenile courts has brought to light the great influence on children's behavior of parental overprotection and overindulgence ("spoiling"), hostility, neglect, and exaggerated educational ambitions and expectations. Many studies exist with regard to the bearing of a child's position in the family in order of birth on the one hand and tendency to behavior difficulties on the other hand. The only child has been the object of special curiosity. According to Campbell (1934), "Stanley Hall is said to have considered being an only child a disease in itself." Recent studies have been rather contradictory. While some declared only children to be physically inferior and given to restlessness and dissatisfaction, others could not agree that they were in any way different from other children. Blatz and Bott (1927) learned that only children had the best behavior rating among 1400 Toronto school children. The same discrepancy exists in the literature concerning first-born and youngest children. Goodenough and Leaky (1927) said in conclusion of an interesting investigation that "there is no position in the family circle which does not involve, as a consequence of its own peculiar nature, certain special problems of adjustment."

The relationship between siblings from the point of view of rivalry and jealousy and behavior difficulties arising on that basis has received particular attention from Levy (1937a), whose interpretations of the results of standardized play investigation tend, however, to see sibling rivalry too readily in everything that a child does.

Next to the home, the school is the greatest and most powerful socializing agent. It is a child's protracted experience with competitive living within a group under direction. But in the course of years, a considerable number of difficulties may grow out of the school situation. The outstanding pathogenic elements are: unhealthy relations to teachers, unhealthy relations to classmates, physical illness, lack of recreational outlets, grade misplacement of children with retarded or superior endowment, frequent changes of schools, long absences from school, experience of failure, and parental interference with the school regulations. The best discussions of the contributions made by the school to children's behavior and its deviations come from Wickman (1928), Sayles (1929), and Cameron (1933).

Neighborhood influences have been investigated largely in connection with juvenile delinquency. Almost all juvenile courts now have maps of their districts showing the distribution of residences of the offenders brought to them. Such maps invariably show at first glance that some sections are heavily dotted, while others are almost entirely free from delinquents. Shaw (1929) has shown in his excellent study that disintegrating areas have the highest delinquency rates, that in large cities these areas are located near the business and heavy industrial sections, that the delinquency rate decreases in proportion to the distance from the center of the city; and that there is a definite correlation with poverty, overcrowding and absence of recreation centers. Plant (1930) gave a brilliant account of the effects upon children of crowded living conditions, which he summed up as follows:

> Children living in large families in crowded quarters (and neighborhoods) have presented to us certain traits which run through much of the entire group. Those which seem very common, very fundamental and reasonably to be ascribed to crowding are five: (1) Difficulty in developing a self-sufficient entity or personality. (2) Destruction of illusions about other people—with a consequent difficulty in building heroes and a real personal idealism. (3) Destruction of illusions about sex, with a concomitant factor that the child grows to value the physical sexual life *per se* rather than as a symbol of idiomatic relationships. (4) A "mental strain"—a constant wear and tear from constantly having to "get along" with other people. (5) Failure in developing a habit of objectification of self or those phenomena impinging upon the self.

THE CONSTITUTIONAL FACTOR.—While the physical, intellectual, emotional and situational factors are accessible to direct and concrete observation, the concept of constitution has remained an abstraction and has not even been clearly and uniformly defined as such. This seeming difficulty is perhaps the greatest tribute to the uniqueness of each human individual. In the absence of a clear-cut definition, we might say generally that "constitution" is that which a child has inherited from his parents plus that which he brings with him into the world as an unduplicated experiment of nature, an individual *sui generis*. Only on this basis can it be explained that different children react differently to the same environment. We know that inherent potentialities differ with regard to attainable size, configuration of the body, physiognomy, and other characteristics. We are forced to assume that they also differ with regard to personality difficulties and behavior tendencies, over and above the inroads made on a child by all the factors discussed above; even some of those, notably the factor of innate intellectual endowment, can be ascribed to "constitution." Previous attempts to judge constitutional weakness from so-called stigmata of degeneration have been as fruitless as later efforts to single out a neurotic or neuropathic constitution or the habit of speaking glibly of constitutional inferiority or immaturity.

FUSION OF FACTORS.—In the clinical study of any child, with or without behavior difficulties, none of the motivating factors can be considered alone, detached from the others and, above all, detached from the child. They are all fused in a particular manner. It is this fusion, understood only in terms of the child's biography, which brings about the constellation of the moment in a developing integrated person. Constitutional uniqueness, health, intelligence, environment, and type of emotional response melt into a oneness, the child under consideration. That is why even the finest statistical calculations regarding this or that factor can never be applied diagnostically, prognostically or etiologically to the next child who comes along.

Manifestations of Children's Behavior Disorders

In accordance with the great manifoldness of causative factors and the almost limitless possibility of their combinations, the symptoms, manifestations, or expressions of disordered behavior are very numerous, indeed. This becomes especially clear if one considers the many functions which can be impaired: "intelligence," memory, judgment, thinking, emotional responsiveness, the routine performances connected with food intake, elimination and sleep, motility, habit formation, attitudes toward parents, siblings, teachers and playmates, physical health, attitude toward health, sense of security, acquisition of self-dependence, regularity of school attendance, truthfulness, respect for property rights, sexual adjustment, speech, ability to comprehend, reading, numerical and mechanical abilities, and many other items. The differences in degree cannot be emphasized enough; there is a wide range from very severe and sometimes ominous illness affecting all spheres and phases of performance to minor and minimal, often only temporary, deviations from "normal" activity. It is well to remember that perfection is not a human attribute. Just as even the healthiest child is subject to an occasional cold, sore throat or bruise, so can—and does—every child in the course of his first decade and a half of life at times display forms of behavior which are comprised under the heading of behavior disorders. A sense of proportion and relativity is therefore indispensable in the consideration of complaints about the behavior of individual children. The common minor anomalies have been well designated by Thom (1927) as the "everyday problems of the everyday child."

Behavior Disorders Forming Essential Features or Sequels of Physical Illness.—This group is composed of those disorders which are intimately connected wtih permanent or transient damage to the body or selected organs or organ systems.

IRREVERSIBLE STRUCTURAL DAMAGE TO THE CENTRAL NERVOUS SYSTEM.—Pathologic changes of the cerebral tissues are mostly allied with a loss, deficit or arrest of the mental functions. Congenital malformations of the brain result in slow and insufficient intellectual development and in those personality disorders which go with the existing somatic handicaps (paralyses, contractures, abnormal motility, blindness, deafness). The prototypes are: porencephaly—a lack of cerebral substance, "a hole in the brain"; microcephaly—unusual smallness of the brain; hydrocephalus—accumulation of an abnormally large quantity of cerebrospinal fluid in the ventricles or in the subarachnoid space; amaurotic family idiocy or Tay-Sachs disease—a widespread degenerative process affecting the ganglion cells of the entire central nervous system;

tuberous sclerosis or Bourneville's disease—very rare, characterized by multiple sclerotic areas of the cortex and tumors of various internal organs. Mongolism also belongs in this group, even though the pathologic brain condition is not as unequivocally established as in the other diseases; it is recognized from a peculiar Mongoloid physiognomy, certain anomalies affecting chiefly the shape of the head, the eyes, the tongue and the extremities, considerable hypotonia of the muscles, and a marked defect in the mental development (Brousseau, 1928).

Acquired brain lesions may affect the child in the sense of complete or partial standstill of mental growth, a dropping out of functions already possessed, or a general change of emotional, adaptive, and social reactivity ("change of personality"), with or without intellectual impairment. In acute illness, there may be a varying degree of reduction of consciousness, ranging from mild drowsiness and delirium to profound coma. In the chronic diseases, memory, judgment, comprehension, and the capacity for verbal communication may suffer. Among the sequels of brain disease are intellectual inadequacy, epileptiform conditions, faulty utilization of experience, confusional states, and antisocial trends.

Brain tumor, brain abscess, meningitis, encephalitis, juvenile paresis, and cerebral trauma are the main such conditions affecting personality development and behavior. Epidemic or lethargic encephalitis was plentiful in the wake of the grippe epidemic during the latter part of the First World War. Jelliffe (1927) stated: "In the monumental strides made by neuropsychiatry during the past ten years no single advance has approached in importance that made through the study of epidemic encephalitis. No individual group of diseased reactions has been as widely reported upon, as intensively studied, nor as far reaching in modifying the entire foundations of neuropsychiatry in general." Its clinical manifestations are polymorphous and almost unlimited. Thiele (1926) distinguished three types of behavior disorders following this disease: (1) pathogenic, process-determined character changes; (2) reaction tendencies which had been a part of the patient's original personality make-up, made dormant by adequate training, and becoming activated under the influence of the disease; (3) reactive misbehavior arising from a response to being ill and the closely associated changes in the living conditions and in the attitudes of the environment. A good general orientation about the behavior disorders connected with, and resulting from, this disease is offered by Hohman (1922) and by Bond and Appel (1931). Symptoms and sequels similar to those of the epidemic form can also be brought about by sporadic incidents and cases of encephalitis associated with infectious diseases (measles, chicken pox) and with lead poisoning.

Juvenile paresis is a disease based on congenital syphilis and the invasion of the brain by spirochetes. The principal features of the mental disturbance consist of progressive intellectual deterioration, impairment of comprehension, memory and judgment, habit disorganization, and emotional instability. Aside from this "simple" form, some children display the "expansive" form with delusions of grandeur or a "depressive" form. The monograph by Menninger (1936) gives a thorough account of the disease and the most complete bibliography to be found anywhere.

Cerebral trauma may be due to antenatal injuries about which little is known except for those which lead to miscarriage, stillbirth or early death, birth injuries or postnatal head injuries. Schroeder (1929) found distractibility and overactivity to be the characteristic behavior traits in the birth injuries. Figures about the frequency and degree of intellectual retardation vary in the reports from different investigators, because the neurological handicaps make an exact and sometimes even an approximate estimation exceedingly difficult. It may be said, however, that the last two decades have brought considerable hope to birth-injured children, who are now much better understood and trained (Rogers and Thomas, 1935; Lord, 1937). Doll, Phelps, and Melcher (1932) have published a thorough study of mental deficiency due to birth injury. The most fascinating and informative presentation of the problem comes from Carlson (1941), who autobiographically describes his ascendency from a birth-injured cripple to a respected specialist in the very field of his own disease; his book gives an excellent illustration of the problems met and presented by such children.

The main results of head injuries sustained during childhood were reported by Bailey (1903) as irritability, temper tantrums, boisterousness, fighting, and unmanageableness, and by Kasanin (1929) as marked emotional instability, antisocial trends, headaches, and inability to stand heat and closed-in places.

TRANSITORY CEREBRAL INVOLVEMENT.—Another set of psychopathologic disorders, also bound to somatic illness, is more transient and depends on temporary metabolic and toxic brain involvement rather than on more or less irreparable tissue alterations. Impairment of consciousness is the outstanding feature. It may appear as delirium with confusion, disorientation, fear and hallucinations, as stupor, coma, or febrile convulsions. Chorea also belongs in this group, though the behavior picture consists largely of increased sensitiveness and irritability. Maniclike excitements and other brief psychotic episodes have been observed in rare instances (Diefendorf, 1912; Davies and Richards, 1931).

THE ENDOCRINOPATHIES.—Dysfunctions of the glands of internal secretion are associated with certain physical anomalies and behavior deviations. Congenital deficiency of thyroid secretion in the form of cretinism goes with a general stunting of growth and mental development. Hyperthyroidism, encountered at the age of pubescence, is accompanied by sensitiveness, excitability, and irritability. Fröhlich's syndrome, a pituitary disorder, produces general intellectual and emotional immaturity. Suprarenal disorders result in precocious sexual development.

Behavior Disorders Expressing Themselves in the Form of Involuntary Part-Dysfunctions.—A considerable and clinically conspicuous portion of the psychopathology of infancy and childhood is made up of localized functional disturbances seemingly limited to a specific organ or organ system, which is itself healthy in the sense of morphology and physiology. The disorder is an involuntary part-manifestation of the not harmoniously functioning totality of the organism, hence it is a disorder of personality and behavior. Singly, the same symptom may be due either to structural pathology ("organic"), to personal pathology ("functional"), or to a fusion of both. Differentiation depends on a thorough investigation of both physical condition and personality.

The relationship between personality and somatic part-dysfunction has been recognized for a long time. It has been less easy to understand the type of linkage and the reason why a particular organ has been selected in the individual instance. A number of explanations has been attempted. The possibility of intensification and automatization of visceral participation in emotional reactions has been mentioned above. Anton (1906) and Peritz (1919) spoke of partial infantilism, denoting that certain organs did not keep pace with the general evolution of the individual. Adler (1907) thought in terms of constitutional organ inferiority; the individual, besides his verbal and gestural language, has an "organ vocabulary" of his own, which is an expression of his struggle to overcome his organ inferiority and furnishes a clue to the understanding of the choice of his neurotic symptoms. According to the Pavlovian school (Pavlov, 1928), the organ selection depends on the specific mode of conditioning which in a given person gives rise to behavior such as vomiting, tics, or enuresis as a response to certain situations. Others speak of substitution of emotional difficulties through somatic symptoms. Substitution with no conscious association of the symptom with a "forgotten" emotionally loaded situation has been termed conversion, a process by which sums of emotion become transformed into physical manifestations. The fusion of personal and organic pathology has in recent years received special attention by an increasing group of physicians who have set out to build up a body of what is called "psychosomatic medicine."

Almost every organ system may lend itself for the somatic part-expression of emotional difficulties. The central nervous system may respond with headaches, the circulatory system with blushing, pallor or palpitations, the digestive apparatus with anorexia, constipation, vomiting, or encopresis, the urinary system with enuresis, the striped-muscle system with tics, or general motor restlessness. Enuresis, encopresis, and tics may serve as examples.

ENURESIS.—Involuntary nocturnal or diurnal passage of urine is usually cited as a typical paradigm of part-dysfunctions of a psychogenic character. An enormous bibliography has accumulated. From 10% to at the most 30% of all cases were found to result from physical causes. The others have their origin in faulty training and in personality features of immaturity, instability, or insecurity. However, we cannot get away from the observed fact that enuresis is sometimes an isolated habit disorder in otherwise well-adjusted children. Enuresis is a frequent manifestation of early remonstrance; it has been found at times to be an expression of jealousy or spite. Attempts have been made to differentiate between a number of "personality traits" of enuretic children. Bissell (as early as 1892) divided them into two groups: those who are active and oversensitive, and those who are slow and phlegmatic. Behm (1923) had three groups: degenerated, phlegmatic, and excitable. Pototzky (1924) had four types: (1) the spiteful-uninhibited children, who wet themselves intentionally to tease the parents and teachers; (2) the shy-inhibited children whose wetting is an expression of fearfulness; (3) the restless, absentminded children, who are so easily distracted that they forget their urinary needs; (4) the indifferent children, who are not sufficiently concerned to acquire proper urinary control.

ENCOPRESIS.—Involuntary defecation of a nonorganic nature is less common than enuresis. Thom (1929, p. 102) said: "One can only say that these cases call for a careful psychiatric examination by the best qualified person available. And it will often test all his skill and ingenuity to understand the mental processes at work that result in such conduct." Shirley (1938) reviewed 70 cases; 33 of those had IQ of more than 80. Exceptionally poor home environment and parental over-solicitude were frequent findings. For the rest, the etiologic factors varied with the individual children.

TICS.—Tics or habit spasms are sudden, quick, involuntary, and repetitious movements of circumscribed muscle groups, serving no apparent purpose. Blinking, grimacing, head shaking, clearing the throat, sniffing, and jerking the shoulders are the forms observed most frequently. Tics may be residuals of intelligible actions, originating as defensive movements against some constant irritations, such as a tight cap, tight suspenders, long hair coming down in front of the eyes, poorly fitting eyeglasses, or an itching skin disease. Imitation of others also plays a part in the etiology. The habit becomes detached from its primary purpose and is no longer useful in the economy of motility. This detachment or automatization takes place in a setting of environmental and emotional stress. The classical monograph by Meige and Feindel (1902) is still the best presentation of the subject.

Behavior Disorders Expressing Themselves Clearly as Whole-Dysfunctions of the Individual.—Psychologically uninformed people find it sometimes difficult to believe that organ dysfunctions, such as constipation, vomiting, enuresis, or tics, can represent "behavior." There is no such difficulty in connection with the largest group of children's behavior problems, which appear obviously and unmistakably as personal performances. They comprise a wide range and variety of deviations from acceptable "average" behavior in all spheres of cognition, conation, and affect. At the risk of being repetitious, it is well to emphasize that there is considerable fluctuation between "normal" and outright psychopathologic behavior of children. The single deviation is relatively negligible or relatively severe according to the extent to which it interferes with the child's own adjustment and well-being, the family's attitude toward the child, and the established standards of our culture and social order. A single instance of "stealing" a few cherries from the neighbor's yard differs essentially from habitual pilfering from stores. A "white lie" of a child driven into a corner and anticipating excessive punishment differs fundamentally from false accusations leading to the arrest and trial of an innocent person. Occasional daydreaming as a spare time pleasure does not have the serious connotations of obsessive preoccupations affecting a child's scholastic and social performances.

The following review of the outstanding problems must of necessity be brief and summary. Wherever possible, the reader will be referred to the best available sources in the literature.

UNHEALTHY EMOTIONAL RESPONSES.—Reactions of jealousy, anger, and fear are the commonest forms of overt emotional disorders of children.

The two principal sources of jealousy are the arrival of a new baby and the practice of contrasting siblings with one another. Its manifestations are manifold; they are designed to center parental attention on the jealous child (Foster, 1927; Levy, 1937a).

Vigorous anger and resentment are expressed by infants in the form of breathholding spells, later through temper tantrums, and still later less explosively through sullenness and crossness. Children have a tendency to react more drastically than adults; this is true even of physical happenings. A child vomits much more readily when ill or as a result of carsickness; the chill ushering in a febrile disease may in children assume the proportion of a full-fledged convulsion. This tendency to explosiveness shows itself particularly in the outbursts of anger. The gradual transition from breathholding with loss of consciousness, sometimes even associated with convulsive phenomena, to the motor and vocal violence of tantrums, and from those to less vigorous pouting, is a very instructive example of the gradually decreasing propensity for emotional explosiveness (Goodenough, 1931).

Fearfulness is not an inherent characteristic of a normal and well-trained child. He learns to recognize real dangers and to avoid them cautiously. Fear of imagined perils is acquired through faulty education and parental example. Hagman (1932) found a close correlation between the fears of preschool children and fears expressed by their mothers. Jersild, Markey, and Jersild (1933) learned that only a negligible number of children had real experiences with regard to objects or situations feared, such as animals, the dark, strangers, or being alone, and of course no experiences, other than threats or frightening stories, with ghosts, kidnappers, and the like.

Full-fledged anxiety attacks are not so uncommon in children as the sparseness of literature would seem to indicate. These occur mostly in the evening or at night and are characterized by sudden terror, palpitations, and acute fear of death. They often begin after an operation, especially one with ether anaesthesia (Richards, 1932, p. 189; Langford, 1937).

Deep-rooted fear may find an outlet at a time when the child is, as it were, caught off his guard. It then is expressed in the form of nightmares and night terrors, which require a study of the fearful dream contents, the child's diurnal preoccupations and fantasies, the environmental constellation, physical condition, and specific events and experiences which may have a more or less direct bearing on the child's emotional difficulties, responsible for the sleep disorder (Strauch, 1919).

DISORDERS OF VERBAL AND GRAPHIC EXPRESSION AND COMPREHENSION.—It is a matter of common observation that inherent intellectual inadequacy ("mental deficiency") is associated with corresponding difficulties in the acquisition of verbal tools for symbol formation and communication. Late onset of speech is followed by deficiencies in both active and passive vocabulary, and in the ability to learn graphic symbolization through reading and writing. This difficulty is, roughly speaking, proportionate to the degree of the intellectual defect. Speech does not only begin at a later age than is usual but articulation, enunciation, grammatical construction, ease of expression and the capacity for the grasp and use of abstractions is impaired in varying degrees.

The development of speech suffers also in cases of certain physical handicaps. The deaf child lacks the usual avenue for receiving, through audition, the verbal symbols common in his environment. He has the choice between mutism and invention of his own verbal representations ("idioglossia"). Neurological diseases affecting the mechanics of the speech apparatus may seriously affect the intelligibility of a child's linguistic performance.

Late onset of speech and faulty articulation, especially in the sense of "baby talk" or retention of an earlier mode of enunciation, occur also in children of normal health and intelligence.

Stuttering is speech of a halting, hesitating nature, with repetition of the initial sounds of a word or sentence. Most stutterers experience no difficulty when they sing or whisper. It has been estimated that nearly a quarter of a million children in the United States stutter. Boys are much more frequently affected than girls; this is also true of the other disorders of speech. In many children, stuttering is associated with a history of changed handedness or with "split laterality." There are many theories about the etiology. It is now commonly agreed that it is the manifestation of a personality disorder which, in turn, creates further emotional problems because of self-consciousness and fear of speaking in anticipation of possible embarrassment. A thoroughgoing discussion of the subject from many angles will be found in the symposium edited by West (1931). Other helpful presentations are those by Bluemel (1930), Travis (1931), Brown (1933), and Orton (1937).

Even though there is consensus about the emotional background of stuttering, no uniform definition of the basic nature of this background exists. This is also true of the so-called specific disabilities, of which reading disability (dyslexia, congenital word-blindness) has received by far the greatest attention. The others are disabilities in writing, spelling, arithmetic, and musical appreciation.

Since Hinshelwood (1917), it has become increasingly clear that many children of normal or even superior intelligence experience an isolated difficulty in learning how to identify written or printed verbal symbols. This condition, like stuttering, is predominant in boys and has correlations with the handedness-eyedness question. Like stuttering, it gives rise to added emotional distress because of the experience of failure not explicable to the child or to the environment which does not understand his handicap. Specific reading disability is often connected with difficulty in writing and spelling and with a tendency to reversal of letters and words in reading and writing ("strephosymbolia"). Methods have been devised to diagnose and measure through reading indices the degree of a child's dyslexia, and special methods of remedial reading instruction have been worked out (Monroe, 1932; Gates, 1935; Betts, 1936).

Congenital word-deafness is a very rare condition characterized by the inability of otherwise intelligent children to comprehend the meaning of words heard. Deafness in the ordinary sense is not present. Some of these children were found by Ewing (1930) to be unable to perceive sounds of a frequency above 256 double vibrations. The patients communicate well through gestures but have no understanding of verbal symbols.

HABITUAL MANIPULATIONS OF THE BODY.—No other culture of the past or present has attributed so much significance to certain habits of children as does our own civilization. This fact indicates on the one hand the laudable desire to record, observe and explain behavior in whichever form it is noted, but on the other hand often furnishes an additional source of parental worry and anxiety. We have in mind motor habits which consist of frequent repetitions of movements which serve no other purpose than that of providing pleasure for the indulging person. Some of them, such as head banging or noisy grinding of the teeth, may indeed become quite disturbing. Some were found to have hedonic implications similar to masturbatory gratification. Olson (1929) divided these "nervous habits" into oral, nasal, manual, hirsutal, aural, irritational (scratching), ocular, genital, and facial. Thumb-sucking and nail biting are the most frequent complaints. Both have been regarded as far more serious than they really are. That the tide of overemphasis of these habits is receding, is best indicated by more recent publications, such as the one by Langford (1939).

ANTISOCIAL BEHAVIOR.—Inasmuch as the subject of delinquent behavior is fully discussed in the following chapter by Lowrey, it is not necessary to enlarge upon it in this place. The present attitude toward juvenile delinquency is one of the most eloquent examples of the shift of public and professional sentiment from impersonal retaliatory "punishment" to interest in the individual child, the motives of his difficulties and steps toward his rehabilitation. Even in this reference to another chapter, the pioneering work of Healy (1915), his life-long effort to understand and treat the antisocial behavior of children, and his profound influence on the establishment and trends of modern juvenile courts must at least be mentioned.

OVERT SEXUAL BEHAVIOR.—In our culture every kind of overt sex behavior of children is immediately viewed as a behavior disorder. If, as in masturbation, no other person is involved, the complaint is usually made to physicians, psychologists, or psychiatrists. If the sexual act implicates more than one person, the performance is classed with the delinquencies. Among the delinquency cases disposed of by 88 courts in the United States in 1930, a total of 2% of the boys and not less than 21% of the girls were arraigned because of sex offenses, mostly heterosexual. The age distribution among children under 14 years was as follows:

Age	Boys %	Girls %
Under 10 years............	2	11
10–11 years............	1	9
12–13 years............	1	15

The commonest complaint with regard to children's sexual performances is that of masturbation. Inquiries made by Exner (1915) and Davis (1929) showed that between 60% and 90% of college-trained men and women remembered having practiced masturbation in their early years. This fact alone should suffice to make one refrain from attaching psychopathologic significance to the act itself. It is safe to say that manipulation of the genitals often does not even have definite sexual connotations in young children beyond the pleasurable sensations common to all other habitual manipulations of the body. Some investigators have reversed this sequence and decided that thumb-sucking and nail biting are masturbatory equivalents. The habit may, as it frequently does, be a transitory type of sexual gratification. It becomes disturbing if it is done in excess, is accompanied by too overpowering fantasies and, above all, if unwarranted prophecies of illness and insanity upset a child's security and outlook into the future (Malamud and Palmer, 1932).

Heterosexual behavior ranges all the way from attachments and "crushes" and naïve courting, "peeping," verbal annoyances, inspection and manual exploration of the genitals of the opposite sex, exhibitionism, and "petting" to sexual intercourse, assault and infantile prostitution. Seduction by irresponsible adults, low standards of housing and intelligence, loose sex behavior in the home and in the neighborhood are some of the factors in the etiology of the serious forms of sexual misconduct, to which instances of incest between siblings must be added as occurrences less rare than is usually believed.

Of homosexual practices among children, that of fellatio forms the most frequent complaint brought to the attention of courts and clinics and involving boys sometimes as young as six or seven years of age. Most of them come from the lowest type of home standards.

The book by Moll (1909), though antiquated and often anecdotal, is still the most comprehensive presentation of the "sex life of children" and its anomalies.

ATTACK DISORDERS.—Children are subject much more frequently than adults to sudden and brief events of first magnitude, "attacks" or "spells," which for a few seconds, minutes or hours involve their total reactivity and exclude them from their usual adaptations and participations. Anxiety attacks have been mentioned before. Temper tantrums, breath-holding spells and night terrors may also be viewed as attack disorders.

The classical picture of attack disorder, known commonly as epilepsy, finds special consideration in this book in a chapter on "Seizure States" by Lennox (see Chapter 31) and will therefore not be dealt with here.

Narcolepsy is a condition characterized by diurnal attacks of sleep lasting about 10 or 15 minutes and initiated by a feeling of drowsiness and irresistible fatigue. It is often associated with cataplexy, a sudden loss of muscle tone precipitated by strong emotions. Though sometimes a sequel of encephalitis or other brain disease, the "genuine" or "idiopathic" form is found in children in whom a cerebral disorder cannot be demonstrated (Adie, 1926; Weech, 1926).

Fainting spells are known to occur in children under emotional stress, especially at the sight of blood and in the excitements of graduation and confirmation exercises. Those children show evidence of inadequate balance of the autonomic nervous system (Stier, 1920).

MINOR PSYCHOSES.—In adult psychiatry, a number of reaction sets are comprised under the general heading of minor psychoses or psychoneuroses, to indicate that, though they represent marked disturbances of personal functioning, they are less sweeping than the psychoses and the patients manage to retain their contact with the environment. The usual subdivisions are: Neurasthenia, psychasthenia, hysteria, hypochondriasis, and anxiety neurosis. Some of these headings can hardly be applied to children; this is particularly true of neurasthenia, which is about the vaguest of all diagnostic concepts. Louttit (1936, p. 505) says rightly: "Guthrie's (1909) statement, to the effect that children may be highly neurasthenic from an early age, must be taken with caution. It is true only if all varieties of behavior problems are subsumed under the term."

Psychasthenia refers to compulsive thinking and acting in a manner which is recognized as irrational and serves no useful purpose. The patient cannot shake off those obtrusive ideas in spite of his awareness of their absurdity. The condition has also been designated as "obsessive-ruminative tension states." The ideational contents are usually divided into obsessive thoughts, doubts and phobias. The commonest obsessions and compulsions of children are fear of contamination with frequent hand washing, fear of sickness, and the urge to do things in a certain way only. The obsessive child is mostly overconscientious, shy, pedantic, punctual, painstakingly addicted to the minutest orderliness, perfectionistic in the evaluation of his own performances (Bender and Schilder, 1940).

Hypochondriasis is a chronic complaint habit. Imitation of observed adult patterns, desire to retain privileges derived during a period of actual illness, overwork with no recreational outlets, parental oversolicitude, and medical mismanagement may all contribute to the development of somatic complaints on a psychogenic basis. The feeling of sickness may seriously interfere with the child's adaptations to the demands of everyday life and create a state of chronic invalidism (Richards, 1923, 1941; Levy, 1932; Kanner, 1937).

Much was written in former years about childhood hysteria. This is largely due to the fact that the term was used indiscriminately to include almost every type of behavior disorder. True hysterical disorders, according to Adolf Meyer (unpublished lectures to students), "can be shown to be substitutions which follow the type of more or less unconscious self-suggestion, i.e., a suppression or repression of incompatible experiences, with substitutive reactions, the connection of which tends to be 'forgotten' and which, themselves, are often unheeded or accepted with indifference and complacency, or with actual satisfaction, but great emotional lability." If these criteria are applied, hysteria in children is rather rare in this country at the present time. The most frequently observed hysterical symptoms in children are "functional" blindness, deafness, and paralysis of a limb.

MAJOR PSYCHOSES.—The two prototypes of not demonstrably cerebrogenic psychoses are schizophrenia and manic-depressive psychoses. The latter of these is almost nonexistent before the age of puberty. A comprehensive review, with case illustrations, of the "functional" (not definitely organic) psychoses in childhood was published by Kasanin and Kaufman (1929).

Childhood schizophrenia, though also rare, has been diagnosed often enough to create a considerable bibliography. The symptomatology in older children approximates that of adult patients. In smaller children the symptoms are fewer and simpler. The outstanding features are seclusiveness, loss of interest in the surroundings, disturbance of affective contact with people, emotional blunting, reversion to primitive forms of behavior, negativism, mannerism, bizarre manner of thinking and speaking, sensitivity to comment and criticism, and physical inactivity. The schizophrenic development is sometimes preceded by grotesquely obsessive behavior (Potter, 1933; Bradley, 1941).

Therapeutic Principles

Even this brief and little more than enumerative outline undoubtedly suffices to demonstrate the heterogeneity of children's behavior disorders. Treatment, therefore, must vary with the individual child and his problems. There are surprisingly few organized presentations of the therapeutic principles involved. By far the best and most comprehensive is contained in the book by Rogers (1939), who discusses the indications, values, and results of treatment through dealing with the individual, modification of his environment, and change of environment.

Treatment of behavior disorders may be defined as the sum total of efforts made in behalf of the adjustment of a child who presents any form of personality difficulty. This usually requires a number of well-defined steps.

Realizing that we deal with a maladjusted person rather than merely with a detached complaint or symptom, it is necessary to establish in the child a condition of security, comfort, and well-being. Any existing physical disorders should be remedied, regardless of whether or not they are directly related to the problem of behavior. The child needs an opportunity to discuss his problems frankly and without fear of ridicule and criticism. The play methods, which we have previously described from the point of view of their investigative advantages, offer at the same time great curative possibilities, by giving vent ("release," Levy, 1939) to the child's emotions, making it possible to relate himself to the therapist (Allen, 1937) and to his life situation (Conn, 1939a), and generally helping him to gain insight and giving him a chance to redirect a hitherto misdirected pattern tendency.

Family collaboration is frequently an indispensable part of the treatment. Not only will it be necessary to influence the parents' modes of managing and training the child, but also to help them with their own personal problems and attitudes which have caused or contributed to the child's difficulties ("attitude therapy").

A considerable part of the treatment depends on community facilities. Certain feebleminded, delinquent, epileptic and psychotic children require institutional care. Certain dependent, neglected, or rejected children need foster home care. The cooperation of the school becomes paramount when grade readjustment of scholastically misplaced children is essential. Often the child is helped when his specific problems and needs are explained to an understanding teacher. Much benefit can be derived from working with recreational agencies. Above all, in many instances the social workers of relief and case work agencies and clinics can render inestimable and, at times, indispensable assistance.

BIBLIOGRAPHY

ACKERSON, L. 1931. Children's behavior problems. Chicago: University Chicago Press.
ADIE, W. J. 1926. Idiopathic narcolepsy: a disease sui generis. *Brain, 49,* 257–306.

ADLER, A.   1907.   Studie über die Minderwertigkeit von Organen.   Berlin: Urban & Schwarzenberg.
——   1924.   The practice and theory of individual psychology.   New York: Harcourt, Brace.
ALLEN, F. H.   1934.   Therapeutic work with children: statement of point of view. *Amer. J. Orthopsychiat.*, *4*, 193–202.
——   1937.   Some therapeutic principles applicable to psychiatric work with children. *Amer. J. Psychiat.*, *94*, 671–680.
——   1939.   Trends in therapy: participation in therapy. *Amer. J. Orthopsychiat.*, *9*, 737–742.
ANTON, G.   1906.   Über Formen und Ursachen des Infantilismus. *Münch. med. Wschr.*, *53*, 1458–1460.
BAILEY, P.   1903.   Fracture at the base of the skull; neurological and medicolegal considerations. *Med. News, N. Y.*, *82*, 918–926.
BEHM, K.   1923.   Bettnässertypen und ihre Behandlung. *Z. Gesundheitsfürsorge u. Schulgesundheitspflege*, *36*, 321–329.
BENDER, L., & SCHILDER, P.   1940.   Impulsions: a specific disorder of the behavior of children. *Arch. Neurol. Psychiat., Chicago*, *44*, 990–1008.
BENDER, L., & WOLTMANN, A. G.   1936.   Use of puppet shows as psychotherapeutic method for behavior problems in children. *Amer. J. Orthopsychiat.*, *6*, 341–354.
BENJAMIN, E.   1930.   Grundlagen und Entwicklungsgeschichte der kindlichen Neurose.   Leipzig: Thieme.
——   1941.   The period of resistance in early childhood. *J. Pediat.*, *18*, 659–669.
BETTS, E. A.   1936.   The prevention and correction of reading difficulties.   Evanston, Ill.: Row, Peterson.
BISSELL, J. B.   1892.   Daytime enuresis in children. *Med. Rec., N. Y.*, *42*, 697.
BLATZ, W. E., & BOTT, E. A.   1927.   Studies in mental hygiene of children. *Pedag. Sem.*, *34*, 552–582.
BLUEMEL, C. S.   1930.   Mental aspects of stammering.   Baltimore: Williams & Wilkins.
BOND, E. D., & APPEL, K. E.   1931.   The treatment of behavior disorders following encephalitis.   New York: Commonwealth Fund.
BRADLEY, C.   1937.   Definition of childhood in psychiatric literature. *Amer. J. Psychiat.*, *94*, 33–36.
——   1941.   Schizophrenia in childhood.   New York: Macmillan.
BRAGMAN, L. J.   1931.   Thumbsucking and other auto-erotic tendencies in children, as portrayed in art. *J. nerv. ment. Dis.*, *74*, 708–709.
BROUSSEAU, K.   1928.   Mongolism. A study of the physical and mental characteristics of Mongolian imbeciles.   (Rev. by G. Brainerd.)   Baltimore: Williams & Wilkins.
BROWN, F. W.   1933.   Personality integration as the essential factor in the permanent cure of stuttering. *Ment. Hyg., N. Y.*, *17*, 266–277.
BROWN, S., POLLOCK, H. M., POTTER, H. W., & COHEN, D. W.   1937.   Outline for the psychiatric classification of problem children.   Utica, N. Y.: State Hospitals Press.
BUSEMANN, A.   1928.   Über das sogenannte "erste Trotzalter" des Kindes. *Z. pädag. Psychol.*, *29*, 42–49.
CAMERON, H. C.   1933.   The nervous child at school.   London: Oxford University Press.
CAMPBELL, A. A.   1934.   The personality adjustment of only children. *Psychol. Bull.*, *31*, 193–203.
CARLSON, E. R.   1941.   Born that way.   New York: John Day.
CHOBOT, R., SPADAVECCHIA, R., & DE SANCTIS, R. M.   1939.   Intelligence rating and emotional pattern of allergic children. *Amer. J. Dis. Child.*, *57*, 831–837.
CLARK, L. P.   1933.   The nature and treatment of amentia.   London: Bailliere, Tindall & Cox.
CLARKE, E. K., & JENSEN, R. A.   1941.   Integration of psychiatric teaching with pediatrics. *J. Pediat.*, *18*, 121–127.
CONN, J. H.   1939a.   The child reveals himself through play. *Ment. Hyg., N. Y.*, *23*, 49–69.
——   1939b.   The play interview, a method of studying children's attitudes. *Amer. J. Dis. Child.*, *58*, 1199–1214.
COSACK, H.   1933.   Psychische Pubertätssymptome und Schizophrenie. *Allg. Z. Psychiat.*, *99*, 51–83.

DAVIES, E., & RICHARDS, T. W. 1931. The psychological manifestations of post-choreic conditions as shown in five case studies. *Psychol. Clin., 20,* 129–153.

DAVIS, K. B. 1929. Factors in the sex life of twenty-two hundred women. New York: Harper.

DE SANCTIS, S. 1925. Neuropsichiatria infantile. Rome: Stock.

DESPERT, J. L. 1938. Emotional problems in children. Utica, N. Y.: State Hospitals Press.

—— 1940. Thinking in schizophrenic children and in children of preschool age. *Amer. J. Psychiat., 97,* 189–213.

DIEFENDORF, A. R. 1912. Mental symptoms of acute chorea. *J. nerv. ment. Dis., 39,* 161–172.

DOLL, E. A., PHELPS, W. N., & MELCHER, R. T. 1932. Mental deficiency due to birth injury. New York: Macmillan.

EWING, A. W. G. 1930. Aphasia in children. London: Oxford University Press.

EXNER, M. J. 1915. Problems and principles of sex education: a study of 948 college men. New York: Association Press.

FORMAN, J. 1939. Importance of mental hygiene in management of the allergic child. *Ohio St. med. J., 35,* 747–749.

FOSTER, S. 1927. A study of the personality make-up and social setting of fifty jealous children. *Ment. Hyg., N. Y., 11,* 53–77.

FREUD, A. 1925. Introduction to the technic of child analysis. (Trans. by L. P. Clark.) *Nerv. ment. Dis. Monogr.,* 1928, No. 48.

—— 1931. Psychoanalysis of the child. In Murchison, C., *Handbook of child psychology.* Worcester, Mass.: Clark University Press. Pp. 555–567.

FREUD, S. 1905. Three contributions to the theory of sex. In *The basic writings of Sigmund Freud.* (Trans. and ed. by A. A. Brill.) New York: Modern Library, 1938.

—— 1909. Analysis of a phobia in a five year old boy. In *Collected papers.* Vol. 3. London: Hogarth, 1925.

GATES, A. I. 1935. The improvement of reading. A program of diagnostic and remedial methods. New York: Macmillan.

GOODENOUGH, F. 1931. Anger in young children. Minneapolis: University Minn. Press.

GOODENOUGH, F., & LEAHY, A. M. 1927. The effect of certain family relationships upon the development of personality. *J. genet. Psychol., 34,* 45–71.

GUTHRIE, L. J. 1909. Functional nervous disorders in childhood. London: Frowde.

HAGMAN, R. R. 1932. A study of fears of children of pre-school age. *J. exp. Educ., 1,* 110–130.

HEALY, W. 1915. The individual delinquent. Boston: Little, Brown.

HENDERSON, D. K., & GILLESPIE, R. D. 1932. A textbook of psychiatry for students and practitioners. (3rd ed.) London: Oxford University Press.

HETZER, H. 1927. Systematische Dauerbeobachtung über den Verlauf der negativen Phase. *Z. pädag. Psychol., 28,* 80–96.

HINSHELWOOD, J. 1917. Congenital word-blindness. London: Lewis.

HOHMAN, L. B. 1922. Postencephalitic behavior disorders in children. *Johns Hopk. Hosp. Bull., 33,* 372–375.

HOMBURGER, A. 1926. Vorlesungen über Psychopathologie des Kindesalters. Berlin: Springer.

HORNEY, K. 1939. New ways in psychoanalysis. New York: Norton.

HOWARD, F. E., & PATRY, F. L. 1935. Mental health, its principles and practice. New York: Harper.

HUFELAND, C. W. 1797. Die Kunst das menschliche Leben zu verlängern. Jena. (Trans. by E. Wilson. *Art of prolonging life.* Philadelphia: Lindsay & Blakiston, 1870.)

HUG-HELLMUTH, H. 1913. Aus dem Seelenleben des Kindes. Leipzig: Deuticke.

JASPER, H. H., SOLOMON, P., & BRADLEY, C. 1938. Electroencephalographic analyses of behavior problem children. *Amer. J. Psychiat., 95,* 641–658.

JELLIFFE, S. E. 1927. Postencephalitic respiratory disorders. New York: Nervous & Mental Disease Publ.

JERSILD, A. T., MARKEY, F. V., & JERSILD, C. L. 1933. Children's fears, dreams, wishes, daydreams, likes, dislikes, pleasant and unpleasant memories. *Child Develpm. Monogr.,* No. 12.

KANNER, L. 1932. Supplying the psychiatric needs of a pediatric clinic. *Amer. J. Orthopsychiat., 2,* 400–406.

KANNER, L. 1933a. The significance of the complaint factor in child psychiatry. *Amer. J. Psychiat., 90*, 171–182.
—— 1933b. The significance of a pluralistic attitude in the study of human behavior. *J. abnorm. soc. Psychol., 28*, 30–41.
—— 1935. Child psychiatry. Springfield, Ill.: Thomas.
—— 1937. The invalid reaction in children. *J. Pediat., 11*, 341–355.
—— 1939. Infantile sexuality. *J. Pediat., 15*, 583–608.
—— 1941. Early behavior problems as signposts to later maladjustment. *Amer. J. Psychiat., 97*, 1261–1271.
KANNER, L., & LACHMAN, S. E. 1933. The contribution of physical illness to the development of behavior disorders in children. *Ment. Hyg., N. Y., 17*, 605–617.
KASANIN, J. 1929. Personality changes in children following cerebral trauma. *J. nerv. ment. Dis., 69*, 385–406.
KASANIN, J., & KAUFMAN, M. R. 1929. A study of the functional psychoses in childhood. *Amer. J. Psychiat., 86*, 307–384.
KLEIN, M. 1932. Psychoanalysis of children. London: Hogarth.
KLIENEBERGER, O. 1914. Über Pubertät und Psychopathie. *Grenzfr. Nerv.-u. Seelenleb., H. 95.*
KLÜVER, H. 1931. The eidetic child. In Murchison, C., *Handbook of child psychology.* Worcester, Mass.: Clark University Press. Pp. 643–668.
LALLEMAND, C. F. 1836. Des pertes seminales involontaires. Paris: Bechet.
LANGFORD, W. S. 1937. Anxiety attacks in children. *Amer. J. Orthopsychiat., 7*, 210–218.
—— 1939. Thumb and finger sucking in childhood. *Amer. J. Dis. Child., 58*, 1290–1300.
LEVY, D. M. 1932. Body interest in children and hypochondriasis. *Amer. J. Psychiat., 12*, 295–315.
—— 1936. Hostility patterns in sibling rivalry experiments. *Amer. J. Orthopsychiat., 1936*, 183–257.
—— 1937a. Studies in sibling rivalry. *Res. Monogr. Amer. Orthopsychiat. Assn.*, No. 2.
—— 1937b. Primary affect hunger. *Amer. J. Psychiat., 94*, 643–652.
—— 1939. Release therapy. *Amer. J. Orthopsychiat., 9*, 713–736.
LEVY, D. M., & TULCHIN, S. H. 1923. The resistance of infants and children during mental tests. *J. exp. Psychol., 6*, 304–322.
—— 1925. The resistant behavior of infants and children. *J. exp. Psychol., 8*, 209–224.
LEVY, J. 1931. A quantitative study of behavior problems in relation to family constellation. *Amer. J. Psychiat., 87*, 637–654.
LINDNER, S. L. 1879. Das Saugen an den Fingern, Lippen, u.s.w., bei den Kindern. *Jb. Kinderheilk., 14*, 68–91.
LORD, E. E. 1937. Children handicapped by cerebral palsy. New York: Commonwealth Fund.
LOUTTIT, C. M. 1936. Clinical psychology. A handbook of children's behavior problems. New York: Harper.
LOWREY, L. G. 1937. Foreword to Levy, D. M., *Studies in sibling rivalry. Res. Monogr. Amer. Orthopsychiat. Assn.*, No. 2.
LURIE, L. A. 1935. The medical approach to the study of behavior disorders of children. *Amer. J. Psychiat., 91*, 1379–1388.
—— 1937. Conduct disorders of intellectually subnormal children. *Amer. J. Psychiat., 93*, 1025–1035.
MALAMUD, W., & PALMER, G. 1932. The rôle played by masturbation in the causation of mental disturbances. *J. nerv. ment. Dis., 76*, 220–233, 366–379.
MALINOWSKI, B. 1929. The sexual life of savages. New York: Harcourt, Brace.
MEIGE, H., & FEINDEL, E. 1902. Les tics et leur traitement. Paris: Masson.
MENNINGER, W. C. 1936. Juvenile paresis. Baltimore: Williams & Wilkins.
MEYER, A. 1928. The "complaint" as the center of genetic-dynamic and nosological teaching in psychiatry. *New Engl. J. Med., 199*, 360–370.
—— 1929. Monismus als einheitlich-kritisch geordneter Pluralismus. *J. Psychol. Neurol., Lpz. 38*, 71–81.
MOLL, A. 1909. Das Sexualleben des Kindes. Berlin: Walther. (Trans. by E. Paul. *The sexual life of the child.* New York: Macmillan, 1912.)
MONROE, M. 1932. Children who cannot read. An analysis of reading disabilities and the use of diagnostic tests in the instruction of retarded children. Chicago: University Chicago Press.

MYERS, G. C. 1929. Problem parents. *J. juv. Res.*, *13*, 146–149.

NEWELL, H. W. 1934. The psychodynamics of maternal rejection. *Amer. J. Orthopsychiat.*, *4*, 387–401.

ORTON, S. T. 1925. Word-blindness in school children. *Arch. Neurol. Psychiat.*, *Chicago*, *14*, 581–615.

—— 1937. Reading, writing and speech problems of children. New York: Norton.

OSGOOD, W. B., & TRAPP, C. E. 1936. Study of 400 juvenile delinquents; statistical report. *New Engl. J. Med.*, *215*, 623–626.

PAPPENHEIM, M., & GROSS, C. 1914. Die Neurosen und Psychosen des Pubertätsalters. Berlin: Springer.

PAVLOV, I. P. 1928. Lectures on conditional reflexes. (Trans. by H. Gantt.) New York: International Publishers.

PAYNTER, R. H., & BLANCHARD, P. 1929. A study of educational achievement of problem children. New York: Commonwealth Fund.

PERITZ, G. 1919. Der Infantilismus. In Kraus, F., & Brugsch, T., *Spezielle Pathologie und Terapie innerer Krankheiten*. Vol. I. Berlin: Urban & Schwarzenberg. Pp. 681–749.

PLANT, J. S. 1930. Some psychiatric aspects of crowded living conditions. *Amer. J. Psychiat.*, *86*, 849–857.

POTOTZKY, C. 1924. Die diagnostische und therapeutische Differenzierung der Enuresisfälle. *Z. Kinderheilk.*, *37*, 12–23.

POTTER, H. W. 1933. Schizophrenia in children. *Amer. J. Psychiat.*, *89*, 1253–1269.

REYNOLDS, M. M. 1928. Negativism of pre-school children. *Teach. Coll. Contrib. Educ.*, No. 288.

RICHARDS, E. L. 1923. The significance and management of hypochondriacal trends in children. *Ment. Hyg., N. Y.*, *11*, 688–702.

—— 1932. Behavior aspects of child conduct. New York: Macmillan.

—— 1941. Following the hypochondriacal child for a decade. *J. Pediat.*, *18*, 528–537.

ROGERS, C. R. 1939. The clinical treatment of the problem child. Boston: Houghton Mifflin.

ROGERS, G. G., & THOMAS, L. C. 1935. New pathways for children with cerebral palsy. New York: Macmillan.

ROGERSON, C. R. 1939. Play therapy in childhood. London: Oxford University Press.

RUPPERT, H. 1931. Aufbau der Welt des Jugendlichen. Leipzig: Barth.

SACHS, B. 1926. The normal child and how to keep it normal in mind and morals. New York: Hoeber.

SAYLES, M. 1929. The problem child in school. New York: Commonwealth Fund.

SCHILLER, M. 1934. Capillaruntersuchungen bei Schulkindern. *Z. ges. Neurol. Psychiat.*, *151*, 700–717.

SCHROEDER, P. L. 1929. Behavior difficulties in children associated with the results of birth trauma. *J. Amer. med. Assn.*, *92*, 100–104.

SHAW, C. R. 1929. Delinquency areas. A study of the geographic distribution of school truants, juvenile delinquents, and adult offenders in Chicago. Chicago: University Chicago Press.

SHIRLEY, H. F. 1938. Encopresis in children. *J. Pediat.*, *12*, 367–380.

SHIRLEY, H. F., & GREER, I. M. 1940. Environmental and personality problems in the treatment of diabetic children. *J. Pediat.*, *16*, 775–781.

SILVERMAN, B. 1935. The behavior of children from broken homes. *Amer. J. Orthopsychiat.*, *5*, 11–18.

STEVENSON, G. S., & SMITH, G. 1934. Child guidance clinics. New York: Commonwealth Fund.

STIER, E. 1920. Über Ohnmachtsanfälle, besonders bei Kindern. *Dtsch. med. Wschr.*, *46*, 372–375.

STRAUCH, A. 1919. Sleep in children and its disturbances. *Amer. J. Dis. Child.*, *17*, 118–139.

THIELE, R. 1926. Zur Kenntnis der psychischen Residuärzustände nach Encephalitis epidemica bei Kindern und Jugendlichen. Berlin: Karger.

THOM, D. A. 1927. Everyday problems of the everyday child. New York: Appleton-Century.

Tissot, S. A. 1760. De l'onanisme ou Dissertation physique sur les maladies produites par la masturbation. Lausanne: Chapuis.

Travis, L. 1931. Speech pathology. New York: Appleton-Century.

Watson, J. B. 1919. Psychology from the standpoint of a behaviorist. Philadelphia: Lippincott.

—— 1928. Psychological care of infant and child. New York: Norton.

Weech, A. A. 1926. Narcolepsy—a symptom complex. *Amer. J. Dis. Child., 32,* 672–681.

West, R. 1931. A symposium on stuttering (stammering). Madison, Wis.: College Typing Co.

Wexberg, E. 1926. Handbuch der Individualpsychologie. München: Bergmann.

—— 1928. Individualpsychologie. Leipzig: Hirzel.

Wickman, E. K. 1928. Children's behavior and teachers' attitudes. New York: Commonwealth Fund.

Wille, W. 1898. Die Psychosen des Pubertätsalters. Leipzig: Deuticke.

Ziehen, G. T. 1917. Die Geisteskrankheiten des Kindesalters, einschliesslich des Schwachsinns und der psychopathischen Konstitutionen. (2nd ed.) Berlin: Reuther & Reichard, 1926.

Chapter 26

DELINQUENT AND CRIMINAL PERSONALITIES

By LAWSON G. LOWREY, A.M., M.D.

IT IS THE THESIS of this chapter that, despite extensive research and
many ingenious efforts to delimit them, there are no such entities as
"delinquent" or "criminal" personalities. To be sure, there are delinquents and criminals and, naturally, each has a personality, normal or
abnormal, but all attemps to establish a distinctive delinquent or criminal
type have eventually come to naught. It is necessary to review some of
the past efforts and examine them in the light of present-day knowledge
of personality, its evolution, driving forces and relationships to behavior,
whether the latter be social or unsocial.

With this specific orientation it is essential to define certain terms
freely used throughout. These definitions are not necessarily those employed by other writers, nor do they cover all possible variations of usage
and shades of meaning. They are, however, clinically acceptable and
adequately confine the discussion to reasonable and understandable limits.

Definitions

Behavior.—In general terms, behavior is composed of the reactions
of an individual to situations which pile up tension or energy, discharged
by the reactions. All reactions of the organism, internal or external, to
all stimuli, internal or external, would therefore be included in the general
definition (Lowrey, 1926). This discussion, however, is limited to certain specific aspects of human behavior: the externalized, observable responses, reactions or activities of the individual. These aspects represent
the social behavior, i.e., comprise the various ways in which the individual reacts to persons and things. More particularly, it is the socially
disturbing behavior which must be considered in this chapter.

Social behavior may be viewed in various ways. In moralistic terms,
it may be judged good or bad; in legal terms, as delinquent or law-
abiding; in psychiatric terms, as normal or abnormal, etc. For reasons
to be presented, none of these dichotomies is adequate for understanding
behavior, more specifically, delinquent and criminal behavior.

Behavior may be satisfying to the individual in the sense that it meets
the inner need of a drive or tension for discharge. Or, the behavior may
fail to satisfy the drive or tension, in which case the organism continues

in a state of partially or completely unrelieved tension. Behavior may also be healthy or unhealthy, in accordance with its effects upon the individual's physical and mental health. Finally, behavior may be socially acceptable or socially unacceptable, in accordance with the mores or legal concepts of the culture in which it occurs.

If behavior is satisfying, healthy, and socially acceptable, it obviously presents no problem to individual or group. If it is satisfying to the individual, but socially unacceptable, the result is "problem" behavior, delinquency or crime. Behavior which does not satisfy the individual's needs, but is socially acceptable, would result in some form of inner disturbance or illness; while behavior not satisfying to the individual and socially unacceptable would represent a form of neurotic or psychotic delinquency.

Crime and Delinquency.—Certain types of behavior are classified as crimes, which are, for the most part, defined in penal codes. Definitions usually include omissions and commissions of acts forbidden by public law and punishable upon conviction. A crime, therefore, in the abstract is an illegal act for which the perpetrator, if apprehended and convicted, may be punished. Without going into technicalities, minor offenses are arbitrarily defined as "misdemeanors" and major offenses are called "felonies." The latter are more severely punished and involve the loss of certain civil rights. While some types of offenses are described as being such from their own nature or by natural law, for present purposes the term crime will be used to refer to those offenses proscribed in penal codes, with prescribed punishments.

Delinquency is a milder term referring to misdeeds, faults and misdemeanors. Technically, it seems to be applied only to the offenses of juveniles under the age of sixteen or eighteen, and refers to any kind of offense committed by children.

Both crime and delinquency are, in our culture, legal conceptions and, as such, present variations in definition at various times and places. Both imply a conspicuous deviation from the accepted standards of behavior, as embodied in the laws governing the particular community and representing the social code of behavior. Codes may or may not be psychologically well founded; when they are not, or a particular item is not, widespread disregard ensues and the public attitude is one of condoning the offender and his offense. Furthermore, many transgressions are viewed more seriously by a family group than by the law, and vice versa. In the present discussion the terms crime and criminal are not applied to merely unethical or immoral, unprincipled or stupid conduct or persons, but are used in the specific senses given.

Criminal and Delinquent.—Technically, these terms are applied only to those proven by plea or by conviction to be guilty of crime or delinquency. The general tendency is to use the terms loosely to refer chiefly to the repeated offender, or recidivist, but this is not entirely correct. It is true that the recidivist group has been most closely studied in the various efforts to establish a criminal type or delimit delinquent personality. Furthermore, it is stated by Morris (1941) that 80% or more of penitentiary prisoners have previous criminal records.

To some extent the differentiation of delinquent and criminal behavior is dependent upon the standards of individuals or, more particularly, families. Behavior acceptable to some families or social groups may be regarded as serious transgression in others. Children reared in such family or social groups are likely to share the views, with corresponding freedom of action, or guilt and anxiety, in accordance with these group standards. In general, however, the differentiation of criminal and delinquent persons is dependent upon legal conviction of exhibiting behavior punishable by law.

It is recognized that this sharp delimitation to those who have actually been adjudged delinquent does not take into account the large number of individuals who are charged with delinquent behavior, or who actually are delinquent over long periods of time without being apprehended. This restriction is, however, both theoretically and practically essential since, for the most part, adequate data are available only in the cases of those whose delinquencies are acknowledged or proven. Further, and tritely, incidental delinquency, witting or unwitting, is universal because of the vast number of laws intended to govern social behavior. Studies of various crime commissions have shown a wide disparity between the number of crimes reported, the number of individuals arrested and charged, those convicted and sentenced and the final carrying out of sentence. Menninger (1938, p. 202), in discussing the problem of criminality and possible differences in personality of those who are apprehended and those who are not, cites a survey of criminal justice in Missouri in 1926 as showing only one offender actually punished for every thousand crimes committed.

All in all, therefore, it seems desirable to discuss personality factors only in the actually proven delinquent and criminal. The resulting conclusions may be open to criticism from the statistical standpoint, but no other way is seen to delimit the population group to be studied.

Personality.—Many and varied are the definitions which have been proposed for this term, which is vaguely used in many senses. Aside from the presentations in other chapters of this book, Allport (1937) has contributed a discussion of some fifty definitions. For present purposes the definition given in Webster's Dictionary is accepted as adequately comprehensive, without being too specific or too exclusive: "Personality implies complex being or character having distinctive and persistent traits, among which reason, self-consciousness and self-activity are usually reckoned as essential."

It seems probable that the stress on "total personality" in psychiatric literature during the last few decades is dependent on the point that there was a previous tendency to restrict the use of the word to particular aspects of "distinctive personal character."

Each person is an entity; as such, there is an independent physical and mental being, a specific character, a series of attitudes, reactions and behavior patterns. Many adjectives are used to describe various aspects of personality, all of them referring to reactions of the individual to situations which he encounters and to which he must respond. Many "systems" of classification of normal and abnormal personality have been devised, but none so far has stood the test of prolonged critical examination. Several classifications of body types, with associated temperaments, have been presented, now upon one bias, now upon another. A recent one is that of Kretschmer (1926), describing four anthropological types—pyknic, asthenic, athletic, and dysplastic; and two major temperamental types—cyclothymic and schizothymic (schizoid). This system is apparently not of great practical significance in psychiatry, judging by the small space devoted to it in recent textbooks (one voluminous text does not even mention it) and the failure to include measurements derived from Kretschmer's scale in the section on examination methods.

Actually, classifications are not especially important. The essential point is to understand the mechanisms underlying the behavior of individuals and groups, especially, perhaps, of individuals in groups.

At any given point of study, personality is a complex derivative of biological constitution and experiences interacting together. Its external manifestations constitute the behavior we study. To a considerable extent behavior and personality are socially determined, especially through early experiences in the family, but neither behavior nor personality is dependent solely on either social or cultural factors. With this point in mind, the study of personality with reference to delinquent and criminal behavior obviously must consider physical, intellectual, emotional, instinctual (drives) and social factors, their interaction and integration into a harmonious or unharmonious whole.

Abnormal Personality and Delinquency.—The common thread in the many approaches to the delimitation of a criminal type lies in the obvious attempt to prove the criminal to be a variant from the normal, a person set apart, different from the rest of the population. Also, and quite specifically, it was evidently hoped that the criminal personality might be recognized before it swung into action. Gross (1911) states that the real criminal is different from the majority of people, adding that the difference is great and essential, since a single characteristic does not constitute a criminal (p. 411).

Ideas concerning crime, the criminal, and punishment have complicated the picture, while themselves being complicated by concepts derived from religion, philosophy and general group mores. Frequently, the argument seems to run along the line that the individual committing a delinquency (a socially disapproved act) *must* be abnormal, which is to say, "he must be different from me." Michael and Wechsler (1940, pp. 20–24), after previously discussing complexities regarding what kinds of behavior shall be made criminal by law, and how criminals shall be punished, attribute the interest in objective study of the characteristics of criminals primarily to the endeavor to discover the causes of crime, with the ultimate end of elimination of causes, thus making possible the control of crime. Noting that considerable material descriptive of examined individuals has been secured, they point out that much importance is attributed in contemporary criminal law to the individual characteristics of offenders. They, as do most writers on the subject, note that the factors, especially the external factors, to which delinquency may be, and often is, attributed, also operate in the lives of non-delinquent individuals. This point has been made especially clear by Healy and Bronner (1936) through the study of 105 pairs of delinquent and non-delinquent siblings, including eight pairs of twins.

While analysis of the personality of the delinquent cannot avoid the inclusion of social factors, it should be emphasized that they are discussed only with reference to their dynamic influence as they are incorporated into and influence the evolution of personality. Causes of crime, as such, are not under consideration, except as particular personality sets enter into such causation. Evidence is cumulative that distortions of personality play a large part in the exhibition of delinquent behavior; indeed, that certain conflicts, defects and mental mechanisms appear very frequently in delinquents. In some instances it can be shown that specific traits are present more frequently in delinquents, i.e., those delinquents who have been studied, than in the general population. In other cases it remains somewhat obscure as to why one individual reacts with delinquent behavior and another does not, although the mental mechanisms seem to have similar origins and intensity.

In any case, the important point seems to be that careful, complete study of the delinquent individual is essential to an understanding of his personality, how it evolved, how it is related to the delinquency, and what happens to the personality as a result of the delinquency.

Criminological Theories

Early Concepts.—Even cursory survey reveals a wide variety of explanations for criminal behavior, often offered with masses of supporting data. In general, they are characterized by a comparatively narrow attempt at one-to-one correlation, without taking into account the complexity either of human personality or of the situations to which the person must react. Of course, attempts at classifying people—especially other people—are as old as the human race. The fact that so many theories have been offered to explain delinquent behavior proves the enormous complexity of the problem.

POSSESSION BY THE DEVIL.—Perhaps the oldest theory used to explain deviant behavior is that of "demoniacal possession," once a favorite explanation also of mental disease. This notion is still deeply imbedded in general viewpoints, as witness many phrases in everyday use, such as,

"The devil is in him." There are widely held beliefs in witchcraft, "hexing," the "evil eye," and the like, which testify to the strength of these ancient beliefs. Bromberg (1937, p. 44) cites an instance of witch prosecution in New Jersey in 1936. (For a fairly comprehensive account of these concepts, see especially pp. 43–66 of Bromberg's book.) A number of accounts of "hexing" have appeared in the newspapers during the last few years. A more modern way of expressing much the same idea is to speak of the "two sides of man," i.e., the good and the bad. Any such concept of the essential basis for human behavior is, of course, entirely too divorced from reality to be of service.

MORAL INSANITY AND MORAL IMBECILITY.—A concept which received great attention during the nineteenth century was that of "moral insanity." The term was introduced by Prichard (1835), who defined the condition as one apart from the "intellect or knowing and reasoning faculties" and without "insane illusion or hallucination." The feelings, temper, moral dispositions and natural impulses were subject to "morbid perversion."

The condition itself had been called *manie sans délire* by Pinel. Rush (1812) defined *moral derangement* as a state "when the will becomes the involuntary vehicle of vicious actions, through the instrumentality of the passions" (p. 262), and elsewhere emphasized the fact that there is no "disease in the understanding." In 1810 he had limited "the morbid operations of the will" to two acts, viz., murder and theft. In the later work here cited, he added lying and drinking. The description of the "lying disease in the will" is an excellent thumb-nail sketch of pathological lying as we know it today. In another chapter (p. 356) Rush treats "derangement of the moral faculties" and cites three cases of "total derangement." This he defines as innate and preternatural, and probably due to "an original defective organization in those parts of the body, which are occupied by the moral faculties of the mind." Although Rush wrote extensively on the topic, Prichard's description seems to have been the one most influential in stimulating the long controversy regarding this concept. In this country most of the leading alienists were involved on one side or the other, as were lawyers and sociologists.

Ray (1838), whose work on medical jurisprudence occupied a foremost position during much of the last century, classified moral insanity, partial or general, under affective mania. The general type involved the entire moral nature, while the partial was confined to one or a few of the affective faculties, the remainder of the moral and intellectual constitution being unimpaired. Crimes were committed whose motives were equally inexplicable to the criminal and to others. Ray likened the course of events to the working of a blind, instinctive impulse which was irresistible. He laid especial stress on the propensity to destroy, and attempted a differentiation between homicidal mania and criminal homicide.

Most of the polemics which followed had to do, as might be expected, with problems of legal and moral responsibility. To many psychiatrists, moral insanity was only a convenient term to excuse acts committed as a result of ordinary desires or passions; or just another name for wickedness or depravity.

Fink (1938), in his comprehensive and valuable discussion of this concept (Ch. III, p. 48 ff.) to which the reader is referred for details, points out that the trial of Giteau for the assassination of President Garfield spelled the doom of the doctrine of moral insanity, but later shows that similar concepts under other names have appeared.

Complicating the issue of moral insanity was the doctrine of heredity and the concept of degeneration. Kiernan (1884) was among the first to advocate the term "moral imbecility" to replace moral insanity, since the condition was regarded as innate, and so hereditary, following Spitzka's use of the term (Spitzka 1883, preface and p. 281). Again, however, there was lack of clarity in definition. Tredgold (1915) gives a particularly good account of the "moral defective" (a term he preferred to moral imbecile), in which he states (p. 313) that the moral defective never developed the power of regulating personal conduct in the moral and social sphere. He advanced the belief that defect of the moral sense may occur without intellectual impairment, and distinguishes between this type of person and the incorrigible criminal, stating that the latter condition implies some degree of mental impairment (p. 321). He lists three types of moral defectives: (1) the morally perverse, or habitual criminal; (2) the facile type (with defective will); (3) the explosive type. Most of his case illustrations are mental defectives with "moral" difficulties added. This is a good example of the confusion regarding the categories of moral insanity and moral imbecility, and explains many of the apparent contradictions of theory and observation.

Tredgold (p. 321) says, ". . . my experience is that most persistent criminals are the offspring of a decidedly neurotic or mentally abnormal stock, and that they possess many characteristics identical with those occurring in ordinary aments" (his term for the mentally defective or feebleminded of all classes). He had previously pointed out that the various "senses or sentiments" making up the mind differed in development, partly due to special hereditary tendencies, and partly due to early environmental influences. Especially, there must be sufficient will to follow a course known to the individual to be right and ethical, and the ability to inhibit antisocial and immoral impulses. He further noted that, to a child growing up in an atmosphere of selfishness, vice and crime, acts of thieving, lying and licentiousness would be meritorious.

Fernald (1908) expressed the view that every imbecile is a potential criminal, needing only a particular environment and opportunity for the expression of criminal tendencies. It was his definite opinion that there were no moral imbeciles who were not true imbeciles. He also thought the "instinctive criminal" of Lombroso (vide infra) might be a typical adult imbecile who had had opportunity and experience in the community.

In England, the category of moral imbecile was legally established in the Mental Deficiency Act of 1913, in which moral imbeciles were defined as "persons who from an early age display some permanent mental defect coupled with strong vicious or criminal propensities on which punishment has had little or no deterrent effect." The intent of this passage seems clearly to be that of first establishing the diagnosis of mental defect, which is primarily a matter of intellectual defect. Accordingly, this is not the same type of moral imbecility as that defined by Prichard.

Various terms were proposed to apply to individuals of this type, among them psychopathic personality (Ransom, 1896; Hitchcock, 1909, et al.) and constitutional inferiority (Wright, 1913). Wholey (1914) stressed the inherent deficiency of the moral sense.

It remained for Healy (1915) to dispose of this debate rather neatly. Pointing out that different authors discuss different things (p. 782 ff.) and paying his respects to the problem of a "moral sense," he states that there was no point on which he expected more positive data than the moral imbecile, i.e., a person not subnormal or mentally diseased, yet devoid of moral feeling. *Not a single case was found.* Cases brought to him as moral imbeciles were mentally defective or otherwise disordered, or the victims of environment or mental conflict, but not devoid of moral feeling. His final conclusion is, " . . . that probably all moral imbeciles are primarily mentally abnormal" (p. 786).

Considerable space has been given to this discussion of "moral insanity" and "moral imbecility" because, despite the confusion evident among the disputants, these concepts have their place in determining present-day views.

Much of the debate centered around the problem of free will. Thus the various *monomanias*—dipso-, pyro-, eroto-, klepto-, and homicidal— were described as having in common an intellectual recognition of the wrongness of the act, which the individual would avoid if he could, but volition was too weak to resist the impelling power. There was, until Healy (1915) presented his case studies, a marked tendency merely to group people according to their behavior, rather than to make careful, individual case studies. The interplay of personality and environment was glimpsed, but neither understood nor analyzed.

Even so able a student as Hall (1904, Vol. 1, p. 330) states that "Moral insanity, which sometimes precedes and sometimes comes out at puberty, is characterized by incapacity for education, distaste for family life, marked peculiarities of character, extreme cleverness in certain directions, bad sexuality and criminality. The more passionate and instinctive men are, the more they resemble children in these respects and the more egoistic they are."

ANTHROPOLOGICAL THEORIES.—To explain deviation in social behavior, our predecessors (ca. 1850–1900) were sure there must be anatomical or physiological differences between persons, in the organism as a whole or in the nervous system. The criminal reacted differently because he was organically different. In general, this is in line with the expanding scientific thought of the times, when anatomical and pathological laboratories were the chief centers of research.

Lombroso (1911) (see also Ferrerro, 1911) is universally credited with the initiation of the concept of "criminal man" as a distinct type. He insisted that the criminal was essentially atavistic, morphologically a savage. Fink (1938) credits E. P. Fowler with the first American publication in this field, an article in 1880 on the topic, "Are the brains of criminals anatomical perversions?" Atavism, reversion to type, instinctive savagery and arrested development were favorite terms. Arrested development referred particularly to the persistence of instincts normal among savages and the semi-civilized, but regarded as evidence of failure of development when occurring in our civilization. For example, the inclination to assault or kill was explained as a persistence of animal or subhuman ancestral traits. To many writers, the criminal was an abnormal person to whom crime was a normal function. Furthermore, retrogression from generation to generation was claimed.

Many anatomical deviations were noted in all parts of the body, with special reference to the head. Particular attention was paid to the "stigmata of degeneration," some of which were the following: facial asymmetry, tower skull, deformed palate (unusually high or pointed arch), prognathism and receding lower jaw, scanty beard, low growing head hair and low forehead, meeting eyebrows, deformities of dental arches and teeth, coarse features, high cheek bones, very broad or very narrow face. The ears were particularly studied for asymmetries, protrusion, adherent lobules, anomalies in conformation and the Darwinian tubercle.

Through such studies, a concept of the criminal as a degenerate, or devoluting type, was evolved and a considerable literature developed. Talbot (1898) set up a classification of degeneracy. "Ethical degeneracy" included crime, prostitution and sexual degeneracy, moral insanity and inebriety. Intellectual degeneracy comprised the insanities, neuroses and epilepsy; sensory degeneracy, deaf-mutism, congenital color blindness, etc.; nutritive degeneracy, goitre, cancer, gout, etc.; and local reversionary tendencies in the various organs were described. Lydston (1904) attributed all degeneracy to a neuropathic constitution, which might not be obvious. but latent, until the neuropsychic degeneration is revealed by inebriety or criminal acts.

The theory of degeneration brought crime, insanity, mental deficiency and pauperism into a sequence of cause and effect, not accidents or due to "satanic interference." Reviewing the period, it now seems that concepts of brain and nervous system, physical constitution, intelligence and will, were quite thoroughly mixed up. A frequent sequence was that defective conduct was rooted in defective brain action, dependent in turn on defective brain structure which was most probably usually inherited. Also, criminality was *either* hereditary *or* environmental in origin; very few considered the possibility of interplay.

The present status of criminal anthropology has been well summarized by Hrdlicka (1939), who says there are recognizable anthropometric differences between the averages of the main criminal classes, but they are not sufficiently characteristic, nor are they universal. Noting that crime is not an organic entity, but a social phenomenon, he concludes that anthropometry and physical examination *cannot aid* in the recognition of the potential criminal.

For about thirty years, there was much interest in the question of a specific type of criminal brain. Benedikt (1881) showed, in nineteen brains of criminals, a simplified type of architecture (confluent fissures). Apparently up to the time of Benedikt's report these anomalies of gyration had been only infrequently noted. Following his report, however, similar conditions were described in brains from many individuals with a wide variety of types of disturbance. The idea of a specific type of brain configuration, never well accepted, was finally abandoned. That gyral interruption or sulcal confluence is common in certain types of disorders and may have a bearing on organization and functioning of the nervous system, is shown by my own observations in 100 brains, in which 44% of 63 cases of organic and toxic psychoses revealed these anomalies, while practically 95% of 37 cases of functional or endogenous disorders presented such findings (1920). While emphasis has shifted to the social and psychological aspects of crime and the criminal, it remains true that nothing has been produced to show any relationship between the brain of the criminal and his acts or habits, aside from those pathological manifestations which are related to certain types of mental disorders which, of course, may be complicated by crime.

Much the same comments could be made regarding the findings of craniology. Fink (1938) credits August Drähms (1900) and Frances A. Kellor (1901) with producing the first two works on the American criminal. Significantly, neither was able to demonstrate a type of cranium peculiar to the criminal.

To sum up, it may be said that no distinctive physical type of criminal has been proven to exist. There are observations indicating certain trends toward inferior constitutional endowment, but these are not specific for the criminal.

HEREDITY.—The theories of degeneration, of moral insanity and moral imbecility, and of the criminal anthropological type, were all complicated by ideas of hereditary transmission. While the doctrine of heredity was perhaps particularly stressed in relation to degeneration, it was argued pro and con with reference to all the other theories, and mental disease and mental defect as well.

Of the great mass of literature which accumulated, only three works will be cited here. The first was Dugdale's (1877) study of a family he called the Jukes. This study has often been used in support of the thesis of hereditary transmission of criminal characteristics. Yet the author himself was careful to point out that not only hereditary blood lines, but similar environment, were involved. It was his view that hereditary characteristics produce a corresponding environment and so tend to perpetuate the characteristics. He regarded heredity as an organized result of the environment which produces habits which tend to become hereditary. While this is not acceptable doctrine today, his statements to the effect that capacities are limited by heredity, and the use to which they are put is governed by environmental influences, is thoroughly in accord with the most modern views.

The second study is that of Goddard (1912) on the Kallikak family. Here again, a numerous family was traced through many generations. Goddard concluded that criminals are made and not born. But in this and other works, he also stressed the importance of feeblemindedness in the production of criminality, and further concluded that feeblemindedness was inherited. Hence there might appear to be some equivocation in this argument. It was his opinion that Lombroso's criminal types may have been feebleminded individuals who became criminal because of environmental circumstances.

Finally, Spaulding and Healy (1914), in a study of a thousand young recidivists, found no evidence of direct inheritance of criminality, but did find familial incidence of insanity, epilepsy and feeblemindedness which could have been of indirect importance.

It seems justifiable to conclude that, in so far as heredity is concerned, even the proponents of the theory have shown only that certain fundamental defect states are transmitted in familial lines, and that these must be combined with environmental influences to result in criminality.

CONCLUSIONS.—It is clear that all the efforts described in this section were concerned with (a) the delimitation of a criminal type or types, and (b) the causes of criminal behavior. The orientation was chiefly in physical and neurological terms, with only here and there reference to sociological and psychological factors. Despite an apparent abstractness, these studies were of importance because of the gradually increasing emphasis on the study of the individual, rather than of a type or of the crime. This has permitted the emergence of our present concepts of the personality difficulties of delinquents. Furthermore, the failure of these efforts led to a definite shift in the search for causes from a somatic to a psychological orientation. With the increased study of psychological factors, and the perfection of diagnostic techniques, there came an increasing emphasis on social or cultural components in human behavior. Both problems in behavior and in personality must be studied in relation to environmental influences, as well as in terms of psychobiological constitution. Finally, the most significant finding of twentieth century psychiatry has been the demonstration of the continuity of mental life, and, as a corollary, the far-reaching influence of past experience, especially early experience, in determining personality and behavior patterns.

Actually, it is to the dynamics of mental life that we must turn for the explanations of behavior. As Healy (1915, ¶ 23) put it, we deal with the motives and driving forces of human conduct, a product of mental life. Hence the problems are essentially those of individual and differential psychology. To this we would add the importance of cultural factors in producing the psychology of the individual. Significantly, we shall not find a doctrine of monocausation tenable. Instead, especially in the field of behavior, multiple causation is clearly demonstrable. This is one of the most significant contributions of the child guidance work of the past twenty years.

Mental Disorders

Leaving to one side such uninformed judgments as those proclaiming that all criminals are insane or feebleminded, or that criminality is a diseased condition of the human character, or that the criminal is a psychopath whose dominant passion is to commit a crime, it has been found that some of those who commit crimes are mentally disordered. The relationship of the major types of mental disorder—the psychoses, mental deficiency, epilepsy, the neuroses, and psychopathic personality— are separately discussed.

Psychoses.—There is considerable discrepancy in figures on the relative incidence of the psychoses among criminals. In most states, provision is made for special institutional care of the criminal insane who are committed under special legal provisions. In case of recovery from the psychosis, offenders may frequently be tried for the original offense if that was not adjudicated at the time of the commitment.

In ordinary prisons, the proportion of psychoses, either present on admission or developing during incarceration, seems to vary considerably. Variations in diagnostic standards, in methods of keeping statistics, and in ideas regarding punishment, probably contribute to the apparent variations. From 5% to 15% of prisoners have been reported to be psychotic.

Reporting on 9,958 cases (the largest series found in the literature) examined at the New York Court of General Sessions, *after* conviction or a plea of guilty, Bromberg and Thompson (1937) presented the following findings:

Psychoses	1.5%
Mental deficiency	2.4
Psychopathic personality	6.9
Psychneuroses	6.9 (of 7,100 cases)
Average or normal	82.0

While the rate of psychoses is considerably higher than in the general population, it is clear that the presence of a psychosis does not account for any substantial proportion of criminal activity. These figures seem particularly important because they are based on *complete* examination of all convicted adult offenders and so comprise a random sample large enough to be representative. The standards of psychiatric work in this court clinic are of the best.

By contrast, Bernard Glueck (1918) studied 608 admissions to Sing Sing Prison and reported 12% with mental disease; 28% mental deficiency; 19% psychopathic personality; or more than half of the cases with some definite type of mental abnormality.

Another index of the incidence of psychoses in relation to criminal activity might conceivably be found in the number of cases becoming psychotic in prison. While such figures are extremely misleading, it may be noted that, of a total of about 12,000 inmates (average daily census), 156 were transferred from correctional institutions to state hospitals in New York in 1939 (Commission of Correction Annual Report, 1940).

These later reports are not, of course, based on any such conceptions of "moral insanity" as have been previously discussed. Their validity might be questioned with respect to general social and legal attitudes toward "the criminal" and the need for, and effects of, punishment. Nevertheless, according to the best modern studies, psychoses are not overwhelmingly important factors in delinquency. On theoretical grounds alone this should be expected, since the types of symptom formation in the psychoses and in delinquency are, on the whole, quite different.

Mental Deficiency.—Some earlier views respecting the relationships of mental deficiency to crime have already been presented. Modern studies may be said to date from the introduction of the Binet-Simon test in this country in 1910 by Goddard. Reports multiplied from all parts of the country, dealing with all types of delinquents (as well as socially and educationally defective). Most extraordinary were the proportions of diagnoses of feeblemindedness reported. Figures of 25% to 90%, and in some small series of cases, 100%, were reported (see Goddard, 1910, 1914). It is easy to understand why these extraordinarily high figures were received with great skepticism by the majority of psychiatrists. These studies are not listed in detail, because it soon became clear that much depended on methods of scoring and interpretation. At first, feeblemindedness was estimated in terms of mental age and number of years of retardation; then, in certain tests, by the number of points; later still, in terms of intelligence quotient (see, for example, Haines, 1916). The most reliable results were eventually found to be through the use of batteries of tests. Especially the Army experience during 1917 and 1918 showed the need for care in standardization and, at the same time, gave an enormous random sample of males of considerable age range and varied socio-economic, cultural and racial backgrounds.

The study of the intelligence levels of criminals by Tulchin (1939) is the most comprehensive yet to appear and gives the most complete answer obtainable to the question of the relationship between feeblemindedness and criminal behavior. The data include the results of a 1920 survey of all inmates in Illinois penal and correctional institutions, followed by routine psychometric testing of all admissions through 1927, comprising 10,413 prisoners. The standard procedure was to use the Army group intelligence tests, Alpha or Beta as indicated, followed by individual testing of all those with rating below C— (Alpha) or 45 points (Beta), except that, in the latter part of the study, use of the Beta test was eliminated, and all who would have been chosen for this test were given individual tests instead. With the exception of two groups, totaling 517, who made low Alpha scores and left the institution before individual examinations could be administered, all diagnoses of feeblemindedness were based on individual tests. The data were subjected to detailed analysis and comparison with the test results reported for the Illinois Army draft. The major conclusions may be briefly summarized.

There are a number of important differences between the populations of the State Penitentiary and the State Reformatory, and some differences are shown between the 1920 survey results and the 1920–1927 study. But, so far as intelligence is concerned, the outstanding point is that *the percentages of inferior, average, and superior men in the prison population are extremely similar to those for the Illinois Army draft* (see Tulchin, pp. 11–14). In point of fact, tests of nearly 5,000 men in the Reformatory showed a higher proportion of superior test results, and a smaller proportion of inferior, than did the Army draft. The entire institution population revealed 20.4% inferior, 67.6% average, and 11.9% superior results, by comparison with 25.9% inferior, 63.5% average, and 10.6% superior for the Army draft.

With specific reference to the occurrence of inferior intelligence (mental ages below 10.9) the following percentages were found: Army draft, 25.9; 1920 survey of the penitentiaries, 24.4; seven-year admissions to the State Penitentiary, 23.4; similar study at the Reformatory, 15.0.

The difference between the several groups is to be explained, according to the report, by differences in proportion of native-born whites, foreign-born, and Negroes in the Reformatory, the Penitentiary, and in the Army draft sample. The latter compares much more closely with the penitentiary population in average age and in distributions by nativity and race than it does with the reformatory group. Marked variations were found in intelligence distributions on comparing the several nativity and racial groups, and these must be taken into account when comparing intelligence distributions. Cultural and educational factors were found to be definitely important in relation to test scores.

It is of great significance, however, that for all nativity and racial groups, test results from the institution population approximate the distribution for the Army draft. In most instances where there is discrepancy, it is that the reformatory group shows a lower proportion of inferior test scores and a higher proportion of superior scores.

The final conclusion, for our present purposes, is that a most adequate study has failed to produce evidence of any significant disproportion of test scores for male delinquents when compared with scores earned on the same tests by a draft group from the same areas. Some nativity and race groups in both series show quite high percentages of inferior ratings. As pointed out in the report (pp. 33–35), it would be absurd to label these large groups feebleminded. The only direct comparison made for those of lowest rating (E, below MA 9–6, or IQ 60) is for the native-born whites, where the percentage for Army and the penal group is approximately the same, 3.5% to 4.0%.

Some relationship is found between the level of intelligence test scores and type of crime, in that the highest median scores were made by the men committed for fraud; the lowest by those committed for sex crimes. Individuals of all grades of intelligence were found in the six crime groups listed (fraud, robbery, larceny, burglary, murder, and sex crimes, in about that order for intelligence levels).

How shall we explain the high proportions of mental defect reported in the early studies, up to 100% in some instances, and the much lower proportion found in this Illinois study, with a curve of distribution practically identical with the Illinois Army draft? It has been mentioned that there were wide variations in types of tests used and, more especially, in the interpretations placed on the findings. Besides this important point, it seems probable that many delinquent or potentially delinquent younger feebleminded were committed to training schools for mental defectives, with the development of greater interest in their training and the provision of more facilities. Or, they may have been put under some form of prolonged social supervision, operating to reduce the incidence of delinquency among the defective. Tulchin brought out the fact that recidivists have somewhat higher median scores, chiefly because of a reduction in the percentage of inferior scores (pp. 42–49). He suggests several possible explanations, among them longer sentences for the defective, more rigid supervision on parole, and commitment to training schools.

The conclusions drawn from the Illinois study regarding the incidence of mental defect among delinquents are, to a considerable degree, supported by the findings of Bromberg and Thompson (1937). Among 4,396 convicted prisoners, 2.2% were found to be feebleminded, and an additional 26.3% inferior, by contrast with the finding of 7.1% feebleminded and 17% inferior among 94,000 white draftees used as a control. The major difference in their findings from those in Illinois was that only 2.5% of their prisoners were superior in intelligence rating.

Feeblemindedness, then, is not the universal factor in delinquency it was once thought to be (see Lowrey, 1928a). Even inferior intelligence, broadly conceived, cannot be considered to be an outstanding feature of the personality of delinquents, since the incidence of inferiority is, in general, so nearly the same as with the Army draft.

These studies of the incidence of the psychoses and mental defect among delinquents deal only with convicted adult and adolescent offenders, and so may be criticized. However, these are the known offenders, with known, punishable offenses. The important point is that *this most deviant behavior group* proves to be, so far as we have norms with which to compare them, a reasonably fair cross-section of the population.

Epilepsy.—This is one of the rarer forms of mental disorder, but an especially important one in relation to delinquency because of the bizarre features often found. These include the amnesia (often mistaken for malingering) and the extraordinary brutality of many of the crimes in which epilepsy is regarded as the important factor in causation. Cases of epilepsy are, fortunately, rare, and so are their delinquencies. In many reports consulted, epilepsy was not mentioned. Foxe (1938), noting that epilepsy was rare in his experience with prisoners, suggested that epilepsy may be a form of criminal behavior lived out on oneself.

Neuroses.—Fully developed neuroses are relatively rare as causative factors in delinquency. Bromberg and Thompson (1937) reported an incidence of 6.9% among 7,100 prisoners examined. In general, hysteria is the neurosis most commonly involved, an especial complication being the amnesia frequently found with respect to the delinquency.

This low incidence of neuroses in the causation of delinquent behavior is to be expected, since neurotic mechanisms tend to appear in the form of symptoms of disturbed function. Medical experience indicates a much higher proportion of neuroses in the nondelinquent population. Minor degrees of disturbance in social relationship are common symptoms in neurotics, in line with the disturbances of physiological functions.

Recently psychoanalytic studies of delinquents have appeared with greater frequency, and these indicate that delinquency more frequently represents the working out of neurotic conflicts than had been believed (see especially Alexander and Healy, 1935; Lippman, 1937; Aichhorn, 1935; and Menninger, 1938). Of particular importance are (1) the unconscious need to be punished, (2) displaced aggression, and (3) various compulsions based on unconscious needs, many of which, in individual cases, may be shown to have a sequential relationship to the other two. Most frequently the compulsions are related to suppressed aggression, often directed against the self. In other words, the crimes of the neurotic are symbolic, as are other symptoms.

So far as present reports are concerned, there is more evidence that repressed hostile impulses lead to guilt formation and neurosis than the reverse. Gutheil (1941a, b) has given an outline of the method of repression and conversion of the primitive hostile impulses into various neurotic symptoms. He presents the point that the neurosis acts as an immobilizer of criminal trends as part of the constant conflict between hostile impulses and the need, both psychological and social, to be part of a group.

After all, only two ways are open to a psychological impulse. One is to act on it, thus discharging the energy. The other is to suppress it, which leads to anxiety and symptom formation.

Psychopathic Personality.—This diagnostic term is, in at least one sense, a lineal descendant of the "moral insanity" discussed in a previous section. Conditions included under this diagnosis have been variously named, described, grouped, and interpreted. For discussion of the psychopathic states from several points of view, including relationship to delinquency, Preu's chapter in this book (Chapter 30), Kraepelin (1915), Henderson (1939), Cleckley (1941), Caldwell (1941), Karpman (1933, 1940), Healy (1915, p. 575 ff.), and Partridge (1930) may be consulted. A particularly concise discussion may be found in Noyes (1934), while an excellent survey of the literature will be found in Maughs (1941).

For present purposes, it may be noted that a variety of terms have been used to describe types of personality and behavior regarded as aberrant and socially or personally destructive. Psychopathic personality, constitutional psychopathic inferiority, constitutional inferiority, constitutional psychopathic state, and psychic constitutional inferiority, are the most common. Latterly, there has been a trend toward calling similar cases "neurotic character" (e.g., Bartemeier, 1931; Alexander and Staub, 1931; Alexander and Healy, 1935; Lippman, 1937).

Inclusions of cases in this group have been of two major types: (1) those showing personality characteristics which, if exaggerated or developed by the addition of certain other symptoms, would represent a psychosis; and (2) those showing deviations from generally accepted, though vaguely defined, norms of personality integration, together with antisocial behavior, commonly as a repetitive pattern. In the main, it is the latter type which is of present concern. Interpretations have also followed two main lines: (1) that of constitutional, innate, hereditary factors; and (2) disturbances in personality development and integration, primarily dependent upon the nature of early experience, especially emotional relationships.

Questions concerning types of cases to be included, factors in causation and interpretation have recently again come to the fore and this interest is reflected in the rising tide of literature. It is worthy of note that some psychiatrists deny the existence of the condition [see, for example, the discussions by Brill and Menninger of Sprague's (1941) paper]. To others, all criminals would seem to be psychopathic.

Probably because of the uncertainties of diagnostic standards in these borderline cases, there is considerable variation in reported incidence. Although recognizably ill and repeatedly failing to profit by punitive experience, these cases are held fully responsible in legal procedure.

In the early '20's in the Psychopathic Laboratory of the Chicago Criminal Courts, the great majority of the cases studied were called "dementia praecox," in addition to any other conditions which might have been found, and *poverty of affect* was regarded as the most important single point in the makeup of the criminal (see reports issued in those years). Anderson (1914, 1915) had already noted that the constitutional psychopath—one not feebleminded, not psychotic, but with such personality disorganization that he could not adjust to the social environment—was as frequent as the feebleminded in his court clinic. He differentiated between the mental defective (the defective delinquent, for whom special provision has been made in some States, notably New York), the psychopaths, and the "mental delinquent" with an acquired, reformable delinquency.

Glueck (1918), reporting 19% of psychopaths among 608 admissions to Sing Sing Prison, showed, among other things, that the incidence of recidivism in this group was high; that various types of unstable, more or less antisocial behavior were common; that school and work careers were usually irregular and inefficient; that marked deviations from average behavior were found in childhood histories. Many of the latter disturbances were in the nature of rebellion against all types of authority, restrictions, etc.

Healy (1915) reported that "mental abnormalities and peculiarities" appeared as a main causative factor in 455 of 823 cases. There were 20 cases designated as "constitutional inferiority, including marked neurasthenic and psychopathic types" (pp. 130–132). This, by contrast with the 58 cases in which "mental conflict" was given as a major causative factor.

Healy and Bronner (1926, pp. 152, 273) reported 2.8% of psychopathic personality among 2,000 juvenile offenders, and 2.0% of constitutional inferiority. Among 675 cases used for a follow-up study, there were 14% of psychopaths, 16% of whom were also classed as feebleminded (p. 274).

In their latest report (1939) these authors dealt with 400 cases followed up five to eight years after study. Of these, 207 had presented "personality and behavior problems"; while 35 were classed as having "definitely abnormal personality." Of these, 14 were called psychopathic personality, 9 constitutional inferior, and 5 unclassified. Another 9 were called "probably abnormal personality." At most, then, the psychopaths constitute only 3.0% to 5.0% of juvenile delinquents, according to these figures.

For adults, Bromberg and Thompson (1937) reported, as previously noted, 6.9% of psychopathic personality among almost 10,000 cases examined. These included the schizoid, paranoid, cyclothymic, sexual, constitutional inferiority, drug addiction, and the explosive (epileptoid). A survey of their "normal or average" types shows at least 22.2% which might be included in the psychopathic group, at least according to the brief descriptive notes [emotionally unstable, 11.3%; egocentric (character defect) 5.3%; dull, adynamic, 2.5%; adult immature, 3.1%]. In any case, only 17.2% were recorded as "balanced or adjusted," with another 3.6% of "low cultural level" and 7.2% showing characteristics of the psychology of adolescence; or, perhaps at most, some 27% to 30%

of reasonably average or normal types. (In a personal communication, Bromberg reports that these cases are being restudied, with special reference to the problem of the neurotic character. The figures are, therefore, subject to other interpretations.)

It is accordingly necessary to leave in abeyance the question of the quantitative occurrence of psychopathy among delinquents. It may be noted that surveys of county jails, houses of refuge, etc., where so many recidivist misdemeanants are sent for short sentences, have revealed much higher percentages of psychopaths than is shown in the studies here cited. Experience in correctional institutions indicates some 20% to 25% of psychopathic personality among inmates. This may be related to a variety of factors—the repetitive behavior pattern, with high incidence of recidivism, the characteristic, egocentric failure of the psychopath to profit by experience, the rather obvious social disabilities, etc. It should also be noted that not all psychopathic personalities are delinquent in the strict sense used here; in many instances their inability to adjust socially is worked out in other ways. The diagnosis of psychopathic personality is never to be based on the occurrence of delinquent behavior, or even on its repetitiveness, but upon rather specific personality pictures.

Summary.—While the most recent figures available show considerable variation, it would appear that all personality disorders of the most marked types (psychoses, mental defect, neuroses, epilepsy and psychopathic personality), judged by the best modern studies, account for only about one-fifth to at most one-third of the cases of delinquency, at least for the more serious types. There are some differences according to age. Thus, there are very few psychotics among children, among whom the percentage of mental deficiency is higher than among adult offenders. Healy (1915) reported 11% of mental defectives among 832 juvenile delinquents, and juvenile court reports commonly show a skew of the curve of intelligence distribution to the left. Neuroses are considerably more frequent than psychoses, yet not extremely numerous. Most numerous of all, and the most complex to diagnose and treat, are the psychopathic personalities or character defects, which appear to be more numerous in adults than in children. It is clear, however, that there is no such entity as a "criminal type," either physical or mental. On the contrary, it would appear that there are complex psychological patterns involved, and that we must turn to a consideration of the individual delinquent and particular mental mechanisms.

The Delinquent Individual

Personality Types.—From the preceding discussions it appears that the delinquent is not especially different from the general population so far as gross personality disturbances are concerned. The neuroses are apparently more frequent in the general population; mental deficiency appears to occur with about the same frequency among delinquents and

comparable sections of the general population; psychoses and psychopathic states are apparently more frequent among delinquents.

To function normally in terms of social behavior requires not only
freedom from mental disorder of all types, but also adequate physical
and mental equipment for a well-balanced personality. As part of this,
inhibiting powers are necessary. Mental activity is necessarily directly
antecedent to criminal behavior, as to any other. Inhibitory powers are
a direct function of the super-ego, in so far as they pertain to social
behavior. One of the characteristics of an inadequate personality is
weakness of inhibitory activity, a sign of failure of development, or, in
the broad sense, immaturity. In such cases, faulty ego-ideals and imperfect transformation of the original, normal, egocentricity are also
evident. These and other deviations in personality formation occur and
profoundly influence behavior, without necessarily resulting in grossly
abnormal personality.

Healy (1941), after more than 30 years study of the problem, concludes that both biological and social factors are components in the production of delinquency and criminality. This point, which the child guidance work of the past twenty years has emphasized from the beginning,
is most important in considering the delinquent individual. Healy further concludes from the researches of his group, that there are two types
of abnormal personalities who became delinquent and criminal. One type
proves to be inadequate in personality makeup, and he calls them constitutionally inferior personalities. The other group shows abnormally egocentric and unstable personalities. These conclusions may be viewed in
the light of the finding by Healy and Bronner (1936) that 23.5% of 153
cases were definitely abnormal in personality, while inclusion of those
"probably" and "possibly" abnormal would raise the figure to 30%.

Bromberg and Thompson (1937) list 18 different groupings among
the 82% of "average or normal" types reported in their study of court
cases, based on particular traits which predominated in the total personality makeup. They finally emerge with 17% to 21% of "balanced or adjusted" among their cases. Types occurring with considerable frequency
in their groupings are: aggressive, 7.3%; emotionally unstable, 11.3%;
egocentric (unmodified ego as character defect), 5.3%; shiftless, 8.4%;
weak and submissive (suggestible), 5.2%. They also list an "unethical"
group (2.5%) who pursue carefully planned criminal careers. To another 1.0%, called the primitive, is ascribed simple, instinctive behavior
of a delinquent nature.

It would appear, therefore, that there are dominant traits, or factors in
causation, which may be important in individual cases, but not to the
extent that they may be regarded as personality types. Some sociologists,
notably Reckless (1940), believe that the search for causative factors is
a hopeless task, but this view seems extreme and unjustified by the data
at hand. There are many environmental factors which enter into the production of delinquent behavior, but they in turn must be transmuted
in the subtle alchemy of personality integration. Certain mechanisms

within the personality have been shown to be especially important and frequent among delinquents. No attempt is here made to assign any statistical frequency, or to indicate the rich variations of combinations which are encountered.

Fundamental Mechanisms.—

INDIVIDUAL DIFFERENCES, AND THE CONFLICT OVER DIFFERENCE.— An outstanding characteristic of contemporary life is its competitiveness in a wide variety of fields, affecting many phases of mental life. The effectiveness of the individual in many of these competitive fields is often directly related to the problem of competence (general or special disabilities or abilities). Frequently, however, it is not so much a question of actual competence as it is the individual's feelings about himself, the well-known *inferiority complex*, or, as it has been called for well-defined reasons, the *conflict over difference* (Lowrey, 1928). Healy and Bronner (1936) report conscious feelings of inferiority in one-third of their delinquency cases (p. 46), and later noted (p. 49) that there were marked feelings of inadequacy or inferiority in some situations or activities in sixty-one of 143 cases, or 43%. In my own experience with young offenders, this conflict as a precursor of socially disturbing behavior is very common, occurring with especial frequency in cases of stealing, truancy and running away, extremely aggressive, attention-compelling behavior (as a compensatory mechanism) and where submissive, withdrawn behavior is related to the delinquency, often as a part of so-called increased suggestibility.

The conflict may arise with respect to any attribute of the individual —physical abilities and appearance, intellectual abilities, emotional and behavior characteristics, economic and social status of the family or self, race, religion, vocation (especially where there is a difference between vocational interests and the vocation actually engaged in), etc. The mechanism of the conflict is related to the ego-ideals, real or imagined, of the individual and the group or groups in which he wishes to be accepted and valued and, perhaps, be a leader. Anything at all which happens in group relationships to indicate that the individual is not acceptable, or is actually regarded with hostility, may activate the mechanism. Often nicknames are especially expressive of the underlying emotional attitudes of a particular group, since they so frequently emphasize rejection of some reality factor which the individual cannot control. Color of hair, race and associated cultural patterns, and physical build are good examples of such reality situations which may be painfully impressed upon the developing ego. The manners and customs of the family group may contrast sharply with those of families in the neighborhood, with resulting conflict, as, for example, in the case of children whose foreign-born parents attempt to maintain their foreign patterns of personal and family life in the face of the quite different patterns of their neighbors.

There are several elements involved in the conflict. One is the drive for self-maximation, which involves (a) the realization of a sense of personal adequacy to meet the everyday demands made upon the individual, and (b) the realization of security in the group, as measured by the real or imagined expressions of the group. Under ordinary circumstances, an individual is not able to develop a complete feeling of personal adequacy, or complete group security. But, for the average situation, there are compensating satisfactions to be gained in some way, which offset with reasonable completeness the frustrations.

In addition to this ego drive, there is also the drive for group conformity, which has libidinal as well as ego components. This is worked out in relation to many groups, two of especial importance being the family and the own age group of companions. Frequently the standards of these two groups are in conflict. Particularly in the later adolescent years, when delinquency rates are especially high, the need for own age group conformity is unusually great. This is complicated by a variety of factors having to do with the establishment of independence from the home, resolution of the Oedipus situation, heterosexual adaptation and achievement of vocational and societal status.

That this is a period of great conflict between instinctual drives, and between certain drives and inhibiting factors, derived in part from within and in part from without, is clearly indicated by the high incidence of delinquency. Healy and Alper (1941, pp. 6–10) cite figures demonstrating this from several points of view. It is shown, for example, that arrests for major offenses amount to 2.68% of all nineteen-year-old males in the population. This age, nineteen, appears to be particularly crucial in their several tables. From age sixteen through age nineteen, there is a sharp increase in arrests for serious offenses, with subsequent decline to age 25, though this is not true when all offenses, including traffic violations, drunkenness, etc., are taken into account.

Any existing conflict over difference is sharply accentuated at this period, when so many changes confusing to the adolescent's judgment of himself are taking place. Aggression, often based on real hostility, flares up and may lead to delinquent acts which may have any of several values to the adolescent. Delinquent behavior may operate to demonstrate to the adolescent and to others his masculinity; it may be a carry-over of rebellion against family authority (father) to all forms of authority; it may represent revenge on the family, perhaps a particularly infantile method of returning to an earlier dependent state; it may have simpler values with reference to economic factors, in the absence of long-time goals; occasionally it represents a need for failure and punishment. A great deal of the delinquency in this period, however, in so far as it is an expression of personality as opposed to social factors, is a matter of compensation for the conflict over difference.

It is within this area that intellectual inferiority, with inadequate provision for educational potential, is especially important. Pressures for success and conformity in standard educational procedures, derived from the family, the school, and class competitions. frequently operate to force the inadequate individual toward delinquent behavior as a means of compensation for his own feelings of inadequacy, and as proof to the group of his adequacy.

IDENTIFICATION.—Sometimes delinquency may be shown to be equivalent to identifying with the group. Under such circumstances the individual merely takes over the pattern of the family or the neighborhood and has no special feelings of guilt or anxiety about his behavior. The need for a "hero" (ego-ideal) is well known, as is the tendency to identify with the most widely publicized individual of the neighborhood or a larger community.

Under the most favorable circumstances, the ego-ideals are derived (at least primarily) from father or mother, who represent not only authority, but also competitive careers. In case the family or neighborhood pattern is chiefly one of delinquency, then for a child to go contrary to this pattern would certainly produce conflict and at least some symptoms of abnormality. There is much evidence to the effect that there are delinquency areas, in the sense that an unusually high proportion of children in such areas appear in court. However, even in such areas, there are many nondelinquents, always, so far as known, exceeding the delinquents in number.

It should be noted that many instances could be cited in which the child reverses the patterns of parents or neighborhood, apparently in reaction to other identifications from which the super-ego is derived.

FAMILY SITUATIONS.—The most important factors leading to delinquency are undoubtedly to be found in the variations of the "family drama," those interpersonal relationships so important during the early, formative years.

Some studies have attempted to show that the "broken home" is a basically important factor, chiefly in terms of incidence among delinquents, without adequate controls. Clinical experience has, however, amply demonstrated that it is not the broken home as such which is directly responsible, but the reactions of the individual which are important. Thus it can be shown in case after case that a psychologically broken home, with disharmony, quarreling, and the use of the child as a buffer between parents, is far more important in determining attitudes conducive to delinquency than are actual, physical breakdowns in the makeup of the family.

Another family situation often studied is that of the ordinal positions of the delinquent among siblings. Particularly, the only child has been studied, primarily, apparently, because of a general idea that the only child is necessarily indulged, and so is not stimulated to (a) grow beyond the original narcissism so far as love object relationships are concerned; or (b) learn to forego the pleasure of the immediate future in favor of more remote gains. No definite evidence has yet been produced to indicate that the only child is more liable to delinquency than any other child in the family setting. A recent study by Hart and Axelrad (1941) points to some differences in personality traits among delinquent boys who are only children or members of large families, but there is definite indication that family size is not the important item. Common observation shows that, from the psychological standpoint, several or all of a family of children may occupy an "only child" situation. This is clear for all oldest and youngest children; because of spacing and changes in sex of succeeding children, it may apply to all in a particular family.

The factor of rivalry and jealousy among siblings is of considerable importance. Of practically universal occurrence, whether or not it becomes sufficiently marked to be related to delinquent behavior apparently depends to a great extent upon parental recognition and management.

The most important family situations have to do with emotional relationships, especially those subsumed under rejection, as felt by the child, or overprotection, as expressed by the parent. Ordinarily the child derives early ego-ideals, feelings of personal adequacy, security in the group, evidences of affection, and love objects from the family group. In case of severe family disharmony, none of these needs may be satisfied. Particularly, the child may actually be rejected or may be made to feel that he is rejected. He may find no anchorage for his affectional needs, nor stimuli to become less narcissistic. These feelings of being unwanted, neglected, thwarted in self-expression, and of insufficient importance to lead to stable, adequate, and consistent discipline in the home, produce a variety of feelings of insecurity and inadequacy which may be important in the evolution of a delinquent career.

Overprotection operates in a somewhat different way, since no penalties are exacted for transgressions and many aggressive reactions run on. That being the case, there is no particular super-ego formation; infantile hedonistic egocentricity is not checked; there is no stimulus to accepting personal responsibility, since someone else always assumes it. Normally developing sexuality is likely to be checked. Not infrequently it happens that such overprotection operates to make the child feel that he is not valued (as frequently he is not, much overprotection springing from parental guilt feelings over rejecting the child), since limits are not consistently set for him as they are for other children he knows, whose family relationships seem less strained than his.

AGGRESSION, HOSTILITY, AND FRUSTRATION.—These mechanisms are particularly ascribed to the delinquent, probably because so many crimes involve "acts of aggression" toward the person or property of others. Essential to the development of hostile aggression is *frustration*. Simple aggression or hostility have other meanings in terms of personality makeup (Lowrey, 1938) but where many frustrations are in evidence, either or both may rise to the point where the resulting behavior reactions are distinctly delinquent in type. Especially important are the frustrations arising in the family, interfering with normal identifications, love relationships, and the development of the sense of personal adequacy and group security. Frustrations arise from parental rejection, sibling rivalry, and oversolicitousness. The resultant hostility is due to the inability to accept the unfavored position, or to uninhibited ego evaluation.

PSYCHOSEXUAL DEVELOPMENT.—Various abnormalities in the course of psychosexual development are frequent in delinquents. These have chiefly to do with problems in relationships, especially object love relationships. Here again, family experiences are extremely important. It is quite characteristic of the delinquent that the capacity for lasting, friendly, emotional relationships is greatly diminished or absent.

In cases where sexual delinquency predominates, various difficulties in personality development, either constitutional or acquired, are usually found. However, many individuals presenting similar physical or mental findings achieve an adequate sublimation.

GENERAL PERSONALITY CHARACTERISTICS.—The delinquent personality is, in general, characterized by immaturity, egocentricity, and inability to establish emotional relationships with others, primarily because of lack of ability to identify or because of actual hostility.

By immaturity is meant a failure to develop in various ways, aside from mensurable biological inferiorities. Specifically, inability to restrain present impulses to pleasurable activity in the face of imminent penalty, or in favor of long-time goals; inadequate control of emotional reactions; and lack of poise and balance commensurate with age and position are some of the ways in which immaturity is shown.

Egocentricity appears in the search for personal pleasure, lack of consideration for others, absence of sense of guilt, often resulting in blaming others for difficulties really dependent on the individual, and a carping, critical attitude toward others. Not only does the delinquent tend to believe he is right and others wrong, but he feels that his emotional outbursts should be accepted without complaint by others. General moral and ethical ideas are considered only in the light of their advantages to the self.

It has been noted that there is a tendency for the delinquent to become stabilized, i.e., to mature emotionally, at about age 30 (for example, Foxe, 1938). This is true of nondelinquents as well, and is probably an expression, for both groups, of maturational factors so important in personal and social adjustment at different ages.

To sum up, a great many factors have been found important in the evolution of the personality of delinquents. *Not one is peculiar to the delinquent.* The most important points are found to be factors leading to increased hostility, egocentricity, and lack of consideration for others. These may depend primarily on abnormalities of constitution, or upon the effects of early, distorted, or thwarted relationships in the family or its substitute. *Delinquency is probably most frequently due to the subtle effects of interactions between individual and environment, leading to the establishment of particular personality sets.*

BIBLIOGRAPHY

AICHHORN, A. 1935. Wayward youth. New York: Viking.
ALEXANDER, F., & HEALY, W. 1935. Roots of crime. New York: Knopf.
ALEXANDER, F., & STAUB, H. 1931. The criminal, the judge and the public. New York: Macmillan.
ALLPORT, G. W. 1937. Personality: a psychological interpretation. New York: Holt.
ANDERSON, V. V. 1914. An analysis of one hundred cases studied in connection with the municipal courts of Boston. *Bost. med. surg. J., 171,* 341.
—— 1915. A proper classification of borderline mental cases among offenders. *Bost. med. surg. J., 173,* 466.
BARTEMEIER, L. H. 1931. The neurotic character as a new psychoanalytic concept. *Amer. J. Orthopsychiat., 1,* 512.
BENEDIKT, M. 1881. Anatomical studies upon brains of criminals. (Trans. by E. P. Fowler.) Baltimore: William Wood.
BOWERS, P. E. 1914. The recidivist. *J. crim. Law Criminol., 5,* 407.
—— 1915. Clinical studies in the relationship of insanity to crime. Michigan City, Ind.: Dispatch Printers.
BROMBERG, W. 1937. The mind of man. New York: Harper.
BROMBERG, W., & THOMPSON, C. B. 1937. The relation of psychosis, mental defect and personality types to crime. *J. crim. Law Criminol., 28,* 1.
CALDWELL, J. M., JR. 1941. The constitutional psychopathic state. *J. crim. Psychopath., 3,* 171.
CLECKLEY, H. 1941. The mask of sanity. St. Louis: Mosby.
CROTHERS, T. D. 1893. The disease of inebriety from alcohol, opium and other narcotic drugs. New York: E. B. Treat.
CURRAN, F., & SCHILDER, P. 1940–1941. A constructive approach to the problems of childhood and adolescence. (In two parts) *J. crim. Psychopath., 2,* 125, 305.
DRÄHMS, A. 1900. The criminal: his personnel and environment. New York: Macmillan.
DUGDALE, R. 1877. The Jukes: a study in crime, pauperism, disease and heredity. New York: Putnam.
FERNALD, W. E. 1908. The imbecile with criminal instincts. *Amer. J. Insan., 65,* 731–749.
FERRERO, MME. 1911. Criminal man according to Lombroso. New York: Putnam's.
FINK, A. E. 1938. Causes of crime: biological theories in the United States 1800–1915. Philadelphia: University Pennsylvania Press.
FOXE, A. N. 1938. Psychiatric classification in a prison. *Psychiat. Quart., 12,* 617.
—— 1939. An additional classification of criminals. *J. crim. Law Criminol., 2,* 232.
GLUECK, B. G. 1916. Studies in forensic psychiatry. Boston: Little, Brown.
—— 1918. A study of 608 admissions to Sing Sing Prison. *Ment. Hyg., N. Y., 2,* 85.
GLUECK, S. S. 1925. Mental disorders and the criminal law. Boston: Little, Brown.
GODDARD, H. H. 1910. The criminal imbecile. New York: Macmillan.
—— 1912. The Kallikak family: a study of the heredity of feeblemindedness. New York: Macmillan.
—— 1914. Feeblemindedness, its causes and consequences. New York: Macmillan.
GODDARD, H. H., & HILL, H. F. 1911. Feeblemindedness and criminality. *Train. Sch. Bull., 8,* 6.
GROSS, H. 1911. Criminal psychology. (Trans. from the 4th German ed. by H. M. Kallen.) Boston: Little, Brown.
GUTHEIL, E. A. 1941a. Neurosis and crime. *J. crim. Psychopath., 2,* 444.
—— 1941b. The criminal complex in compulsion. *J. crim. Psychopath., 3,* 253.
HAINES, T. H. 1916. Relative values of point scale and year scale measurements of one thousand minor delinquents. *J. exp. Psychol., 1,* 51.
HALL, G. S. 1904. Adolescence: its psychology and its relations to psychology,

anthropology, sociology, sex, crime, religion and education. (2 Vols.) New York: Appleton-Century.

HAMILTON, A. McL. 1883. Manual of medical jurisprudence. New York: Bermingham.

HART, H. H., & AXELRAD, S. 1941. The only-child delinquent contrasted with delinquents in large families. *J. crim. Law Criminol., 33,* 42.

HEALY, W. 1915. The individual delinquent. Boston: Little, Brown.

—— 1923. Mental conflict and misconduct. Boston: Little, Brown.

—— 1941. The psychiatrist looks at delinquency and crime. *Ann. Amer. Acad. polit. soc. Sci., 217,* 138.

HEALY, W., & ALPER, B. S. 1941. Criminal youth and the Borstal system. New York: Commonwealth Fund.

HEALY, W., & BRONNER, A. 1926. Delinquents and criminals, their making and unmaking. New York: Macmillan.

—— 1936. New light on delinquency and its treatment. New Haven: Yale University Press.

—— 1939. Treatment and what happened after. Boston: Judge Baker Guidance Center.

HENDERSON, D. K. 1939. Psychopathic states. New York: Norton.

HITCHCOCK, C. W. 1909. Imbecile, criminal, or both? *Amer. J. Insan., 65,* 510.

HOOTON, E. A. 1939. Crime and the man. Cambridge: Harvard University Press.

HRDLICKA, A. 1939. The criminal. *J. crim. Psychopath., 1,* 87.

KARPMAN, B. 1933. Case studies in the psychopathology of crime. Washington, D. C.: Mimeoform Press.

—— 1939. The delinquent as a type and personality. *J. crim. Psychopath., 1,* 24.

—— 1940. Principles and aims of criminal psychopathology. *J. crim. Psychopath., 1,* 187.

KARPMAN, B., *et al.* 1924. The psychopathic individual: a symposium. *Ment. Hyg., N. Y., 8,* 174.

KELLOR, F. A. 1901. Experimental sociology. New York: Macmillan.

KIERNAN, J. G. 1884. Moral insanity—what is it? *J. nerv. ment. Dis., 11,* 562.

KRAEPELIN, E. 1915. Psychiatrie. (8th ed.) Band IV. Leipzig: Barth.

KRETSCHMER, E. 1926. Physique and character. New York: Harcourt, Brace.

LEVY, D. M. 1932. On the problem of delinquency. *Amer. J. Orthopsychiat., 2,* 197.

LIPPMAN, H. S. 1937. The neurotic delinquent. *Amer. J. Orthopsychiat., 7,* 114.

LOMBROSO, C. 1911. Crime, its causes and remedies. (Trans. by H. P. Horton.) Boston: Little, Brown.

LOWREY, L. G. 1920. Note on a certain anomaly of gyration in brains of the insane. *Amer. J. Insan., 77,* 87.

—— 1926. Environmental factors in the behavior of children. *Amer. J. Psychiat., 6,* 227.

—— 1928a. Competitions and the conflict over difference. *Ment. Hyg., N. Y., 12,* 316.

—— 1928b. Feeblemindedness and behavior disorders. *Proc. Amer. Assn. Stud. Feeblemind., 33,* 96.

—— 1936. The family as a builder of personality. *Amer. J. Orthopsychiat., 6,* 117.

—— 1938. Problems of aggression and hostility in exceptional children. *Proc. 5th Inst., Child Res. Clin. Woods Schs.,* 22.

LYDSTON, G. F. 1904. The diseases of society. Philadelphia: Lippincott.

MAEDER, L. M. A. 1941. Diagnostic criteria: the concept of normal and abnormal. *Family, 22,* 171.

MAUGHS, S. 1941. A concept of psychopathy and psychopathic personality: its evolution and historical development. *J. crim. Psychopath., 2,* Part 1, p. 329; Part 2, p. 465.

MAY, J. V. 1912. Mental diseases and criminal responsibility. *St. Hosp. Bull., 5,* 339.

MENNINGER, K. A. 1938. Man against himself. New York: Harcourt, Brace.

MICHAEL, J., & WECHSLER, H. 1940. Criminal law and its administration. Chicago: Foundation Press.

MORRIS, A. 1941. Criminals' views on crime causation. *Ann. Amer. Acad. polit. soc. Sci., 217,* 138.

NEW YORK STATE COMMISSION OF CORRECTION, 1939 REPORT. 1940. Ossining: Sing Sing Prison.

NORTH, E. A. 1940. Psychopathic personality. *Dis. nerv. Syst., 1,* 136.

NOYES, A. P. 1934. Modern clinical psychiatry. Philadelphia: Saunders.

PARTRIDGE, G. E. 1930. Current conceptions of psychopathic personality. *Amer. J. Psychiat., 10,* 53.

PATTERSON, R. J. 1877. Report on moral insanity. *Trans. Amer. med. Assn., 28,* 359.

PRICHARD, J. C. 1835. A treatise on insanity and other disorders affecting the mind. London: Sherwood, Gilbert & Piper.

RANSOM, J. B. 1896. The physician and the criminal. *J. Amer. med. Assn., 27,* 788.

RAY, I. 1838. A treatise on the medical jurisprudence of insanity. Boston: Little, Brown.

RECKLESS, W. C. 1940. Criminal behavior. New York: McGraw-Hill.

RUSH, B. 1812. Medical inquiries and observations upon the diseases of the mind. (3rd ed., 1827.) Philadelphia: J. Grigg.

SPAULDING, E., & HEALY, W. 1914. Inheritance as a factor in criminality: a study of a thousand cases of young repeated offenders. *Bull. Amer. Acad. Med., 15,* 4.

SPITZKA, E. C. 1883. Manual of insanity. (2nd ed., 1887.) New York: E. B. Treat.

SPRAGUE, G. S. 1941. The psychopathology of psychopathic personalities. Abstract, *J. nerv. ment. Dis., 94,* 193. (Also in *Bull. N. Y. Acad. Med., 17,* 911.)

TALBOT, E. S. 1898. Degeneracy: its causes, signs and results. New York: Scribner's.

TREDGOLD, A. F. 1915. Mental deficiency. (2nd ed.) Baltimore: William Wood.

TULCHIN, S. H. 1939. Intelligence and crime. Chicago: University Chicago Press.

WHOLEY, C. C. 1914. Cases of moral insanity arising from inherent moral defectiveness. *J. Amer. med. Assn., 62,* 926.

WRIGHT, H. W. 1913. The problem of the criminal in the light of some modern conceptions. *J. Amer. med. Assn., 61,* 2119.

Chapter 27

UNFIT PERSONALITIES IN THE MILITARY SERVICES

By A. Warren Stearns, M.D.

IT IS DIFFICULT TO SAY when the concept of personality disorder first came into the human mind. Insanity and mental deficiency have long been recognized. References to mental disease and defect date back to the very remote past. The earliest references to what now seem to have been psychopathic personalities appeared under the heading of moral lunacy. Battie, who published in 1758, mentions nothing which could be so classified. However, Benjamin Rush, in 1812, speaks of an oration delivered before the American Philosophical Society in the year 1787 as giving an account of the nature and offices of the moral faculty of conscience. He gives several cases, three of which had come to his attention, and says, "How far the persons whose diseases have been mentioned should be considered responsible to human or divine laws for their action and where the line should be drawn which divides free agency from necessity and vice from disease I am unable to determine." Moreover, Sampson, writing first in 1841, gives an excellent case, which would seem to indicate that at least as early as 1819 the problem was a vexing one.

In the Richmond Lunatic Asylum, Dublin, Mr. George Combe saw a patient in 1829, who had been confined for ten years. He exhibited a total want of moral feeling and principle, yet possessed considerable intelligence, ingenuity, and plausibility. He had been a scourge to his family from childhood—had been turned out of the army as an incorrigible villain—had attempted the life of a soldier—had been repeatedly flogged—and had since attempted the life of his father. Respecting this man, Dr. Crawford, Substitute Physician at the Asylum, made the following remarks:—"He never was different from what he now is; he has never evinced the slightest mental incoherence on any one point, nor any kind of hallucination. It is one of those cases where there is great difficulty in drawing the line between extreme depravity and insanity, and in deciding at what point an individual should cease to be considered as a responsible moral agent, and amenable to the laws. The governors and medical gentlemen of the Asylum have often had doubts whether they were justified in keeping him as a lunatic, thinking him a more fit subject for a Bridewell. He appears, however, so totally callous with regard to every moral principle and feeling, so thoroughly unconscious of ever having done anything wrong, so completely destitute of all sense of shame or remorse when reproved for his vices or crimes, and has proved himself so utterly incorrigible throughout life, that it is almost certain that any jury, before whom he might be brought, would satisfy their doubts by returning him insane, which, in such a case, is the most humane line to pursue. He was dismissed several times from the asylum, and sent there for the last time for attempting to poison his father; and it seems fit he should be kept there for life as a moral lunatic: but there has never been the least symptom of diseased action of the brain, which is the general concomitant of what is usually understood as insanity. This, I consider, might with propriety be made the foundation for a division of lunatics into two great classes—those who were insane from original constitution, and never were otherwise—and those who have been insane at some period of life from diseased action of the brain, either permanent or intermittent.

Prichard, writing in 1835, is frequently given as the originator of the concept of moral lunacy. A careful reading of his chapter on *moral insanity*, however, would seem to indicate that it has nothing to do with constitutional inferiority, but is an attempt to group mental diseases according to emotional differences. The cases given would appear to be what are now called dementia praecox and manic depressive insanity.

Most psychiatric works from this time on grapple with this problem. As early as 1817 the *Habitual Criminal Law* was passed in Massachusetts recognizing that there are certain individuals who were prone to commit crime. Meanwhile, Lombroso (1911), and other members of the positivist school had developed the idea of a born criminal. Their belief was that this was an atavistic matter and they laid great stress upon physical stigmata of degeneration. Many went so far as to claim that by an examination and measurement of a child they could predict his future criminal life. Partridge (1930) states that, "The wider conception of psychopathic inferiority dates from Koch's statement in his *Leitfaden der Psychiatrie* (1888) and in his *Psychopathische Minderwertigkeiten* he refers to this as a new term."

Maudsley, in 1876, states, "Many cases of moral insanity will be found to be connected with more or less congenital moral defect or imbecility." Spitzka, in 1883, states, "Disorders of the moral sentiments may be congenital and equivalent to partial imbecility, as the father of American science, Rush, first pointed out." Later, speaking of moral insanity, Maudsley suggests that moral imbecility would be a better term. Nisbet, in 1893, states, "Without being positively insane, a person may have what is called the insane temperament, a condition characterized by singularities of thought, feeling, and action. He is eccentric in his habits; he does apparently purposeless acts, and he is often either extremely obstinate or given to violent fits of temper. Rarely, he lands in an asylum. . . . Moral insanity is another name given to insane temperament. The deficiency of moral feeling may be of a different kind, or it may be an ordinary deficiency analogous to lack of musical sense or color blindness."

In 1904, Dr. Walter E. Fernald stated the following:

To a trained observer the class of boys and girls in truant schools and in industrial and reform schools includes a rather large proportion of defectives where the intellectual defect is relatively slight and is overshadowed by the moral deficiency. The history of a case of this sort during infancy and early childhood, from a medical and psychological standpoint, is that of an abnormal child. While they generally present definite physical evidences of degeneracy, they are physically superior to the ordinary imbecile. Their school work is not equal to that of normal boys of the same age, but they are often abnormally bright in certain directions. They may be idle, thievish, cruel to animals or smaller children, wantonly and senselessly destructive and lawless generally. They are often precocious sexually and after puberty almost always show marked sexual delinquency or perversion. They are often wonderfully shrewd and crafty in carrying out their plans for mischief. They instinctively seek low company and quickly learn everything that is bad. They have little or no fear of possible consequences in the way of punishment. They acquire a certain spurious keenness and brightness and possess a fund of general information which is very deceiving on first acquaintance. They are apt to be accomplished liars. The great army of police court chronic criminals, vagrants and low prostitutes is largely recruited from this class of "moral imbeciles." These children are not simply bad and incorrigible, but they are irresponsible by reason of the underlying mental defect. The mental defect and the moral lack are alike the visible effects of incurable affection of the cerebral cortex. No method of training or discipline can fit them to become safe or desirable members of society. They cannot be "placed out" without great moral risk to innocent people. These cases should be recognized at an early age, before they have acquired facility in actual crime, and permanently taken out of the community to be trained to habits of industry and as far as possible contribute to their own support under direction and supervision. They are not influenced by the simple system of rewards and deprivations which easily serves to control the conduct of the feebleminded. They do not class well with the rather simple types of ordinary imbecility. When the actual number of this dangerously potential class of moral imbeciles is fully realized, they will be given lifelong care and supervision in special institutions combining the educational and developmental methods of a school for the feebleminded and the industry and security of a modern penal institution. Such provision would only be a rational extension of the principle of the indeterminate sentence, and, if safeguarded by careful and repeated expert examination and observation, could do no injustice and would greatly diminish crime in the immediate future.

Also, in 1908, Dr. Walter E. Fernald wrote:

The patients described vary greatly in intelligence and in the amount of definite knowledge which they have acquired, but they greatly resemble each other in their childish tastes, excessive vanity, unreliability, aggressive boastful egotism, selfishness, moral insensibility, fondness for malicious mischief and trouble-making, indolence, willingness to run great risks for the sake of some small gain, untruthfulness, lack of shame and remorse, lack of sympathy, etc.

The cases described fairly represent the criminal imbecile type. I have no doubt as to the actual imbecility and the resulting moral irresponsibility of every one of these cases. As a group, the female cases especially well illustrate the so-called "high-grade imbecile." In fact, the physical and psychical stigmata exhibited by this group of imbeciles, selected because of their criminal tendencies and acts, are merely the usual signs and symptoms found in the ordinary case of imbecility, modified only in degree and not in mind.

This class of borderline cases with criminal tendencies now constitutes a troublesome and puzzling factor in our institutions for the feebleminded. They are often malicious, deceitful, and inciters of mischief and insubordination. They have a wonderful power of suggestion over their simple-minded fellow-patients. They are generally committed to the institution against the wishes of their parents. The efforts of their friends to obtain their release are constant and perplexing. If a case of this description is taken before the Supreme Court on a writ of habeas corpus, it is more than likely that the patient will be released. Indeed, it is not difficult to find reputable medical men who would testify that the case "is by no means a fool," and that he ought not to be deprived of his liberty. It is evident that clinical types and shadings of mental deficiency have become familiar to the alienist which have not yet been so definitely formulated and classified as to be readily recognized by the profession generally. It is equally true that the legal definitions and precedents pertaining to ordinary cases of imbecility are inadequate when applied to these high-grade imbeciles. We have, therefore, to face the anomalous fact that it is easy to have a class of patients committed to our institutions who are promptly discharged by the higher courts because these lesser types of deficiency have neither been adequately formulated nor recognized legally.

Dr. Guy Fernald, in 1912, wrote the following:

There is urgent need of special legal recognition of the class of defective delinquents, and of suitable provision for their proper commitment and permanent detention. The law should recognize that such a class exists by making a distinctive legal definition. There should be a definite form of procedure for the commitment of the defective delinquent similar to that used for the commitment of the insane. This procedure should be equally applicable to cases in the courts or in the community, to youthful and adult criminal defectives, and to cases which develop in the institutions for the feeble-minded. They should be committed to permanent care and custody, under special institutional conditions combining the educational and developmental methods of a school for the feeble-minded with the industry and security of a modern penal institution. Under proper conditions, perhaps in a farm colony, the directed labor of these persons would materially reduce the cost of their support. Their immoral and criminal depredations would be prevented, the cost of repeated arrests, trials and commitments would be avoided, and they would not be able to bring helpless children into the world. Provision should be made for the safeguarding of the rights of the individual by periodical expert examination and observation, and by the possibility of ultimate release under parole.

From this time on constitutional inferiority and constitutional psychopathic inferiority are frequently found in American psychiatric literature. Dr. May, again according to Partridge (1930), states that Dr. Meyer told him that he used the term psychopathic inferiority in connection with the Thaw case in 1908. By 1910, it was customary to classify individuals committed to hospitals for mental disease who were neither feebleminded nor insane, but whose conduct was extremely disordered, under the heading "constitutional inferiority." The concept at that time was not especially different from our present concept, but more emphasis was put upon evidence of nervous irritability during early childhood and upon evidence of physical inferiority. In the author's study (1914) of the population of the Bridgewater State Hospital for criminals, nineteen such individuals were found to be committed there as insane, usually because of the commission of atrocious crimes.

At the time of the opening of the Boston Psychopathic Hospital in 1912, American psychiatry was very much under the influence of Kraepelin, who spoke of congenital states of morbid personalities, morbid criminals and born swindlers. However, he later clarified the matter by speaking of psychopathic personalities and divided them into the paranoid, inadequate, and emotionally unstable. This classification was current for some years, but the last war resulted in a recurrence of constitutional inferiority and many constitutional psychopathic states.

For many years there have been occasional case studies such as "Jesse Pomeroy" by Folsom; Haberman's "A case of psychopathic constitution resembling so-called moral insanity"; and more recently, Thom's "A case of juvenile delinquency." During recent years many writers have sought to clarify the matter by elaborate psychopathological studies (see Kahn, 1931; Partridge, 1930; Kraepelin, 1915; Healey, 1936; Preu, Chapter 30; and many others). More recently Alvarez (1942) has used the term constitutional inadequacy to cover a certain number of chronic nervous invalids.

Cases Seen in Military Service

With the onset of the war the writer, in charge of a neuropsychiatric service in a naval hospital, was forced to deal with the matter in a practical way. Patients were daily being received who did not show gross physical disease, who were not insane or feebleminded, and yet who had shown vagaries of conduct making them appear undesirable as members of the Navy. Of the first 500 admissions, 16% were classified as personality disorders, to use the Navy nomenclature. No attempt was made at exactness in terminology. Those cases who were neither insane nor feebleminded but who showed persistent vagaries of conduct were assumed to be psychopathic and placed in this group. The following is the classification used in the U. S. Navy Diagnostic Nomenclature (1938).

1501.　Constitutional psychopathic inferiority without psychosis
1502.　Constitutional psychopathic state, criminalism
1503.　Constitutional psychopathic state, emotional instability
1504.　Constitutional psychopathic state, inadequate personality
1505.　Constitutional psychopathic state, paranoid personality
1506.　Constitutional psychopathic state, pathological liar
1507.　Constitutional psychopathic state, sexual psychopathy

One who uses this concept extensively is faced with a dilemma. Most individuals whose conduct departs widely from the conventional pattern show certain constitutional tendencies which may be called psychopathic. Yet, there is little sense in substituting the word psychopathic for criminal or pauper. At best, the concept in its application seems to be entirely behavioristic. At one end of the scale we have those who are so erratic in their conduct that they cannot get along in the most carefully regulated environment. At the other end of the scale we have those so well adjusted that they can meet the vicissitudes of the most adverse environment. Where shall we draw the line between the medical problem called the psychopathic and the social problem called normal? Obviously, a decision must be made arbitrarily. It is the writer's belief that certain criteria should be insisted upon. In other words there should be some evidence that the disorder is constitutional, e.g., a tendency such as stealing or homosexuality which can be traced from early childhood, or else the reaction being so out of line with what might be expected as to justify a belief in a psychopathic constitution.

The following analogy has been a help in understanding the concept. If a man is six feet in height, we characterize him as tall; if he is six and a half feet we say he is very tall; but if he is ten feet in height we no longer use the ordinary standards by which bodily height is expressed, but use the term giant, implying the existence of a morbid process. Likewise, if a person is short enough there comes a time when we call him a dwarf, inferring the existence of a monstrosity. If we assume as normal and healthy a child who develops through its first few years according to a fairly definite schedule, who upon going to school progresses along with the other children and gradually tends to mold his conduct like that of other children, after which he goes through the adolescent period with only minor changes and embarks upon adult life, gets a job at which he specializes and excels, establishes a home and from then on leads a conventional life, we are forced to consider variations from this conventional pattern as abnormal. These variations may be due to intellectual defect which is a fairly well established concept at the present time, or the development of a psychosis, where again we have fairly definite criteria. If neither of these conditions is found we have two possibilities left, a normal reaction to an abnormal environment, or an abnormal re-action to a normal environment. Unfortunately, the abnormal environ-ment and the abnormal personality are often associated and it comes down to a matter of individual judgment as to with which we are dealing (see Chapter 24 by Faris).

It is obvious that we can have as many types of eccentric people as there are human traits. Their only common denominator is that they behave ineffectually. There are certain inadequate personalities, aesthetic in type, lacking in drive, who do not meet their obligations and frequently resort to alcohol or a neurosis as an escape. These, of course, are closely related to Kraepelin's inadequate personalities as well as to Alvarez' con-stitutional inadequacies. The individuals in another group are well, but they also lack drive, or they are emotionally unstable and so have diffi-culty in making the sustained effort to support themselves and have to be assisted by friends or relatives or the public. The members of still another group are from their earliest days rebellious and intractable (the trouble-makers) and have all the other characteristics so frequently described as criminal. If 50% of the population are so constituted, obviously the concept has no validity, as they are just average people. In other words, it is folly to extend the group to include all of the social problems of society. It should be reserved for persons who stand out grossly as variants.

Illustrative Cases.—It must be confessed that an attempt to abstract cases shows the use of the concept by us to have been largely utilitarian. A study of the record of the individual and an analysis of the episode which led to his coming to the hospital has convinced us that it would be imprudent to send him back to duty. Whereas some of this group would undoubtedly make good, they belong to a category which as a group offers little promise. A gleaning of a few data from the cases following will perhaps help to show the sort of problems that have occurred al-though fuller case study makes it very difficult to find "the least common denominator" in these cases.

H. D. V. Sent in because of tendency to seek a weapon when he lost his temper. Much trouble in the Navy through violent attempts upon others with weapons. A haughty, belligerent, egoistic, individual, thoroughly un-reliable on the ward, a bully and a petty thief.

T. J.F. A sneak thief with many house-of-correction sentences, lived with prostitutes at their expense; traveled in a carnival, ran away shortly after enlistment.

B. F. A somewhat talented, artistic person who went to theological school, left after a short while, when he became involved in a homo-sexual episode. Then entered law school, stayed one term. Went to theo-logical school of another denomination and gave up after a short while. Enlisted in Army and in a few months bought out, then enlisted in the Navy, very unhappy, discontented, talked of suicide. and said he couldn't stand it. Given medical discharge. Went to another theological school, stayed a little while, and again changed his mind.

A. G. Backward in school, borderline feebleminded, irregular work at odd jobs. Wife works steadily. Shortly after enlistment, while on guard, shot himself with a 30-30 rifle through the foot. Very much depressed, soon cleared up and not considered psychotic.

S. A. H. Somewhat of a problem child, left high school against parents' wishes, returned a year later, started college and gave it up to join the Navy. Contracted gonorrhea and syphilis from one exposure. Very much depressed, took poison and nearly killed himself. Sent to hospital as manic-depressive. Soon cleared up.

J. H. On parole from state reform school, a roamer and persistent parole violator, petty thief, deserted soon after enlistment. Very dull, borderline feebleminded.

V. M. N. Committed to a reform school in early childhood, frequent runaway and parole violator, said not to be vicious but intractable and undependable. Returned from abroad for refusal to obey orders. Borderline feebleminded. Ran away from hospital.

R. F. M. Two years of high school, involved in domestic friction at home, left school because of grief over parents' quarrels. Shy, easily fatigued, complained of his stomach. In brig for going to sleep while on watch, which he persistently did. Many somatic complaints suggesting psychoneurosis.

R. C. O. States that he has never been attracted by females, and since 15 years of age has habitually had sexual satisfaction with males. No difficulty in Navy but in acute anxiety state for fear he might get into trouble and be sent to prison.

G. J. O. Backward in school, borderline feebleminded, frequently runs away. One term in reformatory, deserted from Army and ran away shortly after entering Navy. Many complaints suggesting neurosis. Dizziness, headache, and so on.

E. W. O. Left third year of high school to enter Navy, very homesick, seasick, and couldn't stand duty on tanker as member of gun crew. Cried, very unhappy, and talked of suicide but cleared up promptly in hospital.

C. H. P. Sent in for headache, having been A. W. O. L. complained of headache, indigestion, and history showed that he had always been asthenic, frequently going to doctors as a child. Caused neurasthenia but difficulty appears to be constitutional. His previous instability was carefully verified but he has recently written in saying that he lied about his headache and now wishes to join the Army and asks help in getting him in.

J. H. R. Backward in school, worked with father, drank creosote in brig while awaiting trial for being A. W. O. L., ran away from hospital, cried when discussing problem, yet he immediately did it again and also drank Clorox while in the brig.

A. D. A. Many arrests for vagrancy—bad conduct discharge before this enlistment. Ten days A. W. O. L. Alcoholic. Sent in with a question of alcoholic delirium. Surveyed C. P. S. without psychosis.

A. J. A. Backward in school, professional fighter, alcoholic. Much naval disciplinary trouble. Sent in from the brig of his ship for scabies. Returned to duty, no disease, but subsequently showed utter irresponsibility. Should have been called C. P. I.

J. P. A. Upon going to sea was very much frightened, so frightened by gunfire that he could not perform his duty. A dull, asthenic individual, who went two years to high school. Simply lacking in the stamina required for military duty.

J. W. E. A somewhat dull man, completed ninth grade at 17. During any excitement went into hysterical attacks. On one occasion was mute for several days. On another occasion, frenzied excitement, particularly upset by gunfire.

R. S. F. Sent in under arrest for homosexual advances. Entertainer at night club, bell boy in hotel, roamer. States that at 15 had first homosexual experience. Women never attracted him, males always. Somewhat effeminate in his manner.

B. E. C. An adopted child who graduated from high school, worked with his foster father in a female beauty parlor; on the stage in the evening impersonating a female; picked up spare money by prostitution to male homosexuals. Admitted in acute anxiety state afraid he would transgress in Navy and get sent to prison.

E. M. B. A persistent runaway at home, irregular attendance at school, petty thief diagnosed as kleptomaniac before enlistment. Ran away 10 days after enlistment. Suicide attempt in brig.

D. G. F. Previous history negative. At 21 fell in love with a 16-year-old girl whose parents would not consent to her marriage. Much friction because girl did not marry him. He went out into a park, cut his wrists, and drank sulphanaphthol.

F. X. B. Began stealing in early childhood. During high school forged checks and ran away and enlisted in Marines. Ran away and was sent to hospital where he again escaped. Attempted suicide by gas. Following a medical discharge he enlisted in Navy; immediately ran away, and again attempted suicide and was sent to this hospital.

J. J. D. A good boy, devoted to his mother, became discouraged over failure to get a type of transfer he wished. Given leave, went home, somewhat sad, hated to go back. Brother took him to train, later found him in the evening in an alleyway with both wrists cut and having drunk a bottle of mercurochrome. Cleared up rapidly in hospital. Did not appear to be psychotic.

W. J. D. Eighth grade at 16. A runaway and a petty thief, committed at 14 to state reformatory during minority, and in and out of this and other reformatories. Five commitments to hospitals for mental disease for observation. Only work as laborer at carnivals. Married to a similar character. Enlisted and soon ran away.

F. F. I. A problem child, a runaway from home. In early youth committed to reformatory at age 10. Frequent runaway, characterized by police as worst man in town. Traveled with circus and carnivals, no steady work. When attempt was made to take blood from his arm, he went into hysterical convulsions. Petty thief.

F. J. C. At 10 years of age in juvenile court; 75 arrests in Suffolk County, discharged from Navy as undesirable in 1917. Has had commitments to seven different hospitals for the insane, usually for observation and delirium tremens. Has served sentences in at least four different prisons. Little or no work.

W. W. K. Problem child, juvenile court, many arrests usually for drunkenness and wife beating. Irregular employment. Enlisted when drunk and immediately ran away.

J. E. P. A dull boy who had nearly finished high school, constant complainer, considered an invalid, only job as errand boy. Left school because his eyes hurt, unable to keep up with others in the Navy and sent to hospital on account of eyes. Considered inadequate personality.

J. C. A. A backward person in school, family on welfare. Several trips on the Merchant Marine. No steady work. Walked and talked in sleep. Frequent runaway, enlisted in Navy, ran away from training station, attempted suicide when put in brig for punishment.

E. J. A. Backward in school, on parole from reformatory when enlisted. Committed to state hospital as insane in 1940 during an episode. While in our brig refused food, stood mute in fixed posture for several days, attempted suicide. Spent a day or two making rhythmic motions, saying the same thing over and over again, suggestion catatonia. Cleared up promptly. Considered C. P. I. with psychosis.

R. O. B. Expelled from high school, roamer, petty thief, pathological liar, posed as a college man and borrowed all the money on the ward. Problem child. Ran away shortly after enlistment.

E. L. B. Subject to outbursts of temper. Habitually sought a weapon during these outbreaks. In many courts and fighting; all the traits of the feebleminded, with IQ of 75. Cried violently if sad, or into a frenzy if irritated.

J. B. Juvenile delinquent, backward in school, persistent runaway. Enlisted in Navy and almost immediately ran away. Rebellious and intractable.

E. P. C. Race track habitue, made his living as a pimp and petty gambler. Alcoholic. Lived on the income which his wife received as a prostitute. Ran away shortly after enlistment.

R. J. C. Backward in school, good family, on probation for breaking and entering when enlisted. Many arrests for petty offenses. Rebellious at home. Ran away shortly after enlistment.

J. E. C. Backward in school, many jobs of short duration. Quarrelsome and unmanageable at home. Deserted shortly after enlistment.

A. M. D'A. Committed to reform school as a stubborn child at 12. Persistent parole violator and petty thief. Borderline feebleminded. IQ 71. Deserted shortly after enlistment. Ran away from hospital.

H.S. Said to have received a head injury as a child. Ran away from home at 10 and roamed throughout the United States traveling on freights. No known arrests, undesirable discharge from the Army in June, enlisted in Navy in September and soon ran away; ran away from hospital.

P. J. Z. Backward in school, frequent truant on probation in juvenile court, discharged from C. C. C. for disciplinary reasons. A nomad, admitted to the hospital once, worked well, and returned to duty but after 10 days ran away. Attempted suicide by hanging in brig.

C. S. Y. An older man, aged 53, enlisted as 46. In the Army in last war. Father was a doctor and mayor of a large city in West. Ran away at 16 and has never seen his family since. A soldier of fortune roaming all over the face of the earth as a common sailor and for last 16 years as a stunt man in Hollywood. Lived alone, had little or nothing to do with other people, no friends, paranoid, egoistic, vain, very proud of his body and his exploits. Called "Pap" by sailors which led to frequent outbreaks of temper. Thought he was being discriminated against by everybody.

S. C. Several arrests as a young man, served one sentence in prison. In 1937 when out of work and in domestic trouble had period of amnesia lasting 12 days, brought to hospital by shore patrol in cataleptic state, did not speak for several days, cornea insensitive, claims amnesia for period of about 10 days. Had recently served a sentence in brig for A. W. O. L. and a fine of $150. Now cleared up completely but still claims amnesia.

J. H. S. Background excellent, a normal, healthy young man, homesick, returned to his home and told his parents that he had leave, stayed two weeks, started back for ship and 10 days later was brought to hospital claiming that he did not know his name or who he was. Now cleared up but still claims amnesia for period of about two weeks.

It will be noted that of these 42 cases, 20 were definitely problems of delinquency; 16 were problems of emotional instability; and but three were sexually peculiar. There were but two who appeared to be definitely sick, and only one who was paranoid. It is quite obvious that had we been working on a medical service, especially with the gastro-intestinal group, we would have had a very much larger number of sick and a smaller number of delinquent cases.

In studying large groups of incompetent people the writer has for many years used the gross subdivision of the sick, the poor and the bad. This may be a good way to classify personality disorders. It is certain that in the Navy part of them come to the attention of the disciplinary officers because of delinquency; another part are problems for the divisional officers because of inaptitude, and an unknown number are at the sick bay projecting their disabilities into symptoms of physical disease.

BIBLIOGRAPHY

ALVAREZ, W. C. 1942. Constitutional inadequacy. *J. Amer. med. Assn., 119,* 780–783.

BATTIE, W. 1758. A treatise on madness. London: J. Whiston & B. White.

FERNALD, G. G. 1912. The recidivist. *Amer. J. Insan., 68,* 866–875.

FERNALD, W. E. 1904. Care of the feeble-minded. In *National Bulletin of Charities and Corrections.*

—— 1908. The imbecile with criminal instinct. *Amer. J. Insan. 65,* 731–749.

HEALEY, W. 1936. New light on delinquency and its treatment. New Haven: Yale University Press.

KAHN, E. 1931. Psychopathic personalities. New Haven: Yale University Press.

LOMBROSO, C. 1911. Crime, its causes and remedies. (Trans. by H. P. Horton.) Boston: Little, Brown.

MAUDSLEY, H. 1876. Responsibility in mental disease. New York: Appleton-Century.

PARTRIDGE, G. E. 1930. Current conceptions of psychopathic personality. *Amer. J. Psychiat., 10,* 53–99.

PRICHARD, J. C. 1835. A treatise on insanity and other disorders affecting the mind. London: Sherwood, Gilbert & Piper.

RUSH, B. 1812. Medical inquiries and observations upon the diseases of the mind. Philadelphia: Kimber & Richardson.

SAMPSON, M. B. 1841. Criminal jurisprudence considered in relation to cerebral organization. London.

SPITZKA, E. C. 1883. Manual of insanity. (2nd ed., 1887.) New York: E. B. Treat.

STEARNS, A. W. 1914. A survey of the inmates of the Bridgewater State Farm.

—— 1916. A survey of defective delinquents under the care of the Massachusetts State Board of Insanity. *Amer. J. Insan., 72,* 427–437.

U. S. NAVY. 1938. Diagnostic nomenclature for the Medical Department of the U. S. Navy. Manual of the Medical Department. Ch. 15, Appendix, p. 53.

Chapter 28

THE PSYCHONEUROSES

By WILLIAM MALAMUD, M.D.

IT HAS LONG BEEN RECOGNIZED by the medical profession, and particularly by those working in the field of psychiatry, that the psychoneuroses occupy a unique and important place in the study of human adjustment. Their frequent incidence, the rich variability of their clinical pictures, and the fact that they afford a link between the more serious mental disorders and normal personality functions and between psychiatry as a specialty and medicine in general make them a natural starting point for the discussion of mental diseases in the medical curriculum. In a handbook whose purpose is to present personality functions and their disorders to a group that extends beyond the limits of the medical profession, an understanding of the nature, characteristics, manner of development, and methods of treatment of the psychoneuroses gains even greater fundamental value for the following reasons:

The Prevalence of Psychoneuroses.—It may be said without fear of exaggeration that the number of persons whose adjustment is interfered with because of the various forms of psychoneurotic disturbances is greater than that found in any other single type of medical disease known to the profession. A well-known and reliable specialist in internal medicine, who was, at the time, the director of one of the largest general hospitals in the country, estimated that of the entire clientele of the outpatient department of his institution computed over one year, fully 75% were suffering either from pure psychoneurotic syndromes or psychoneurotic superimpositions upon somatic diseases. Even if this may be an unusual proportion of the incidence of these disorders, other men working in the field and equipped with the training and interest enabling them to evaluate their material properly have varied in their estimates from a conservative 40% to the high 75% mentioned above (Strecker, 1930; Ebaugh, 1940). When we consider the fact that there are a great many people in the general population who are afflicted with difficulties of this type but who rarely consult a physician or particularly one who specializes in psychiatry, we can form an idea of the high proportion of individuals who are more or less incapacitated in their adjustment by psychoneurotic ailments. Any attempt to understand personality disorders, therefore, must include an acquaintance with the nature and mechanisms of the psychoneuroses.

833

Even if we disregard the question of disorders in the functions of the personality and deal with the behavior of the average individual, we are still confronted continually with the need to understand the factors which have been brought to light by students of neurotic behavior. Students of normal psychology are well aware that our knowledge of human behavior, and particularly our knowledge of its dynamics and motivation, has been greatly enriched by contributions from this field. The impetus that has been given to the progress of dynamic psychology by psychoanalysis (see Chapters 3, 6, 7, 8, 9, and 20 in this book), by studies of experimental neuroses in animals (Anderson and Parmenter, 1941; Masserman, 1943; see also Chapters 12 and 13), of war neuroses, of children's disorders, and others is well known and requires no further elaboration. If, in addition to the study of personality functions in the individual, we consider the problems of social pathology and group behavior in general, we find hitherto isolated but recently more concerted attempts to understand the disorganization of group behavior on the basis of what we know takes place in the development of a neurosis. Such problems as disturbances in morale, class unrest, and the reaction of the general population to catastrophes have been subjected to analyses of this kind which have added considerable clarification. For instance, the studies recently published in England by Glover (1941), Bion (1940), and Sargent (1940) have shown that the development of unusual attitudes, anxieties, and resentments in the group can be understood in relation to the stress and strain to which society is subjected in more or less the same manner in which a psychoneurotic syndrome develops in the individual.

Paradoxical as it may appear, considering the widespread incidence of such disturbances and the somewhat glib use of the word *neurotic* not only in academic vocabulary but in everyday conversation, there is a surprising lack of unanimity and clarity as to what is meant by the concept of psychoneurosis, what its limitations should be, to what particular forms of behavior it should be applied, and under what conditions it develops. At the outset, therefore, I should like to consider what we might call a definition of the psychoneuroses and proceed from it to a discussion of their manner of development, clinical manifestations, differential diagnosis, and treatment. To the psychiatrist it is clear that there are certain cases with syndromes so definite that there is no doubt as to their being representative of a typical psychoneurosis. Such a syndrome can be utilized here for the purpose of abstracting from it the features that render it typical of this form of disturbance and with this as a nucleus we can develop the concept of what the term stands for. With this in mind, I should like to present the following case:

A 28-year-old married man was brought into a general hospital with the chief complaint of blindness. The events leading up to his admission were as follows: Shortly before admission he was involved in a minor automobile accident. The patient apparently sustained only minor scratches, but directly after the collision he complained of the fact that he could not see.

The hospital examinations failed to show any signs of physical injury aside from a few abrasions, and no organic reason could be found for the blindness. He was referred to the psychiatric department with the diagnosis of Psychoneurosis, Hysteria.

The first interview brought to light the fact that the patient sustained the accident while driving to visit his wife, who had just been confined with the first child. His first spontaneous remark was to the effect that since he was now blind and would probably remain so for life, his first duty to his wife was to divorce her, thus obviating the necessity of tying her down to a blind man. A careful physical and neurological re-examination failed to show any organic basis for this symptom, and an analysis was undertaken of the life history of the patient in order to understand why that symptom had developed. Briefly, the facts were as follows: The patient was an only child. The father was physically of slight build, of a meek, dependent type of personality, economically unsuccessful. The mother was the direct antithesis, ample of body and "strong" in character. She ruled the household with an iron hand, serving both as master and support of the father and of the patient. The patient had inherited a queer combination of the father's physical characteristics and the mother's indomitable and independent character. Early in life, as usually happens, he had built up his attitude toward the sexes on the basis of his own parents. His feelings toward them were ambivalent. He liked the sympathetic and kind father, but pitied his weakness and dependence. He respected the mother, but at the same time hated her and revolted against her domineering attitude. Two important factors developed as he reached puberty. Fearing a fate similar to that of the father, he had determined never to get married. Seeking independence and freedom, he decided to cut away from home and make his own way. He succeeded in this quite well and as far back as early adolescence he became self-supporting in a position that furnished him comfortable means. He adhered to his original decision not to get married, although since he was apparently sexually a normal person he was attracted to members of the opposite sex. He had several affairs which invariably took the same pattern. As long as it was a matter of friendship only or uncompromising sexual contacts, he continued the relationship, but as soon as any hint of marriage appeared, he found some means of dissolving the contact. His present wife was, of course, the last of these affairs. He became very much attached to her and a unique but understandable relationship was established between them. She was very similar in character to his mother, or at least she appeared so to him, and early in their contacts he began to seek her advice in business affairs, and let her make decisions for him. The more he did so, the greater became his discomfort in her presence, but nevertheless he could not find the necessary strength to break the relationship. In the course of events she suggested that they get married and in a weak moment he acquiesced. At his instigation they had decided that care should be taken to avoid children at least for a while, although economically he was in a position which would have permitted the expense necessary for the support of a family.

About two years after the marriage she became pregnant. A quarrel ensued and he accused her of deliberately allowing this to happen. He tried to convince her that she should have an artificial abortion but she refused. All through her pregnancy, as became apparent in the analysis, he had hoped that the pregnancy would not mature. The realization came to him during the analysis that he still had had hopes of some day breaking away from his wife, but that the birth of the child would place an insuperable barrier in his way. When she was taken to the hospital for delivery he spent a few days in his home in great anxiety, conscious of fears that something would happen either to the wife or to the child. Then the news came that he was the father of a normal boy and that both the child and his wife were in good condition. On his way to the hospital after this news, the accident occurred which resulted in his blindness. As the analysis progressed he became aware of the reason for the symptom and for his attitude toward women in general and toward his wife and his mother in particular. His symptom disappeared but the adjustment of the patient to the situation became possible only after further interviews not only with him but with the wife. It became apparent to both of them that his relationship with her, particularly his dependence upon her and her function of leader in the family, was something that she did not want at all but which developed on the basis of the fact that she felt his need and search for these. With all his natural independence and desire to make his own decisions he was hampered by his early conditioning at home and unconsciously began to seek these when he met a person who resembled his mother physically. The discussions with the two resulted in his gaining the position in the house which he always feared was impossible between man and woman, and both of them were quite contented in the newly-gained relationship.

An analysis of the important issues in the above-described case brings to the fore a series of features which can be regarded as fundamental in the concept of psychoneurosis. These can be discussed under three main headings. In the first place, we find a certain manner of development which logically leads up to the formation of the symptom-complex. Secondly, we deal with a clinical picture of the fully developed disorder equally representative of this disease, and finally, we notice the absence of certain characteristics which led to the exclusion of other types of personality disturbance. It is true that in the case quoted we are dealing with a special type of psychoneurotic symptom-complex. In other cases we may find additional possibilities in etiology and clinical picture. In the development of our concept of what constitutes a psychoneurosis we shall first bring to the foreground the essential features in the case quoted and then add to these such factors as are related to them and are found in other forms of this syndrome, thus completing what can be designated as a definition of the concept of psychoneurosis.

Etiology and Manner of Development.—A certain degree of importance must be ascribed to the original personality make-up of our patient. We spoke in a general way of the fact that this young man had "inherited" a combination of characteristics belonging to each of his parents and that this was of importance in laying the foundation for his subsequent attitudes toward life and seemed to be characteristic of him since the earliest days of his childhood. Whether or not this can be regarded as actually transmitted by germ plasm is a question. It is significant that in his family history a number of instances of so-called psychopathic trends occurred somewhat more frequently than in the case of the average individual. I should prefer to regard these personality traits as more properly constitutional in the sense of characteristics which were either inherited or acquired very early in life but in either case had become more or less rigidly fixed so that they could not be affected to any great extent by further cultural impact. In addition to this constitutional foundation, however, and much more important both in the formation of the symptoms and in the influence which analytic treatment could exert upon them, we have a series of experiences running through his whole early history which have made him the arena of conflicting emotional tendencies. His natural desire for freedom and for the supremacy of his sex was counterbalanced by the feeling of respect toward and dependence upon the mother. We see in the subsequent development that with all his apparent determination to retain his independence, he finally succumbed to the tendency to reestablish the early protective environment afforded by the mother as soon as he met the person with whom he fell in love and who represented most clearly the mother image. A similar conflicting issue was the one introduced in his early adolescence when his growing need for heterosexual contacts clashed with his original determination not to get married. Before this, when the need for such contact was not biologically as strong, he could hold to his determination with much less difficulty.

Other opposing trends somewhat less obvious may nevertheless be considered as possibilities; for example, the unconscious desire to enjoy once more the protective and guiding hand of the mother introduced the need of identifying his wife with the mother and thus placing himself in a position of incestuous relationship with all the feelings of guilt and fear of punishment that it usually involves. It is interesting to note that his avenue of escape in the form of functional blindness reenacted the age-old story of Oedipus, who paid with his eyesight for the unnatural act of marrying his mother. It might be added here that an indirect investigation proved conclusively that, at least consciously, this man knew nothing of the myth of Oedipus Rex. Finally, we had in the events immediately preceding the development of the disease the reenactment of the early home situation. It is true that, superficially, early in the analysis the patient came to regard the pregnancy and the birth of the child as simply a stronger bond in the marital situation and, therefore, removing the possibility of his regaining his freedom. Later on, however, it became evident that of greater importance was the fact that the birth of the child was a living proof before the world of his having assumed the role of his own father in relationship to a woman whom he had identified with his mother. We also see that it was by his own maneuvering that he had forced his wife into a position where she had to act toward him in the same way that his mother had done toward his father.

To recapitulate, therefore, etiologically we find the following three essential features: (a) a certain type of personality which serves as a foundation or suitable soil for the development of this form of reaction; (b) a series of life experiences leading to conflicting tendencies out of which the person himself sees no solution; and (c) a reenactment of the original setting which, given an opportunity, finds a solution in the pathological symptom complex. These three features can be found to serve as etiologic factors in the development of psychoneuroses, with this proviso, however, that the development of the disease syndrome depends upon the relative severity of each of these factors. Given a strong personality predisposition, the other two factors need not be much more marked than we find in the lives of normal people. Similarly, given a severe conflict, the personality and reenactment of the situation need not be definitely unusual; and finally, given a reenactment of a particularly severe type, the first two factors may be of a degree which in all probability would not in themselves have led to the development of a psychoneurosis. This is particularly apparent in the cases of the development of such disturbances in situations as trying as, for instance, one finds in war.

Clinical Manifestations.—Outstanding in the clinical picture of this case is the creation of a somatic symptom without any basis in the form of physical pathology in the organ involved. Moreover, we find a certain characteristic affective attitude toward the symptom. At no time during his blindness did this man show any great distress over his condition and, in fact, from the beginning was more concerned about the future of his family than his own. It is the lack of proper concern over symptoms that has traditionally been referred to as "la belle indifference" of the hysterical patient. It seemed as if he had excluded his eyesight from the sphere of his personality and treated it in a more or less academic, objective fashion. This is a characteristic combination of features in one particular form of psychoneurosis. A general survey of the field indicates a variety of other possible clinical pictures which fall into three main categories.

CONVERSIONS.—By this we mean the transformation, as it were, of a psychic conflict into a somatic symptom, and here we have several possible configurations: (1) the creation of physical symptoms without underlying organic pathology; (2) exaggeration of organic symptoms or their persistence when the cause no longer exists; (3) production of organic pathology such as hypertension, mucous colitis, etc.; (4) creation of pseudo-psychotic symptoms.

ANANKASTIC REACTIONS.—That is, ideas or activities which the patient feels himself forced to entertain against his own will. Here we have (1) obsessions, which are anankastic thoughts; (2) phobias, which are unwarranted fears; (3) compulsions, which are forced activities such as continuous uncalled-for hand washing.

FAULTY CONTROL OF EMERGENCY REACTIONS.—This is a concept used by Rado (1939) and has reference to the unwarranted utilization of measures that biologically are intended to serve only in actual emergencies. Anxiety, fatigue, sense of guilt or of inadequacy, and irritability when they develop in situations that do not warrant their occurrence belong to this group of symptoms.

We shall return in the following pages to a discussion of the various forms of manifestations that can be grouped under each of these general headings. At present we might say that all of these could be regarded as features characteristic of the psychoneurotic picture or, in other words, *positive* phenomena.

Differentiating Features.—These are symptoms which are characteristically absent in the psychoneurosis and whose presence would militate against such a diagnosis. We designate them as *negative* phenomena and, unlike the positive features, they must all be *absent* in a given case if it is to be regarded as psychoneurotic. They are as follows:

1. *Demonstrable organic pathology* relevant to the etiology of the symptoms. This does not mean that a psychoneurotic patient may not have organic disease of one kind or another. If the disturbance, however, is to be regarded as psychoneurotic, as, for instance, the blindness in the case quoted above, there should be no demonstrable lesion anywhere in the visual apparatus which could be regarded as an adequate basis for the symptom.

2. *Consistent and lasting deterioration* in the intellectual functions, such as, for example, disturbance in orientation, judgment, memory, etc., as they are found in the psychoses.

3. *Primary disturbances of the mood* or affect as they are found in the manic-depressive and schizophrenic psychosis respectively; and finally,

4. *Persistent distortion of external reality*, such as projections.

On the basis of the above analysis we can now present a definition of the psychoneuroses as follows: psychoneurotic reactions are disturbances in the function of the personality which usually develop in certain types of personality make-up, and are the expressions of emotional conflicts whose nature or relationship to the symptoms are not consciously understood by the patient. They are characterized by clinical features of a positive type (conversions, anankastic reactions, or faulty control of emergency measures) and negative features consisting of the absence of relevant organic pathology, deterioration of intelligence, primary disturbance of mood or affect, and consistent and lasting distortions of external reality.

With the above definition and its analysis as a background, we shall now attempt a more detailed discussion of the manner of development and nature of the psychoneuroses. This discussion is to be presented in three sections along the lines that were followed in the analysis of the definition, that is: (1) *etiology*; (2) *symptomatology and clinical syndromes*; (3) *the differentiation of the psychoneuroses* from other forms of personality disturbances.

Etiology

As was pointed out above, the determining factors of the case presented could be arbitrarily divided into constitutional, developmental (in terms of the formation of the conflict), and the immediate precipitating factors in which, usually, a reenactment and accentuation of the conflict situation takes place. These three sets of determinants are found in all the cases, although it must be emphasized that their relative importance differs in the individual cases so that first one and then another may be brought into the foreground as the deciding etiological factor. In any case, however, if the treatment is to be carried out in a rational manner, due consideration must be given to all three. With this in mind, let us see what role each one of these is likely to play in the causation of these disturbances.

Constitutional.—The use of the word *constitutional* rather than *hereditary* is purposeful because we are interested primarily in personality traits which either by virtue of hereditary transmission or strong influence early in life become so deeply rooted in the make-up of the individual that they are not easily influenced by environmental factors either during the later development or the attempts at treatment. Furthermore, it is an almost impossible task to differentiate personality traits which are inherited from those which have been acquired early in life. With our present available means of investigation we depend upon historical data in the estimation even of the hereditary factors, basing this entirely on the frequency with which they recur in the family history of the individual. It is obvious, however, that since the early and most impressionable years of the patient's life are spent in the closest proximity with and dependence upon various members of the family, they can just as easily be acquired as inherited. It is best, therefore, to speak of them in a general way as constitutional and to take as criteria of their belonging to this category the following: the presence of similar traits in a comparatively large number of the family antecedents, their consistent manifestation from the earliest days of life and throughout the whole history of the individual, and the appearance of traits of this type under conditions which, in the average person, would not lead to such behavior.[1] Two such sets of characteristics are of importance in the development of the psychoneuroses, that is, general constitutional types and special character traits.

In the first case we deal with a general type of psychobiologic make-up. It has long been recognized that human beings in general, but particularly those in whom mental diseases develop, tend to fall into special groups of mental and physical make-up which, as far as we can see, are constitutional in nature and act as suitable soil for the develop-

---

[1] It is to be emphasized that this concept of "constitution" is at variance with that of other authors. One of the clearest statements of this controversy is given in W. H. Sheldon's Chapter 18 in this book.

ment of personality problems. In the field of the physical types we find the most systematic presentation in the work of Ernest Kretschmer, who described a series of such categories (1921). Thus we have the *leptosome* with the thin, short torso, narrow shoulders, flat chest, long limbs, and inverted, egg-shaped head. Contrasted to this is the short, pudgy, round-headed, paunch-bellied, heavy-jowled, and short-limbed *pyknic*, and finally, the coarsely-muscled and boned, broad-shouldered, narrow-hipped, and square-jawed *athletic* type. Occasionally we find people who present combinations of the athletic with either of the other two and we speak of these as the *mixed* types. In rare instances we meet with various dysplasias such as dwarfs, giants, eunuchoid men, or masculine women, which are spoken of as *dysplastics*. Kretschmer's own studies and those of other workers in this field have led to the conclusion that certain behavior characteristics are frequently associated with the physical type, especially in people who represent the extremes of these types. The familiar descriptions of the *extravert-introvert* dichotomy and the closely associated cyclothymic and schizothymic types occur most frequently in relationship to the pyknic and leptosome physical make-up respectively. There is no question but that where the two occur together, predispositions toward certain forms of reactions are frequently found. Thus we find that the introspective, brooding, rationalizing behavior with its tendency to daydreaming, egocentricity, and the development of fantastic and impractical forms of behavior is most usually found in persons who are constitutionally of the leptosome and introverted type of make-up. On the other hand, we find that the easy-going, suggestible, anaklitic person who continually plays up to the gallery and dramatizes his reactions is most likely to be constitutionally of the pyknic and extraverted make-up. It is easy to see that in the choice of symptom formation in the psychoneurotic reaction, these constitutional characteristics must play a definite role. Furthermore, the ease with which an abnormal personality reaction is assumed when one is faced with a difficult situation will also be definitely influenced by such constitutional predispositions. It must be pointed out, however, that a large number of people who present these characteristics, even in extreme fashion, need not necessarily develop psychoneurosis unless other factors come into play.[2]

Still more important in this connection are the special constitutional factors which we find in certain people. They actually seem to dispose the person toward the development of certain psychoneurotic manifestations. Thus we have the individuals who, throughout their lives, have been known to be pathologically *sensitive*. From their very earliest days they exhibit special susceptibility to any kind of emotionally colored stimuli. They suffer under ridicule, always seek for reassurance, react in an exaggerated fashion to success and failure, and distort statements made to or about them. We can easily see how such a person may go on

---

[2] One of the most impressive and systematic presentations on this subject is the recent work by W. H. Sheldon (1940).

to develop feelings of inferiority and suspiciousness, anticipations of injustice and retaliations, and so on. Another form of pathologic constitutional trait is found in the *chronic complainer*. From early childhood, he exaggerates physical symptoms and continually lives under the fear of developing some disease. The careless suggestion by an outsider of the presence of some physical anomaly may serve as the nucleus for the development of an ever-widening set of symptoms whether or not any physical basis exists. A third commonly encountered characteristic of this type is the so-called *obsessive* form of reaction. Here we find individuals, unusually scrupulous and pedantic, who tend to analyze even trivial occurrences in the most minute fashion. They tend to dwell with remarkable tenacity on thoughts which come into their minds and if these thoughts are related to some actual or imagined danger, they may gradually turn into true obsessions from which the person cannot free himself.

In evaluating the true nature of these constitutional characteristics it is well to remember that no matter how deeply rooted any one of them may appear to be, they are nevertheless likely to have been caused by faulty development (see Chapter 20 by Ribble). This is especially frequently seen in the cases showing deviations in their sexual life. Emphasis has been placed here on the fact that homosexuals, for instance, are characterized by such features as effeminacy in the male and masculine mannerisms or even physique in the female. One could argue, however, that even these may be developed on the basis of early conditioning or identification.

Developmental Determining Factors.—The effect of developmental influences upon behavior and their importance in the causation of abnormal reactions is too complex a subject to present fully in a short discussion of this type. The literature is replete with theories and observations which must be digested fully before one can abstract that which is pertinent to the subject. The reader will be well advised to refer to these, some of the more important of which are given in the bibliography. Since other chapters in this book will deal more fully with some of the special phases of this subject (see Parts IV and V), the following discussion will be limited to a general résumé and will not venture into the more controversial and speculative aspects of it.

The process of development starts out with a certain number of given factors as a foundation. On the one hand we have the basic biological needs or instincts of the individual as an organism and those potentialities which we have discussed under the headings of constitutional characteristics. On the other we have the environmental setting into which the individual is born. Development as a dynamic process will have as its goal the proper adjustment of these two sets of factors at any given time to the changes that take place in both of them throughout the course of time. It is logical to assume that at first the individual recognizes no needs other than those that emanate from himself, and it is only through his contact with the outside that he begins to establish patterns of behavior in relationship to it. The nature of these patterns will depend primarily upon the fact that environmental factors differ in regard to their relationship to the individual. Thus some of them become the basis for inhibition or prevention. Others, by virtue of their assistance in the gratification of instinctive needs, will be considered as beneficial and protective and characteristic of persons to be emulated because of their ability to do things which the individual himself desires to do, and will serve as objects of imitation, as models for the development of ideals. At the same time the individual undergoes changes by virtue of his potentialities as a growing person. Changes take place in his size, shape, features, in the functions of his endocrine glands, etc. Conditions which are acceptable at one stage during this process of development become obsolete at another stage, and are displaced by new needs and new forms of behavior. Thus, a component develops in the personality which has to deal on the one hand with the relationship of the individual to the environment as a whole, and to himself as a changing organism on the other. This component assumes a special relationship to his primitive needs, sanctioning them at one time and preventing their free flow toward gratification at another. In the course of this development minor clashes occur throughout one's existence, but at certain times the conflicting tendencies are in particularly strong opposition and greater difficulties in adjustment will occur. It is at those points that the foundations of the psychoneuroses are most likely to be laid.

It must be remembered also that the forces which run counter to instinctive needs exert pressure upon the individual not only at the time of their original occurrence, but if repeated may establish patterns which will lead to conflicts even where the original setting is not present. Various forms and combinations of such influences are possible. In the first place we must consider the effect of faulty conditioning. A person who has been repeatedly subjected to the simultaneous effect of two opposing trends in his early childhood will, in his later life, when one comes to the surface, react to the situation as though both were present. Thus, for instance, a child who has had repeated frightening or disgusting experiences in relation to eating some special food may later experience feelings of anxiety or disgust whenever the food alone is presented. This is particularly important in relationship to the social taboo that is attached to sexual activities in the childhood of a great many individuals. Another factor of importance, particularly in relationship to the development of the psychosexual life but also true in other phases of behavior, is that which develops in conjunction with changes occurring with growth. At any stage during the growth of the individual, objectives and ways of gratification of instinctive needs may be experienced as satisfactory and socially approved but at another stage will have to be radically changed. This requires an emancipation from a form of behavior which has become deeply rooted both by virtue of personal gratification and approval by society. It is difficult enough, even in the normal individual, to have to break this routine and adjust himself to new forms of behavior. The success of accomplishing such a change will naturally depend upon two factors, that is, the strength of attachment to the original pattern and the force of attraction of the new one. If, because of accidental or purposeful occurrences, either one of these is affected, this change may be rendered either more easy or more difficult. Thus, for instance, the child who in his early years is overprotected by the home environment and is then called upon to adapt himself to an independent existence at school may find it difficult to emancipate himself from the constant need of the affection and care of the home. If such a child, in addition, happens to have the misfortune of attending a school where conditions are particularly difficult for adjustment, his ability to emancipate himself may be rendered impossible and in the search for a solution, pathological means of solving the problem may develop. The actual choice of the manner of escape may be accidental or suggested by definite patterns. If the child, for instance, has on previous occasions learned that physical disease can be used as a means of securing extra sympathy and protection, he may adopt that. Or if a pattern at home has been established wherein some member of the family utilizes a certain form of escape in difficult situations, that may present itself as a possibility. The most commonly occurring examples of this type of reaction are to be found in the psychosexual life, first because in our form of social organization it is likely to be burdened with more taboos and social restrictions than any other phase of behavior and secondly because it is in this field that the most drastic changes take place in the development of the individual himself.

Other possibilities for the development of such reactions must be considered. A great deal of emphasis has been placed on the importance of feelings of inferiority developed in early life in relation to some actual or imagined physical or mental inadequacy. In his search for compensation for this inferiority a person may attempt to excel in some other aspect of his activities and if that is impossible may develop neurotic manifestations as a means of securing sympathy or superiority. A similar mechanism may be observed as a result of indirect effects of organic diseases. The child who, early in life, has suffered an attack of a disease process such as infantile paralysis and has been left with some obvious physical defect will have to go through life with the feeling that he is not only different from but also inferior to others. He will not be able to have the normal outlets and pleasures that sports and games afford and may even feel himself discriminated against or disliked by the rest of the group. He will become sensitive, insecure, and will naturally search for other means of gaining the limelight to a point where this may come to be his sole interest in life.

So much for a discussion of the general and more obvious possibilities in regard to developmental factors. In the fields of instinctive organization and social adjustment a large number of more complex relationships are encountered and for a discussion of these we refer the reader to the chapters dealing particularly with the psychoanalytic concepts and the influence of social impacts upon the development of personality functions.

SITUATIONAL FACTORS.—In the case used in our definition it was seen that the actual development of the abnormal behavior came in relationship to a special situation, that is, the patient's marriage and the birth of the child, and that the symptoms served as a method of escape from this particular situation. It is true that had there not been a special personality background and specific conflicts established in the early life of the patient, the precipitating situation probably would not have caused any further strain on the adjustment than is usual in such circumstances. It can be argued just as well, however, that had the patient not married this particular type of person, and had pregnancy and the birth of a child not taken place or even had there been no collision in which he was involved, the particular symptom complex would not have come about. Neither of these two arguments is justified any more than the arguments offered in the age-old controversy concerning the relative importance of constitution and environment. The causes of the psychoneuroses must always be looked for in a constellation of circumstances rather than in any one single factor. It is true, however, that a certain relationship must exist between all these factors if they are to converge upon some particular form of behavior at a given time. Thus it is that given a certain weakness in the personality it can serve as suitable soil for a particular type of emotional conflict developed in early life. Similarly, given a combination of these two it will take a special form of immediate strain that will lead to the appearance of symptoms. In some cases it may be some social upheaval, such as war, in other cases threatened loss of economic security, in still others some physical disease. All of these factors may be described as situational determining factors. It is obvious that they can be of infinite variety just as all possible experiences in life are of infinite variety, but for purposes of practical approach we can arbitrarily reduce them to several main classes.

SOCIAL FACTORS.—In the discussion of the development of the individual it was emphasized that patterns of behavior develop during the life of the individual in relationship to the group in which he lives. He must learn to take into consideration the established standards and demands of the group and to a certain extent fit his own needs to these. While certain needs may be allowed gratification, others must be inhibited or delayed. In a stable social situation in adult life the individual, if he adjusts, will have established certain standards to which he can adhere, and from which he need deviate only within very narrow limits depending upon minor changes. With the appearance of more critical upheavals in the group these standards of behavior may have to be radically changed and then the ability of the person to adjust is proportionately taxed. We need only mention the strain upon adjustment which has come about from the various sociological disturbances that have developed in the last few years. The rapid changes in political and economic situations in Europe or even in this country have taken their toll in failures in adjustment of a large number of people. It is true that not all of them developed neuroses. Given a robust personality and an adequate development it is surprising and gratifying to see how flexible the adjustment of a human being to the most radical changes in established social organization can be, but there will always be a certain number who will succumb to the final situational disturbance.

The nature of the change need not be one that involves a whole group, but may be one that develops in the life of the particular person. Immigrants, for instance, who find themselves forced to adjust to strange standards and forms of behavior may find difficulty in making the transition, and similarly people who change their milieu within the same group by moving from a rural to an urban community, from agricultural to industrial forms of life, and so on. Within the family itself there are numerous possibilities of this type. The child who has been brought up in a family where certain relationships between the various members exist may find it difficult to orient himself after marriage if forced into a new type of environment. The everyday relationships of husband and wife, of child and parent, even forms of food or dress may produce a constant state of irritation which can lead to a gradual development of psychoneurotic reactions. Religious differences, gaps in ideologies, education, and various other interests may cause similar strain on the ability to adjust. All of these are much more important than one may be led to believe by those who tend to minimize the importance of precipitating factors and place the main emphasis on the earlier experiences as personality foundations. The fact remains, however, that even in practical therapeutic work we find that social difficulties of this type, if they can be removed, will frequently in themselves help in alleviating the symptoms.

ECONOMIC FACTORS.—The stress and strain of the struggle for existence which has become particularly acute in modern life, where security so often is expressed in terms of the quantity and quality of worldly possessions, must be regarded as another important group of possible situational factors. Economic disasters either of the type that affects the whole group or only the particular individual, loss of home or material possessions especially if it is sudden in its development may, in certain individuals, be the determining factor in causing a breakdown. Here, of course, as in the case of the other forms of precipitating conditions, the availability of other assets is of great importance. Of deciding influence are such circumstances as the socially acceptable values, possible forms of compensation, the breadth and diversity of interests, the age of the individual and his resilience, etc.

PERSONAL FACTORS.—It was emphasized above that the changes in the individual himself that occur with the passing of years, although they are of a continually progressive type, nevertheless present at certain stages more drastic transitions than at others. Whether it is because of social tradition or because of biological development, they mark critical periods in the life of the individual and are known to be particularly vulnerable spots in the development of mental diseases. Such is, for instance, the critical period that confronts the child when he is more or less suddenly forced out of the protective environment of the family into the competitive life at school. Another stage of even greater critical stress is that of puberty, with its implications both social and biological. The rapid development of endocrine and other physical changes introduces new needs and a change in objectives of instinctive urges, and at the same time the person is socially expected to act as an adult in contrast to the privileges and patterns of behavior of the child. Marriage and the introduction of new responsibilities and the need to adjust to an almost totally different mode of life as may be true in some cases is another example of this form of drastic change. Finally, there is the impending change that looms with such great importance in the life of most individuals at the involutional period. The necessity of giving up activities and interests which in the case of some people have become the only ones that matter, the need to resign oneself to what may be regarded as an unproductive, and at times dependent, old age is quite frequently one of the most important causes in the development of a serious personality disturbance.

ORGANIC FACTORS.—In discussing the definition of the neuroses, it was emphasized that one of the distinctive features of these syndromes is the fact that they do not show etiologically relevant organic pathology. To what extent an organic disease may in itself by a breaking down of tissues lead to development of neurosis is not definitely known, and is considered by a great many as unlikely. It is true, however, that in an indirect way somatic disease may serve as a definite situational factor. It must be remembered that from a psychological point of view a disease process, aside from its organic effects, must be considered as an occurrence of great importance in the life of the individual, and the adjustment to it will depend materially upon the extent to which it renders the individual uncomfortable, endangers his feeling of security, and jeopardizes his subsequent ability to function at the original level. In addition to this, certain aspects of diseases and their social significance play an important role. Feelings of guilt and shame that accompany certain diseases, social isolation, traditional attitude of hopelessness as, for instance, in the case of tuberculosis or cancer, and other psychological factors may result in reactions altogether out of keeping with the actual severity of the disease.

Clinical Manifestations

The presentation of the clinical manifestations of the psychoneuroses with the full range of deviations from normal behavior and experience that can be encountered in this field is a difficult task in the limits of a short discussion. There is hardly any function, physiological or psychological, that may not be the site of some one or another psychoneurotic symptom. Here we must confine ourselves to a brief description of some of the more familiar and striking symptoms with the hope that those who are interested in a more detailed study will seek this information in available texts, some of which will be indicated in the bibliography. It is proposed to present these symptoms under the headings of the subdivisions presented in our definition and designated as "positive" features. At the same time we shall attempt to gather these symptoms under the groupings of their clinical manifestations, utilizing the terminology accepted by psychiatric textbooks. This will be especially convenient since to a large extent the major diagnostic entities correspond with the subdivisions that were described in the definition. With this in mind, let us first consider the various phenomena which can be grouped under the subdivision of the conversions, and which are usually included under the clinical entity of the hysterias.

The Hysterias (Conversion Neuroses).—In the case used in our definition we found in the center of the clinical picture the symptom of complete blindness which, on the one hand, seemed not to be based on organic pathology and, on the other, served the purpose of offering an escape mechanism to a person who was faced with an apparently insoluble problem. This can serve as a typical example of a conversion, whereby we mean the transformation of an emotional conflict into some specific symptom, somatic or mental. Four different types of conversions, all of them representing different forms of hysterical reactions, can be generally recognized. They are as follows:

1. *The creation of physical symptoms where no signs of organic pathology can be found.* We meet here a most astounding variation of manifestations and it can be safely said that there is hardly a somatic function anywhere in the organism that does not in some case or another serve the purpose of these conversions. The most commonly involved are first of all the various sensory functions: blindness, deafness, disturbance of the sense of pain and other representatives of common sensation, disturbance of sense of smell, etc. The disturbance may be one of complete loss of sensation, such as, for instance, in the cases of hysterical analgesia where a pin can be stuck right through the tissues without causing any apparent experience of pain, or the case of complete blindness described in our illustration. There may, however, be simply a diminution or restriction of the function of the particular sense organ such as hypesthesia, hypalgesia, concentric restriction of the field of vision, diminution of hearing, etc. Finally, these conversion symptoms may manifest themselves in an increased sensory impression such as is shown in some of the painful paresthesias or hyperalgesias. Motor function also may be disturbed. Loss of ability to produce sounds (aphonia), paralyses or pareses of voluntary movements of the arms or legs, difficulties in breathing, retention of urine with an apparently decreased tone of the bladder often occur. Here, too, the loss need not be complete. One

may find hoarseness or whispering instead of aphonia, or simply a restriction of the scope of movement of voluntary musculature rather than
complete paralysis. Occasionally we may have the development of dys-
kinesias (distortion of movement) of various types, such as tremors of
various parts of the body, dystonias, tics, choreiform movements, and
sometimes generalized convulsions following the special patterns that
have been so frequently described under the name of major hysteria.
Painful sensations of various types are quite frequent as conversion
manifestations. Headache, precordial pain, abdominal distress, arthritic
pains, backache, and coccydynia are among the most common. Visceral
manifestations such as persistent vomiting, incontinence of urine, painful
or disturbed menstruation, dysfunctions of the sexual activities such as
impotence or frigidity, disturbance of gastro-intestinal functions, and
many others are also frequently found.

In all of these it is important to appreciate that we are dealing here
with expressions not of recognizable organic systems but of their psychological representations. By this we mean that in the case of loss of
sensation in the limbs we get such symptoms as glove-and-stocking
anaesthesia. This would mean that the hand or foot is affected rather
than an area of the body supplied by some particular nerve or center, and
similarily with visual disturbances, where we get such things as double
vision that persists even when one eye is covered, or a telescopic constriction of the field. This is an important consideration not only in the
recognition of the symptom as such with its psychological basis but also
in the differentiation of these symptoms from organic disease.

2. *Exaggeration of organic symptoms* or their persistence when the
cause no longer exists. Here we deal with conditions where organic disease is present or has existed at some time in the past, but the symptoms
are unconsciously exploited either beyond their scope and intensity or
after the organic basis for them has ceased to exist. They are encountered especially in the so-called industrial, war, insurance, and traumatic
neuroses. Sometimes it is difficult to differentiate them from pure malingering, to which reference will be made further on. They differ from
the group described above in that by their nature they are much more
likely to follow actual anatomical distribution. Into this group also falls
the common tendency to exaggerate normal sensations or discomforts
produced by the heart-beat, gastro-intestinal motility, noises in the ear,
and other physiological functions.

3. *Production of organic pathology.* It is a well-known fact that emotional experiences are almost always accompanied by changes in some
of the physiological functions. Pulse and blood pressure fluctuations,
mobilization of blood sugar, constriction or dilation of blood vessels,
changes in the function of the adrenal and other glands, gastro-intestinal
motility, etc., can be shown to undergo demonstrable organic changes.
It is logical to expect, therefore, that, depending upon the intensity or
duration of a given set of emotional experiences, definite and sometimes
irreversible pathology may occur. During the last few years a great deal

of work has been done in this field, and today it forms a large portion of the field of psychosomatic medicine. Our reference to these will be very brief since another chapter in this book deals with them more extensively. They are of particular importance since the functions affected in this way may be of vital importance and of such intensity as to interfere seriously with the health of the individual. Skin lesions, often of a severe type and showing stubborn resistance to somatic treatment, are frequent. Disturbances of the respiratory apparatus, allergic reactions of various types, and dysfunctions of menstruation often develop on the basis of psychoneurotic mechanisms and can be treated accordingly. Hypertension with various disturbances of the circulatory system and kidney function form a special chapter in this subject. A great deal of work has been done on the occurrence of pathological conditions in the gastro-intestinal tract which find their origin in emotional conflicts. Gastric ulcers, mucous colitis, spasms of the sphincters in this tract are a few of the important types of lesions that have been discussed under this heading. The subject is still in its early stages of development and speculation perhaps goes beyond actually known facts at times. It has even been suggested by some that such well-known diseases as multiple sclerosis, nephritis, and even some new growths may be largely dependent upon psychoneurotic mechanisms. It must be emphasized that we must proceed very cautiously in this not yet clearly defined subject, but its importance both from a theoretical and therapeutic point of view has perhaps not been fully realized.

4. *Creation of pseudo-psychotic symptoms.* Conversion manifestations may find their expression not only in symptoms referable to somatic functions but also in the form of mental disturbances more or less similar to those found in the more serious personality disturbances known as the psychoses. The hysterical amnesias belong to this group. They may cover periods of time lasting only a few moments or may produce gaps of a longer duration sometimes even to the extent of blotting out the individual's whole past life. They may be complete or may permit the patient patchy memories of isolated events. They may have reference to periods during which the patient behaved normally or they may erase events of a pathological nature such as a delirious condition or convulsions. Other reactions of this type are the hysterical "twilight states" during which the patient may appear partially confused or dazed, dreamstates, stupors, fugues, etc. Most of these are characterized by dramatic and fantastic performances. The patients apparently believe themselves transported into a magic world in which they see wonderful visions, hear heavenly music, or are terrified by blood-curdling monsters. In the course of some of these states the patient can be found to live out an accentuated drama of an unfulfilled wish or to regain the possession of a lost love-object. It is during these states that the hysterical patient may manifest hallucinatory or delusional experiences which more closely resemble a dream experience than do those that we find in the psychoses.

Psychasthenias (Anankastic Reactions).—In this group are placed forms of psychoneurotic reactions which, although different in many respects, have in common the fact that the patients feel themselves compelled by some inner force and against their own will or reason to think, act, or feel in an abnormal manner. Three major forms of symptoms are found here.

OBSESSIVE THINKING.—The characteristic feature of this symptom is the recurrence of undesired and discomforting thoughts of which the patient is unable to rid himself even if he is quite able to understand their illogical nature and protests constantly his innocence of wishing to entertain such thoughts. The religious person who is continually tormented by sacrilegious thoughts and who may, to his great consternation, even feel himself forced to make blasphemous statements; the woman who experiences thoughts related to injuring her husband or children; men who continually fight against thoughts of homosexual activities, all fall into this category. The development is usually gradual, frequently beginning with occasional ruminations which can at first be easily dismissed from the mind, but even then accompanied by anxiety lest these thoughts may become more deeply rooted and may actually lead to abnormal, asocial, or immoral acts. Unlike the hysterical symptoms, they are often accompanied by marked depressive emotional reactions, the person making determined efforts to displace them, and the more he does so the greater is the stubbornness with which they return to his mind. It is a well-known fact that as a rule the danger of persons actually carrying out these thoughts is minimal if it ever occurs, although the mere fact that the thoughts cannot be gotten rid of may occasionally lead to desperate measures, sometimes even suicide. Very often a great many ritualistic activities are undertaken to deal with these thoughts; peculiar movements such as tics, stamping of feet, stereotyped gestures, etc., may develop in order to counteract the thoughts.

PHOBIAS.—These are unwarranted fears which, much like the obsessions, the person feels himself forced to experience although he consciously recognizes the fact that no actual danger exists. A large variety of these have been described and various Greek names applied to them. A few of the more common ones include *claustrophobia*, the fear of confined spaces; *agoraphobia*, the fear of open spaces; *aichmophobia*, the fear of sharp objects; *mysophobia*, the fear of contamination, and numerous others. The distinguishing feature of these fears as contrasted, for instance, with the delusional fears of the psychotic is the fact that the person realizes that these fears are born within himself. They can prove definitely incapacitating, however, as, for example, in the case of a person with a claustrophobia who will not enter a small room or narrow passage even when it is essential to do so. Even when threatened by danger, his phobia may prevent him from saving himself by taking refuge in a small but safe place. Phobias are frequently complicated by obsessive thoughts so that the patient thinks constantly of the particular object of his phobia and experiences as much discomfort as when he is faced with the actual fear-stimulus.

COMPULSIVE ACTS.—These are forms of behavior which the person carries out consciously either without knowing the reason for such activity or for reasons which he knows have no logical foundation. One of the most common of these is the so-called "hand washing" compulsion. The individual realizes only that he is being compelled by some inner force to wash and scrub his hands continuously although he admits quite freely that there cannot be any dirt or contamination on them. This often goes with a mysophobia, the person expressing the fear of possible danger of infection to himself or of carrying it to other people. Attempts to avoid touching possible sources of contamination usually accompany it. Objects are handled by using gloves, clothing, or other coverings, or the person becomes quite skilful in opening doors with his elbows, moving objects by pushing them with parts of the body which are covered by clothing, etc. Other examples of this form of behavior are found in *kleptomania,* or the compulsion to steal; *pyromania,* or the compulsion to set fires; *poriomania,* or the need of moving from place to place. In a great many of these the person does not even attempt to justify these acts, simply falling back on the excuse that he cannot help himself.

Although in certain cases any one of the forms of psychasthenia described above may occur as the single expression of the neurosis, they more usually occur together and sometimes one develops as a sequel to the other, such as the development of a hand washing compulsion because of the fear of contracting a disease. It is important to emphasize the fact that one usually finds the psychasthenic syndrome developing in a certain type of personality. Long before the actual outbreak of the fully developed symptom we find these persons exhibiting such characteristics as rigid pedantry, scrupulousness, tendency to hair-splitting, stubbornness in their convictions, and so on. In a more general way the personality make-up of such an individual is very likely to be that of the introverted, self-centered, daydreaming type as contrasted with the suggestible, extraverted, demonstrative person that is so frequent amongst the hysterical patients. From a practical point of view it is important to appreciate, furthermore, that such personality characteristics are more frequent and more deeply rooted in the psychasthenics than in the other neuroses and therefore present less favorable prognoses. Fortunately these cases occur considerably less frequently than those described under the hysterias.

Faulty Control of Emergency Reactions.—The first two categories, that is, the hysterias and psychasthenias, have been frequently referred to in the literature as the *true* psychoneuroses, particularly since, in their development, one usually finds the sequence of events described in our sample case. By this is meant the development of the original conflict in early life without any immediate symptoms, the latter manifesting themselves in relationship to a reenactment of the original setting (Freud, 1895). In the early psychoanalytic literature these reactions were differentiated from what were called the *"actual"* neuroses in which the symptoms were considered as primarily dependent upon an immediate situation.[3] The clinical pictures described in this group corresponded to the two syndromes known as "anxiety neuroses" and "neurasthenia." It has since been recognized that such a distinction is not really a valid one but that early experiences in terms of the establishment of conflicts are as important here as in the other forms (Malamud, 1931). Therefore, in the present discussion, we shall assume that whereas in general the etiologic mechanisms follow the same principles, the type of clinical pictures presented is different.

As was suggested earlier in this chapter, the type of symptom formation that we find here can be best described as a faulty control of emergency reactions (Rado, 1939). Biologically, the organism is capable of responding with a certain mobilization of safety devices when it is faced by an actual emergency. Thus when an animal is in danger, various psychological and physical activities come into play. The emotional experience of fear is accompanied by changes in endocrine functions, blood chemistry, circulatory reactions, respiration, etc. All of these may be grouped under the general term of fear or anxiety. Similarly when muscular exertion has reached a point where all the readily available energy has been strained and reserve supplies must be tapped, the phenomenon of fatigue develops. Such emergency measures are, of course, considered normal when they develop in relation to conditions which call for them. If, however, anxiety should develop without an actually existing danger, or fatigue be experienced without adequate exertion, then we might speak of faulty emergency reactions.

ANXIETY NEUROSIS.—Clinically, this disturbance expresses itself in attacks of vague, unexplained but intense fear which, at least in the beginning of the disease, does not seem to be attached to any particular object. It can best be described as being near to a normal fear of a vital danger, but is different from it in that no such danger is present and, in most cases, not even imagined to be present. The concomitant symptoms are usually of the same kind as found in real fear—a kind of paralyzed state of the musculature, cold shivers, a sense of pressure in the head and precordial regions, profuse cold sweating, palpitation of the heart, and at times relaxation of the sphincters. As time goes on the attacks may be consciously associated with some of the concomitant symptoms. The person may develop the fear that his heart may stop, that something will burst in his head, or that some serious disease is developing in his gastro-intestinal system. The concomitant symptoms may also assume the controlling feature of the picture, and thus instead of pure anxiety attacks we may have tachycardia, alternating constipa-

---

[3] Systematic psychoanalytic accounts of the psychoneuroses are available in Fenichel (1934) and Brown (1940).

tion or diarrhea, dizziness, or even vertigo, and others. It has been emphasized particularly in the early psychoanalytic literature (Freud, 1895), that the most important etiologic factors of this form of neurosis are to be looked for in some interference with normal sexual activities, such as prolonged abstinence in the presence of constant stimulation as in protracted engagements, coitus interruptus, and so forth. It is true that these factors are very commonly found in the immediate history of the development of such conditions. It must be emphasized, however, that in the background and serving as the basis for such reactions, one can find mechanisms akin to those encountered in the forms described above. This is a consideration which is of great practical importance in the treatment of the anxiety neuroses.

NEURASTHENIA.—This term has, more than any other, been misused in its application to a great many conditions both organically and psychogenically produced which in reality belong to other symptom complexes. In its pure form it is characterized by feelings of physical and mental inadequacy, complaints of fatigability without adequate exertion, paresthesias in the back of the neck, and a sense of general weakness. In the more chronic and severe forms of this disturbance the patients usually describe themselves as mental and physical "wrecks." They cannot concentrate on any activity, they wake up in the morning feeling exhausted, "fagged out," unable to get started on any work. Increased irritability, feeling of lack of sexual vigor at times amounting to impotence, and a vague sense of anxiety may complicate the picture. In contradistinction to the anxiety neuroses, these states are usually monotonously chronic without any great degree of variation and as is too frequently the case the patient seeks for help only after long duration of the symptoms. Here we find, as in the psychasthenias, a premorbid personality whose characteristics merge into the symptoms of the neurosis so gradually that it is sometimes difficult to tell what is the original endowment of the person and what are the symptoms of the disease. Because of this such cases are often difficult to treat and the prognosis is frequently poor.

Delimitation and Relationship to Other Forms of Personality Adjustment

In the definition it was emphasized that the psychoneuroses are characterized not only by a certain set of symptoms peculiar to them but by the absence of clinical features which belong to other forms of personality maladjustments. This group of "negative" features can serve in outlining a differential diagnosis. The scope of the present discussion does not permit an analysis of this aspect of the problem as complete as one would find in a medical textbook. Other chapters of this book will present discussions of a number of related personality disorders. It is important, however, to emphasize not only the differentiation but also the relationships of the psychoneuroses to these other forms of behavior, since the manner of symptom formation of the psychoneuroses is one which is closely related on the one hand to normal behavior and on the other to that encountered in the psychoses and reactions to somatic disease. This means that in a large number of personality disturbances which are found at the borderline between the psychoneuroses and these other conditions we are apt to find symptom complexes that depend as much on psychoneurotic mechanisms as they do on other determining factors. From the point of view of treatment and management of these problems, it is essential to understand to what extent the disturbance depends upon the psychoneurotic mechanisms. We can then treat this aspect of the disturbance psychotherapeutically and at the same time deal with the other aspects of the disease on the basis of what we know about its etiology. With this in mind let us consider some of the conditions with which the psychoneuroses can be most easily confused.

Somatic Disease.—Since the psychoneuroses, particularly the hysterias, tend to manifest themselves in the form of somatic complaints, the differential diagnosis here has long been considered very difficult. An adequate knowledge of medicine is obviously imperative in arriving at a correct diagnosis. No one who is not equipped to make an adequate physical examination and to recognize the existence of a physical disease should undertake to make a final diagnosis in such conditions. Given such a preparation, however, one should experience little difficulty with clear-cut conditions. On the one hand, given a fundamental knowledge of the pathognomonic symptoms of psychoneuroses, one realizes immediately their difference from the somatic disease. On the other hand, the various diagnostic aids and laboratory methods developed in medicine should serve as reliable criteria for differentiation. Physical examination of the heart and the electrocardiogram in the case of cardiac disease, temperature rises, blood changes and bacteriological tests in the case of infectious diseases, blood chemistry and examination of the urine in kidney diseases, and many others should serve as dependable evidence of organic etiology and should exclude purely psychogenic reactions. In the case of organic disease of the nervous system we have already referred to the fact that the psychoneurotic counterpart of an organic nervous ailment such as paralyses, sensory changes, etc., does not follow the anatomical distribution but the psychological idea of the part involved. Reference has been made to such things as "glove and stocking" anaesthesia, concentric restriction of the field of vision, etc. It is conceivable, however, that psychogenic mechanisms may be associated with or engrafted upon an organic disease. In such cases, provided we realize the presence of both, the treatment will have to be planned with due consideration of both. Inasmuch as the maladjustment is psychoneurotic in nature, we shall try to discover the reasons in terms of life experiences and correct them. At the same time, however, we shall keep in mind the organic factors and try to eliminate them if possible. Thus the psychological reaction to and utilization of the symptoms of diabetes will have to be attacked on the basis of the personality factors involved at the same time that dietetic and medicinal therapy is instituted. One of the greatest achievements of the workers in the field of psychosomatics has been the recognition of such combinations, which has led to a more successful form of treatment in the way of cooperation between the internal medical man and the psychiatrist. We cannot refrain from the temptation of pointing out that in a great many of these conditions the organic disease at this stage of our progress in medicine is practically beyond any successful therapeutic influence. On the other hand, the reeducative and analytic approaches often succeed in ameliorating the maladjustment materially in such patients.

The Psychoses.—The differentiation of the psychoneuroses from the so-called functional psychoses—the manic-depressive, schizophrenic, and paranoid groups (see Chapter 29 by Cameron)—should not present any great difficulties in the clear-cut cases. The primary mood disturbance of the manic-depressive syndrome, the typical affect and association disturbance of schizophrenia, and the reality distortion that characterizes paranoid psychoses are features that should not be present in a case definitely diagnosed as psychoneurotic. This is also true of clear-cut and lasting intellectual deterioration. Here, too, however, we find borderline conditions which seem to correspond to the nature and mechanisms of both psychoneuroses and psychoses. It is well known that a great many psychoses may begin with symptoms characteristic of the psychoneuroses which may also have developed in much the same manner. Also we find cases that have been justifiably considered to be psychoneuroses developing into psychoses in some inexplicable fashion. From a practical point of view, cases of this type should be dealt with as combinations of both psychoses and psychoneuroses. The etiologic factors of a psychoneurotic type should be adequately treated although in the management of the case it should be borne in mind that psychotic manifestations may develop. Special consideration should be paid to the personality disturbances that develop in the involutional and senile periods. It is highly probable that we have been too prone to consider them all as depending entirely upon organic tissue destruction. Actually we find that environmental stress and strain, previous life experiences, and numerous conditioning factors are of the utmost importance in the development of a large number of these conditions.

Constitutional Personality Deviations.—A great deal of controversy has developed in relationship to the differential diagnosis between psychogenically produced personality maladjustments and those which depend upon faulty endowment. We have already referred to this in our discussion of constitution. Furthermore, the subject is to be dealt with in other chapters of this book (see Chapter 30 by Preu, Chapter 27 by Stearns, Chapter 26 by Lowrey, and Chapter 25 by Kanner). At this point it is sufficient to emphasize that constitutional defects in personality such as the psychopathies and mental deficiency do not preclude the further superimposition of psychoneurotic manifestations. This would mean, of course, that successful treatment of the latter would still leave the original defect. At the same time it must be stressed that what may often appear to be an inborn defect (and we would include here interference with the intellectual functions) may actually depend upon such mechanisms as social rejection, faulty conditioning, early fixations, frustrations, and so on. We often find an improvement in adjustment in those cases where such causes are found and removed or ameliorated.

Malingering.—This term has been used to designate consciously motivated, deliberate, and sustained simulation of symptoms in order to secure a desired end. It is unfortunate that in the minds of most people this has become almost synonymous wtih psychoneurosis. It should be appreciated that although psychoneuroses, too, are related to some definite purposes these are neither conscious nor need they be actually desired by the adult person. As a result, we find that the psychoneurotic symptom is frequently not related at all to the situation in which the person finds himself at the time, but is relevant to a much earlier setting. Similarly, because it depends upon unconscious motivation, the psychoneurotic, unlike the malingerer, not only does not object to examination but actually searches for frequent and thorough investigation of his symptoms. Secondly, it should be emphasized that the symptoms described above are just as characteristic of the psychoneuroses and are as difficult to simulate as are the symptoms of organic disease. But it must also be remembered that malingering is not really a normal reaction and may in itself depend upon a personality organization which could profit from an analytic revision and readjustment. Finally it must be borne in mind that some of the cases may be combinations of both and whatever the attitude of the physician may be to the malingering component he should regard the psychoneurotic element as an expression of disease and treat it as such.

Treatment

In any discussion of a medical subject, it is important to include some statement concerning that phase of it which, to the physician, forms the goal of his work—that is, the treatment. It is obvious, of course, that in the present discussion we cannot take up the techniques as they are practically applied, and, for those interested, references will be given in the bibliography. In addition to this a special chapter on treatment is to be included in the handbook (see Chapter 34 by Appel). Here we should like to mention only the general principles of treatment in the psychoneuroses, the goals toward which the therapist aims, and some indication of the methods available. We must emphasize primarily that treatment, particularly in this field, does not presume to provide substitutes for disturbed functions but is dependent upon the ability to mobilize whatever assets the patient has and guide him toward a better use of these in dealing with his particular problem. In order to do this the therapist must aim first at two primary objectives. These are: (1) a proper evaluation of the personality functions in relation to the given setting, which will set clearly before us both the problem and the life experiences that have led up to it; (2) an understanding of what useful assets the person possesses and how these can be utilized in the readjustment. An analysis of the situation when it succeeds in attaining these two objectives forms the basis of a *rational* therapy of the psychoneuroses. In addition to this, however, and in most cases to be considered as auxiliary to it, we have at our command a series of other therapeutic methods the purpose of which is to treat symptoms as they arise during the period prior to the successful completion of the rational treatment and other manifestations of poor health which may be only incidental to the neurosis. This is what we call *symptomatic* treatment and it should be understood by both the therapist and the patient that it is either a temporary stop-gap or ancillary measure and is not to be taken for the treatment of the disease as such.

Rational Treatment.—It is useful to remember in carrying out any form of rational treatment that we are trying to accomplish the following things: (1) *The grasp of relationships in the given setting.* This is the primary task of the analysis of the person's relationships to his environment at the time of the development of the problem and a search for the dynamics in terms of life experiences which have led up to the establishment of the present difficulty. (2) *Emotional participation.* The therapeutic success of such work depends materially upon the degree of emotional contact that exists between the patient and his physician and the extent to which the patient is willing to throw himself into the work emotionally as well as intellectually. Merely attaining a verbal understanding of the problem and its dynamics without actually reliving the affective components of the incidents leading up to the problem is not likely to benefit the patient any more than if he were to be told of the occurrences in the life of someone else. (3) *The removal of causative factors.* Where a social situation exists which is not compatible with a proper adjustment of the patient regardless of how well he appreciates the relationships and feels their importance, it is essential to help the patient extricate himself from such deleterious circumstances. In addition, therefore, to the analysis, it is important in a great many cases to undertake social therapeutic measures in order to remove as far as possible the factors which contribute toward creating the problem. (4) *Reconstruction and emancipation.* It is a well-known fact that in most cases if the treatment is successful the patient at first develops a strong emotional attachment to and dependence upon the therapist. His ability to act independently in the post-treatment period is as vital a need as is the understanding of the situation and the eradication of the cause. No treatment, then, should be considered as completed unless this dependence upon the therapist is dissolved and the patient is rehabilitated to the extent where he can act on his own resources. This is especially important in cases where the patient is being treated in an institution or, as it may sometimes be necessary, away from the situation in which he lived before and to which he has to return.

A number of methods have been developed for the purpose of carrying out rational therapy of this type. Perhaps the most systematically organized of these is the *psychoanalytic* method introduced by Freud and further developed by some of the representatives of that school. More commonly used and less time-consuming is a method which can be termed *exploratory* and which, although utilizing to a large extent contributions of psychoanalysis, is nevertheless more direct and technically less complicated. It consists essentially in a thorough face-to-face analysis of the history of the person with particular reference to those incidents that appear to be logically related to the origin of the problem. A great deal of importance is to be placed upon the proper *guidance* and *re-education* of the patient wherever the facts brought up by analysis indicate the existence of faulty judgment, immature attitudes, lack of insight, and so on. Numerous other methods have been described both before and after the introduction of the psychoanalytic method. It must be appreciated that none of the methods should be established as necessarily the only one which must always be used. Perhaps the most successful procedure is to be guided by the developments as one works with the patient, and it may be useful to shift from one method to another.

Symptomatic Treatment.—The psychoneurotic symptoms are quite frequently sources of discomfort or pain both to the patient and to the therapist. Persistent vomiting or headaches, convulsions, or insomnia in addition to the suffering they cause may also interfere with the proper administration of treatment. Under such conditions it becomes imperative to utilize methods of treatment which deal directly with the symptoms even though they do not strike at their roots and therefore are not likely to produce lasting results. Sedatives, anodynes, suggestion, and hypnosis are all useful aids, provided, as we said before, the physician and the patient both realize their value as temporary measures only. Finally, we must remember that psychoneurotic patients are just as likely to suffer from incidental somatic diseases as any other person. A good therapist will see the wisdom of dealing with such problems as they arise. This serves two purposes. Inasmuch as the old dictum of "sound mind in a sound body" contains a great deal of truth, the correction of physical ailments is of great help in increasing the capacities of the patient to deal properly with his personality problem. In addition to that, confidence of the patient in the good judgment and healing abilities of the physician goes a long way in securing the success of treatment, regardless of what kind it is. The interest that the physician shows in the patient as a whole person and the fact that he pays attention even to minor physical disturbances will enhance this confidence and render the patient more receptive to the advice and guidance of the therapist.

BIBLIOGRAPHY

ADLER, A. 1917. The neurotic constitution. New York: Moffat-Yard.

ANDERSON, O. D., & PARMENTER, R. 1941. A long-term study of the experimental neurosis. *Psychosom. Med. Monogr., 2,* Nos. 3, 4.

BROWN, J. F. 1940. The psychodynamics of abnormal behavior. (With the collaboration of K. A. Menninger.) New York: McGraw-Hill.

DUNBAR, H. F. 1938. Emotions and bodily changes. New York: Columbia University Press.

EBAUGH, F. G. 1940. The care of the psychiatric patient in general hospitals. Chicago: American Hospital Assn.

FENICHEL, O. 1934. Outline of clinical psychoanalysis. New York: Norton.

FREUD, S. 1895. The justification for detaching from neurasthenia a particular syndrome: the anxiety neurosis. In *Collected papers,* Vol. 1. London: International Psychoanalytical Press, 1924.

—— 1909. Selected papers on hysteria and other psychoneuroses. (Trans. by A. A. Brill.) *Nerv. ment. Dis. Monogr.,* 1920, No. 4.

—— 1920. Introductory lectures on psychoanalysis. New York: Liveright.

—— 1924. Neurosis and psychosis. In *Collected papers,* Vol. 2. London: Hogarth, 1924.

GLOVER, E. 1941. Psychological effects of war conditions. *Int. J. Psycho-Anal., 22,* 132.

HENDRICK, I. 1934. Facts and theories of psychoanalysis. New York: Knopf.

JONES, E. 1920. The treatment of the neuroses. London: Bailliere.

KARDINER, A. 1941. The traumatic neuroses of war. *Psychosom. Med. Monogr., 1,* Nos. 2 & 3.

KRETSCHMER, E. 1923. Hysteria. (Trans. by O. H. Boltz.) *Nerv. ment. Dis. Monogr.,* 1926, No. 44.

—— 1925. Physique and character. New York: Harcourt, Brace.

MALAMUD, W. 1931. The psychotherapy of neurasthenia. *J. Ia St. med. Soc., 21,* 489.

—— 1936. Modern trends in psychoneurotic reaction types. *J. Ia St. med. Soc., 26,* 625.

—— 1938. The psychoneuroses. In *Tice Practice of medicine,* Vol. 10. Hagerstown: Prior. Ch. 18.

MASSERMAN, J. H. 1943. Behavior and neurosis: An experimental psychoanalytic approach to psychobiologic principles. Chicago: University of Chicago Press.

MILLER, E. (Ed.) 1940. The neuroses in war. New York: Macmillan.

NÜNBERG, H. 1932. Allgemeine Neurosenlehre. Bern: Huber.

RADO, S. 1939. Development in the psychoanalytic conception and treatment of the neuroses. *Psychoanal. Quart., 8,* 427.

ROSS, T. A. 1937. The common neuroses. Baltimore: William Wood.

SHELDON, W. H. 1940. The varieties of human physique. New York: Harper.

STRECKER, E. A. 1930. Psychiatric education. *Ment. Hyg., N. Y., 14,* 797.

WECHSLER, I. 1929. The neuroses. Philadelphia: Saunders.

WHITE, B. V., COBB, S., & JONES, C. M. Mucous colitis. *Psychosom. Med. Monogr., 1,* No. 1.

Chapter 29

THE FUNCTIONAL PSYCHOSES

By NORMAN CAMERON, Ph.D., M.D.

UNDER THE FUNCTIONAL PSYCHOSES it is customary to group those sweeping disorders for which no organic lesions and no toxins have consistently been demonstrated, namely, schizophrenia, paranoia, mania, and most severe depressions. This use is a common one in medicine where, for example, functional heart disorders are recognized as a clinical group for which neither drugs, toxins, nor lesions are responsible. Three interpretations are current with respect to the functional psychoses: (1) that their determining factor lies in a hidden lesion, somewhere in the brain or other organ, that has not as yet been discovered, or in predetermined hereditary defect comparable with the situation in Huntington's chorea, or that some unknown toxins, infections, or general metabolic disorders are directly responsible; (2) that organic activity or change when present is quite incidental, the real disturbance being located in a semi-independent psyche with its own needs and other-worldly attitudes; and (3) that the influences of environmental, social, and personal organizations are fundamental, the fact of biological activity in every form of human behavior being always taken into consideration and accepted as sufficiently demonstrated. The first may be termed the structural view, the second is the psychic approach, and to the third may be applied the term *bisocial*.

It makes a great deal of difference both in practice and in research as to which view the worker embraces. (1) The structuralist, who represents the traditional medical attitude, will direct his efforts toward the organism as a structural, physiological, and biochemical unit, leaving the environmental, social, and personal aspects to the psychologist, the sociologist, and the theologian, as if it were their special concern. His contributions throw light upon the inner workings of the system of organs which go to make up the human machine. (2) The advocate of a separate psyche with its own phenomenal world is the direct intellectual descendant of rationalistic philosophy. For him there are also two worlds of reality, but he believes that the efficient causes of human action are to be found in a special psychic realm. His contributions focus upon the desires, thoughts, and dreams as parts of that psychic realm, and tend to reinterpret organic, social, and environmental reality in its terms, or else to relegate it to the history takers. (3) The remaining attitude differs chiefly in rejecting the dualism of both the other two, and in adopting the simple pragmatic stand that the world we move about in is not only the real world but the only world, and that desiring, thinking, dreaming, and doing all belong in it. For them the psyche is a myth. The contributions of these pragmatists in the study of personality and behavior disorders emphasize man as a person operating in an environmental field, whose difficulties may arise from several sources—visceral, environmental, personal, or interpersonal. The distinct opposition of the pragmatic and the psychic views has been recently set forth by N. Cameron (1942a, 1943d).

The practical difference that general orientations make becomes very evident in the different ways of handling the functionally disordered. Strong faith in the role of heredity and constitutional type leads to mere diagnostic sorting and sterilizing; belief in toxins, infections, lesions, and metabolic disturbances as the basic disorder leads to medicinal and surgical measures or else to a fatalistic custodial attitude; conviction as to the primary efficacy of a separate psyche encourages introspective techniques and mentalistic interpretations; while belief in an everyday world of reality with everything in it leads to a naturalistic orientation which compels the devotion of adequate attention to all human functioning, irrespective of traditional and academic divisions.

The Major Problems

Etiology.—There is no topic around which greater controversy centers than that of the origins and the exact character of the functional psychoses. Each hypothesis has its protagonists, its evidence, and its practical results, as set forth for instance in the symposium on the material of human nature and conduct in which the approaches of the psychologist, the psychoanalyst, the biochemist, the psychopathologist and the psychobiologist are outlined (Meyer, 1935). To each set of postulates we owe the opening up of some special field of investigation in which the workers have looked for solutions to the questions which their particular approach raises.

HEREDITY.—The role of inheritance is by no means settled. Apart from the inevitable statistical problems involved, the most trying task is that of determining how dependable the information is regarding ascendants and collaterals of the patient. Even in a stable population there is so much concealment from generation to generation, because of the disgrace implied by such familial taints as "insanity," that the most reliable informant may unknowingly omit important data. In the other direction, past generations made little distinction between psychosis, oligophrenia, epilepsy, cerebral accidents, and antisocial behavior. What they did pass on to their descendants consisted largely of inexpert interpretations which the descendants then give to the investigator as facts. Finally there is little uniformity within the profession as to diagnostic criteria, so that one cannot even be sure in making studies from case records that the same term is used similarly by different workers (Noyes, 1939).

It seems to be generally accepted that the functional psychoses appear significantly more often in certain family trees than in the general population (N. Lewis, 1923; Myerson, 1925; Landis and Page, 1938; Kallman, 1938). Statistical analyses based upon records of the New York State psychiatric hospitals, whose standards are relatively uniform (Cheney, 1934), have been made by Pollock, Malzberg, and Fuller (1939). According to these authors, functional psychoses appear significantly in excess of the complete expectation, provided a correction be made for the anticipation of further cases among the relatively young. Whether the psychotic attack shall be predominantly affective in character, or belong more to the disorganized psychoses, seems to them to be related more to the family history than to the precipitating situation; for there is a signficantly greater incidence of either one or the other in certain family groups, when corrections have been made for anticipation because of the youth of siblings of patients at the time of study. In their statistics, the particular conditions at the time of onset under which affective psychoses appear seem not to differ essentially from those under which schizophrenic and paranoic disorders arise. Presumably the personality organization of the individual at the time is of great importance in determining the general character of the disturbance; and this organization they ascribe chiefly to family inheritance. What evidence there is indicates that the single-factor hypothesis is incapable of accounting for inheritance in the functional psychoses (Malzberg, 1940).

PHYSICAL CONSTITUTION.—Attempts to tie up bodily types with the psychoses have a long history; the writings of the ancients and the medievals are peppered with them; current popular beliefs in the relationship are strong. In modern times the psychiatrist Kretschmer (1925) has done most to awaken serious study of this problem. What might have been a valuable lead, however, has suffered at his hands from inaccurate method and unprecise formulation, and from the difficulty in getting agreement as to diagnosis in a sizable proportion of cases (Wertheimer and Hesketh, 1926; Raphael, et al., 1928). Gibbs has made studies of sex development in schizophrenics (1923, 1924). Critical analyses have been presented by Burchard (1936) and Farber (1938), while Cabot (1938) has indicated the indirect social effects of physical characteristics upon the person having them. A new and more detailed study, conceived along Kretschmerian lines, has recently been carried out by Sheldon, et al. (1940, 1942, see also Chapter 17).

CENTRAL NERVOUS SYSTEM.—Organized attempts to establish definite brain pathology that can be definitely and dependably correlated with the functional psychoses have been carried out for many decades. Among the more influential workers in relatively recent times should be mentioned Southard (1910, 1914), Mott (1920a), Nissl and Alzheimer (1921), Josephy (1923), and Buscaino (1924). General reviews with bibliographies may be found in Stransky (1911), Lange (1928), Spielmeyer (1930), Steiner (1932), and N. Lewis (1936). A critical analysis of technique and criteria for adequate examination of autopsy material comes from the hand of Dunlap (1923, 1928) who found that, when adequate criteria were followed, it was impossible to single out the brains of schizophrenics from among a group of nonschizophrenic ones. Elvidge and Reed (1938) have attempted to diagnose schizophrenic brain changes during life by means of biopsy material removed through trephined openings. Stein and Ziegler (1939), stimulated by physiological studies of thalamic function in relation to emotion, have subjected the thalami of schizophrenic and of manic-depressive patients to a biometric analysis, but without conclusive results.

In critically reviewing the evidence for and against specific structural pathology for schizophrenia, Conn (1934) considers the quest to have been progressively unproductive, while Skalweit (1938) remains confident, in spite of the failures and mutual contradictions among structuralists, that an anatomical basis will finally be demonstrated. There always remain those who like Jung (1908) believe in the presence of toxic or intermediate metabolic substances in excess, the effects of which appear clinically as schizophrenic or affective disturbances but which may not leave pathology to be found at autopsy. This would be a strong fort into which to retire were there no convincing evidence of psychogenic factors in the predisposition to or precipitation of these illnesses. In addition the recent work that has been done upon the problem of deterioration, particularly the studies of Kendig and Richmond (1940), seems to make the position of those who have insisted upon the prevalence of organic defect, at least in schizophrenia, almost if not quite untenable.

PSYCHOSURGERY (LOBOTOMY, LEUCOTOMY).—In spite of our rather meager information concerning the neurophysiological correlates of abnormal behavior, brain surgery is being carried out quite widely in the treatment of functional disorders. Moniz (1937) developed a technique variously referred to as psychosurgery, lobotomy and leucotomy. This operation originally involved the production by a blunt loop dissection in the prefrontal subcortex of necrotic tissue "cores"; access to the brain was achieved through bilateral burr holes. Watts and Freeman (1938) have radically altered the procedure by inserting a blunt instrument horizontally through burr holes in the coronal suture 6 cm. above the zygomatic process on each side. After certain preliminaries, a periosteal elevator is passed into the brain to a depth of 5 cm., swung in an arc downward and upward as far as the bony opening permits and then withdrawn; the incision is then irrigated and the galea and scalp incisions sutured closed.

The goal of this operation is the severance of connection between thalamus and prefrontal cortex, although more destruction than this may occur. Freeman has summed up the rationale for this therapy as follows: "We believe that the frontal lobe is concerned with the picture that we have of ourselves, both as a unit of society and a collection of organs. The thalamic connection mediates the affect attached to that ego-image. When the image of the ego gets too painful for the individual so that a psychosis develops, and the egocentricity gets so marked that the patient thinks that people . . . are interfering with his adaptation to life, then some whittling down of this ego-ideal, let us say, some bleaching of the affect attached to the ego, renders the individual again capable of taking interest in outside things" (1942). From their results Freeman and Watts conclude that the central or Rolandic fissure divides the cerebral cortex into two portions of essentially different function, so that, "Just as the post-Rolandic cortex is concerned with the past, the pre-Rolandic cortex is concerned with the future. Aside from certain small areas . . . the frontal cortex is, according to our hypothesis, concerned with the projection of the whole individual into the future" (1942, pp. 302–303). Clinical descriptions of the after-effects of psychosurgery appear in the papers of Watts and Freeman (1938), Lyerly (1941), and Strecker, Palmer, and Grant (1942). The last-named consider this to be a mutilating operation and would restrict it to chronic psychotic cases with whom other methods have already proved fruitless. Bailey (1942), however, interprets the objections of psychiatrists to such radical treatment as "indignation resting on the subconscious conviction that the removal of the brain robs a man of his 'soul'."

A recovery strikingly similar to some described for psychosurgery from severe depression has been reported (Lebensohn, 1941) in which a self-inflicted bullet wound involving both prefrontals left the patient without the depression and with the emotional flattening, euphoria, facetiousness and lack of foresight reported for lobotomized patients. The remarkable summary of methods, results and theory in this field by Freeman and Watts (1942) should be consulted.

Focal Infections.—Surgery was at one time extensively employed in attempts to eradicate focal infections which were believed to be the determining cause of functional psychoses. Hunter, in the early days of bacteriology (1900), connected chronic sepsis with neurasthenia, depressions and severe "nervous breakdowns." Cotton (1921) summarized the spectacular therapeutic results he had obtained through dental extractions, and by drainage or surgical removal of viscera, including colonic resection; and he urged (1933) the subordination of everything else to a surgical attack upon the functional psychoses, mental deficiency, and delinquency. Hunter (1927a, 1927b) and Moynihan (1927) presented further data, the former proclaiming the discovery of the role of focal infections to be "a new era" in psychiatry and even suggesting that many functional psychoses be renamed *septic psychoses*. These interpretations were promptly challenged by Henderson (1927) and Menzies (1927) and later by the work of Beck, Ogden, and Whelen (1935a, 1935b), since when evidence has been collected on both sides (Kopeloff, 1941). Interest in this new era has waned considerably during the past decade and others have taken its place; but one still finds psychotic patients whose first treatment has been wholesale extractions or surgical subtractions.

ENDOCRINES.—Investigations of the endocrine system have likewise given inconclusive results. Kraepelin (1909–1913) taught that dementia praecox (schizophrenia) is due fundamentally to a metabolic disorder resulting in some form of autointoxication. Mott (1920a, 1920b, 1922a), on the basis of autopsy material, reported consistent pathological changes for schizophrenics in gonads, adrenals, and pituitary, together with degenerative cell processes especially in those of the cerebral cortex and the basal ganglia. These degenerations he attributed to inherited vital deficiency in the fertilized ovum. N. Lewis (1923) found in similar patients characteristic degenerative changes in testes, adrenals, and thyroid, although not in the pituitary. Morse (1923) has seriously challenged such claims on the basis of further pathological studies, calling attention to the many technical sources of error in determining norms for endocrine tissue, and to the marked effects of malnutrition and of fatal disease upon endocrine structure, which the other workers had apparently not considered. Lewin (1927) found no evidence in his material for "anatomico-psychiatric correlation" and characterized the hypotheses advanced by others on the basis of comparable material as untenable, particularly with reference to dementia praecox.

Bamford (1929) contended that in acute dementia praecox there were demonstrable infantilism of the cardiovascular system, a macrocephalic brain, and fibrosis of the endocrine glands. N. Lewis (1931) presented autopsy reports on eight cases of affective disorder which in his opinion indicated excessive compensatory reactions in both circulatory and endocrine structures; but his cases were aged 45, 51, 60, 62, 65, 76, and 85 years respectively and only one, who suicided, was free of complicating systemic factors preceding death. Hutton and Steinberg (1936) reported pituitary dysfunction in functional psychoses, and Clegg (1937) claimed gonadal deficiency in schizophrenia and pituitary deficiency in the affective group. Carmichael (1938), however, has called attention to the lack of crucial evidence for or against close relationship between endocrines and mental disorders. The endocrinologist Hoskins (1941) characterizes the relationship between the endocrines and personality as indeterminate in broad outline and in detail definitely confused. He doubts that any relationship between endocrines and behavior disorders has been demonstrated and considers this an important but almost unexplored area.

BIOCHEMISTRY AND PHYSIOLOGY.—The case for and against the hypothesis that consistent biochemical changes are the fundamental facts in the pathology of the functional psychoses has been critically reviewed by Malamud and Miller (1931) and by McFarland and Goldstein (1938, 1939). The dependable and consistent results they were able to sort out were very meager and even those were difficult to interpret. Physiological studies in relation to the functional disorders in general have been reviewed by Jasper (1937), Shock (1939), Knott (1941), D. Cameron (1941), Jasper (1941), Liddell (1941), and N. Cameron and Harlow (1943), and with special relation to manic and depressive disturbances by N. Cameron (1942b). Shipley and Kant (1940) have reviewed physiological and psychological aspects of chemical shock therapy. Research upon the physiology and biochemistry of the functional psychoses is being vigorously prosecuted at the present time. It cannot fail ultimately to prove enlightening in some direction; but whether or not it will produce the final and complete answer, as many hope and expect, is another matter. Final and complete solutions of the functional disorders seem less likely than they did 50 years ago when tendencies to study the individual as an isolated organism were less challenged than they are today.

PSYCHOGENESIS.—There are three main groups of persons who give first place to a psychogenic etiology for the functional psychoses. (a) One follows the older academic psychologists in looking upon the mind or psyche as something separate from the body or soma, the psyche somehow exerting an effective influence upon the soma and the soma upon the psyche, both through mediation of the central nervous system. This group of workers usually ascribes the greater reality to the soma, regarding the psyche as intangible, often as unpredictable, but at the same time as potentially a powerful influence. This is essentially the position of the psychosomatic school; the weak link in their causal chain is always the question of just how psyche and soma interact, a question which has never received a scientifically acceptable answer.

(b) The second group includes those whose theories of the unconscious crystallized in the rationalistic atmosphere of the late nineteenth and early twentieth centuries (Zilboorg and Henry, 1941), mainly through Freud's work. The many varieties within this group agree in ascribing the greatest effectiveness and reality to unconscious components of the psyche which to them are more primary and causal than either conscious psychic processes or somatic conditions. They, also, have been unable to solve the riddle of the mind-body or psychosomatic dualism which they have inherited along with their general philosophical position; but there is currently a concerted effort being made in this direction, in which both groups are participating (Dunbar, 1938). A minority of psychoanalysts is inclined to regard the functional psychoses as primarily organic diseases (e.g., Schilder, 1938, 1942).

(c) A newer interpretation of psychogenesis is unique in rejecting the traditional separation into a world of psychic and a world of physical reality. It lies farthest from theories of mental causation and closest to pragmatism and instrumentalism (Cameron, 1942c, 1943d). The term "psychogenesis," although a misnomer, is retained for the same reason that modern psychiatry retains "hysteria," i.e., it has become too thoroughly incorporated into the literature to be dropped. Instead of searching for first causes, however, this approach attempts to determine the conditions under which functional disorders arise and progress or disappear, be these predominantly in fantasy, conflict, disappointment, maladaptation, or in physiopathology, in trauma in the interrelationships with other persons, or in social, economic and other environmental circumstances. Such so-called "mental processes" as desire and fantasy, for example, are included as complex forms of organismic behavior, which involve biological activity in the same sense that signalling or talking to oneself or to another person does. Defective development of role-taking skills in the individual, as an important predisposing factor in functional disorders, has recently been introduced (Cameron, 1938a, 1943a, 1943b). For this view the *functional psychoses* are major disorders in which the direct effects of structural, physiological, and biochemical pathology are minimal or absent, while personal and social factors are maximal.

Adolf Meyer, although at the time brain pathologist at Worcester State Hospital, was among the first to present functional psychoses as reactions of the total personality in terms of social environment and personal organization (1906). He indicated the development of dementia praecox from normal reactions, as habit deteriorations, without falling back upon either pseudoneurology or psychosomatic dualism. According to him, the slightness of histological evidence "suggests a mere bankruptcy under anomalous or even ordinary demands with insufficient funds of adjustment" to meet them (1906, 1910a, 1910b). He worked out a conception of paranoia that did justice both to the unusual personality organization of the patient and to the forms of maladjustment in paranoiacs (1903, 1908, 1913). In 1896, Freud reported a case of "chronic paranoia" which he interpreted as a defense against childhood sex memories and homosexual fantasies; and in 1911 he came out with an analysis of the published autobiography of a paranoid schizophrenic patient of Flechsig's, in which Freud set forth his oft-quoted paradoxical denials and reversals of homosexual wishes (Knight, 1940).

Stransky (1903) postulated a schism between emotion and intellect, or *thymopsyche* and *noopsyche*, as the fundamental process underlying the deterioration in dementia praecox. This formed a basis not only for Bleuler's theory, but also for the rationale behind lobotomy, or "psychosurgery," which tries deliberately to produce apathy by a cerebral insult designed to separate thinking from emotion (Freeman and Watts, 1942). Bleuler (1906) and Jung (1908, 1939) described emotional interference and distortion in relation to paranoic and to disorganized thinking respectively. Gross (1906) gave reasons for considering the illness a disintegration rather than dementia and urged adoption of Wernicke's term *Dementia sejunctiva*; while Zweig (1908), reporting a case with an onset after the age of 30 years, called attention to the inappropriateness of the term praecox and suggested as a substitute *Dementia dissecans*.

Bleuler (1911) wrote an extensive monograph on dementia praecox to which he gave the name of *schizophrenia,* which is the most acceptable term today. Although Bleuler also considered dissociation to be fundamental in schizophrenia, he was never able to free himself from the histological theories of Alzheimer, Nissl, and Josephy, who maintained that cortical degeneration and glial proliferation were the essential parts of the disease picture (Bleuler, 1930a, 1930b). Accounts of the evolution of modern etiological theories of *schizophrenia* have been given by Meyer (1928b), Gruhle (1932c), Conn (1933), and Wittman (1937) ; of *paranoia* by Meyer (1913) and Kehrer (1928) ; and of the *affective* group by Stransky (1911), Lange (1928), Jelliffe (1931), and A. Lewis (1934a). The psychoanalytic theories have been traced by Rickman (1927) and Fenichel (1934).

The conviction is becoming widespread among psychiatrists, psychologists, and sociologists that the same kind of personal, social, and environmental factors are operative in preparing the ground for and in precipitating the functional psychoses as in the case of the neuroses. The intimate interrelationship between neuroses and functional psychoses has been brought out by Freud (1896), Meyer (1906), Dooley (1931), Myerson (1936, 1938), Miller (1940), and Caldwell (1941). There is nothing to be gained by listing the factors that have been implicated in the precipitation of functional psychoses ; obviously almost any incident toward which an individual may have become sensitized can tip the balance. Sullivan (1925, 1927a), Harrowes (1931a), Bonner (1931), Brew (1933), and Fox (1942) discuss psychogenic etiological factors in the affective psychoses ; Hutchings, Cheney, and Wright (1928), Wittman (1937), and Terry and Rennie (1938), in the schizophrenias.

Duration and Prognosis.—The duration of the functional psychoses is highly variable. Obviously many of the factors involved in precipitating the illness may operate in perpetuating it. Personality organizations that are too rigidly organized (Muncie, 1931) or too loosely (Diethelm, 1933) are apt to recover slowly or not at all. Rennie (1942) finds recovery in affective disorders correlated with an "outgoing personality." In general, a large proportion of paranoic and schizophrenic patients run a long course, and recover only partially or not at all. Involutional melancholias, because of aversion and anxiety characteristics as well as relatively advanced age, show a great tendency to become chronic, as do also a few manias. Uncomplicated depressive, manic, and some schizophrenic attacks, in persons with reasonably good personality assets, have a fairly good outlook provided treatment is begun early. What therapeutic method is employed makes far less difference than how early and how selected the cases are (Stalker, 1939; Notkin, *et al.,* 1939, 1940).

Great confusion has resulted in attempts to compare (a) chemically treated patients with (b) those treated by planned psychiatric methods and with (c) those left to themselves in a protected environment, because there has been a striking failure to state in the reports just how the patients were selected for specific therapy. This error, plus the suggestibility of the patients, the physicians, and the authors, have led to the same misleading claims in relation to endocrine therapy, to the elimination of "autointoxication" and focal infections, to psychosurgery and in relation to some of the more recent shock therapy (Henderson and Gillespie, 1940, Ch. 9). It is well known that reports of 90% to 95% complete cures have more than once been made in the literature, and by honest and responsible practitioners of the past, for forms of treatment that today are no longer considered worth talking about (Deutsch, 1937; Cheney and Drewry, 1938; Diethelm, 1939). Even the medical historian may lose his perspective. Garrison in 1924 indicated that the Abderhalden ferment reaction had discredited Meyer's view of schizophrenia as a functional rather than a gonadal disorder (pp. 700–701); but within a decade the Abderhalden technique had proved to be mere self-deception.

Prognostic studies in relation to a wide variety of factors have been reported, for the *affective* group, by Strecker, *et al.* (1931), A. Lewis (1936), Anderson (1936), Hunt (1938), and Rennie (1942); for the *schizophrenias*, by Sullivan (1924, 1928), Harrowes (1931b), Strecker (1931), N. Lewis and Blanchard (1931), Terry and Rennie (1938), Malamud and Render (1939), Stalker (1939), Henderson and Gillespie (1940), and Gottlieb (1940); and for the clinical mixtures of these, sometimes called schizaffective psychoses, by N. Lewis and Hubbard (1931) and Hunt and Appel (1936).

Classification.—All current attempts at classifications of functional personality disorders are unsatisfactory; this is true for the neuroses as well as for the psychoses. No causal organisms have been implicated, hence we cannot fall back upon them as we can in the specific infectious diseases. There are no characteristic organic lesions as there are in the systemic diseases; and the central nervous system exhibits no consistent changes that can be correlated with the syndromes as in neurological disorders. Physiological and biochemical studies do not support the older assumptions that fundamentally different metabolic processes underlie different forms of personality disorder (McFarland and Goldstein, 1938, 1939; Cameron, 1942b).

To date the least unsatisfactory classifications are those based upon clinical and behavioral differences. These suffer in a pronounced form, however, from the same limitations as those found in other clinical classifications; for one seldom encounters a pure clinical case of anything outside a textbook (Cameron and Cameron, 1938). It is unusual to find a depression without a little disorganization, or schizophrenia without some evidence of elation, sadness or hopelessness (Bonner and Kent, 1936). Even the manic patient is apt to have brief episodes of real sadness, or paranoid delusions and perhaps some incidental disorganization. Paranoics often show euphoria and elation, or show depression even to the point of suicide. In any discussion of clinical groupings, however, these admixtures, shadings, and contradictions have to be largely ignored in the interest of clarity; but it is important that they be not completely forgotten afterwards. Most of the confusion and the contradictions in the literature on functional psychoses can be traced to the wholly unjustifiable practice of treating the heterogeneous mass of major depressive and manic disturbances as if they really constituted a single illness, Kraepelin's "manic-depressive insanity," and of lumping together the schizophrenic disorders likewise as a homogeneous disease entity as though it were as uniform as chicken-pox.

It is important for persons working in the abnormal field to realize that the current official psychiatric classifications are not based upon final and convincing scientific evidence. They are children of practical necessities. Decisions as to the group in which a given behavior disorder shall fall depend upon schemata that actually were adopted, both in this country (Cheney, 1934) and in Great Britain (Fleming, 1933), by a majority vote of the practicing members of large associations. In some very fundamental respects these systems of classification represent frank compromises between dissident factions, as one can readily observe by reading the successive committee reports (Fleming, 1932, 1933, 1934). One should therefore avoid an attitude of finality toward the interrelationship among the behavior disorders that our official classifications, if taken too literally, seem to imply. It is obvious to any reasearch worker that questions of etiology, of clinical and physiological characteristics, and of the course, the therapy and the prognosis, cannot be decided for good purely on the basis of a majority vote. The most this can express is the majority opinion as to a useful expedient in administrative decisions. It does not necessarily represent even the most advanced opinion in scientific matters, particularly when the science is young and the evidence is very conflicting.

Diagnosis.—For simplicity's sake this account will follow the classical division of the functional psychoses into (a) affective disorders, including mania and depressions, (b) schizophrenic disorganizations, and (c) paranoic and paranoid psychoses. This follows in general the Kraepelinian schema adopted in a modified form by the American Psychiatric Association (Cheney, 1934). In the great majority of functional depressions, hopelessness and either sadness or an overwhelming anxiety dominate the picture; in manic excitements optimism with great joy or self-assertion usually prevail. In both of these latter groups there is relatively little disorganization of thought, speech and action. The experienced normal person is therefore more easily able to keep in satisfactory rapport with these patients than with schizophrenics. The manic patient is, of course, quite easy to differentiate from the depressed, since the prevailing emotional disturbance appears to be in an opposite direction.

The schizophrenic patient can readily be distinguished from mania and depression if, as is often the case, he shows definite disorganization; otherwise the distinction may be arrived at only after prolonged study of the case. There is still considerable need for better techniques in uncovering slight or early thought disorganization even though much research in the past decade or two has been devoted to this problem. The schizophrenic may be excited or slowed up but, unlike typical affective patients, his rapport with the experienced normal person is apt to be definitely poorer and less stable. He usually undergoes a certain degree of social disarticulation and in severe cases he may become almost completely shut off from the participative behavior of others (Cameron, 1938b, 1943b). Marked oddities of thought, speech, and action often develop which may grow into extraordinary permanent mannerisms.

Finally, paranoia deserves separate discussion because of its potential psychological importance. In the paranoic we are dealing with delusional systems, often well and convincingly organized, which more or less dominate the individual's living but do not necessarily lead to noteworthy disorganization. Outside of the delusional system itself the person may seem fairly clear and reasonable.

Incidence.—Closely tied up with the problems of classification are those of incidence. Some variation will be found in reports as to the incidence of the functional psychoses because of existing differences in classificatory criteria. According to Dayton (1940) there were 12,820 first admissions diagnosed dementia praecox in Massachusetts mental hospitals between 1917 and 1933, constituting 19.46% of total first admissions, of whom 6,253 were males and 6,567 females. During the same period there were 6,368 first admissions of manic-depressives, or 9.66%, of whom 2,552 were males and 3,816 females; there were 1,433 first admissions diagnosed involutional psychosis, or 2.17%, of whom 460 were males and 973 females; and there were 1,340 first admissions of paranoics, or 2.03%, of whom 484 were males and 856 females. The highest incidence of dementia praecox was found in males below and in females above 30 years of age; while in manic-depressives the highest incidence for males was above 50 and for females between 30 and 49 years. Paranoia and the involutional psychoses had their range of highest incidence between 50 and 79 in both sexes.

Malzberg (1940) bases his figures on first admissions to all mental hospitals in New York State during the fiscal years 1929–1931. During this period there were 7,539 diagnosed dementia praecox, constituting 26.3% of total first admissions, of whom 4,163 were males and 3,376 females. There were 3,846 manic-depressive first admissions, or 13.4%, of whom 1,530 were males and 2,316 females; 810 diagnosed involutional melancholia, or 2.8%, of whom 274 were males and 536 females; and 287 paranoia and paranoic conditions, or 1.0%, of whom 131 were males and 156 females. Average ages of first admissions diagnosed as dementia praecox are given as, for males, $31.8 \pm .01$ (S.D. in years $= 10.5 \pm .1$) and for females, $36.5 \pm .01$ (S.D. $= 11.6 \pm .1$); manic-depressives, for males, 38.3 ± .2 (S.D. = 13.7 ± .1) and for females, 36.2 ± .2 (S.D. = 12.4 ± .1); involutional melancholia, for males, 54.9 ± .3 (S.D. = 6.9 ± .2) and for females, 52.1 ± .2 (S.D. = 7.0 ± .1); and paranoia or paranoic conditions, for males 50.1 ± .7 (S.D. = 11.8 ± .5) and for females, 50.5 ± .6 (S.D. = 11.8 ± .4). Malzberg also presents analyses on the basis of environment, marital status, nativity and parentage, race, order of birth, economic factors, and literacy (1940).

In interpreting such data as these it must not be forgotten that hospital statistics cannot be applied directly to general population studies. They represent minimal figures since only those persons whose illness is fairly marked or whose home facilities are inadequate are usually sent to these hospitals. The approximately 500,000 patients in mental hospitals could undoubtedly be matched by an equal number who have never been in one. Paskind has attacked this problem, so far as the affective group is concerned, in a series of studies (1930a, b, c) reporting data on over 600 patients seen in private practice and not hospitalized. His patients turned out to be older on the average than in hospital statistics, the males slightly outnumbered the females, and the average duration of the attacks was much shorter than that given in hospital reports.

Major Affective Disorders

Under the major *affective* or *mood* disorders are usually grouped the elated excitements, the retarded depressions, and the anxious and agitated depressions. It is not customary to include here depressive and elated reactions occurring in the setting of organic brain disease or of systemic intoxications. In some quarters the depressions of middle life, especially those occurring in women at about the period of the menopause, are given separate treatment as "involutional melancholia"; in others they are simply included among the other depressions, or else placed with disorders of metabolism and endocrine function. Minor and incidental depressions clearly developing out of specific situations are conventionally grouped with the neuroses. This convention had its origin in the older theories that distinguished between the profound depressions as endogenic, i.e., of structural or metabolic origin, and the milder ones as psychogenic, i.e., psychologically or situationally determined.

Early History.—Recognition of some fundamental relationship between excitements and depressions goes back into antiquity. Hippocrates mentioned mania and melancholia in the fourth century B.C. By the first century A.D. they were already coming to be regarded by many physicians as part of one illness; thus Aretaeus wrote that melancholia "is a lowness of the spirits without fever; and it appears to me that melancholy is the commencement and a part of mania." In the sixth century Trallianus introduced the circular conception, which appears today in the term "cycloid personality," when he wrote of persons "not suffering from melancholia only, for they tend to become maniacal periodically and in a cycle" (Whitwell, 1936). General medical attitudes by the sixteenth century were thus summed up by Jason Pratensis: "Most physicians associate mania and melancholia as one disorder, because they consider that they both have the same origin and cause, and differ only in degree and manifestation; others consider them to be quite distinct" (Whitwell, 1936). Undeniably, many syndromes were then included under mania and melancholia which today would be grouped with other psychoses and neuroses. None the less, the modern tendency to look upon manias and depressions as phases of one disease represents the continuation of an old and established tradition.

Apparently the first persons to unite the two names to cover a single syndrome were Bonet, who wrote in 1684 on *folie maniaco-mélancolique* (i.e., manic-depressive insanity), Schacht, who in 1747 wrote on *delirium melancholico-maniacum,* and Herschel, who wrote in 1768 on *morbis melancholico-maniacus.* The French psychiatrist Falret senior introduced the term *folie circulaire* in 1851. Three years later both he and Baillarger published independently clinical descriptions of mania and depression occurring in the same person. Falret's son in 1879 described mixed states as transitional between mania and depression; and Kahlbaum in 1882 put the finishing touches by claiming that mania and melancholia were always phases of a single disease.

The Present Situation.—Kraepelin crystallized these attitudes in the eighth edition of his remarkable four-volume textbook (1909–1913). All severe depressions and all elated excitements became in his hands only manifestations of a single phasic disease-process, of which excitements were at one pole and depressions at the other. The widespread official acceptance of this hypothesis has profoundly affected therapy and research everywhere. Beneath the surface of this agreement for clinical convenience, however, there lie innumerable unsolved problems and some fundamental contradictions (Meyer, 1917; Partridge, 1931; Oberndorf and Meyer, 1931; Rosanoff, 1938). Of these, Partridge goes farthest in questioning the validity of any research reports that compare groups, for example, of unselected manic-depressives with groups of schizophrenics as though these were two relatively homogeneous disease entities. This criticism seems to have enough justification, from both the biological and the psychological evidence, to throw serious doubt upon the usefulness of a very large proportion of such research data. The controversy has recently been summarized and its relation to physiological and biochemical research reviewed by N. Cameron (1942b).

The psychoanalytic school, beginning with the writings of Abraham (1927) and Freud (1921), while introducing their own special concepts, has deviated surprisingly little from the Kraepelinian position. Glover (1932) and Klein (1935, 1940) show an increasing tendency to oppose depression to paranoia rather than to mania, mainly on the basis of adultomorph speculations upon the thinking of suckling babes. Radó (1928), however, seems clearly to be attempting a fusion of Kraepelin with psychoanalytical theory when he asserts that, "The manic condition succeeds the phase of self-punishment [depression] with the same regularity with which formerly, in the biological process, the bliss of satiety succeeded to hunger."

Because of the many unsolved problems in this field the more doctrinaire and speculative attitudes will be avoided as much as possible. In this way what facts there are may be presented as they actually appear, rather than as they may have been interpreted according to one or another system of postulates.

Mania.—

HISTORICAL.—Our conceptions of mania today have come from an ancient distinction which sorted out from the excitements a group neither accompanied by .fever nor arising from the ingestion of toxic substances. Aretaeus, for example, in the first century A.D. defined mania as a continuous disorder of the mind without fever; and he stated definitely that deliria arising from the taking of specific substances should not be included (Farrar, 1908; Jelliffe, 1931). He also wrote that mania has recurrent periods and is curable; his recognition of its relation to depression has already been discussed. In modern times Kraepelin, whose classificatory system is the model for most current schemes, divided "manic states" into *hypomania, mania, delusional forms,* and *delirious forms* (1908–1913). Under "mixed states" which, following Falret *fils,* he regarded as transitional between mania and depression, Kraepelin distinguished "depressive mania," "mania with poverty of thought," "manic stupor," "angry mania," and "nagging mania." Of these so-called mixed manic states only manic stupor seems to be surviving in the literature. He also recognized "chronic mania," following Schott (1904), whose classical descriptions have been reviewed in English and added to by Wertham (1929).

The current trend is away from Kraepelin's tendency to make finer and finer subdivisions, and toward a simple subgrouping on the basis of severity into *hypomania, acute mania,* and *delirious mania.* Objections have been raised to these terms because hypomania gets confused with *hypomanic personality,* while delirious mania reintroduces a confusion with toxic deliria which even the ancients were at great pains to avoid. The writer suggests *subacute mania, acute mania,* and *hyperacute mania* as simpler terms that cover the same categories. As for the other two commonly used distinctions, the "manic stupor" is only a manic attack in which the patient is mute; while "chronic manias" are attacks of very long duration and usually of mild or moderate intensity. The other Kraepelinian varieties are little used and can largely be ignored.

DEFINITIONS.—*Mania* may be defined as excitement in which the person characteristically is elated and overactive without serious disorganization, and for which no underlying consistent physiopathology or structural pathology has been demonstrated. *Subacute mania* ("hypomania") is a mild degree of mania which shades imperceptibly into normal elated overactivity; *acute mania* represents mania that has got seriously out of hand; *hyperacute mania* ("delirious mania") is manic excitement so severe as to involve serious disorientation and such extreme overactivity as to endanger the patient's life. Mania characteristically comes in attacks having a fairly definite beginning and end (Harrowes, 1931a), but, like most other personality disorders, it may have a long prodromal period and is subject to recurrence.

SUBACUTE MANIA ("HYPOMANIA").—Subacute mania may at first appear to be only an episode of normal mild euphoria. Its onset may date from a mere increase in elation or in general activity, or from a shift to elation and a more active attitude in a person who is ordinarily quiet and retiring. Thus to both the subject and his associates the change is often taken to be an improvement; and encouragement is usually given him by his associates to continue along this direction of development. Subacute mania may follow a depressive episode. The typical early clinical appearance is often compared to that of mild alcoholic intoxication; the person becomes gay or aggressive, or both, is often witty and jolly, relatively uninhibited in speech and general conduct, inclined to increased initiative without a corresponding increase in effectiveness, more self-confident than usual and less concerned over the risks involved in his plans and their execution. Sleep-loss, constipation, and weight-loss are common.

It may be difficult in practice to establish to others' satisfaction the fact that the patient is not at this time completely well; for he feels better than usual, he may really be enjoying himself, and he may show none of the more obviously pathological features of a full blown mania. None the less in this phase he often will, if not curbed, indulge in entertainments and in enterprises, unwisely conceived and poorly thought out, which may have disastrous consequences for his economic, social or personal status. Usually his family and his close friends recognize that there is a change in his personality, especially if he grows domineering, sleepless and increasingly erotic. Often subacute manic attacks, lasting several weeks, are successfully handled without hospitalization and even without competent medical guidance; but the dangers to the person's health, to his reputation and to his future are very real and should never be ignored by those in any way responsible for his wellbeing. The milder excitements may subside or go on after a period of a few hours, days, or weeks into a more acute phase.

ACUTE MANIA.—The intelligent layman, unless himself the patient, can usually recognize the acute manic attack as definitely pathological. The general picture one sees is that of a very excited, distractible, overactive, overconfident, and continuously talkative person with whom nevertheless rapport is usually good. There may be little or nothing in his behavior that is incongruous with exaggerated and uninhibited elation. This is an important point because a very persistent tendency is still present to consider every acute excitement, no matter how disjointed and bizarre, as manic. The patient is restless, busy, impatient, and sleepless; he feels little or no fatigue in spite of the extreme and continual activity. He may sing loudly and gaily, shout himself hoarse, prance about, do calisthenics, and even destroy things or injure other persons in a spirit of anger, or as a demonstration of strength and domination. Some manic persons become especially arrogant and abusive to those in authority or to those who are responsible for curbing them. The rapid flow of talk is typically peppered with quips, puns, rhymes, and plays on words; there is a constant quick shifting from topic to topic without, however, unintelligible gaps in continuity. Personal comments, vulgar or obscene talk, and gestures are common. Many patients engage in a great deal of writing, drawing, painting, or decorating; and these productions likewise are not, as a rule, bizarre or inexplicable to the ordinary observer.

The very elated mood may shift easily to irritability, anger, and furious resentment if interference or restraint is arbitrarily introduced. It is at this point often that, somewhat late for the patient's own good, inpatient care in a psychiatric hospital is decided upon. The tendency of manic patients to dominate situations, to interfere aggressively in others' activities, and to engage in teasing, prankishness, and unbridled criticism makes their separation from other patients often desirable; their own need for a nonstimulating neutral environment may make it practically indispensable. At the same time bodily restraint, solitary confinement without occupation or materials of any kind, and the imposition of rigid discipline are unnecessary in a well-organized psychopathic hospital and are fast disappearing from the modern treatment of acute mania.

In manic attacks the personal needs of the patient are frequently lost sight of because of the ease with which manic conduct arouses anger, ridicule or reprisal in those around. In spite of his uncontrolled clowning, his facetious or obscene talk, and his almost complete lack of consideration for others, the manic is often himself very sensitive, childishly proud, and completely intolerant of criticism or ridicule. He benefits from a friendly and tolerant atmosphere; but he also needs, much more than a normal person does, to be treated with a respect and consideration which his own conduct does not automatically elicit. Diethelm (1936) gives an unusually sympathetic picture of this aspect of the manic patient based upon many years of clinical experience; this work should be consulted on questions of therapeutic handling.

Thinking disorders in the manic attack stem partly from the general overactivity and from the elation and self-assertion. In addition to the rapid shifting of topic and the distractibility already mentioned, there may develop grandiose delusions of achievement, power or possessions. The exact character of the delusive beliefs will naturally depend upon the general personality, the past experiences and the present situation.

Expansive, powerful, important, and erotic roles are after all congruous with elation and self-assertion. From unsuccessful or frustrated efforts may also be derived delusions of interference, of malice or of persecution by others. Hallucinations when present are transitory and relatively unimportant. Religious or magical interpretations may intrude themselves into the picture; but in the manic these are not dominant, nor are they usually lasting. As in mild depressions talented persons may produce valuable artistic work related to their mood, so also in manic attacks there may be productions of some value; usually, however, the shifting attention prevents completion of things even if well begun (Anastasi and Foley, 1940, 1941a, 1941b, 1941c).

The acute manic person, even more than the subacute, needs special attention to general hygiene and particularly to food intake and elimination. There is some confusion on this point. Abraham (1927) described as typical of mania a patient in whom a ravenous appetite with gobbling was prominent and evacuation very rapid. On this single observation he built up a theory which still influences many current explanations (Radó, 1928; Glover, 1932; Fenichel, 1934; Klein, 1935, 1940). Actually it is very often a difficult task to get manic patients to eat and to evacuate adequately; they are too busy and active to bother. If after some urging the manic bolts his food, it is characteristically done in a hurry, as everything else is, not eagerly and "cannibalistically" (Roheim, 1923), and the patient turns at once to other things or uses the food for decoration and play. Moreover, Henry (1931), on the basis of X-ray studies, reported that gastrointestinal motility in acute mania is actually slower than in the normal.

HYPERACUTE MANIA ("DELIRIOUS MANIA").—Acute manic attacks occasionally develop to the point where the patient is wildly excited, disoriented, and uncontrollable. His activity is continual, he is out of rapport, frequently hallucinates, grossly misinterprets events and misidentifies persons; delusional material is common. Because of the grave and often fatal consequences of such violent excitement, which throws tremendous strain upon the cardiorespiratory system, hypercute mania has been called in the past "delirium grave," "collapse delirium," and "typhomania." Something like it was described by Bell and it is still often referred to as "Bell's mania." Kraines (1934) has reviewed its history and described cases. It is questionable whether or not extreme manic excitements deserve separate discussion; certainly at their height enough disorganization develops to make them nearly or quite indistinguishable from any other wild excitement.

Depression.—

HISTORICAL.—The present-day attitudes toward melancholia or depression, like those toward mania, have their origins in a more or less continuous history reaching back into antiquity. Hippocrates, over 2,000 years ago, differentiated no less than six kinds of melancholia, some of which apparently included clinical pictures that modern diagnosticians would group with paranoia, schizophrenia, and the neuroses (Jeliffe, 1931). Aretaeus, in the first century A.D., defined melancholia as "a lowness of spirits from a fixed and single fantasy, without fever" (Farrar, 1908). From his clinical descriptions it is evident that he, too, included syndromes that we would not call depressions today. Down through the ages to the present there have been repeated discourses on the nature, etiology, and treatment of melancholia. The last psychiatric renaissance, beginning with the sweeping therapeutic reforms of Chiarugi, Daquin, Pinel, Tuke, and others, ushered in a new era of clinical observation in the mental disorders, while the growth and dissemination of medical periodicals made the reports and discussions of cases widely accessible in Europe and America (Deutsch, 1937). One immediate result was that the almost countless psychiatric syndromes until then given separate status were reduced drastically in number, which greatly simplified the task of those entering upon the study of mental disorder, as, for example, in the system of J. P. Falret published in 1851 and 1854, and that of Baillarger in 1854. The latter constructed a table showing "the forms of mental diseases," in which he has listed four syndromes as curable, viz., *monomania, melancholia, mania,* and *insanity of double form* (presumably manic-depressive), and two syndromes as incurable, viz., *incoherent dementia* and *simple dementia.* In addition he listed as sometimes curable and sometimes not, *delirium tremens, drug deliria,* and mental diseases associated with *cerebral affections,* including general paresis, convulsive disorders, and local organic brain disease. As an "appendix" he grouped imbecility and cretinism. During the latter half of the nineteenth century there were gradually separated out a few definite forms of depressive illness, largely through the work of Guislan, Griesinger, and Kraft-Ebing, which led through the conceptions of Kahlbaum and Hecker to Kraepelin's system (Jelliffe, 1931).

Kraepelin unintentionally wrote a clinical history of modern psychiatry in the successive editions of his great textbook. He came to differentiate six varieties of depression, viz., *melancholia simplex, stupor, melancholia gravis, paranoid melancholia, phantastic melancholia,* and *delirious melancholia*; and among the so-called "mixed states" he placed *depressed mania, agitated depression, depression with flight of ideas,* and *partial inhibition.* In his eighth edition (1909–1913) Kraepelin had decided that most of the depressive syndromes, including involutional melancholia to which he had in earlier editions given separate status, were only parts of the single disease entity "manic-depressive insanity." This decision was accepted by a committee of the American Psychiatric Association in 1934 as final, and it was crystallized in an official classification adopted first by the association and later by various state and federal bureaus. A noteworthy exception was the exclusion of involutional melancholia from this group and its quite premature inclusion under "Psychoses due to disturbances of metabolism, nutrition or endocrine function." The state and federal bureaus also followed the association in listing separately, under the psychoneuroses, a "reactive depression" supposedly different from the "endogenous" manic-depressive disease in being situationally determined and responsive to psychotherapy. The otherwise less adequate British official classification (Fleming, 1933) rather wisely refused to commit itself on the as yet unsettled etiology of involutional melancholia.

In what follows, three groups of depressions will be singled out for discussion. Two of them, the *retarded depression* and the *agitated* or *anxious depression,* are easily distinguishable syndromes. The third, *involutional melancholia,* is the subject of so much controversy today that for this reason alone it deserves special mention.

RETARDED DEPRESSION.—*Definitions.* The retarded depression is a condition of dejection and underactivity without serious disorganization for which no underlying consistent physiopathology or structural pathology has been demonstrated. The degrees of retarded depression customarily distinguished are *mild depression, marked* or *acute depression,* and *depressive stupor.* We shall follow the procedure adopted in the section on mania by substituting for these, *subacute, acute,* and *hyperacute retarded depressions.* Subacute retarded depression shades imperceptibly over into normal discouragement; acute retarded depression represents depression that has got seriously out of hand; hyperacute depression ("depressive stupor") refers to a degree so severe that the patient shows almost no reaction to changes in his environment and in himself. Like mania, retarded depression typically occurs in attacks having a fairly definite beginning and ending; usually attacks are preceded by prodromal symptoms, often beginning months before the outbreak; occasionally they are preceded by a frank manic episode.

Subacute Retarded Depression ("Mild Depression"). This may early be indistinguishable in appearance from discouragement, malaise, or fatigue. As time goes on without improvement, however, there is generally some recognition by others that the person is not up to par; and his associates may attempt to increase his activity through advice, entertainment, and new environment. Sometimes such measures help the patient for a while at least, sometimes they do not; very often they only increase his sense of inadequacy and make his depression worse. Typically the person seems to grow sad and retiring, or irritable and resentful. He loses interest and initiative, cannot see the light side of life, has lost much of his usual self-confidence and self-assertion, and his behavior, speech, and thought are slowed down. Sleep is poor, constipation is the rule, and loss of appetite and weight usually appear.

It is quite possible to conceal subacute depressive episodes and pass them off as ordinary fatigue, laziness, or worry. It is also common for others to give them such a misinterpretation even in the face of frank statements of hopelessness and gloom on the patient's part. The dangers even in relatively mild depression may be very great. Suicide is an ever-present threat which must never be discounted (Jameison and Wall, 1933; Jameison, 1936); associates of the depressed patient are much too easily misled by his reassurances on this score. There is a wholly unfounded belief that if a person repeatedly threatens suicide he will not do it; this is a fatal error of judgment to make. There is also a real possibility of homicide among depressed persons with dependents or loved ones whom they picture as facing hopelessness, suffering, or disaster with them. Only less severe are the dangers to health, business, or family welfare, and to economic status arising from neglect, poor judgment, or incompetence in a person still able to go on with his or her routine. As with some subacute mania, it is often possible in the milder retarded depressions to carry the patient over the depression without hospitalization; the far greater incidence of suicide in depressions, however, makes their treatment always a grave responsibility for the therapist, who must be competent to recognize danger signals of all kinds (Diethelm, 1936). A subacute episode may or may not usher in the acute retarded depression.

Acute Retarded Depression. Even the acute depression may impress others as only unusual worry, malaise, or inertia. Typically the person is very slowed up and deeply dejected, with general behavior, speech, and thinking difficult and monotonous. Initiative is conspicuously impaired. Lack of self-confidence and of self-assertion increases to hopelessness, and to severe self-disparagement and self-accusation. Expectation of punishment or of persecution is common. Sleep becomes wretched, amounting often to only an hour or two in the twenty-four. Appetite decreases markedly, becoming inadequate even for the now greatly diminished level of general activity, so that weight falls off alarmingly. Spoon-feeding and coaxing frequently become necessary; and the patient may have to be reminded to chew the food lying in his mouth after he has admitted it. Some patients complain of difficulty in swallowing food after mastication, which may be related to a reduction in salivary secretion (Strongin and Hinsie, 1938). Complaints of dry mouth, dry skin and hair are frequent, and they help along delusions of body change.

Hypochondriacal complaints are usual and in some persons dominate the picture (Ziegler, 1929), although these are generally more prominent among the agitated than among the retarded. Delusions are common and hallucinations also are reported (Bowman and Raymond, 1931a, 1931b; A. Lewis, 1934b). Sometimes nihilistic delusions referring especially to gastrointestinal function appear, most often in middle-aged and elderly persons; patients may insist they have no stomach or no bowels, or that they have not had an evacuation for months. These delusions are undoubtedly associated with the greatly slowed up gastrointestinal activity (Henry, 1931) and the digestive disturbances incident to such malfunctioning.

In acute retarded depression it is the rule for the person to be adversely affected by the urgings and expostulations of his associates and advisers, who may still not recognize the change as an illness. His efforts bring failure and this only emphasizes for him his actual inadequacy. The danger of suicide is very great, many acutely depressed persons being unremitting in their plans and attempts at self-destruction (Lendrum, 1933; Shapiro, 1935; Piker, 1938). The vigilance and imagination necessary to prevent this all too common termination of depression can be appreciated only through personal experience in the treatment of it. Inevitably some of these continuously planned attempts will be successful, even under expert psychiatric hospital treatment; but the great majority of them can be prevented or, better still, avoided through removing opportunities and providing helpful occupation and competent psychotherapy. A recurrence severe enough to demand hospital care occurs in about 50% of recovered cases (Pollock, 1931).

Hyperacute Retarded Depression ("Depressive Stupor"). In the most extreme form of retarded depression, the person if left alone will lie almost motionless and fail to respond to all attempts at establishing or maintaining rapport. He will neither eat nor drink, and anything placed in his mouth is likely to remain there until removed; tube feeding may then become necessary to preserve life. Evacuation often will not occur without definite aid and this may have to be manual; impactions in neglected cases are common. Even lethal threats may be ignored. It is, of course, very difficult and often impossible to differentiate depressive from schizophrenic stupor on a phenomenological basis, since both denote a state of profound unreactivity; the previous and subsequent history provides the best basis.

There is a somewhat confusing use of the term *depressive stupor* to cover also those cases of retarded depression in which patients who although not so extremely depressed remain entirely mute. Diethelm (1936) ascribes such mutism to fear and aversion. An interesting account of what were taken to be "benign" stupors, i.e., functional stupors with a good prognosis, was published in 1921 by Hoch. A follow-up study of those of Hoch's cases still traceable was reported in 1935 by Rachlin, who found that the greater number had shown developments indistinguishable from catatonic stupors with an unfavorable outcome. Gottlieb (1939) reported that rate of blood-flow seems to be affected neither in mania nor in deep depressive stupor. The literature on stupor has been reviewed by Munn (1933).

AGITATED AND ANXIOUS DEPRESSIONS.—The agitated depression is differentiated from the retarded depression on the basis of activity. In both forms hopelessness, unworthiness, and self-accusation may be experienced, but whereas the retarded, depressed person is slowed up in every respect, the agitated depressed is typically overactive and overtalkative. He may be unable to remain in bed or in a chair, instead pacing the floor, wringing his hands, moaning, or ejaculating phrases of premonition and despair. Sleep, appetite, and weight suffer badly. Usually there are numerous hypochondriacal complaints, probably associated with the disruptions of normal functioning which the total clinical picture includes. Delusional expectations of punishment, torture, and public disgrace are very common. The need of these persons for protection from the stimulating or protesting environment of the home, as well as from their own strongly impulsive suicidal attempts, is often very great. Their need for simple occupation and encouragement is too easily overlooked because any directive effort on their part appears to the inexperienced to be entirely out of the question; but actually this is a group that in the long run is very likely to repay every effort at constructive therapy made on the occupational level.

Falret *fils* in 1879 considered the agitated depression to be a mixed state, part manic because overactive and part depressed for obvious reasons. Such is the prevalent attitude today thanks to its adoption by Kraepelin (1909–1913), whose decision in this respect was incorporated into our official classification (Cheney, 1934). The logic of this position is, however, not compelling. Overactivity and talkativeness do not belong exclusively to mania, neither are they foreign to the normally discouraged or apprehensive person. It is more useful and less confusing to recognize under depression these variants, themselves counterparts of normal variation, than it is to postulate equal parts of mania and of melancholia mixed together in a human beaker to make an agitated depression. The *anxious depression* may best be understood as a subacute or mild degree of agitated depression.

INVOLUTIONAL MELANCHOLIA.—According to the official American classification, involutional melancholia includes depressions of middle and later life characterized chiefly by agitation, uneasiness, sleeplessness and often self-condemnatory trends, but without organic intellectual defects. If these symptoms appear in a person who has ever in his life had a previous attack of excitement or depression, however, his illness is not to be classed as involutional melancholia but as manic-depressive psychosis (Cheney, 1934). This contradictory exception illustrates particularly well the confusion in our classificatory attitudes. Henderson and Gillespie (1940) consider involutional melancholia a fairly common and definite illness whose essential features are anxiety, unreality feelings, hypochondriacal or nihilistic delusions, and depression without retardation, occurring in women between 40 and 55, and in men between 50 and 65 years of age. They acknowledge that the same syndrome may occur in the twenties and thirties in women and before the fifth decade in men; and they go farther than the American classification in excluding all persons who have had any previous psychosis whatever, even though they may have all these symptoms and also be within the involutional period.

Hoch and MacCurdy (1922) felt it necessary to subdivide cases usually called involutional melancholia into chronic and recoverable. Among the chronic they separated off all those showing ridiculous delusions, infantile sexuality, insufficient emotional reaction, and antisocial conduct. These they regarded as cardinal symptoms of schizophrenia; and they placed such cases in that group. Strecker and Ebaugh (1940), however, consider that by restricting the age incidence to the involutional period they eliminate schizophrenia as even a possibility. Hoch and MacCurdy disposed of the rest of their chronic cases by calling them "organic insufficiency" because they seemed to reflect a fundamental and general senescence. They also eliminated any recoverable cases showing typical retarded or agitated depressions, and all reactive depressions when these happened to occur during the involutional period regardless of past history. The group left, which they considered the only genuine involutional melancholias, shows fears of impending death, delusions of poverty and bodily disease, often with vivid hallucinations and great agitation and restlessness, but otherwise without intellectual impairment. MacCurdy (1925) explained away the occurrence of this syndrome in young persons by making it depend upon "a certain type of regression."

Meyer (1938) refers to "involutional psychoses" as including averse and peevish depressions with judgment defects, less plastic and adequate affective factors, and a tendency to rut-formation with an unfavorable outcome. Diethelm (1936) emphasizes surliness and irritability, distorted hypochondriacal delusions, untidiness, and often incontinence of urine and stool. Henry (1938) stresses anxiety and restlessness, intensification of normal hypochondriasis, self-accusatory delusions, and a striking ability to smile and be merry for brief periods. Jameison and Wall (1931) conclude that involutional melancholia is in itself probably not a complete clinical entity. General agreement as to clinical designation has not yet been reached.

Etiological problems in involutional melancholia are exaggerations of those involved elsewhere among the functional psychoses. A few workers take it for granted that failure of adequate sex hormone production is the one important causal agent involved; others, like MacCurdy (1925), use symptoms so strictly as criteria that young adults can be included and the original age-period connotation is lost; while some, like Pearson (1928), attempt psychoanalytic interpretations in terms of libido regression. Titley (1936) reports "an almost constant pattern of traits" that distinguishes the prepsychotic personality from those of normal persons and of manic-depressives. From the hereditary standpoint, Farr, Sloane, and Smith (1930) found significantly fewer cases of "taint" among relatives of patients diagnosed involutional melancholia than of the manic-depressive. Farrar and Franks (1931) discuss the relationship between menopause and psychosis from several standpoints.

One therapeutic test of the role of sex hormones is obviously that of administering them to patients under controlled conditions. Although details of treatment do not lie within the scope of this chapter, a brief discussion of results of this method is in order. The reports in recent papers are quite contradictory. Thus, while Werner, *et al.* (1936) reported hormone therapy with theelin as curative in involutional melancholia and even recommended its use as a test in differential diagnosis,

Schube, *et al.* (1937) found it of no value at all. In a second study, Werner and his associates (Ault, Hoctor, and Werner, 1940) claimed 90% recoveries through sex hormone therapy and regarded shock therapy unjustified unless estrogenic treatment had already been tried; and in 1941 they reasserted this general claim with additional supporting case material (Werner, Hoctor, and Ault). All this is contradicted by the results obtained by Palmer, Hastings, and Sherman (1941), who found estrogenic therapy of no avail while they credited metrazol shock treatment with 73% recoveries or social remissions. Ripley, Shorr, and Papanicolaou (1940) combined the experience of a clinical psychiatrist, an internist, and an endocrinologist in a study of menopausal and post-menopausal depressions. In this report, estrogenic hormone therapy did not influence the patients' depression but only contributed to their comfort through directly affecting vasomotor symptoms.

The involutional period of life involves many difficulties in addition to endocrinological imbalance. There is a gradual decline in physical vigor and health. Chronic illnesses in oneself, or in one's kin and friends, grow commoner and call one's attention to the passage of time. The realization of ambitions becomes obviously less likely. There is apt to be less personal plasticity and less interest in new friends and new adventures. In women the loss of youth and the end of child-bearing, and in men the prospect of diminished powers and of retirement, undoubtedly operate as etiological factors. Diethelm (1936) and Noyes (1939) give considerable weight to these aspects. Billings (1939) considers involutional melancholia as only an agitated depression that happens to fall in the middle life-period.

MANIC-DEPRESSIVE CYCLES.—A brief history of the development of this concept has been included above. In the process of apparently recovering from a depressive attack a minority of persons go over into mania, and a larger percentage goes from a manic illness over into depression. This sequence has been recognized for at least 2,000 years; there is no controversy about the fact of its occurrence. Two main questions may be mentioned. First, how long after apparent recovery from depression may a manic attack occur and still be considered part of such a cycle? The majority opinion and the official classification of the English-speaking world maintain that there is no time limit. If any person has a depressive attack and years later has an elated excitement, these are considered to be two phases of a single disease. A minority dissents from this opinion, maintaining that these are most usefully treated as separate affective disorders in a susceptible person.

Secondly, suppose a person to have only one attack in his life of either mania or depression. Officially, even if only one depression or one elated excitement occurs in a life-time, such an attack must be considered as a phase of the manic-depressive psychosis. The one official exception to this ruling is the occurrence of an agitated depression after forty, which is then to be considered as *involutional melancholia* and a thing apart

(Cheney, 1934; Fleming, 1934; Henderson and Gillespie, 1940). Anyone having clinical experience with attacks of depression knows that
during the recovery period there may be a slight and transitory period
of overoptimism. According to the two-phase theory of affective disorders this represents a small swing through the opposite phase and
therefore completes the cycle and corroborates the theory; but an alternative interpretation is that it represents a mild overreaction to recovery
from a long and distressing illness in an emotionally reactive person.
Cameron (1942b) has suggested that manic attacks are not mere supplements of depression but are coordinate affective disorders playing a
psychological role very similar to that of depressions; and in this sense
they may be considered as depressive equivalents which often arise under
personal and situational conditions that correspond closely to those
giving rise to depressive attacks.

Bond and Partridge (1924), after analysis of 40 cases, concluded
that "the principle of unity that would make the phases of manic-
depressive reactions take their place as aspects of one fundamental psychological or physiological process is wanting." They challenge assumptions that the small minority of patients showing alternate manic and
depressive attacks necessarily passes through a normal phase between;
they regard both as below the normal level. In the almost complete
absence of biological evidence for opposed physiological or biochemical
processes in mania and depression (Cameron, 1942b), their relationship
remains at least an open one. The importance of this to research workers
especially is that grave doubts are cast upon the validity of the prevalent
custom of comparing "manic-depressive patients" with "schizophrenic
patients" as though these represented well-defined and homogeneous
groups. Actually there are large variations in behavior and psychopathology within each of these clinical groups so that such comparisons
become almost meaningless, unless careful selection within each group of
comparable and homogeneous material is carried out. A large part of the
work done in the past has probably been invalidated because of this
uncritical custom (Partridge, 1931).

Schizophrenia

Nowhere else in the field of psychopathology are there more fundamental problems for the clinician and the research worker, nowhere else
is there less agreement on so many important points than in schizophrenia. The first common denominator that led up to the concept of this
functional psychosis was that of a deteriorating process, occurring in
young persons, which progressed to a demented end-stage, hence the obsolescent term *dementia praecox*. The first important revision of this basic
conception came when data accumulated showing that identical clinical
disturbances developed in persons who were in their thirties and forties.
The second important revision is now in progress. There is a growing
body of experimental and clinical evidence tending to discredit the

notion of a demented end-stage in all but a small minority of cases. The answers to such questions as these problems not only help to shape our theoretical structures but they determine just as much our whole therapeutic orientation. The present status of schizophrenia can become intelligible only if its recent historical development is appreciated.

History.—The early historical precursors of the modern concept of schizophrenia are more difficult to identify than are those of the affective disorders. Such characteristic features as progressive apathy and stupor, disorganized excitement and ecstasy, silly or incongruous behavior, and symbolic disorders of motility were easily confused with manic and depressive attacks, or with phenomena similar in appearance occurring in general systemic and in organic brain disease. On the side of classification an important development immediately preceding the contemporary era was that of the isolation and description by various persons of four clinical groupings which Kraepelin then proceeded to fuse into a single disease entity. One of these resembled paranoia in having delusions as its most prominent constituent; but unlike what was then called "true paranoia," the delusions in these cases were poorly systematized and there always appeared to be a tendency toward deterioration. This group early received the name *dementia paranoides*.

Kahlbaum set up another group in 1868 which he called *catatonia* or *tension insanity*; he described it as a form of brain disease in which the clinical pictures of melancholia, mania, stupor, confusion, and dementia were supposed to follow upon one another. But the pathognomonic features were characteristic disturbances of motility; and these were said by Kahlbaum to be just as specific for catatonia as other motility disturbances were for paresis. His assumption of a basic structural brain disease was made upon purely hypothetical grounds and has never been substantiated. A third clinical entity was put forward by Hecker in 1871 and named *hebephrenia*. According to Hecker, this was a progressive disease of puberty and adolescence which began with a prodromal depressive phase, went over into a silly, bizarre excitement, and then terminated rapidly in a mental decline.

Hecker's hebephrenia was actually quite similar to a much older group first described in England, and a century later in France; it finally got its name in Belgium, and this was then adopted in the Latinized form, *dementia praecox*, by the Germans from whom the English-speaking world received it again. The great English brain anatomist, Willis, in 1674 described "young persons who, lively and spirited and at times even brilliant in their childhood, passed into obtuseness and hebetude during adolescence" (Meyer, 1928b). In the late eighteenth and early nineteenth centuries Pinel and Esquirol gave similar descriptions, the latter calling the condition "accidental or acquired idiocy," which he ascribed to unwise blood-letting, to head trauma, to masturbation or the suppression of menses. In 1849 Connolly wrote, "Young persons not infrequently fall into a state somewhat resembling melancholia, without any discoverable cause of sorrow, and certainly without any specific grief; they become indolent or pursue their usual occupations or recreations mechanically and without interest; the intellect, the affections, the passions, all seem inactive and the patients become utterly apathetic" (Noyes, 1939).

It was the Belgian Morel who in 1860 introduced the term *démence précoce*. He, too, emphasized the rapid decline of formerly talented or precocious persons into dementia; but influenced by certain French and Italian traditions he considered this an hereditary degenerative disease. The term gained increasing currency until finally Kraepelin adopted it as *dementia praecox*. He at first included it among the "degenerative psychoses"; and he considered it to be the same thing as Hecker's hebephrenia but independent of, and coordinate with, Kahlbaum's catatonia and the dementia paranoides. Later on, in line with contemporary anatomical and metabolic theories, Kraepelin decided that these clinical pictures together constituted a single unitary disease that was endogenous rather than heredodegenerative in nature, and without recognizable environmental cause. To this whole disease entity he applied Morel's term, dementia praecox, distinguishing *hebephrenic, paranoid,* and *catatonic* forms, and eventually adding a *simple* type also. This represents the official and most widely accepted conception today.

Meanwhile there was a growing emphasis in other quarters upon personal and situational factors. The earlier work of Mesmer, Braid, Liebault, and Charcot on hypnosis and suggestibility laid the foundation. Toward the close of the last century there appeared in quick succession Bernheim's book on suggestive therapeutics (1886), Janet's works on psychological mechanisms (1889) and on the psychology of hysteria (1893, 1894), and Breuer and Freud's studies in hysteria (1893, 1895). Freud had gone to Paris in 1885 for a year with Charcot; and upon his return to Vienna had translated some of his works and attempted to win over his medical colleagues to Charcot's views. In 1889 he spent a brief period studying with Bernheim in Nancy. Describing in their first publication the method of arousing old memories, together with their affect, and having the patient thoroughly talk out the recollections, Breuer and Freud pointed out that, "In the interesting book of Janet, *L'automatisme psychologique*, Paris, 1889, we find the description of a cure brought about in an hysterical girl by a process similar to our method" (1893). The importance of these cross-fertilizations for the problems of schizophrenia cannot be overestimated.

The Present Situation.—The modern era so far as schizophrenia is concerned begins with the work of Bleuler in Switzerland (M. Bleuler, 1931) and of Adolf Meyer in the United States (Campbell, 1937; Ebaugh, 1937). Bleuler ranks with Kraepelin in his thorough first-hand mastery of clinical material, in his organization, and in his clear and concise exposition. Psychologically he was an associationist and therefore ready for some of the psychoanalytic interpretations. He had already

(1906) published a monograph on the important role of emotion and suggestibility in paranoia when he came into contact with Freud. He was the first outstanding psychiatrist to recognize the value of psychoanalytic emphases and urged the members of his hospital staff to master Freud's theories. Some of Freud's most important disciples were recruited from among Bleuler's assistants—Jung, Abraham, Riklin, and Brill. In 1908 Jung's study of the psychology of dementia praecox appeared in which the influence of emotional factors or "complexes" was illustrated by means of a word-association method adapted from Galton and Wundt (Hunt, 1936). Abraham's theoretical paper contrasting the emotional orientations in hysteria and in dementia praecox came out the same year. In 1911 Freud brought out his analysis of the published autobiography of a prominent paranoid schizophrenic patient, the Schreber case.

In 1911 Bleuler's great work on schizophrenia also appeared, in which he made this important and generous acknowledgment: "A great part of the attempt to build up farther the pathology is nothing more than the application of Freud's ideas on dementia praecox. I think every reader will see without further comment how much we owe to this author, even though I do not cite his name everywhere. I have further to thank my colleagues in Burghölzli; I name only Riklin, Abraham, and above all Jung. It is not possible to distinguish what belongs to the observations and ideas of the one or the other among us" (1911). This monograph and Bleuler's textbook (1930), first published in 1912, have had a profound effect upon the attitudes of the whole psychiatric world. Although always convinced that brain pathologists had satisfactorily demonstrated characteristic cell changes for this illness, in spite of the mutually contradictory nature of their reports, Bleuler nevertheless went a long way toward developing the modern conception of schizophrenia as an outcome of individual difficulties in personalities with many liabilities; and he continually emphasized on the basis of his own great clinical experience the fact that social recoveries occur in schizophrenia.

The influence of Adolf Meyer's original and more nearly behavioral approach (1906, 1910a, 1910b) has been mentioned; his dynamic conception appeared independently of, and indeed prior to, the formulations of Bleuler's staff. It has served as a basis for numerous interpretations of schizophrenic disorders in this country that attempt to do justice both to human biology and to the performance of the person in a naturalistic environment. Variants of this approach may be found especially in Meyer (1934, 1938), Kanner (1935, 1940, 1942), Diethelm (1936), Billings (1939), Muncie (1939). Meyer from the first has insisted upon beginning the study of every patient by going directly to whatever data can be obtained, starting always with the patient's own complaints in their setting and their genetic order, and leaving interpretations, inferences, and even technical terms until the end, then to be used sparingly and with caution (1928a). Although this procedure has long been accepted clinically and experimentally in other branches of natural science, including medicine, the old rationalistic prejudices that dominate psychology and psychopathology even today have conspired with Meyer's difficult style of exposition to delay general adoption of his eminently sound and naturalistic attitude. In many respects Meyer's position in psychopathology is strikingly similar to that which James held during the last decade of his life, in psychology (Cameron, 1942a). Today when many well-trained psychiatrists, psychologists, sociologists, and anthropologists are attacking the same problems in schizophrenia, and with a degree of collaboration and mutual respect unheard of three decades ago (Hoskins, *et al.*, 1934; Hunt, 1936), the outlook for broader and more empirical attitudes seems very promising.

Definitions and Symptomatology.—The term *schizophrenia* (*dementia praecox*) covers a large group of major personality disturbances appearing commonly but not exclusively in adolescence and young adulthood, the most obvious characteristic of which is a disorganization of thinking and doing, but with preservation of relatively good orientation and memory. Following Meyer's account (1906, 1938), schizophrenic reactions may be described as having in common "twists and fundamental or fancy-born incongruities more or less foreign to average mature waking life," which develop often in tense, withdrawn or "shut-in" persons who indulge in vague autistic fantasies, in empty ambitions with inadequacy of performance and false overcompensations, and a tendency to ascribe their predicament to the malice or interference of other persons or their machinations.

They see fancied meanings in the behavior of others. With disorganization of thought and the development of automatisms, the conviction may appear that something is wrong in the atmosphere, that hypnotism is being practiced or their minds being read, that they are being compelled to do things and think things, that machines are being used on them or that parts of their body are undergoing some kind of a strucural change (Schilder, 1935; Angyal, 1935, 1936). Hetero-, homo-, and autoerotic preoccupations are common. Religious-like dramatizations and episodes of fantastic symbolic behavior often appear; the apparent grotesqueness of some delusional beliefs has virtually no limits. Hallucinatory experiences are nowhere more common, except perhaps in disorienting deliria and specific alcoholic hallucinoses. Schizophrenic hallucinations are most often auditory, less often visual, olfactory, gustatory, tactile, and visceral. The question as to whether these experiences are "genuine" hallucinations or not is still being discussed (Campbell, 1930; Lundholm, 1931; Gruhle, 1932b; Schilder, 1933; Hill, 1936).

There is often an inadequate blending of preference and aversion (ambivalence), with sudden unaccountable shifts in affection and hate sometimes leading to impulsive episodes. In many schizophrenics, at least on the surface, the emotional reaction compared with the action may seem strikingly incongruous (Stransky, 1903). Indifference and apathy are frequent but not constant features.

Meyer emphasized the strange, odd, bizarre character of the activity; the staring, the posturing, and the mannerisms, often stereotyped; the indecision, negativism, catalepsy, mutism, and stupor; and the complaints of unnatural interference with and unaccountable interruptions of thought (blocking). He describes talk as "scattered" or else verbigerating (word salad), occasionally echolalic, and showing condensation. Difficulty in understanding metaphors and proverbs in their derived sense has been demonstrated by Frostig (1929), Hadlich (1931), Vigotsky (1934), Muncie (1937), and Wegrocki (1940). An extensive review of the artistic productions of schizophrenics has been included in the reports of Anastasi and Foley (1940, 1941a, 1941b, 1941c).

On the basis of studies of their behavior in situations requiring verbal and manipulatory solutions, N. Cameron characterized the talk of disorganized schizophrenics as (1) *asyndetic*, i.e., lacking in essential connectives; (2) *metonymic*, i.e., lacking in precise definitive terms for which approximate but related terms or phrases are substituted (many of these being personal idioms); and (3) *interpenetrative*, i.e., having parts of one theme appearing as intrusive fragments in another unrelated theme (1938a, 1938b, 1939a). Their problem-solving in a grouping test brought out in both talk and manipulation (4) *overinclusion*, i.e., environmental and imaginal material often only remotely related not being eliminated from the problem; (5) frequent *noncorrespondence* between what the schizophrenics did and what they said about that which they had done; (6) the calling for *transformations* in the rules of procedure and in the materials to justify failures; and (7) varied and shifting verbal *generalizations* concerning solution hypotheses which were, however, usually inadequate (1939b).

Quite apart from the problem of somatogenesis and psychogenesis, already discussed, the question as to what psychological or behavior disturbances are basic in schizophrenia has received many answers. Among others may be mentioned regression to infantile narcissism (Freud, 1911) or to the level of primitive man (Storch, 1924; Werner, 1940); habit deterioration (Meyer, 1906); reduction in association tension (Bleuler, 1918); loss of thought-initiative (Gruhle, 1932a); reduction in the range of attention and in central control (Beringer, 1926); intrapsychic ataxia (Stransky, 1903); agnosia and apraxia of thought (Bychowski, 1935); overdevelopment of inner inhibition (Pavlov, in Kasanin, 1932); loss of sustained effort and attention (Kendig and Richmond, 1940); loss or impairment in abstract behavior and concept formation with substitution of concrete behavior and perceptual thought (Kleist, 1930; Vigotsky, 1934; Goldstein, 1939); social disarticulation resulting from the cumulative replacement of communication by private fantasy, in persons who have been unable to establish themselves firmly in their cultural pattern, because of failure to develop adequate role-taking skills (Cameron, 1938a, 1938b, 1939b, 1943b).

Some of these views take a definite stand on another significant question for schizophrenia: (a) is there psychological continuity between the normal and the frankly schizophrenic, or (b) is there a chasm between them that cannot be bridged except at the structural level? The weight of authority is heavier on the side of the latter alternative (Kraepelin, 1909–1913; Jaspers, 1922; Kleist, 1930; Vigotsky, 1934; Bychowski, 1935; Goldstein, 1939; Hanfmann and Kasanin, 1942). Although the hypothesis that in schizophrenia one drops from a conceptual or abstract to a perceptual or concrete mode of thinking need not necessarily imply the intervention of cerebral histopathology, in actuality the two assumptions usually go together.

The opposite view that normal behavior shades over into schizophrenic without any essential chasm also has many advocates. Few today doubt that there is continuity between normal and neurotic; hence the common occurrence of anxiety, hypochondria, and compulsive behavior as precursors or early symptoms of schizophrenia (Brown, 1940; Harrowes, 1931b; Miller, 1940) may be taken as another span in the bridge between the two extremes. The preoccupation of earlier workers with the functioning of single organs and systems has been gradually shifting in psychopathology to emphasis upon the performance of the total intact organism. The writer believes that this theoretical progression must be carried still farther to include not only the total organism but also the social fields within which all human organisms operate.

The most recent studies indicate that heredity plays a relatively unimportant role in schizophrenic developments (Henry, 1938); the evidence offered for an origin in organic brain disease has turned out, in spite of recurrent positive claims, to be neither consistent nor acceptable (Henry, 1938; Noyes, 1939); and no endocrine pathology has as yet been established (Noyes, 1939; Henderson and Gillespie, 1940). The changes involved in biological maturation during pubescent or adolescent periods often play a very important role in directing and intensifying certain urges, and particularly sexual ones; but the prevailing emphases today include more than this, recognizing the schizophrenias as a group of habit disorders developing in persons who, because of emotional and social maldevelopments and inadequacies, are especially susceptible (Sullivan, 1927, 1929). Accordingly, neither a study of the immediately precipitating situation nor of the person's constitutional make-up alone is adequate; nor can liberal interpretations in terms of the psychic life do much more than push the problem out of the range of scientific and clinical attack. To understand the etiology of a schizophrenic disorder in a given person one must begin by mastering, as nearly as possible, his particular life history.

CLASSIFICATION INTO SUBGROUPS.—For convenience in description and in hospital management, the schizophrenic disorders have been subdivided by the official American classification (Cheney, 1934) into Kraepelin's four types: the *simple*, the *hebephrenic*, the *catatonic*, and the *paranoid*. The act of placing an individual schizophrenic reaction in one of these subgroups signifies only that certain characteristics predominate in the clinical picture; it does not mean that the patient "has" this or that disease-type. It is quite possible that during the illness the dominant behavior characteristics will shift from those of one to those of another subgroup. Also, the features of other subgroups are rarely if ever entirely absent from any schizophrenic development taken in its entirety. For instance, paranoid thinking is demonstrable in most schizophrenics regardless of "type." Patients placed in the paranoid subgroup often show "deterioration" and catatonic features. Hebephrenics also "deteriorate," express paranoid interpretations, and often assume catatonic postures. Catatonics show these characteristics too; and they may develop the silly giggling or grimacing of hebephrenia. This overlapping will be obvious in the account of the subgroups which follows.

These subgroups are much more easily distinguishable early in the illness, in acute episodes or in those cases which reach a relatively stationary adjustment. If the disorder progresses very far, the patient's social disarticulation grows, and the disorganization that follows may lead toward similar behavior patterns almost regardless of the start. It was this similarity of end-product in chronic cases that led the nineteenth century classifiers to ascribe the illness to biological degeneration.

SIMPLE TYPE (SIMPLE DETERIORATING; SCHIZOPHRENIA SIMPLEX). —This corresponds most closely to the descriptions of Willis in 1674 and of Connolly in 1849, and to Morel's *démence précoce* (1860). The patient gradually loses interest and, instead of increasing effectiveness during adolescence and early adulthood, tends to decrease in his ability to meet environmental demands. His unconcern and apathy at first are seldom understood by those about him, and often not until his illness has progressed a long way and for a long time; then it is frequently too late to expect adequate social recovery. Some persons, promising enough in childhood, as they mature drift into simple clerical or manual work where they make no progress and usually resist efforts to change or complicate their routine. Many others become irresponsible idlers, vagrants or prostitutes, or lead an asocial existence as neighborhood eccentrics, apparently incapable of more than simple occupations.

The striking thing about the pathological development of those placed in the simple group is that it is not marked by emotional outbursts, or by strikingly peculiar behavior or obvious hallucinatory and delusional episodes. Like all negative diagnoses, however, this group is very apt in practice to include persons whose early manifestations were simply not noticed or not taken seriously by others, as well as persons whose secretiveness in concealing hallucinatory and delusional episodes had been unusually complete and successful. The more painstaking the anamnesis by the physician is, and the greater the attempts carried out to contact effectually the relatives and friends of patients placed in this group, the smaller becomes the remnant finally left in it. Any number of hallucinated and delusional patients are reported to the physician initially as experiencing neither, both by the relatives with whom they have been living and by themselves. The question as to the presence or absence of delusions and hallucinations, either at the time of the original examination or in the past, can often be decided only after a close personal study. In too many hospitals the psychiatric case load is so extremely heavy (100–1,000 per physician), and in many active clinics the period of stay is so brief for such a purpose (1–3 weeks), that even the most interested and competently trained medical attendants lack the opportunity for adequate investigations. No factors are more responsible for retarding the progress of psychopathology and psychiatry than the almost universally inadequate provisions for medical, nursing, and research personnel in psychiatric hospitals and clinics.

HEBEPHRENIC TYPE.—Officially this subgroup includes those schizophrenic persons in whom silliness and incongruous or inappropriate smiling and laughter are prominent (Kant, 1942), in whom bizarre notions are expressed, neologisms are common (Domarus, 1924; Frostig, 1930; C. Schneider, 1930; Bryan, 1933), and hallucinations of a pleasant sort predominate. This conception differs somewhat from Hecker's original characterization (1871). The onset is insidious and usually begins early in adolescence; the delusions are vague, unsystematized, and often fragmentary; there often appear grimacing and odd symbolic mannerisms (Rosenzweig and Shakow, 1937). In these individuals any interference with their fantasies or activities is apt to elicit sudden impulsive retaliation; often they become hostile and aggressive on the basis of their belief that "influence machines" or other semi-magical agents are being used against them. Certain of these individuals become incontinent and show a strong interest in urine and faeces, often using the latter in smearing the walls or their persons. This activity and the silly, incongruous antics are taken by some writers to be evidence of a return to childhood; but in terms of clinical actualities, the behavior of the hebephrenic bears little resemblance to that of a child. There is in some quarters also a tendency to use hebephrenia as a "waste-basket diagnosis" for those cases which do not fit into any one of the other three categories (Noyes, 1939).

CATATONIC TYPE.—In this subgroup are to be found schizophrenic patients in whom motility disorders predominate, including phases of stupor and of excitement, as well as the less dramatic reactions of posturing, gesturing, and grimacing in repetitious, stereotyped behavior patterns. The onset often appears in an acute attack which may be precipitated by an obviously disturbing incident. Careful study of each case, however, usually reveals other and earlier episodes which also belong to the clinical development at least as premonitory signs—e.g., increasing seclusiveness and loss of interest, preoccupation, fantasy, passivity and negativism, or else disorganized overactivity, reports of conversion or of mystical experiences, fervor or ecstasy, and occasional ill-conceived or impulsive attempts to cope with environmental demands. Kahlbaum (1874), when he introduced this group, considered it to be a degenerative disease of the central nervous system whose symptoms could be accounted for by the location of supposed lesions. It is recognized today, however, that these disorders are highly symbolic in character, and that the so-called automatism and negativism represent deep-seated attitudes and responses on a personal basis. The behavior patterns and the stream of talk in overactive catatonic patients, in spite of the disorganization, exhibit a variety of symbolic postures, gestures, and expressions not matched in other excitements (Homburger, 1932; Mayer-Gross, 1932).

Catatonic mutism and stupor present many interesting psychological problems (Coriat, 1909; Munn, 1934; Hunt, 1936; Last and Ström-Olson, 1936; Darrow and Solomon, 1940; Cameron, 1941). Persons mute for weeks or months may converse freely with a visitor, or suddenly ask for their physician, become fairly voluble for a time and then lapse again into a protracted silence. The stupor in catatonic schizophrenics is apt to be an active, not a passive, immobility. Attempts by another to raise the patient's eyelids and to change the position of his limbs or trunk usually meet with resistance. In spite of his evident lack of reactivity, the stuporous patient may be quite observant. He is often, for example, able afterwards to recall surprisingly well many events, and even the names and utterances of medical attendants, belonging wholly within the period of a prolonged and apparently continuous stupor. His going into or coming out of stupor may be quite sudden; sometimes in response to an hallucinatory command a previously rigid, motionless patient may suddenly attack a person violently and then relapse into stupor.

Some of the phenomena usually associated with hypnosis also appear in catatonics, e.g., heightened or greatly reduced suggestibility, changes in reactions to pain (Grabfield, 1915; Bender and Schilder, 1930; Huston, 1934), catalepsy, etc. The occurrence of *flexibilitas cerea* in a hospital provides a rough measure of the adequacy of the general treatment of cases, its frequency being more or less inversely related to the psychiatric expertness of the staff (Diethelm, 1936). Landis, *et al.* (1934) found that waxy flexibility in catatonia disappears during sleep. Landis reported that normal college students during a fraternity initiation were able to maintain fixed postures for periods of time comparable with those seen in catatonia. Gaylor and Wishart (1933) found that when postures were adopted by normals, in imitation of catatonics, their metabolic rate was 20% greater than that of these catatonics. Landis, *et al.* (1934) found, contrary to prominent hypotheses concerning the "fetal" character of catatonic sleep, that actually they assumed "fetal postures" during sleep less frequently than did normals and in the waking state more often.

PARANOID TYPE.—When delusions dominate the clinical picture in a schizophrenic development, the disorder is classed as paranoid schizophrenia. The delusions are most often persecutory or grandiose in character, less often expansive or derogatory. Billings (1939) found that in almost all his schizophrenic patients somatic complaints (often hypochondriacal) were prominent, some of them delusional. Hemphill (1939) has discussed the visceral etiology of certain somatic delusions and Angyal (1935, 1936) attempts to demonstrate some mechanisms of their origin. Paranoid delusions may at first be quite restricted in scope, fairly logical and with congruent attitudes of resentment, aggression, self-aggrandizement, anxiety, etc. Most observers agree that early in the delusional development the personal wishes, needs, and fears are often fairly obvious (Campbell, 1927) ; although Gruhle (1932b) denies categorically that there is any such connection. With increasing disorganization, however, the scope and variety of delusional topics increase and for a time they become less stable and less logical. Vague mystical and magical forces or influences appear, and their explanations grow bizarre and fantastic. Ultimately, if the illness becomes chronic the delusions may appear as stereotypes and lack adequate emotional participation; then one sees other evidences of disorganization, such as scattering or incoherence of speech, posturing, mannerisms and grimacing, a generalized suspiciousness and aloofness, or indifference and apathy. Hallucinations, most often auditory, may be present from the beginning; they usually correspond in topic and mood with the delusional developments, at least early in the illness. While the onset in the paranoid subgroup is usually later than in the others, no age period seems to be exempt.

Resemblance of Psychotic Thinking to Dreaming and Fatigue States.—Psychotic thinking has been likened to normal dreaming and hypnagogic states at least since the early nineteenth century, appearing in the writings of Guislan, Moreau, and Griesinger. Pelletier (1903) specifically compared the symbolism and thought sequences gathered verbatim from dementia praecox patients with dreaming and, following Masselon, attributed the product in both to attention disturbances. Stransky (1903), Bleuler (1911), and in more recent years Beringer (1924, 1926), C. Schneider (1925), and Mayer-Gross (1930) have made the same comparison but with different data. Jung (1908) characterized the schizophrenic as a dreaming man in an awake world, which Mayer-Gross (1932) approves, but which Gruhle (1932b) rejects as greatly overdrawn. Comparisons with the thought and speech of normal fatigued persons have also been made (Kraepelin, 1906; Bumke, 1924). C. Schneider believed that every schizophrenic phenomenon could be understood in terms of the phenomena in fatigue and the hypnagogic and hypnopompic states (1930).

Deterioration.—We have seen that progressive intellectual deterioration in dementia praecox was practically taken for granted up to the turn of the century, and to the great majority this also meant progressive brain deterioration. Meyer since 1906 has emphasized rather a habit-deterioration and, himself a neuropathologist, the slenderness of histological evidence of brain degeneration. Neisser (1909) called deterioration in dementia praecox only an appearance. While Kraepelin (1909–1913) built up his disease entity on the assumption that all its forms tend toward a deteriorated end-stage, he considered the dementia mainly one of emotion and will, and only to a lesser extent of judgment and memory; he did not rule out the possibility of improvement even in profound dementia. Gatewood (1909) ascribed his schizophrenics' inferior performance in learning to their frequent shifts in method and a loss of thought control. Ricksher (1909) noted that the degree of dementia was apparently not related to duration of the illness, some old chronic patients showing less deterioration in affect and less apathy than more recent cases.

Bleuler (1911), under the influence of Freud and Jung, called attention to the selective character of the dementia both as to topic and as to time, and the liability of a shift in the defect from one topic or activity to another. For him the primary disturbances were in association and affectivity (1918); where "clouding of consciousness" occurred, or where disorders appeared in sensation, perception, memory, orientation, or even in motility, Bleuler considered them secondary to other more fundamental processes. Apathy and reduced attention he ascribed to loss of interest; and he, too, denied the inevitability of a genuinely demented end-stage. The influence of associationistic psychology upon both Kraepelin and Bleuler is obvious; their own influence upon current hypotheses regarding schizophrenia is incalculably great.

According to Kent (1911) schizophrenics whom she regarded as very deteriorated were still capable of learning new tasks. Cotton (1912), using Kraepelin's method of continuous addition, found the performance of schizophrenics only slightly inferior to that of his normal controls, and this difference he attributed to disturbance of the will. Hart and Spearman (1914) investigated dementia praecox by means of a number of separate tasks and concluded that there was a diffuse generalized lowering of intellectual level, for which they postulated an impairment in the reinforcing or supporting function of the whole cerebral cortex. To them, their results seemed to rule out specific defects in association, judgment, concept-formation, memory, etc.; they considered the inequality in specific performance existing in normal subjects quite comparable with that found in psychotics.

Pressey (1917) using the Yerkes Point Scale found that schizophrenics and alcoholics surpassed feebleminded subjects with the same mental age rating in ability to define abstract words. Wells and Kelley (1920) reported that schizophrenic patients showed little or no clear reduction in intelligence; they attribute the poor performance to apathy and negativism and follow Kraepelin in regarding the basic defect to be affective and volitional. Rawlings (1921), using tests of information, association, genus-species, and the Yerkes-Bridges Point Scale, considers reasoning and memory to be equally as impaired as the volitional and affective functions.

Mühl (1922) observed that a mumbling, apparently confused and demented schizophrenic could write down satisfactory answers to questions although unable to give them vocally. Mott (1922b) on the basis of clinical and anatomical studies (1920a) characterized dementia praecox as progressive and irreversible. Wentworth (1923), in a study of 200 schizophrenic patients, in which the Stanford-Binet was used, concluded that intellectual deterioration occurred in only a small minority; she corroborated Ricksher's findings that the degree of deterioration was not directly related to duration of the illness in terms of hospitalization, and accepted defective will and judgment as primary. The paranoid schizophrenic patients tested by Barnes (1924) gave a performance on the Stanford-Binet in 70% of the cases that was not below the level for the general population. It is noteworthy that in the foregoing studies of Pressey, Wells and Kelley, Wentworth, and Barnes there are no data for normal controls run under comparable conditions. None of the schizophrenics in a group studied by Davies (1926) fell below Terman's "dull" level; he found defects in memory and association but attributed them to lack of interest incident to the emotional disturbances and their consequences; their loose thinking was noted but regarded merely as a necessary economy.

Babcock (1930) attempted to set up an objective means of estimating deterioration in schizophrenia through contrasting vocabulary age, which she believed represented the prepsychotic level of intelligence, and the performance on a variety of nonvocabulary tests; she calls this difference score the *efficiency index*. Her assumptions are partly based upon the high positive correlation found between vocabulary score, taken alone, and the mental age on the Stanford-Binet scale for normal children (Terman, 1919) and upon the results of work on psychotics reported by Wells and Kelley (1920) in which the vocabulary tests of the Binet were relatively well preserved. Babcock (1933) regards schizophrenia as fundamentally a progressive deterioration on an organic basis comparable to that in senile dementia. The studies of Schwarz (1932) and Davidson (1937) in general support these results; Altman and Shakow (1937) could not correlate the difference scores they obtained with their own criteria of deterioration and concluded that it might result from the schizophrenic thinking disorder. Wittmann (1933) was unable to find evidence with the Babcock test for mental deterioration in schizophrenia. Kendig and Richmond (1940) give a detailed and critical evaluation of Babcock's investigations and conclusions on the basis of their own work with 500 schizophrenic patients.

May (1931) considers intellectual deterioration so frequent and characteristic an outcome as to justify a return to Kraepelin's conception although he actually goes farther than Kraepelin; he postulates "lack of harmony between the intellect and the emotions and volition." Gruhle (1932a) with at least as good reason insists that the intelligence of schizophrenics remains intact. Vigotsky (1934) has no doubt that schizophrenia is an organic deteriorative brain disease in which reduction from conceptual thinking to associative thinking, or thinking in "complexes," although fundamental to emotional and other disturbances, is itself only the outcome of central nervous system weakness and a loss in psychic energy. "I am not at all inclined," he writes, "to regard schizophrenia as a psychogenic disorder." Harbinson (1936) followed the Babcock method but substituted visual-perceptual tests of "G"; according to his criteria deterioration was found in about 30% of schizophrenics. Piotrowski (1937) made the interesting observations that schizophrenic children seldom deteriorate in childhood and that they are inferior to congenitally defective children in their approach and in their method of handling concrete material. Trapp and James (1937) retested 41 patients to find the loss relatively small in paranoid schizophrenia but large in the simple, hebephrenic, and catatonic types, results that were in direct opposition to those of Kendig and Richmond (1940) with a comparable group. Gruhle (1932a) insists that both intelligence and speech remain potentially intact in schizophrenics.

N. Cameron (1938b) made a qualitative comparative study of the logical completion of 15 sentence fragments, each ending with *because*, in 25 disorganized schizophrenics, 22 senile psychotics, 29 children, and 20 normal adults. The results fail to provide evidence that schizophrenic disorganization yields a product in logical manipulations comparable to that in senile deterioration or in normal children. The same disagreement was also reported by Cameron (1939a, 1939b) between seniles and schizophrenics both as to verbal and nonverbal behavior using the Ach-Sakhorov technique; and he criticized the use of both *regression* and *deterioration* to characterize schizophrenic disorganization. Partial recovery in one of the schizophrenics tested was accompanied by restitution of normal logical forms (1938a). Malamud and Palmer (1938) compared the performance on the Stanford-Binet in schizophrenia, in organic psychoses, and in oligophrenia; they were able to differentiate the groups on the basis of patterns characteristic for each, the schizophrenic failing most conspicuously where practical judgment is necessary.

The attitude of Darrah (1940) exemplifies a recommendation recurrent in the literature that we distinguish as schizophrenia a form with sudden onset and negative family history that never deteriorates, and call the deteriorating type dementia praecox. This plan ignores the lack of agreement as to just what is deteriorated and whether the deterioration is genuine, the difficulty in such an unstable population as ours of reasonable certainty as to family histories, the innumerable unexpected improvements and recoveries from apparent deterioration and the equally unexpected disorganization of persons after a decade or two of formally correct and adequate behavior with only a few paranoid episodes. Prophecy is nowhere more hazardous than in schizophrenia. Lehrman (1940) in a study of 20 clinical cases concludes that neither is deterioration inevitable nor irreversible and recommends that the term deterioration be reserved for organic cases. Similar conclusions may be drawn from the results of chemical shock therapy (Zubin and Thompson, 1941) and before that, from the results of injury, febrile illness, prolonged narcosis, cold water shock and many other incidents (Deutsch, 1937; Diethelm, 1939).

The report of Kendig and Richmond (1940) furnishes an historical and critical evaluation of the whole problem. They studied performance on the Stanford-Binet test of 500 cases of schizophrenia, 460 non-schizophrenic hospital cases, 217 nurses and 129 other employees of St. Elizabeth's Hospital. Although in general their schizophrenic patients tested considerably below normal and showed an appreciable loss according to the Babcock test, Kendig and Richmond found no evidence of genuine intellectual deterioration and no selective impairment of particular functions of intelligence. On retest, patients showed no general tendency on the test to an interim loss in adequacy. They believe that emotional maladjustments beginning long before onset of the psychosis render some of these persons progressively incapable of successful competition and help precipitate the attack, while others perhaps begin with poor native endowment and develop a schizophrenic picture for similar reasons. Their schizophrenic patients failed most conspicuously in all tests demanding sustained effort and attention; upon the impairment in these they place the blame for schizophrenic difficulties in selection and in generalization.[1]

Regression Hypothesis and "Levels" of Thinking.—It is claimed today in many quarters that schizophrenia represents regression to the level of a child or of a primitive man. The comparison with the child was implicit in the older accounts which held that the dementia of adolescents was definitely an heredodegenerative disease bringing development first to a standstill and then leading to a return to a childish level. Variations of this hypothesis have played an important role in interpretations of schizophrenia during the past three decades. It was given special meaning and occupied an essential position in psychoanalytic developments, where the regression was depicted as taking place in the *psyche* (e.g., Freud, 1911; Abraham, 1916). Piaget (1923) placed the thinking of the schizophrenic midway between the autistic thinking of the child and the logical thinking of the normal adult. Parallels have been drawn between schizophrenic symptoms and the behavior of the normal child (Wildermuth, 1923). Gardner (1931) on a similar basis attempted to equate psychotic symptoms with the behavior of normal children in constructing a schedule from which a measure of regression, called by him the "psychotic age," might be computed. However, studies of the speech of normal children and of schizophrenics (McDonald, 1915; Cameron, 1938b) and of normal preschool children with older schizophrenic children (Despert, 1940) do not support the hypothesis. Piotrowski (1933a, 1933b) has shown that schizophrenic children differ from defectives making the same test score in repeating errors less frequently but also in failing to react to praise or to urging; moreover, they

---

[1] For further experimental results concerning this topic of deterioration, see Chapter 32 by Hunt & Cofer.

do better on verbal tests than on performance tests whereas the opposite is true of defectives.

Another form of regression hypothesis as applied to schizophrenia developed partly under the influence of the older anthropologists (Lévy-Bruhl, 1923; Róheim, 1923). "Primitive" man, actually man in contemporary nontechnological civilizations, has been quite uncritically accepted as providing an accurate picture of any early stage in our own biological and social evolution. This primitive man in common with infrahuman animals was supposed, on purely *a priori* grounds, not to be endowed with rationality but to be restricted in his thinking to simpler perceptual complexes and pseudo-concepts. The child in our own contemporary technological civilizations was supposed also to think by means of these subrational tools until pubescence when he somehow graduated to conceptual thought.

These two forms of regression hypothesis have become inextricably entangled in most presentations (Storch, 1924). In spite of the contrary evidence growing out of more recent advances in genetic psychology and in anthropology, they are still applied to problems of schizophrenic thinking essentially unaltered. In the clinical field, for example, Levin (1930, 1931) treats both regression hypotheses as fundamental to an understanding of schizophrenia; Sprague (1940) does the same for catatonia; and Osborne (1940) recommends our changing the name of schizophrenia to *palaeophrenia* for this group of disorders. Kant (1940) has introduced a three-fold personality stratification into somatic, vital, and psychological levels within which schizophrenic changes are to be comprehended.

Clinical, observational, and experimental investigations into the language and thinking of schizophrenics are very numerous and only a few can be considered here. The reviews of Bleuler (1911), Berze and Gruhle (1929), C. Schneider (1930), Gruhle (1932b), Hunt (1936), and Kendig and Richmond (1940) may be consulted. Rawlings (1921) making use of the Yerkes-Bridges Point Scale and tests of association and imagination found marked impairment of abstraction and generalization in schizophrenia with a tendency toward "concrete" rather than "abstract" thinking. Piaget (1923) advanced the opinion, chiefly on the basis of his work with children (1928, 1932), that schizophrenic logic lay midway between the logic of normal prepubescent children and that of the normal adult. Domarus (1923, 1927, 1929) arranged thinking into *prearchaic, archaic-paralogical,* and *paralogical-logical*; the latter two he considered to be typical of primitive savages and common in schizophrenia, and the first as typical of man's anthropoid progenitors and of schizophrenic stupor.

Storch (1924), stimulated by Freud's "Totem and Taboo" (1904) and the hypotheses of Reiss (1921) and Kronfeld (1922), described schizophrenic thinking as the outcome of a crumbling of the "rational superstructure" which laid bare primitive archaic modes of dealing with situations, and which substituted for conceptual thinking an inferior form based upon concrete perceptual complexes. Wentworth (1923) using the Stanford-Binet test found defective generalization in schizophrenics. Kleist (1930) related schizophrenic disturbances to motor and sensory aphasia. Vigotsky (1934, 1939), following Piaget (1923, 1928, 1932) and Goldstein (1924; Gelb and Goldstein, 1925), on the basis of results they obtained with the Ach-Sakharov test, concluded that children before puberty are confined to concrete complexes, and only after puberty develop genuine abstraction. While flatly rejecting the possibility of psychogenic origins for schizophrenia, Vigotsky believed an impairment in the function and formation of concepts to be "the most important deterioration of thought occurring in schizophrenia." In connection with the regression hypothesis, he declared that, "in ontogenesis complexes precede concepts and actually form the inner layer on the old substructure beneath the new layers of concepts" (1934).

Bychowski (1935) reported defective categorization in his study of schizophrenic logic, as well as a dropping out of concepts and inability to retain an abstract attitude. He compared his results with those obtained in organic defect cases by Goldstein (1924), Gelb and Goldstein (1925) and Pötzl (1928), and concluded that schizophrenic thinking depends upon an agnosia and apraxia of thought. Meanwhile Bolles (1937), following Gelb and Goldstein's approach to the study of organic deficit reactions, compared the performance of schizophrenics with that of oligophrenics and normal children. Normal children were able to give responses "to objects as representatives of a class or category," whereas both oligophrenics and schizophrenics were restricted to responses "primarily determined by sensory impressions." The first of these she calls "abstract behavior" and the second "concrete behavior." Her schizophrenics were also unable to shift from one aspect of the problem situation to another when instructed to do so. Bolles and Goldstein (1938), using similar technique and definitions, reported impairment of "abstract behavior" in schizophrenia as well as difficulty in shifting attitudes and in stating verbally why objects they grouped together seemed to belong together. They concluded that the *categorical attitude* (Gelb and Goldstein, 1925), upon which they believe the use of true concepts depends, is reduced or lost in schizophrenia.

Kasanin and Hanfmann (1938) followed Vigotsky's lead in using the Ach-Sakharov test, and like him they found reduction or loss in conceptual thinking and, like Bolles and Goldstein, loss of the categorical attitude. Hanfmann (1939a) corroborated these findings in an intensive study of one case. Shipley (1940a) has developed a vocabulary test on the basis of which he derives an "abstraction age" and a "conceptual quotient" (1940b) as indices of intellectual impairment. These and other results have been critically summarized by Kendig and Richmond (1940) and Hanfmann and Kasanin (1942).

Cameron (1938a, 1938b) studied schizophrenic logic by a method similar to that used with normal children by Piaget (1928). Comparisons of these results with those obtained in the same task from normal children and deteriorated seniles provided no support for regression hypotheses. Diminishing social sharing and increasing preoccupation in fantasy permit a functional impairment of communication and of other forms of cooperative behavior, and a condition of *social disarticulation* results (1939a, 1943b). Slotkin has recently reported examples of such decay in social interactions (1941) ; while Despert (1940) failed to find in normal children the confusion of reality and fantasy which Hanfmann had reported for adult schizophrenics (1939b), but did find it in schizophrenic children. Kendig and Richmond (1940) found in an extensive study the performance of adult schizophrenics impaired, not selectively in eductive or "abstract" tests, but in all tests requiring sustained attention and effort, "including those of memory and association." Wegrocki's experimental results (1940) contradicted both the dichotomy of thought and the regressive hypothesis in relation to schizophrenics.

Cameron (1939b) later reported that, when adequate rapport and cooperation had been established, even very disorganized schizophrenics could be led to generalize rather freely and to shift their mode of attack from one method or "category" to another. Although contrary to most current reports, this is not an isolated observation. In fact Gatewood (1909) found that shifting attitudes in memorizing problems were especially characteristic of schizophrenics; and Hunt (1936) has suggested that this may help account for their relatively poor showing in recognition and recall. Nevertheless, Hanfmann and Kasanin (1942) arbitrarily reject all the solutions which Cameron's schizophrenics offered, based on shape, color, mass, weight, material, name, type, radius, angles, opposition and equalization, apparently because these happen not to be the particular generalizations demanded by the Ach-Sakharov test. In effect, this is to say, "Unless you think of this problem the way I have learned to, you are not generalizing at all!"

Goldstein and Scheerer (1941) deny that the schizophrenic can spontaneously evolve groupings according to material, form or color; but Cameron's extremely disorganized schizophrenic patients with marked asyndetic and metonymic thinking, both characteristic schizophrenic disorders, did evolve such groupings using the Ach-Sakharov materials and method, and quite without promptings or suggestions, as the verbatim shorthand records of his transactions plainly show (1939b). If one accept Goldstein and Scheerer's criteria for the "abstract capacity level" (1941), it is obvious to the writer on the basis not only of test situations but of several years devoted to daily close communication with intelligent schizophrenics of every degree of severity, that the "abstract capacity level" can be found in most schizophrenics provided the painfully patient technique necessary for effectual rapport with this group is developed. Actually the criteria for the "abstract attitude" seem to be those customarily employed in demonstrating the intervention of consciousness which, the writer believes, have no more valid application in abnormal than they have in normal behavior (see also interpretation in Chapter 32 by Hunt and Cofer).

There is good reason for doubting the usefulness, to say nothing of the validity, of these determined efforts to maintain separate categories of "abstract" and "concrete" behavior. The notion is based upon an equally hypothetical differentiation between "perceptual" and "conceptual" thinking; and upon inspection this will be found to reduce to little more than the ancient narcissistic flattery that granted rationality to adult human thought but denied it to children and animals—some stoutly denied it to women also. The current form of this dichotomy is grounded in certain nineteenth century evolutionary doctrines of ontogeny and phylogeny which, paradoxically enough, were originally designed to establish not such breaks or chasms between species but an essential *continuity* between the structure-functions of human beings and other animals. The distinction between "abstract" and "concrete" attitudes developed out of studies made upon aphasic patients with focal lesions of cerebral structures; its transfer into the functional schizophrenic field must be justified on a behavioral basis if it is to be justified at all, since the evidence for focal lesions and even for genuine aphasia is wanting, and the schizophrenic speech disorders very often fluctuate between normal and unintelligibly pathological forms in relation to situational factors.

The fact that schizophrenic disorders do appear among adults in "primitive" (i.e., nontechnological) civilizations and among young children of our own contemporary technological civilizations, as well as the results of comparisons that have been made between the logic of normal children and adults and that of schizophrenics, contradicts the regression hypotheses. Moreover, the contention is supported by the same evidence that schizophrenic disorganization represents neither a retracing of the ontogenetic-phylogenetic path of development, nor a removal of outer layers of thought to expose any "primitive nucleus." Instead, it presents us with a development, new and unique for a given individual's life history, that can be made quite intelligible in behavioral terms.

Paranoia

The term *paranoia* antedates Hippocrates; but in ancient times it was most frequently used in a very general sense, either to designate altered or mad thinking which might occur in many disturbances, or even more generally as the equivalent of our popular current term "insanity." Paranoia practically disappeared from the medical literature with Celsus, around the second century A.D., and did not reappear until Vogel picked it up in the eighteenth century. Both Celsus and Vogel seem also to have used it as the equivalent of insanity. The term enjoyed a short-lived popularity in the eighteenth century as a class-name for delirious and delusional disorders, only to be dropped again when Pinel reformed and simplified the then florid Linnean nomenclature of psychiatry.

According to Jelliffe (1913), the roots of nineteenth century controversies over paranoia, as well as of some contemporaneous attitudes, are to be found in Heinroth's classification of 1818. In the spirit of Kantian psychology, Heinroth divided "mental disturbances" into disorders of the intellect, of the will and of the feelings. Exalted disturbances of intellect he called *paranoia*, and of the feelings, *paranoia ecstasia*. In addition he distinguished among intellectual disturbances three "mixed" confusional states—*paranoia anomala* or simple confusion, *paranoia anomala catholica* or general confusion, and *paranoia anomala maniaca* or confusion with furor. He introduced the terms "Wahnsinn" and "Verrücktheit" which are still used in German psychiatry, the latter in Heinroth's sense, for paranoia.

One line of development from Heinroth has been relatively sterile; it culminated in the position of Ziehen, who early in our century still defined paranoia in such a way as to embrace everything in which "primary" delusions or hallucinations dominate, therefore most of the toxic-infectious deliria as well as some hysterias, schizophrenias, etc. Griesinger (1876) used *Wahnsinn*, as identical with *paranoia ecstasia*, to designate a group of disorders in which expansive and often fantastic delusions and hallucinations were prominent, and dementia the usual outcome. He spoke of partial *Verrücktheit*, in which, and in his dementia, he grouped patients who started off with an excited or depressed episode and slowly developed a changed character with apathy, indifference, fixed delusions, and usually hallucinations. It is obvious that most of these patients would today be included among the schizophrenias.

After Kraepelin had set up his dementia praecox, with its four subtypes, there was little left for paranoia. Kraepelin restricted the term to chronically developing cases of intellectually produced, fixed delusions of endogenous origin but without personality deterioration. Secondarily he set up a provisional group supposed to be transitional between paranoia and dementia praecox, the *paraphrenias*; but they have not proved helpful and are little used (Henderson and Gillespie, 1940).

Freud (1896) made an exceedingly important step forward in describing a case of "chronic paranoia" as a *defense psychosis* and comparing it with hysteria and obsessions. This marked the point of departure from classificatory interests and Kantian psychology to a more dynamic preoccupation with the origin of symptoms. Freud postulated a gradual weakening of defenses against repressed self-reproaches as part of the paranoic process, resulting in their return to consciousness but now ascribed to others in the form of delusions and hallucinations; for this development he introduced the term *projection*. Freud's analysis of the Schreber autobiography (1911) also introduced the system of paradoxical denials and transformations by which homosexual wishes may give rise to persecutory and grandiose delusions.

Meyer (1903, 1908) stressed the inability of paranoics to adapt the trend of personal thoughts and their elaborations to the facts, their growing inclination to isolation, their excessive concern over what others might think, their progressive failure to attempt real verification of suspicions, and their inadequate realization of a need for correction. In his critical and historical review (1913) he includes material from Bjerre's successful treatment of a case of paranoia of ten years' standing (Bjerre, 1912).

Bleuler (1906, 1926) worked out the relationship of affect to suggestibility and of both these to paranoia. He considered paranoia to be a purely psychogenic development occurring in certain kinds of persons and not a "disease-process" as, it will be recalled, he regarded schizophrenia. Bleuler ascribed the development in one person of hysteria and in another of paranoia to a premorbid lability of mood in the former and to excessive stability in the latter. He held that the errors and misinterpretations paranoics made were the same as those a normal person might make under the same circumstances; the pathological feature was the fixity of the errors, leading thus to delusions which, by expanding to include more and more, ended up in paranoia. He opposed the still prevalent doctrines that persecutory delusions come first, while self over-evaluation and grandiose delusions are secondary and compensatory outgrowths, or that persecutory are necessarily balanced by grandiose delusions (Brown, 1940). For Bleuler, grandiosity was primary wish-fulfilment, while persecutory delusions were always secondary processes covering a conflict based upon unacknowledged incapacities.

Schulte (1924), writing from the Gestalt point of view, has interpreted self-reference as an attempt to fill in a chasm, between an individual incapable of entering into "we-groups" and members of these groups, by transforming the indifference of others toward him, even into acts of criticism and hostility, provided only that by setting up a relationship the "wound is closed." Kretschmer (1927) has attempted to delineate a sensitive characterological type with tendencies toward self-reference that tie up with paranoid and paranoic developments.

Brunswick (1929) presented interpretations of the dreams of a paranoic woman, but her analysis shows considerable internal evidence of indoctrination by the therapist. Kahn (1931) related paranoia and paranoid states to the more active groups of eccentric psychopaths. Brill (1934) and Knight (1940) have reviewed some of the evidence for the often-found relationship between homoerotism and paranoia, the latter stressing more the role of fear in strengthening persecutory delusions. Cameron (1943a, 1943c) ascribes the genesis of both the sensitive asocial personality and the paranoid delusions to a defective development of role-taking in the individual, and to the relative inadequacy in social perspectives that results. In place of the projection hypothesis he introduces the concept of a *pseudo-community*, organized by the paranoic's reactions to his own preoccupations out of fragments of the social behavior of others. This view differs from its predecessors, also, in replacing the mind-body or psychosomatic hypothesis of a double world by the simple interaction between organismic and social behavior, from which can be derived personality development and maldevelopment. The literature on paranoia has been reviewed by Meyer (1913), Bleuler (1926), Lange (1926), and Kehrer (1928).

Definitions.—In its most current use the term *paranoia* designates a group of personality disorders, usually developing in the forties or fifties (Dayton, 1940), characterized by fixed and systematized delusions in the presence of formally correct conduct and good general grasp. There is no striking tendency toward general personality disorganization; and while the course is usually very chronic and the outlook for complete recovery is very poor, the development is not necessarily progressive; the disorder often comes at some point to a standstill, or shows only episodic flare-ups in an otherwise fairly well-adjusted life. No toxic substance or organic lesion has ever been implicated; in fact the paranoic or paranoid episodes that so frequently occur in the course of systemic disease, infection and intoxication are officially excluded from this group (Cheney, 1934). Clinically, paranoia merges imperceptibly into paranoid states (see below), into Kraepelin's paraphrenias (Henderson and Gillespie, 1940), into paranoid schizophrenia, and into the sensitive paranoid psychopath described by Kretschmer (1927). Even the classical cases of Freud (1896, 1911) would be grouped by a large majority of psychiatrists today as belonging among the paranoid schizophrenics rather than in paranoia without, however, detracting in the least from the value of Freud's contributions to our understanding of paranoic thinking. Finally other behavior disorders, whether of organic or of functional origin, often show paranoic or paranoid characteristics; but they are naturally classified according to the over-all picture.

Symptomatology.—For a very long time it has been recognized that certain personality characteristics favor the development of paranoia. The predominant features of the development are, according to Meyer (1903, 1908, 1913), an inability to adapt the personal trend of thought and its elaboration to the facts and to make concessions or accept corrections, while at the same time there are marked overconcern and sensitiveness as to what others may be thinking. Early there are feelings of uneasiness about the future and about what is going on, and a tendency to brood and ruminate with increasing inclination toward isolation from others. With ill-balanced aims and dissatisfactions there come suspicions and dominant notions about the intentions and goals of others. Then to the actually indifferent actions of others, special meanings in some personal relation to the patient are increasingly attributed, along with a decrease in genuine attempts at verification of any conclusions thus arrived at, and often with flat refusal to reconsider or discuss the conclusions. The misinterpretations grow with the brooding and fantasy, and become systematized while falsification of past incidents, retrospectively considered, further distorts the train of events. The excessive self-assertion of the person and his lack of adaptability make it likely that antisocial and often violent reactions against others, who are usually quite unaware of their danger, may occur without warning.

As Bleuler pointed out (1906, 1926), a discrepancy between excessive ambition and relatively moderate ability sets the stage for paranoic or paranoid developments in proud, sensitive, rigid persons who, however, often utilize purely chance occurrences in building their delusional systems, in the same way that normals often do in relation to their pet beliefs. Freud (1911), in his analysis of Schreber's autobiography, posited a homosexual origin for all paranoid psychoses, with the most-loved person of the same sex becoming the persecutor on the basis of ambivalence. Freud demonstrated logically that when a patient presents evidence of heterosexual fixation of delusions, it can still be transformed, by the principle of opposites, into concealed homosexuality.

While the close relationship between sexual conflict and paranoic or paranoid developments has now generally been accepted, Freud's drastic restriction of its genesis to homosexuality or narcissistic repression has not. The relatively common occurrence of paranoic or paranoid syndromes among women of heterosexual interests during the thirties and forties, when marital opportunities have dwindled or forbidden heterosexual attachments have been developed, as well as their occurrence somewhat later in heterosexual men with a very rigid moral code under similar circumstances, seems to most psychiatrists to implicate other sexual taboos. The influence of nonsexual factors, both personal incapacities and situational frustrations, must also be included in any account of paranoic development (Kehrer, 1928; Noyes, 1939).

Meyer attributes special importance to the irresistible tendency of paranoics toward systematization of experiences and false crystallizations, and to their retrospective falsifications and their sudden experiences of matters becoming "all clear" to them. Bleuler, however, sees nothing in paranoic developments that would not occur under the same circumstances in a normal person, given a similar background. These views do not seem irreconcilable.

The relationships claimed for grandiose and persecutory delusions also presents psychological problems. Freud (1911) looked upon delusional grandiosity as secondary to persecutory and as intended to provide an acceptable explanation of persecution to the patient; Brown (1940), who accepts paranoia as regression to an anal level of reality-testing, believes that the persecutory and grandiose represent balancing sets of delusions which stabilize the disease and slow up its progress. Bleuler (1926) and Diethelm (1936), on the other hand, consider grandiose delusions to be direct compensatory developments related to wish-fulfillment; Bleuler gives case illustrations of such developments and of the existence side by side of grandiose and persecutory systems showing no functional interdependence.

Both expansive and depressive episodes appear in paranoia, the former giving it an elated, excited, angry or ecstatic coloring, sometimes with hallucinations, and the latter a gloomy, sullen, unhappy, or hypochondriacal character. Acute intercurrent exacerbations of the whole delusional trend may alternate with relatively quiescent periods, a fact that at one time engendered much nosological confusion when such alternation was considered pathognomonic of the major affective disorders. It was once customary to distinguish four and sometimes five subvarieties of paranoia, e.g., persecutory, gradiose, erotic, litigious, or querulous; but this custom has become obsolescent. Paranoia, as described above, makes up only about 2% of first admissions to mental hospitals (Landis and Page, 1938; Dayton, 1940). Kraepelin and Bleuler reported that 70% of paranoics were men, but this is not substantiated by recent studies in this country. A report of the United States Bureau of the Census shows only a negligible preponderance of male over female paranoics among first admissions to mental hospitals (Landis and Page, 1938); according to Dayton (1940), males made up only 35% of those diagnosed paranoic among first admissions to Massachusetts mental hospitals from 1917 to 1933. In part these are only reflections of the lack of strict comparability with respect to the diagnostic criteria employed by admitting officers.

Paranoid Conditions and Paranoid Personalities.—Paranoia, strictly speaking, may not be of very common occurrence but the number of persons in some way resembling paranoics is large. Wherever evidence of general personality disorganization is found in such a case it is considered to belong to the paranoid schizophrenic group. This differentiation in practice is often very difficult to make and many psychiatrists from Kraepelin on have considered throwing all paranoics into the schizophrenic group; but others have felt that the well-organized and often intelligent and successful persons developing systematized delusions deserve separate treatment. A very large group of sensitive, rather rigid and difficult persons, with strong tendencies to self-reference, is looked upon in many quarters as either potentially paranoic or already partially paranoic or *paranoid*; such persons, showing paranoic-like or paranoid characteristics, are said to be in a *paranoid condition* or *state*. Officially (Cheney, 1934) they are defined as having delusions, usually persecutory in nature, and tendencies in the direction of misinterpretation and illogical thinking, sometimes too with hallucinations, but in any case with little or no tendency to deteriorate. The distinction between this and paranoid schizophrenia can be more easily made on paper than with reference to a real patient; and in practice it is actually not a very important one to make unless, as is sometimes the case, therapy is automatically determined by the diagnosis instead of being designed according to the patient's problems. If one accept *paranoid* as going with misinterpretation, illogical thinking and delusions, it is obvious that almost all psychoses have paranoid ingredients. It is also evident that a very large number of difficult persons, odd eccentrics, faddists, pseudo-reformers, inventors, cantankerous and litigious men and women, usually never seen by psychiatrists, falls legitimately into the group of paranoid conditions or paranoid personalities. Kretschmer (1927), Kehrer (1928), and Kahn (1931) have reviewed and discussed the ramifications of this topic which is of considerable social importance.

BIBLIOGRAPHY

ABRAHAM, K. 1916. The first pregenital stage of the libido. In *Selected papers.* London: Hogarth, 1927.

—— 1927. Selected papers. (Trans. & ed. by C. A. D. Bryan & A. Strachy.) London: Hogarth.

ALTMAN, C., & SHAKOW, D. 1937. A comparison of the performance of matched groups of schizophrenic patients, normal subjects, and delinquent subjects on some aspects of the Stanford-Binet. *J. educ. Psychol., 28,* 519–529.

ANASTASI, A., & FOLEY, J. 1941a. Survey of the literature on artistic behavior in the abnormal: I. Historical and theoretical background. *J. gen. Psychol., 25,* 111–142.

—— 1941b. Survey of the literature on artistic behavior in the abnormal: II. Approaches and interrelationships. *Ann. N. Y. Acad. Sci., 42,* 1–112.

—— 1940. Survey of the literature on artistic behavior in the abnormal: III. Spontaneous productions. *Psychol. Monogr., 52,* No. 6.

—— 1941c. Survey of the literature on artistic behavior in the abnormal: IV. Experimental investigations. *J. gen. Psychol., 25,* 187–237.

ANDERSON, E. 1936. Prognosis of the depressions of later life. *J. ment. Sci., 82,* 559–582.

ANGYAL, A. 1935. The perceptual basis of somatic delusions in a case of schizophrenia. *Arch. Neurol. Psychiat., Chicago, 34,* 270–279.

—— 1936. The experience of the body-self in schizophrenia. *Arch. Neurol. Psychiat., Chicago, 35,* 1029–1053.

AULT, C., HOCTOR, E., & WERNER, A. 1940. Involutional melancholia. *Amer. J. Psychiat., 97,* 691–694.

BABCOCK, H. 1930. An experiment in the measurement of mental deterioration. *Arch. Psychol., N. Y.,* No. 117.

—— 1933. Dementia praecox: a psychological study. Lancaster, Pa.: Science Press.

BAILEY, P. 1942. The present state of American neurology. *J. Neuropath. exp. Neurol., 1,* 111–117.

BAMFORD, C. 1929. Considerations on dementia praecox as a physical disease. *J. ment. Sci., 75,* 120–123.

BARNES, G. 1924. A comparison of the results of tests in the Terman scale between cases of manic-depressive and dementia praecox psychoses. *J. nerv. ment. Dis., 60,* 579–589.

BECK, A., OGDEN, W., & WHELEN, M. 1935a. Experimental studies on the connection of schizophrenia and tuberculosis. *J. ment. Sci., 81,* 514–523.

—— 1935b. The agglutinations of B. coli by the serum of psychotics, especially of schizophrenics. *J. ment. Sci., 81,* 524–527.

BENDER, L., & SCHILDER, P. 1930. Unconditioned and conditioned reactions to pain in schizophrenia. *Amer. J. Psychiat., 87,* 365–384.

BERINGER, K. 1924. Beitrag zur Analyse schizophrener Denkstörungen. *Z. ges. Neurol. Psychiat., 93,* 55–61.

—— 1926. Denkstörungen und Sprache bei Schizophrenen. *Z. ges. Neurol. Psychiat., 103,* 185–197.

BERNHEIM, H. 1886. De la suggestion et de ses application à la thérapeutique. Paris: Alcan.

BERZE, J., & GRUHLE, H. 1929. Psychologie der Schizophrenie: Monograph an dem Gesamtgebiet der Neurologie und Psychiatrie. Berlin: Springer.

BILLINGS, E. 1939. Handbook of elementary psychobiology and psychiatry. New York: Macmillan.

BJERRE, P. 1912. Zur Radikalbehandlung der chronischen Paranoia. *Jb. psychoanal. psychopath. Forsch., 3,* 795–847.

BLEULER, E. 1906. Affectivität, Suggestibilität, Paranoia. Halle: Marhold.

—— 1911. Dementia praecox oder Gruppe der Schizophrenien. Leipzig: Deuticke.

—— 1918. Störungen der Assoziationsspannung im Elementarsymptom der Schizophrenien: eine Hypothese. *Allg. Z. Psychiat., 74,* 1–21.

—— 1926. Affectivität, Suggestibilität, Paranoia. (2nd ed.) Halle: Marhold.

—— 1930a. Lehrbuch der Psychiatrie. Berlin: Springer. [English translation of earlier ed., New York: Macmillan. 1924]

—— 1930b. The physiogenic and psychogenic in schizophrenia. *Amer. J. Psychiat., 87,* 203–211.

BLEULER, M. 1931. Schizophrenia: a review of the work of Professor Eugen Bleuler. *Arch. Neurol. Psychiat., Chicago, 26,* 610–627.

BOLLES, M. 1937. The basis of pertinence. *Arch. Psychol., N. Y.,* No. 212.

BOLLES, M., & GOLDSTEIN, K. 1938. A study of the impairment of "abstract behavior" in schizophrenic patients. *Psychiat. Quart., 12,* 42–65.

BOND, E., & PARTRIDGE, G. 1924. Interpretations of manic-depressive phases. *Amer. J. Psychiat., 81,* 643–662.

BONNER, C. 1931. Psychogenic factors as causative agents in manic-depressive psychoses. *J. nerv. ment. Dis., 11,* 121–131.

BONNER, C., & KENT, G. 1936. Overlapping symptoms in catatonic excitement and manic excitement. *Amer. J. Psychiat., 92,* 1311–1322.

BOWMAN, K., & RAYMOND, A. 1931a. A statistical study of delusions in the manic-depressive psychoses. *Amer. J. Psychiat., 88,* 111–121.

—— 1931b. A statistical study of hallucinations in the manic-depressive psychoses. *Amer. J. Psychiat., 88,* 299–309.

BREUER, J., & FREUD, S. 1893. Ueber den psychischen Mechanismus hysterischer Phänomene. *Neurol. Zbl.,* Nos. 1–2.

—— 1895. Studien über Hysterie. (Trans. by A. A. Brill. *Nerv. ment. Dis. Monogr.,* 1936, No. 61.)

BREW, M. 1933. Precipitating factors in manic depressive psychosis. *Psychiat. Quart., 7,* 401–410.

BRILL, A. 1934. Homoerotism and paranoia. *Amer. J. Psychiat., 90,* 957–974.

—— 1938. The basic writings of Sigmund Freud: translated and edited, with an introduction. New York: Modern Library.

BROWN, J. 1940. Psychodynamics of abnormal behavior. New York: McGraw-Hill.

BRUNSWICK, R. 1929. The analysis of a case of paranoia (delusion of jealousy). *J. nerv. ment. Dis., 70,* 1–22; 155–178.

BRYAN, E. 1933. A study of forty cases exhibiting neologisms. *Amer. J. Psychiat., 90,* 579–595.

BUMKE, O. 1924. Die Auflösung der Dementia praecox. *Klin. Wschr., 3,* 437–440.

BURCHARD, E. 1936. Physique and psychosis. An analysis of the postulated relationship between bodily constitution and mental disease syndrome. *Comp. Psychol. Monogr., 13,* 1–73.

BUSCAINO, V. 1924. Recherches sur l'histologie pathologique et la pathogénie de la démence précoce de "l'amentia" et des syndrome extrapyramidaux. *Encéphale, 19,* 217–224.

BYCHOWSKI, G. 1923. Metaphysik und Schizophrenie. *Abh. Neurol. Psychiat. Psychol., 21,* 1–158.

—— 1935. Certain problems of schizophrenia in the light of cerebral pathology. *J. nerv. ment. Dis., 81,* 280–298.

CABOT, P. 1938. The relationship between characteristics of personality and physique in adolescents. *Genet. Psychol. Monogr., 20,* 3–120.

CALDWELL, J. 1941. Schizophrenic psychoses: report of 100 cases in the U. S. Army. *Amer. J. Psychiat., 97,* 1061–1072.

CAMERON, D. 1941. Objective and experimental psychiatry. (2nd ed.) New York: Macmillan.

CAMERON, N. 1938a. Reasoning, regression and communication in schizophrenics. *Psychol. Monogr., 50,* No. 1.

—— 1938b. A study of thinking in senile deterioration and schizophrenic disorganization. *Amer. J. Psychol., 51,* 650–665.

—— 1939a. Deterioration and regression in schizophrenic thinking. *J. abnorm. soc. Psychol., 34,* 265–270.

—— 1939b. Schizophrenic thinking in a problem-solving situation. *J. ment. Sci., 85,* 1012–1035.

—— 1942a. William James and psychoanalysis. In [Various], *William James, the man and the thinker.* Madison: University Wisconsin Press.

—— 1942b. The place of mania among the depressions from a biological standpoint. *J. Psychol., 14,* 181–195.

—— 1943a. The development of paranoic thinking. *Psychol. Rev., 50,* 219–233.

—— 1943b. Experimental analysis of schizophrenic thinking. In [Various], *Language and thought in schizophrenia: proceedings of the round table on schizophrenia held at the meeting of the American Psychiatric Association in Chicago, May 1939.* Berkeley: University of California Press.

CAMERON, N. 1943c. The paranoid pseudo-community. *Amer. J. Sociol., 49,* 32–38.

—— 1943d. The role of psychological research in psychiatry. In [Various], *Psychiatry and the war.* Springfield, Ill.: Thomas.

CAMERON, N., & CAMERON, E. S. 1938. Personality function and reaction types. In *Contributions dedicated to Dr. Adolf Meyer.* Baltimore: Johns Hopkins Press. Pp. 57–60.

CAMERON, N., & HARLOW, H. 1943. Physiological psychology. In *Annu. Rev. Physiol., 5,* 453–478.

CAMPBELL, C. 1927. Delusion and belief. Cambridge: Harvard University Press.

—— 1930. Hallucinations, their nature and significance. *Amer. J. Psychiat., 86,* 607–618.

—— 1935. Destiny and disease in mental disorders, with special reference to the schizophrenic psychoses. New York: Norton.

—— 1937. Adolf Meyer. *Arch. Neurol. Psychiat., Chicago, 37,* 715–724.

CARMICHAEL, H. 1938. The role of endocrines in mental disorders. *J. abnorm. soc. Psychol., 33,* 205–216.

CHENEY, C. (Ed.) 1934. Outlines for psychiatric examinations. Utica: State Hospitals Press.

CHENEY, C., & DREWRY, P. 1938. Results of non-specific treatment in dementia praecox. *Amer. J. Psychiat., 95,* 203–217.

CLEGG, J. 1937. Some observations on endocrines in the emotional psychoses. *J. ment. Sci., 83,* 52–60.

CONN, J. 1934. An examination of the clinico-pathological evidence for the concept of dementia praecox as a specific disease entity. *Amer. J. Psychiat., 90,* 1039–1082.

CORIAT, I. 1909. Certain pulse reactions as a measure of emotion. *J. abnorm. soc. Psychol., 4,* 261–279.

COTTON, H. 1912. Comparative psychological studies of the mental capacity in cases of dementia praecox and alcoholic insanity. *Nerv. ment. Dis. Monogr., No. 9,* 123–154.

—— 1921. The defective, delinquent and insane: the relation of focal infections to their causation, treatment and prevention. Princeton: Princeton University Press.

—— 1933. The physical causes of mental disorder. *Amer. Mercury, 29,* 221–225.

DARRAH, L. 1940. Shall we differentiate between schizophrenia and dementia praecox? *J. nerv. ment. Dis., 91,* 323–328.

DARROW, C., & SOLOMON, A. 1940. Mutism and resistance behavior in psychotic patients. *Amer. J. Psychiat., 96,* 1441–1454.

DAVIDSON, M. 1937. A study of schizophrenic performance on the Stanford-Binet scale. *Brit. J. med. Psychol., 17,* 93–97.

DAVIES, A. 1926. An interpretation of mental symptoms of dementia praecox. *J. abnorm. soc. Psychol., 21,* 284–296.

DAYTON, N. 1940. New facts on mental disorders. Springfield, Ill.: Thomas.

DESPERT, J. 1940. A comparative study of thinking in schizophrenic children and in children of preschool age. *Amer. J. Psychiat., 97,* 189–213.

DEUTSCH, A. 1937. The mentally ill in America. Garden City: Doubleday, Doran.

DIETHELM, O. 1933. Nonorganization and disorganization of the personality during psychoses. *Arch. Neurol. Psychiat., Chicago, 29,* 1289–1303.

—— 1936. Treatment in psychiatry. New York: Macmillan.

—— 1939. An historical view of somatic treatment in psychiatry. *Amer. J. Psychiat., 95,* 1165–1179.

DOMARUS, E. VON. 1923. Praelogisches Denken in der Schizophrenie. *Z. ges. Neurol. Psychiat., 87,* 84–93.

—— 1924. Beispiel paralogischen Denkens in der Schizophrenie. *Z. ges. Neurol. Psychiat., 90,* 620–627.

—— 1927. Zur Theorie des schizophrenen Denkens. *Z. ges. Neurol. Psychiat., 108,* 703–714.

—— 1929. Das Denken und seine krankhafte Störungen. *Würzb. Abh. prakt. Med., 5,* 369–456.

DOOLEY, L. 1931. Some psychoneuroses that are allied to manic-depressive psychoses. *Res. Publ. Assn. Res. nerv. ment. Dis., 11,* 387–402.

DUNBAR, H. 1938. Emotions and bodily change: a survey of literature on psychosomatic interrelationships. (2nd ed.) New York: Columbia University Press.

DUNLAP, C. 1923. Dementia praecox: some preliminary observations on brains from carefully selected cases, and a consideration of certain sources of error. *Amer. J. Psychiat., 80,* 403–421.

DUNLAP, C. 1928. The pathology of the brain in schizophrenia. *Res. Publ. Assn. Res. nerv. ment. Dis., 5,* 371–381.

EBAUGH, F. 1937. Adolf Meyer, the teacher. *Arch. Neurol. Psychiat., Chicago, 37,* 732–741.

ELVIDGE, H., & REED, G. 1938. Biopsy studies of cerebral pathologic changes in schizophrenia. *Arch. Neurol. Psychiat., Chicago, 40,* 227–268.

FARBER, M. 1938. A critique and an investigation of Kretschmer's theory. *J. abnorm. soc. Psychol., 33,* 398–404.

FARR, C., SLOANE, P., & SMITH, L. 1930. Relative importance of hereditary factors in manic-depressive psychosis and involutional melancholia. *J. nerv. ment. Dis., 71,* 409–411.

FARRAR, C. 1908. Some origins in psychiatry. *Amer. J. Insan., 64,* 523–552.

FARRAR, C., & FRANKS, R. 1931. Menopause and psychosis. *Amer. J. Psychiat., 87,* 1031–1044.

FENICHEL, O. 1934. Outline of clinical psychoanalysis. New York: Norton.

FLEMING, G. 1932. The revision of the classification of mental disorders. *J. ment. Sci., 78,* 387–391.

—— 1933. The revision of the classification of mental disorders. *J. ment. Sci., 79,* 753–757.

—— 1934. Definitions and explanatory notes on the classification of mental disorders. *J. ment. Sci., 80,* 409–410.

FOX, H. 1942. Dynamic factors in the affective psychoses: a comparative study. *Amer. J. Psychiat., 98,* 684–689.

FREEMAN, W. 1942. Discussion appended to Strecker, Palmer, & Grant's "A study of prefrontal lobotomy," *q.v.*

FREEMAN, W., & WATTS, J. 1942. Psychosurgery: intelligence, emotion and social behavior following prefrontal lobotomy for mental disorders. (With special psychometric and personality profile studies by T. Hunt.) Springfield, Ill.: Thomas.

FREUD, S. 1896. Further remarks on the defence-neuropsychoses. In *Collected papers,* Vol. 1. New York: International Psychoanalytical Press, 1924.

—— 1904. Totem and taboo. In *The basic writings of Sigmund Freud.* New York: Modern Library, 1938.

—— 1911. Psychoanalytic notes upon an autobiographical account of a case of paranoia (Dementia paranoides). In *Collected papers,* Vol. 3. London: Hogarth, 1925.

—— 1914. The history of the psychoanalytic movement. In *The basic writings of Sigmund Freud.* New York: Modern Library, 1938.

—— 1921. Group psychology and the analysis of the ego. New York: Liveright.

FROSTIG, J. 1929. Das schizophrene Denken: Phänomenologische Studien zum Problem der widersinnigen Sätze. Leipzig: Thieme.

—— 1930. Beitrag zur Phänomenologie der autistischen Gestalten und Wortneubildung. *Z. ges. Neurol. Psychiat., 125,* 700–733.

GARDNER, G. 1931. The measurement of the "psychotic age." Preliminary report. *Amer. J. Psychiat., 87,* 963–975.

GARRISON, F. 1924. An introduction to the history of medicine. (3rd ed.) Philadelphia: Saunders.

GATEWOOD, L. 1909. An experimental study of dementia praecox. *Psychol. Monogr., 11,* Whole No. 45.

GAYLOR, J., & WISHART, G. 1933. The metabolic cost of sustained postures in normal and catatonic subjects. *Brain, 56,* 282–292.

GELB, A., & GOLDSTEIN, K. 1925. Über Farbennahmenamnesie nebst Bemerkungen über das Wesen der amnestischen Aphasie überhaupt und die Beziehung zwischen Sprache und dem Verhalten zur Umwelt. *Psychol. Forsch., 6,* 127–186.

GIBBS, C. 1923. Sex development and behavior in male patients with dementia praecox. *Arch. Neurol. Psychiat., Chicago, 9,* 73–87.

—— 1924. Sex development and behavior in female patients with dementia praecox. *Arch. Neurol. Psychiat., Chicago, 11,* 179–194.

GLOVER, E. 1932. A psychoanalytic approach to the classification of mental disorders. *J. ment. Sci.*, 78, 819–842.

GOLDSTEIN, K. 1924. Das Wesen der amnestischen Aphasie. *Schweiz. Arch. Neurol. Psychiat.*, 15, 163–175.

—— 1939. The significance of special mental tests for diagnosis and prognosis in schizophrenia. *Amer. J. Psychiat.*, 96, 575–588.

GOLDSTEIN, K., & SCHEERER, M. 1941. Abstract and concrete behavior: an experimental study with special tests. *Psychol. Monogr.*, 53, No. 2.

GOTTLIEB, B. 1940. Prognostic criteria in hebephrenia. *Amer. J. Psychiat.*, 97, 332–341.

GOTTLIEB, J. 1939. Arm to carotid circulation time in abnormal mental states. *Arch. Neurol. Psychiat., Chicago*, 41, 1117–1126.

GRABFIELD, G. 1915. Variations in the sensory threshold for faradic stimulation in psychopathic subjects: III. The dementia praecox group. *Boston med. surg. J.*, 173, 202–205.

GRIESINGER, W. 1876. Die Pathologie und Therapie der psychischen Krankheiten. (4th ed.) Braunschweig.

GROSS, O. 1906. Zur Nomenklatur "Dementia sejunctiva." *Neurol. Zbl.*, No. 26.

GRUHLE, H. 1932a. Geschichtliches. In Bumke, O., *Handbuch der Geisteskrankheiten*, Bd. 9: *Die Schizophrenie*. Berlin: Springer.

—— 1932b. Allgemeine Psychopathologie. In Bumke, O., *Handbuch der Geisteskrankheiten*, Bd. 9: *Die Schizophrenie*. Berlin: Springer.

—— 1932c. Theorien. In Bumke, O., *Handbuch der Geisteskrankheiten*, Bd. 9: *Die Schizophrenie*. Berlin: Springer.

HADLICH, H. 1931. Schizophrene Denkstörung. *Psychol. Forsch.*, 15, 359–373.

HANFMANN, E. 1939a. Analysis of the thinking disorder in a case of schizophrenia. *Arch. Neurol. Psychiat., Chicago*, 41, 568–579.

—— 1939b. Thought disturbances in schizophrenia as revealed by performance in a picture completion test. *J. abnorm. soc. Psychol.*, 34, 249–264.

HANFMANN, E., & KASANIN, J. 1937. An experimental study of concept formation in schizophrenia: I. Quantitative analysis of the results. *Amer. J. Psychiat.*, 95, 35–48.

—— 1942. Conceptual thinking in schizophrenia. *Nerv. ment. Dis. Monogr.*, No. 68.

HARBINSON, M. 1936. An investigation of deterioration of "general intelligence" or "G" in psychotic patients. *Brit. J. med. Psychol.*, 16, 146–148.

HARROWES, W. 1931a. The reactive manic episode, its implications and scope. *J. ment. Sci.*, 77, 127–136.

—— 1931b. The significance of a neurotic reaction as a precursor of schizophrenia. *J. ment. Sci.*, 77, 375–407.

HART, B., & SPEARMAN, C. 1914. Mental tests of dementia. *J. abnorm. Psychol.*, 9, 217–264.

HECKER, E. 1871. Die Hebephrenie. Cited in Bumke, O., *Handbuch der Geisteskrankheiten*, Bd. 9: *Die Schizophrenie*. Berlin: Springer, 1932.

HEMPHILL, R. 1939. Some considerations of the physical factor in delusional states. *J. ment. Sci.*, 85, 119–125.

HENDERSON, D. 1927. Chronic sepsis as a cause of mental disease: discussion. *Brit. med. J.*, Part 2, 817–818.

HENDERSON, D., & GILLESPIE, R. 1940. A text book of psychiatry. (5th ed.) London: Humphrey, Milford.

HENRY, G. 1931. Gastrointestinal motor functions in manic-depressive psychoses. *Amer. J. Psychiat.*, 88, 19–28.

—— 1938. Essentials of psychiatry. (3d ed.) Baltimore: Williams & Wilkins.

HILL, J. 1936. Hallucinations in psychosis. *J. nerv. ment. Dis.*, 83, 405–421.

HOCH, A. 1910. Constitutional factors in the dementia praecox group. *Rev. Neurol. Psychiat.*, 8, 463–474.

HOCH, A., & MACCURDY, J. 1922. Prognosis of involutional melancholia. *Arch. Neurol. Psychiat., Chicago*, 7, 1–37.

HOMBURGER, A. 1932. Allgemeine Symptomatologie: Motorik. In Bumke, O., *Handbuch der Geisteskrankheiten*, Bd. 9: *Die Schizophrenie*. Berlin: Springer.

HOSKINS, R. 1941. Endocrinology: the glands and their functions. New York: Norton.

HOSKINS, R., SLEEPER, F., SHAKOW, D., JELLINEK, E., LOONEY, J., & ERICKSON, M. 1933. A cooperative research in schizophrenia. *Arch. Neurol. Psychiat., Chicago*, 30, 388–401.

Humm, D. 1932. Mental disorders in siblings. *Amer. J. Psychiat., 89,* 239–283.

Hunt, J. McV. 1936. Psychological experiments with disordered persons. *Psychol. Bull., 33,* 1–58.

Hunt, R. 1938. Relation between precipitating situation and outcome in manic depressive psychosis. *Amer. J. Psychiat., 95,* 65–72.

Hunt, R., & Appel, K. 1936. Prognosis in the psychoses lying midway between schizophrenia and manic depressive psychoses. *Amer. J. Psychiat., 93,* 313–339.

Hunter, W. 1900. On sepsis as a cause of disease. *Brit. med. J.,* Part 2, 215–216.

—— 1927a. Chronic sepsis as a cause of mental disorder: I. Relation of focal sepsis to mental disease. *Brit. med. J.,* Part 2, 811–815.

—— 1927b. Chronic sepsis as a cause of mental disorder. *J. ment. Sci., 73,* 549–563.

Huston, P. 1934. Sensory threshold to direct current stimulation in schizophrenic and in normal subjects. *Arch. Neurol. Psychiat., Chicago, 31,* 590–596.

Hutchings, R., Cheney, C., & Wright, W. 1928. Psychogenic precipitating causes of schizophrenia. *Res. Publ. Assn. Res. nerv. ment. Dis., 5,* 159–168.

Hutton, J., & Steinberg, D. 1936. Endocrinopathies and psychoses. *J. ment. Sci., 82,* 773–784.

Jameison, G. 1936. Suicide and mental disease. *Arch. Neurol. Psychiat., Chicago, 36,* 1–12.

Jameison, G., & Wall, J. 1932. Mental reactions at the climacterium. *Amer. J. Psychiat., 88,* 895–909.

—— 1933. Some psychiatric aspects of suicide. *Psychiat. Quart., 7,* 211–229.

Janet, P. 1889. L'automatisme psychologique, essai de psychologie mentale sur les formes inferieures de l'activité mentale. Paris: Alcan.

—— 1893–94. L'état mentale des hystériques. Paris: Rueff.

Jasper, H. 1937. Electrical signs of cortical activity. *Psychol. Bull., 34,* 411–481.

—— 1941. Electrical activity of the brain. *Annu. Rev. Physiol., 3,* 377–398.

Jaspers, K. 1922. Allgemeine Psychopathologie. (3d ed.) Berlin: Springer.

Jelliffe, S. 1913. A summary of the origins, transformations and present-day trends of the paranoia concept. *Med. Rec., N. Y., 83,* 599–605.

—— 1931. Some historical phases of the manic-depressive synthesis. *J. nerv. ment. Dis., 73,* 353–374, 499–521.

Josephy, H. 1923. Beiträge zur Histopathologie der Dementia praecox. *Z. ges. Neurol. Psychiat., 86,* 391–485.

Jung, C. G. 1908. Über die Psychologie der Dementia praecox. Halle: Marhold. (Trans. by A. A. Brill. *Nerv. ment. Dis. Monogr.,* 1936, Ser. No. 3.)

—— 1939. On the psychogenesis of schizophrenia. *J. ment. Sci., 85,* 999–1011.

Kahlbaum, K. 1874. Die Katatonie oder das Spannungsirresein. Berlin: Hirschwald.

Kahn, E. 1931. Psychopathic personalities. New Haven: Yale Univ. Press.

Kallmann, F. 1938. The genetics of schizophrenia. New York: Augustin.

Kanner, L. 1935. Child psychiatry. Springfield, Ill.: Thomas.

Kant, O. 1940. Differential diagnosis of schizophrenia in the light of the concept of personality stratification. *Amer. J. Psychiat., 97,* 342–357.

—— 1942. "Inappropriate laughter" and "silliness" in schizophrenia. *J. abnorm. soc. Psychol., 37,* 398–402.

Kasanin, J. 1932. Pavlov's theory of schizophrenia. *Arch. Neurol. Psychiat., Chicago, 28,* 210–218.

Kasanin, J., & Hanfmann, E. 1938. Disturbances in concept formation in schizophrenia. *Arch. Neurol. Psychiat., Chicago, 40,* 1276–1282.

Kehrer, F. 1928. Paronoische Zustände. In Bumke, O., *Handbuch der Geisteskrankheiten,* Bd. 6. Berlin: Springer.

Kendig, I., & Richmond, W. 1940. Psychological studies in dementia praecox. Ann Arbor: Edwards.

Kent, G. 1911. Experiments on habit formation in dementia praecox. *Psychol. Rev., 18,* 375–410.

Klein, M. 1935. A contribution to the psychogenesis of manic-depressive states. *Int. J. Psycho-Anal., 16,* 145–174.

—— 1940. Mourning and its relation to manic-depressive states. *Int. J. Psycho-Anal., 21,* 125–153.

Kleist, K. 1930. Zur hirnpathologischen Auffassung der schizophrenen Grundstörung: Die alogische Störung. *Schweiz. Arch. Psychiat., 26,* 99–102.

KNIGHT, R. 1940. The relationship of homosexuality to the mechanism of para-noid delusions. *Bull. Menninger Clin., 4,* 149–159.

KNOTT, J. 1941. Electroencephalography and physiological psychology: evalua-tion and statement of problem. *Psychol. Bull., 38,* 944–975.

KOPELOFF, N. 1941. Bacteriology in neuropsychiatry. Springfield, Ill.: Thomas.

KRAEPELIN, E. 1906. Über Sprachstörungen im Traume. Leipzig: Engelmann.

—— 1909–1913. Psychiatrie: ein Lehrbuch für Studierende und Ärzte. (4 Vols.) Leipzig: Barth.

KRAINES, S. 1934. Bell's mania (acute delirium). *Amer. J. Psychiat., 91,* 29–40.

KRETSCHMER, E. 1925. Physique and character. New York: Harcourt, Brace.

—— 1927. Der sensitive Beziehungswahn. (2d ed.) Berlin: Springer.

KRONFELD, A. 1922. Über schizophrene Veränderungen des Bewusstseins der Aktivität. *Z. ges. Neurol. Psychiat., 74,* 15–68.

LANDIS, C., FORBES, T., MAYS, L., DUBOIS, P., SHIPLEY, W., & PIOTROWSKI, Z. 1934. Studies of catatonia. *Psychiat. Quart., 8,* 535–552, 722–744.

LANDIS, C., & PAGE, J. 1938. Modern society and mental disease. New York: Farrar & Rinehart.

LANGE, J. 1924. Über die Paranoia und die paranoische Veranlagung. *Z. ges. Neurol. Psychiat., 94,* 85–152.

—— 1926. Die Paranoiafrage. Leipzig: Deuticke.

—— 1928. Die endogenen und reaktiven Gemütserkrankungen und die manisch-depressive Konstitution. In Bumke, O., *Handbuch der Geisteskrankheiten.* Berlin: Springer.

LAST, S., & STRÖM-OLSON, R. 1936. Chronaximetric studies in catatonia. *J. ment. Sci., 82,* 763–772.

LEBENSOHN, Z. 1941. Self-inflicted bullet-wound of frontal lobes in a depression with recovery: a psychologic study. *Amer. J. Psychiat., 98,* 56–62.

LEHRMAN, S. 1940. Schizophrenic "deterioration." *Psychiat. Quart., 14,* 140–156.

LENDRUM, F. 1933. A thousand cases of attempted suicide. *Amer. J. Psychiat., 90,* 479–500.

LEVIN, M. 1930. Archaic regressive phenomena as a defense mechanism in schizo-phrenia. *Arch. Neurol. Psychiat., Chicago, 24,* 950–965.

—— 1931. The basic symptoms of schizophrenia. *Amer. J. Psychiat., 88,* 215–236.

LÉVY-BRÜHL, L. 1923. Primitive mentality. New York: Macmillan.

LEWIN, B. 1927. A study of the endocrine organs in the psychoses. *Amer. J. Psychiat., 84,* 391–458.

LEWIS, A. 1934a. Melancholia: a historical review. *J. ment. Sci., 80,* 1–42.

—— 1934b. Melancholia: a clinical survey of depressive states. *J. ment. Sci., 80,* 277–378.

—— 1936. Melancholia: prognostic study and case material. *J. ment. Sci., 82,* 488–558.

LEWIS, N. D. C. 1923. Constitutional factors in dementia praecox. *Nerv. ment. Dis. Monogr.,* No. 35.

—— 1931. The pathology of manic-depressive reactions. *Res. Publ. Assn. Res. nerv. ment. Dis., 11,* 340–373.

—— 1936. Research in dementia praecox. New York: National Committee for Mental Hygiene.

LEWIS, N. D. C., & BLANCHARD, E. 1931. Clinical findings in "recovered" cases of schizophrenia. *Amer. J. Psychiat., 88,* 481–492.

LEWIS, N. D. C., & HUBBARD, L. D. 1931. The mechanisms and prognostic as-pects of the manic-depressive-schizophrenic combinations. *Res. Publ. Assn. Res. nerv. ment. Dis., 11,* 539–610.

LIDDELL, H. 1941. Physiological psychology. *Annu. Rev. Physiol., 3,* 487–508.

LUNDHOLM, H. 1931. A hormic theory of hallucinations. *Brit. J. med. Psychol., 11,* 269–382.

LYERLY, J. 1941. Neurosurgical treatment of certain abnormal mental states. *J. Amer. med. Assn., 117,* 517–520.

MACCURDY, J. 1925. Psychology of emotion. New York: Harcourt, Brace.

MALAMUD, W., & MILLER, W. 1931. Psychotherapy in the schizophrenias. *Amer. J. Psychiat., 88,* 457–480.

MALAMUD, W., & PALMER, E. 1938. Intellectual deterioration in the psychoses. *Arch. Neurol. Psychiat., Chicago, 39,* 68–81.

MALAMUD, W., & RENDER, N.   1939.   Course and prognosis in schizophrenia. *Amer. J. Psychiat., 95,* 1039–1057.

MALZBERG, B.   1940.   Social and biological aspects of mental disease.   Utica: State Hospitals Press.

MAY, J.   1931.   The dementia praecox-schizophrenia problem.   *Amer. J. Psychiat., 88,* 401–466.

MAYER-GROSS, W.   1930.   Primäre und secondäre Symptome in der Schizophrenie. *Z. ges. Neurol. Psychiat., 124,* 647–672.

—— 1932.   Die Klinik.   In Bumke, O., *Handbuch der Geisteskrankheiten,* Bd. 9: *Die Schizophrenie.*   Berlin: Springer.

McDONALD, W.   1915.   Mental disease and language.   *J. nerv. ment. Dis., 42,* 482–540.

McFARLAND, R., & GOLDSTEIN, H.   1938.   The biochemistry of dementia praecox. *Amer. J. Psychiat., 95,* 509–552.

—— 1939.   Biochemistry of manic-depressive psychosis.   *Amer. J. Psychiat., 96,* 21–58.

MENZIES, W.   1927.   Chronic sepsis as a cause of mental disease: discussion.   *Brit. med. J.,* Part 2, 818.

MEYER, A.   1903.   An attempt at analysis of the neurotic constitution.   *Amer. J. Psychol., 14,* 354–367.

—— 1906.   Fundamental conceptions of dementia praecox.   *Brit. med. J.,* Part 2, 757–760.   Also: *J. nerv. ment. Dis., 34,* 331–336.

—— 1908.   The problem of mental reaction-types, mental causes and diseases. *Psychol. Bull., 5,* 245–261.

—— 1910a.   The dynamic interpretation of dementia praecox.   *Amer. J. Psychol., 21,* 385–403.

—— 1910b.   The nature and conception of dementia praecox.   *J. abnorm. Psychol., 5,* 274–285.

—— 1913.   The treatment of paranoic and paranoid states.   In White, W., & Jelliffe, S., *Modern treatment of nervous and mental diseases.*   Philadelphia: Lea & Febiger.

—— 1917.   The aims and meaning of psychiatric diagnosis.   *Amer. J. Insan., 74,* 163–168.

—— 1928a.   The "complaint" as the center of genetic-dynamic and nosological teaching in psychiatry.   *New Engl. J. Med., 199,* 360–370.

—— 1928b.   The evolution of the dementia praecox concept.   *Res. Publ. Assn. Res. nerv. ment. Dis., 5,* 3–15.

—— 1934.   The psychobiological point of view.   In Bentley, M., & Cowdry, E., *The problem of mental disorders.*   New York: McGraw-Hill.

—— 1935.   The material of human nature and conduct: a symposium.   *Amer. J. Psychiat., 92,* 271–359.

—— 1938.   Leading concepts of psychobiology (ergasiology) and of psychiatry (ergasiatry).   In *Proceedings of the Fourth Conference on Psychiatric Education.*   New York: National Committee for Mental Hygiene.   Pp. 267–301.

MILLER, W.   1940.   The relationship between early schizophrenia and the neuroses. *Amer. J. Psychiat., 96,* 889–896.

MONIZ, E.   1937.   Prefrontal leucotomy in the treatment of mental disorders. *Amer. J. Psychiat., 93,* 1379–1385.

MOREL, B.   1860.   Traité des maladies mentales.   Cited in Bumke, O., *Handbuch der Geisteskrankheiten,* Bd. 9: *Die Schizophrenie.*   Berlin: Springer, 1932.

MORSE, M.   1923.   The pathological anatomy of the ductless glands in a series of dementia praecox cases.   *J. Neurol. Psychopath., 4,* 1–26.

MOTT, F.   1920a.   Pathology of dementia praecox.   *Brit. med. J.,* Part 2, 781–782.

—— 1920b.   Studies in the pathology of dementia praecox.   *Proc. R. Soc. Med., 13,* 25–63.

—— 1922a.   The reproductive organs in relation to mental disorders.   *Brit. med. J.,* Part 1, 463–467.

—— 1922b.   The genetic origin of dementia praecox.   *J. ment. Sci., 68,* 333–347.

MOYNIHAN, B.   1927.   Chronic sepsis as a cause of mental disorder. II.   Relation of aberrant mental states to organic disease.   *Brit. med. J.,* Part 2, 815–817.

MÜHL, A.   1922.   Automatic writing.   Dresden: Steinkopff.

MUNCIE, W.   1931.   The rigid personality as a factor in psychoses.   *Arch. Neurol. Psychiat., Chicago, 26,* 359–370.

—— 1937.   The psychopathology of metaphor.   *Arch. Neurol. Psychiat., Chicago, 37,* 796–804.

MUNCIE, W. 1939. Psychobiology and psychiatry. St. Louis: Mosby.

MUNN, C. 1934. Historical survey of the literature of stupor with the report of a case of twelve years' duration with complete amnesia for two years. *Amer. J. Psychiat.*, 90, 1271–1283.

MYERSON, A. 1925. Inheritance of mental diseases. Baltimore: Williams & Wilkins.

—— 1936. Neuroses and neuropsychoses: I. *Amer. J. Psychiat.*, 93, 263–301.

—— 1938. Neuroses and neuropsychoses: II. *Amer. J. Psychiat.*, 94, 961–983.

NEISSER, C. 1909. Zur Dementia praecox-Frage. Cited in Bumke, O., *Handbuch der Geisteskrankheiten*, Bd. 9: *Die Schizophrenie*. Berlin: Springer, 1932.

NISSL, F., & ALZHEIMER, A. 1921. Histologie und Histopathologie. Arbeiten über die Grosshirnrinde, mit besonderen Berücksichtigungen der pathologischen Anatomie der Geisteskrankheiten. Jena: Fischer.

NOTKIN, J., NILES, C., DE NATALE, F., & WITTMAN, G. 1939. A comparative study of hypoglycemic shock treatment and control observation in schizophrenia. *Amer. J. Psychiat.*, 96, 681–688.

—— 1940. Comparative study of metrazol treatment and control observations in schizophrenia. *Arch. Neurol. Psychiat., Chicago*, 44, 568–577.

NOYES, A. 1939. Modern clinical psychiatry. (2d ed.) Philadelphia: Saunders.

OBERNDORF, C., & MEYER, M. 1931. Psychoanalytic sidelights on manic-depressive psychoses. *Res. Publ. Assn. Res. nerv. ment. Dis.*, 11, 450–470.

OSBORNE, R. 1940 Palaeophrenia: a re-evaluation of the concept of schizophrenia. *J. ment. Sci.*, 86, 1078–1085.

PAGE, J., LANDIS, C., & KATZ, S. 1934. Schizophrenic traits in the functional psychoses and in normal individuals. *Amer. J. Psychiat.*, 90, 1213–1226.

PALMER, H., HASTINGS, D., & SHERMAN, S. 1941. Therapy in involutional melancholia. *Amer. J. Psychiat.*, 97, 1086–1115.

PARTRIDGE, G. 1931. Personality and the concept "manic depressive psychosis." *Res. Publ. Assn. Res. nerv. ment. Dis.*, 11, 405–412.

PASKIND, H. 1930a. Manic-depressive psychosis as seen in private practice: sex distribution and age incidence of first attacks. *Arch. Neurol. Psychiat., Chicago*, 23, 152–158.

—— 1930b. Manic-depressive psychosis in private practice: length of the attack and length of the interval. *Arch. Neurol. Psychiat., Chicago*, 23, 789–794.

—— 1930c. Hereditary factors in manic depressive psychosis: a comparison of institutional and extramural cases. *Arch. Neurol. Psychiat., Chicago*, 24, 747–752.

PEARSON, G. 1928. An interpretative study of involutional depression. *Amer. J. Psychiat.*, 85, 289–335.

PELLETIER, M. 1903. L'association des idées dans la manie aigne et dans la débilité mentale. Cited in Jung, C. G., *Psychology of dementia praecox*. *Nerv. ment. Dis. Monogr.*, 1936, Ser. No. 3.

PIAGET, J. 1923. La pensée symbolique et la pensée de l'enfant. *Arch. Psychol., Genève*, 18, 273–304.

—— 1928. Judgment and reasoning in the child. New York: Harcourt, Brace.

—— 1932. The language and thought of the child. (2d ed.) New York: Harcourt, Brace.

PIKER, P. 1938. Eighteen hundred and seventeen cases of suicidal attempt. A preliminary survey. *Amer. J. Psychiat.*, 95, 97–115.

PIOTROWSKI, Z. 1933a. The test behavior of schizophrenic children. *Proc. Amer. Assn. ment. Def.*, 38, 332–344.

—— 1933b. Work habits as a means of differentiating native and acquired deficiency (abstract). *Psychol. Bull.*, 30, 728–729.

—— 1937. A comparison of congenitally defective children with schizophrenic children in regard to personality structure and intelligence type. *Proc. Amer. Assn. ment. Def.*, 42, 78–90.

PÖTZL, O. 1928. Die optisch-agnostischen Störungen. Leipzig: Deuticke.

POLLOCK, H. 1931. Recurrence of attacks in manic-depressive psychoses. *Amer. J. Psychiat.*, 88, 567–574.

POLLOCK, H., MALZBERG, B., & FULLER, R. 1939. Hereditary and environmental factors in the causation of manic-depressive psychoses and dementia praecox. Utica: State Hospitals Press.

PRESSEY, S. 1917. Distinctive features in psychological test measurements made upon dementia praecox and chronic alcoholic patients. *J. abnorm. Psychol.*, 12, 130–139.

RABIN, A. 1941. Test score patterns in schizophrenic and non-psychotic states. *J. Psychol., 12,* 91–100.

RACHLIN, H. 1935. A follow-up study of Hoch's benign stupor cases. *Amer. J. Psychiat., 92,* 531–558.

RADÓ, S. 1928. The problem of melancholia. *Int. J. Psycho-Anal., 9,* 420–438.

RAPHAEL, T., FERGUSON, W., & SEARLE, O. 1928. Constitutional factors in schizophrenia. *Res. Publ. Assn. Res. nerv. ment. Dis., 5,* 100–132.

RAWLINGS, E. 1921. The intellectual status of patients with paranoid dementia praecox. *Arch. Neurol. Psychiat., Chicago, 5,* 283–295.

REISS, E. 1921. Zur Theorie der schizophrenen Denkstörung (abstract). *Zbl. ges. Neurol. Psychiat., 25,* 432–434.

RENNIE, T. 1942. Prognosis in manic-depressive psychoses. *Amer. J. Psychiat., 98,* 801–814.

RICKMAN, J. 1927. A survey: the development of the psychoanalytical theory of the psychoses, 1894–1926. *Brit. J. med. Psychol., 7,* 321–357.

RICKSHER, C. 1909. Impressibility in dementia praecox. *Amer. J. Insan., 66,* 219–229.

RIPLEY, H., SHORR, E., & PAPANICOLAOU, G. 1940. The effect of treatment of depression in the menopause with estrogenic hormone. *Amer. J. Psychiat., 96,* 905–914.

ROHEIM, G. 1923. Nach dem Tode des Urvaters. *Imago, Lpz., 9,* 83–121.

ROSANOFF, A. 1938. Manual of psychiatry and mental hygiene. (7th ed.) New York: Wiley.

ROSENZWEIG, S., & SHAKOW, D. 1937. Mirror behavior in schizophrenic and normal individuals. *J. nerv. ment. Dis., 86,* 166–174.

SCHILDER, P. 1928. Introduction to a psychoanalytic psychiatry. (Trans. by B. Glueck.) *Nerv. ment. Dis. Monogr.,* No. 50.

—— 1933. Experiments on imagination, after-images and hallucinations. *Amer. J. Psychiat., 90,* 597–611.

—— 1935. The image and appearance of the human body. London: Kegan, Paul.

—— 1938. Psychotherapy. New York: Norton.

—— 1942. Goals and desires of man: a psychological survey of life. New York: Columbia Univ. Press.

SCHNEIDER, A. 1927. Studien uber Sprachstörungen bei Schizophrenen (Schizophasien). *Z. ges. Neurol. Psychiat., 108,* 491–524.

SCHNEIDER, C. 1925. Beiträge zur Lehre von der Schizophrenie. III. Über die Unterschiede zwischen schizophrener Sprache und Aphasie und zur Theorie der schizophrenenen Sprachstörungen. *Z. ges. Neurol. Psychiat., 96,* 251–274.

—— 1930. Die Psychologie der Schizophrenen und ihre Bedeutung für die Klinik der Schizophrenie. Leipzig: Thieme.

SCHOTT, A. 1904. Klinischer Beitrag zur Lehre von der chronischen Manie. *Mschr. Psychiat., Neurol., 15,* 1–62.

SCHUBE, P., MCMANAMY, M., TRAPP, C., & HOUSER, G. 1937. Involutional melancholia: treatment with theelin. *Arch. Neurol. Psychiat., Chicago, 38,* 505–512.

SCHULTE, H. 1924. Versuch einer Theorie der paranoischen Eigenbeziehung und Wahnbildung. *Psychol. Forsch., 5,* 1–23. (Trans. abstract: In Ellis, W., *A source book of Gestalt psychology.* New York: Harcourt, Brace, 1938.)

SCHWARZ, R. 1933. Measurement of mental deterioration in dementia praecox. *Amer. J. Psychiat., 89,* 555–560.

SHAPIRO, L. 1935. Suicide: psychology and familial tendency. *J. nerv. ment. Dis., 81,* 547–553.

SHELDON, W., & STEVENS, S. 1942. The varieties of human temperament. New York: Harper.

SHELDON, W., STEVENS, S., & TUCKER, W. 1940. The varieties of human physique. New York: Harper.

SHIPLEY, W. 1940a. A self-administering scale for measuring intellectual impairment and deterioration. *J. Psychol., 9,* 371–377.

—— 1940b. Shipley-Hartford scale for measuring intellectual impairment. Hartford: Neuropsychiatric Institute of the Hartford Retreat.

SHIPLEY, W., & KANT, F. 1940. The insulin-shock and metrazol treatments of schizophrenia, with special emphasis on psychological aspects. *Psychol. Bull., 37,* 259–284.

SHOCK, N. 1939. Some psychophysiological relations. *Psychol. Bull., 36,* 447–476.

SKALWEIT, W. 1938. Schizophrenie. *Fortsch. Neurol. Psychiat., 10,* 533–576.

SLOTKIN, J. 1941. The nature and effects of social interaction in schizophrenia. *J. abnorm. soc. Psychol., 37,* 345–368.

SOUTHARD, E. 1910. A study of the dementia praecox group in the light of certain cases showing anomalies or scleroses in particular brain regions. *Amer. J. Insan., 67,* 119–176.

—— 1914. On the topographical distribution of cortex lesions and anomalies in dementia praecox, with some account of their functional significance. *Amer. J. Insan., 71,* 383–403.

SPIELMEYER, W. 1930. Die anatomische Krankheitsforschung in der Psychiatrie. In Bumke, O., *Handbuch der Geisteskrankheiten.* Berlin: Springer.

SPRAGUE, G. 1940. Regression in catatonia. *J. nerv. ment. Dis., 91,* 566–578.

STALKER. H. 1939. The prognosis in schizophrenia: based on a follow-up study of 129 cases treated by ordinary methods. *J. ment. Sci., 85,* 1224–1240.

STEIN, R., & ZIEGLER, L. 1939. A comparison of the thalamus in dementia praecox and manic-depressive brains: a biometric analysis. *J. nerv. ment. Dis., 90,* 709–729.

STEINER, G. 1932. Anatomisches. In Bumke, O., *Handbuch der Geisteskrankheiten,* Bd. 9. Berlin: Springer.

STORCH, A. 1924. The primitive archaic forms of inner experiences and thought in schizophrenia. *Nerv. ment. Dis. Monogr.,* No. 36.

STRANSKY, E. 1903. Zur Kenntnis gewisser erworbener Blödsinnsformen, zugleich ein Beitrag zur Lehre von der Dementia praecox. *Jb. Psychiat. Neurol., 24,* 1–149.

—— 1911. Das manisch-depressive Irresein. Leipzig: Deuticke.

STRECKER, E. 1931. Prognosis in schizophrenia. *Res. Publ. Assn. Res. nerv. ment. Dis., 10,* 119–190.

STRECKER, E., APPEL, K., EYMAN, E., FARR, C., LAMAR, N., PALMER, H., & SMITH, L. 1931. The prognosis in manic-depressive psychosis. *Res. Publ. Assn. Res. nerv. ment. Dis., 11,* 471–538.

STRECKER, E., & EBAUGH, F. 1940. Practical clinical psychiatry. (5th ed.) Philadelphia: Blakiston.

STRECKER, E., PALMER, H., & GRANT, F. 1942. A study of prefrontal lobotomy. *Amer. J. Psychiat., 98,* 524–532.

STRONGIN, E., & HINSIE, L. 1938. Parotid gland secretions in manic-depressive patients. *Amer. J. Psychiat., 94,* 1459–1466.

SULLIVAN, H. 1924. Schizophrenia, its conservative and malignant features. *Amer. J. Psychiat., 81,* 71–79.

—— 1925. Peculiarity of thought in schizophrenia. *Amer. J. Psychiat., 82,* 21–86.

—— 1926. Affective experience in early schizophrenia. *Amer. J. Psychiat., 83,* 467–483.

—— 1927. The onset of schizophrenia. *Amer. J. Psychiat., 84,* 105–134.

—— 1928. Tentative criteria of malignancy in schizophrenia. *Amer. J. Psychiat., 84,* 759–787.

—— 1929. Research in schizophrenia. *Amer. J. Psychiat., 86,* 553–567.

TERMAN, L. 1919. The intelligence of school children. Boston: Houghton, Mifflin.

TERRY, G., & RENNIE, T. 1938. Analysis of parergasia. *Nerv. ment. Dis. Monogr.,* No. 64.

TITLEY, W. 1936. Prepsychotic personality of patients with involutional melancholia. *Arch. Neurol. Psychiat., Chicago, 36,* 19–33.

TRAPP, C., & JAMES, E. 1937. Comparative intelligence rating in the four types of dementia praecox. *J. nerv. ment. Dis., 86,* 399–404.

VIGOTSKY, L. 1934. Thought in schizophrenia. *Arch. Neurol. Psychiat., Chicago, 31,* 1063–1077.

—— 1939. Thought and speech. *Psychiatry, 2,* 29–54.

WATTS, J., & FREEMAN, W. 1938. Psychosurgery: effect on certain mental symptoms of surgical interruption of pathways in frontal lobe. *J. nerv. ment. Dis., 88,* 589–601.

WEGROCKI, H. 1940. Generalizing ability in schizophrenia: an inquiry into the disorders of problem thinking in schizophrenia. *Arch. Psychol., N. Y., 36,* No. 254.

WELLS, F., & KELLEY, C. 1920. Intelligence and psychosis. *Amer. J. Insan., 77,* 17–45.

WENTWORTH, M. 1923. Two hundred cases of dementia praecox tested by Stanford revision. *J. abnorm. soc. Psychol., 18,* 378–384.

WERNER, A., HOCTOR, E., & AULT, C. 1941. Involutional melancholia. A review with additional cases. *Arch. Neurol. Psychiat., Chicago, 45,* 944–952.

WERNER, A., KOHLER, L., AULT, C., & HOCTOR, E. 1936. Involutional melancholia: probable etiology and treatment. *Arch. Neurol. Psychiat., Chicago, 85,* 1076–1080.

WERNER, H. 1940. Comparative psychology of mental development. New York: Harper.

WERTHAM, F. 1929. A group of benign chronic psychoses: prolonged manic excitements; with a statistical study of age, duration and frequency in 2,000 manic attacks. *Amer. J. Psychiat., 86,* 17–78.

WERTHEIMER, F., & HESKETH, F. 1926. Significance of the physical constitution in mental disease. Baltimore: Williams & Wilkins.

WHITWELL, J. 1936. Historical notes on psychiatry. London: Lewis.

WILDERMUTH, H. 1923. Schizophrene Zeichen beim gesunden Kind. *Z. ges. Neurol. Psychiat., 86,* 166–173.

WILMANNS, K. (Ed.) 1932. Die Schizophrenie. In Bumke, O., *Handbuch der Geisteskrankheiten,* Bd. 9. Berlin: Springer.

WITTMAN, M. 1933. The Babcock deterioration test in state hospital practice. *J. abnorm. soc. Psychol., 28,* 70–83.

—— 1937. An evaluation of opposed theories concerning the etiology of so-called "dementia" in dementia praecox. *Amer. J. Psychiat., 93,* 1363–1377.

ZIEGLER, L. 1929. Clinical phenomena associated with depressions, anxieties and other affective or mood disorders. *Amer. J. Psychiat., 85,* 849–879.

ZILBOORG, G., & HENRY, G. 1941. A history of medical psychology. New York: Norton.

ZUBIN, J., & THOMPSON, J. 1941. Sorting tests in relation to drug therapy in schizophrenia. New York: New York State Psychiatric Institute and Hospital.

ZWEIG, A. 1908. Dementia praecox jenseits des 30. Lebensjahres. *Arch. Psychiat. Nervenkrankh., 44,* 1015–1035.

Chapter 30

THE CONCEPT OF PSYCHOPATHIC PERSONALITY

By Paul William Preu, M.D.

It would be desirable to define "psychopathic personality" precisely before undertaking to discuss the historical development of the term and the implications of its use in present-day psychiatry. This logical preliminary requirement for an orderly procedure is difficult to satisfy. The diagnostic label psychopathic personality is a convenient designation, as will be seen, in meeting certain practical necessities of psychiatric practice; but it is one of the vaguest terms employed in modern clinical psychiatry. No agreement exists as to the exact limitations to be placed on its use. Quotation of the definitions offered by leading authorities will make plain the lack of definitive clarity:

Henderson and Gillespie (1930): "Under the heading of constitutional psychopathic inferiority we include persons who have been from childhood or early youth habitually abnormal in their emotional reaction and in their general behavior, but who do not reach except perhaps episodically a degree of abnormality amounting to certifiable insanity, and who show no intellectual defect" (p. 376).

Henry (1938): "Instinctive and emotional deficiency are defects found in large groups of individuals who are commonly referred to as having psychopathic personalities or as representing constitutional psychopathic inferiority. Such individuals are in frequent conflict with social laws because of uncontrollable impulses to satisfy cravings of the present, inability to profit by experience and lack of foresight. Many kinds and degrees of deficiency occur" (p. 223).

Muncie (1939): "The constitutional development disorders include, in addition to the states of intellectual defect, the disorders of personality structure showing disharmony or imbalance of the assets. There may or may not also be intellectual limitation. These reactions constitute the psychopathic personalities, also referred to as constitutional psychopathic inferiorities. Since they are disorders of personality structure of life-long duration, a great variety of types may be expected" (p. 197).

Strecker and Ebaugh (1940): "In general, by the term constitutional psychopathic inferior, we mean an individual who is ill-equipped from birth to meet the demands of the environment. We feel that in true psychopathic inferiority the primary consideration is a defect state. This defect is not like that found in mental deficiency which involves primarily the intellectual assets of the patient, but is a defect consisting of an apparent constitutional lack of responsiveness to the social demands of honesty or truthfulness or decency or consideration of others and perhaps chiefly in an inability to profit by experience" (p. 496).

These selected definitions represent the opinions of the majority of psychiatrists concerning the meaning of psychopathic personality. They may be comprehensively reformulated as follows:

The diagnostic labels psychopathic personality and constitutional psychopathic inferiority designate those individuals who have manifested considerable difficulty in social adjustment over a period of many years or throughout life, but who are not of defective intelligence nor suffering from structural disease of the brain or epilepsy, and whose difficulties in adjustment have not been manifested by the behavioral syndromes which are conventionally referred to as neuroses and psychoses.

The opinions of certain psychiatrists are not covered by this definition. Several dissenting points of view which are of special significance will be considered subsequently. The comprehensive definition which is offered is, however, a fair statement of the majority point of view and therefore will serve as a convenient point of departure for the discussion of the concept of psychopathic personality.

Historical Background

The development of the concept of psychopathic personality has been reviewed by Partridge (1930) and more recently by Henderson (1939) in his Salmon Memorial Lectures. Both accord priority to the English psychiatrist Prichard (1835), who called the attention of the medical profession to the existence of a large group of psychiatric problems not covered by the conventional diagnosis of insanity as used at that time. Prichard devised the terms "moral insanity" and "moral imbecility" to designate this group of conditions, which are now generally classified as psychopathic personality or constitutional psychopathic inferiority. Quoting Prichard: "There is a form of mental derangement in which the intellectual functions appear to have sustained little or no injury, while the disorder is manifested principally or alone in the state of the feelings, temper or habits. In cases of this nature the moral or active principles of the mind are strangely perverted or depraved; the power of self-government is lost or greatly impaired and the individual is found to be incapable, not of talking or reasoning upon any subject proposed to him but of conducting himself with decency and propriety in the business of life."

The term "psychopathic inferiority" was introduced by Koch (1891), who gave to it a broad connotation, employing it to designate not only that group referred to by Prichard as morally insane but also certain hysterical and obsessional neuroses. In the contribution of Koch there appears for the first time the conception of an underlying fundamental and presumably hereditarily determined weakness or inferiority predisposing to psychopathic development.

Since the time of Koch psychopathic inferiority, or some term essentially synonymous with it such as constitutional psychopathic inferiority, constitutional psychopathic state, emotional instability, psychopathic state and psychopathic inferiority, has been employed by the majority of psychiatrists to indicate the presence of a definite personality problem, or disorder, or illness which does not fit conveniently into any of the established clinical categories.

The diagnosis has never been made dependent on the recognition of particular symptoms or kinds of behavior in the direct descriptive sense, nor on the demonstration of the operation of particular behavioral dynamics, nor on the demonstration of the existence of any definite etiologic factor. The emphasis has been predominantly but not exclusively on the occurrence of social maladjustment, particularly on the occurrence of persistent social maladjustment in the absence of the symptoms of the traditional clinical entities of psychiatry.

No general agreement has been achieved on the permissible limits of application of the label "psychopathic." The term has sometimes been used broadly and sometimes employed more narrowly. Thus Kraepelin (1915) included under the general heading of psychopathic personality not only conditions of circumscribed inhibition of personality development in the emotional and volitional spheres but also early and mild stages of psychoses. He stated that in some instances it was a question of choice whether to classify an individual as a psychopath or as neurotic. Schneider (1923) limited the term to include only conditions of "constitutional" defect other than intellectual deficiency.

Those who have attempted to differentiate subgroups within the psychopathic have tended to use adjectives indicating that the problem behavior qualitatively resembled that seen in the various mental "diseases" but quantitatively stopped short of the full-blown picture. On this basis have been elaborated such terms as schizoid, cycloid, and epileptoid psychopathy.

Symptoms and Diagnostic Criteria

The scope and method of application as well as the etiologic implications of the diagnosis of psychopathic personality will be outlined in this and in the following section in a way which it is felt portrays the present consensus. The usage which appears to the reviewer to be typical or average will be presented. It should be kept in mind that differences of opinion between clinicians exist concerning nearly every point.

The diagnosis of psychopathic personality is customarily established in the following way:

1. An individual who has given evidence of outspoken social maladjustment is brought to the attention of the psychiatrist. A psychiatric problem is assumed to be present since social maladjustment exists.

2. The diagnosis of psychopathic personality will be considered if the maladjustment has been continuous or repeatedly recurrent over a long

period of time, particularly if the problem behavior has proved resistant to presumably adequate treatment.

3. The difficulty in adjustment may have been manifested by any kind of symptom or behavioral pattern, provided that it has not been manifested by symptoms clearly indicating defective intelligence, structural disease of the brain, epilepsy, the neuroses, manic-depressive psychosis, or schizophrenia.

If those three criteria are satisfied, a definite diagnosis of psychopathic personality will be made. It is obvious that this is diagnosis by exclusion.

No special symptoms are considered to be specific or pathognomonic of psychopathic personality. It is obvious, however, that symptoms of some kind must be present or no psychiatric problem could be recognized. It has already been stated that the symptoms of intellectual defect and deterioration, and clouding of consciousness, as well as the familiar syndromes of the established neurotic and psychotic descriptive entities are arbitrarily excluded from consideration as evidence of psychopathy (except, as will be shown presently, under special circumstances). It follows, therefore, that the symptoms of psychopathy comprise all other indications of maladjustment. Chief among these are the following:

1. Delinquency and law-breaking in general, including both minor misdemeanors such as truancy, petty stealing, promiscuity and prostitution, as well as serious crimes such as larceny, forgery, and murder. Delinquency of one kind or another constitutes the most frequently utilized symptomatic basis for the diagnosis of psychopathic personality. Not all delinquency is considered to be psychopathic but there is no agreement as to just where the line of differentiation is to be drawn. Various psychiatrists attempt to make distinction between isolated episodes of delinquency and repeated or habitual delinquency, between delinquency which is understandable in terms of the biography of the individual and that which is not, between compulsive delinquency and that which lacks this quality, and between delinquency which is consciously motivated and that which is motivated unconsciously. Such distinctions, needless to say, are not easy to make nor are they usually very convincing.

2. Socially unconventional behavior which seriously interferes with adjustment is also commonly accepted as evidence of psychopathy. Conspicuous lack of sociability may be mentioned here, as well as vagabondage, litigiousness, and pathologic lying, together with a wide variety of oddities and eccentricities, among them peculiar ways of dressing and odd manners, unusual religious beliefs and extremist political and economic opinions, especially if these latter are expressed with an attitude of radical protest. It is of course admitted by all that it is difficult to draw the line between the normal and the psychopathic in terms of social conformity.

3. Emotional instability and other affective liabilities to comfortable social adjustment also constitute a widely accepted basis for the symp-

tomatic diagnosis of psychopathy. Emotional instability is understood to include emotional lability in general and conspicuous excitability in particular as shown by the occurrence of poorly controlled and more or less unpredictable emotional outbursts, especially with irritability and aggressiveness. The individual with such symptoms is sometimes referred to as an epileptoid psychopath. Other affective symptoms of psychopathy include habitual gloomy mood and the occurrence of frequent swings of mood in the direction of depression or elation, the latter characterizing the cycloid psychopath. It is not clear at what point the distinction is to be made between psychopathic mood swings and manic-depressive attacks.

4. Aberrant sexual behavior is considered by most psychiatrists to be evidence of psychopathy but with many clinicians dissenting. Included here are homosexuality, sadism, masochism, and the rarer perversions as well as chronic masturbation.

5. Drug addiction and chronic alcoholism are usually considered evidence of psychopathy, but here also there is much disagreement between various psychiatrists.

The differential diagnosis between psychopathic personality and other psychiatric diagnostic entities is made in a way which is often highly arbitrary.

If outspoken, classical manic-depressive or schizophrenic symptoms are present, a diagnosis of manic-depressive psychosis or schizophrenia is made and not psychopathic personality. If the symptoms which suggest a manic-depressive or schizophrenic condition are mild, a diagnosis of psychopathic personality is usually made, sometimes with the qualifying adjective schizoid or cycloid. Most psychiatrists are reluctant to make a definite diagnosis of manic-depressive psychosis or schizophrenia unless the symptoms are unmistakable and the disorder severe. On the few occasions in which both psychopathic personality and manic-depressive psychosis or schizophrenia are diagnosed, it is commonly assumed that the two conditions are separate and distinct, not that the psychosis is an outgrowth or extension of the psychopathy even though the history of the case indicates such a continuity of development.

Furthermore, an individual previously diagnosed as psychopathic is reclassified as psychotic if outspoken manic-depressive or schizophrenic symptoms develop, with the implication that the previous diagnosis of psychopathic personality was incorrect. The diagnosis of epilepsy (or convulsive state) will also be given precedence retrospectively and the classification will be changed from psychopathic personality to epilepsy if overt convulsive attacks develop or if electroencephalography reveals cerebral dysrhythmia.

Finally, an individual previously classified as neurotic may be reclassified as psychopathic if the symptoms fail to subside or if social maladjustment persists after presumably adequate treatment. The symptoms, it should be emphasized, may have been perfectly typical of anxiety, hysteria, or obsessional neurosis. None the less, treatment having failed, the patient is reclassified as an anxious, hysterical, or obsessional psychopath or a psychopathic personality with neurotic traits.

Etiologic Implications

Since Koch (1891) introduced the term "psychopathic inferiority" the tendency has been to conceive of the basic difficulty as genetically determined and to place the group designated as psychopathic in the class of congenital defect states together with the intellectually defective or feebleminded.

In recent years, many psychiatrists have abandoned the terms "psychopathic inferiority" and "constitutional psychopathic inferiority" in favor of the etiologically noncommittal labels of "psychopathic personality" and "psychopathic state." Notwithstanding this, the psychopath is still thought of by almost all psychiatrists as an individual born in some way defective or at any rate hereditarily doomed to defective development. Thus Henderson and Gillespie (1930), Henry (1938), Muncie (1939), and Strecker and Ebaugh (1940) continue to classify the psychopath in the group of constitutional defectives.

It should be noted that the adjective "constitutional," which so frequently appears in the literature of psychopathy, is commonly understood to refer to something which is genetically determined and not acquired fortuitously or through the process of learning. A few psychiatrists, notably Adolf Meyer, have attempted to use the term "constitutional" in a broader sense to include not only those traits which are genetically determined but also those which are acquired early and thoroughly ingrained into the personality structure. This broadened usage has not been generally accepted. Its appearance has added to the confusion concerning the meaning of psychopathic personality.

Discussion of the Current Usage

The present status of the concept of psychopathic personality is highly unsatisfactory.

It is evident that psychopathic personality is not a diagnostic entity in the ordinary sense of the word. In the practice of all branches of medicine, including psychiatry, the various disorders or clinical entities or syndromes or reaction-types are recognized and differentiated in terms of their symptoms and signs. General agreement exists that a specific disease or clinical entity is to be diagnosed if a particular group of symptoms and signs is present. The disease or clinical entity in question, furthermore, is to be distinguished from others, which it may superficially resemble, in terms of differences in symptoms or signs. Having recognized and distinguished the specific disease or clinical entity it is possible to proceed with a logical systematic study of its natural course and its causes and to evaluate the relative efficiency of various methods of treatment.

The diagnostic entities of psychiatry are not as clear cut or mutually exclusive as those of internal medicine and surgery. Nevertheless quite generally accepted symptomatic criteria have been established for the various personality disturbances (intellectual defect, neuroses, and psychoses) with the exception of psychopathic personality. When an attempt is made to pin down the diagnosis of psychopathic personality in terms of pathognomonic symptoms it vanishes as a clinical entity.

No one symptom and no combination of symptoms which are described as clinical manifestations of psychopathic personality is specific for that condition. Certainly delinquency, socially unconventional behavior, emotional instability, sexual aberration, and alcoholism are encountered in a great variety of personality disturbances. The more general diagnostic criteria which have been proposed for psychopathy are scarcely more satisfactory. The persistence of maladjustment for many years or for a life-time, for example, does not distinguish psychopathic personality from feeblemindedness or from many cases of schizophrenia, anxiety, hysteria, and other neuroses. The psychopath is sometimes described as an individual who, although of normal intelligence, is incapable of learning by experience. The same might be said of the chronic schizophrenic, the paranoid, and many so-called neurotics, depending on the exact meanings assigned to the terms "intelligence" and "learning by experience."

The conclusion seems warranted that psychopathic personality is not a recognizable entity in the descriptive behavioral sense. The psychopathic group includes an indefinite number of poorly delineated problems of personality development and adjustment which do not happen to fit conveniently into the accepted rigid system of psychiatric diagnosis.

What then is implied in the classification of an individual as a psychopath, if this procedure is not diagnosis in the ordinary sense? It is a conclusion that the personality make-up of the individual differs from the normal or average in the sense of having been in some vague way originally defective or in being at any rate permanently warped or pathologic. The question of etiology is theoretically left open, but actually psychopathic personality is conceived of by the majority of psychiatrists as predominantly genetically determined.

The evidence for hereditary predisposition to psychopathic development consists chiefly in the following observations:

1. Psychopathic maladjustment usually becomes evident in childhood. Therefore it is probably hereditarily determined. Psychiatric experience, however, clearly indicates that it is in the early years of childhood that the forces of the social environment, especially as transmitted through the family, exert the most powerful influence upon the development of personality. Learned patterns of maladjustment would therefore be expected to become evident in the early years of life.

2. Psychopathic maladjustment, once established, continues to be evident throughout the life of the individual. Therefore it must have an

hereditary basis. But learned patterns of behavior, once thoroughly ingrained, are well known to be so persistent.

3. Psychopathic maladjustment is often discernible in several members of the same family group. It is concluded on this account that the family stock is psychopathically tainted. This argument again disregards or at least greatly underestimates the importance of the attitudes operating within the family group in shaping the development of personality.

Any discussion of the inheritance of predisposition to the development of personality traits or characteristics needs to be very specific if it is to do justice to the facts. Such factors as intelligence and temperamental make-up do seem to be genetically determined and not significantly affected by learning. The same cannot be said of social attitudes, which are best regarded as learned traits, granted that there must exist a genetically determined potentiality for learning which varies both quantitatively and qualitatively from one individual to another. It does violence to common sense, however, and to accumulated experience with human behavior to maintain that the occurrence of resentful asocial delinquency in parent and child is evidence of innate predisposition to psychopathic development. Such a statement is on a par with concluding that the religiously bigoted child of a religiously bigoted parent has inherited a predisposition to bigotry.

4. Psychopathic maladjustment is resistant to treatment, therefore it is hereditarily determined. This conclusion is flattering to psychiatry but is obviously fallacious, as any clinician can testify who has attempted to treat such a typically learned pattern of maladjustment as hypochondriasis.

5. There is electroencephalographic evidence of cerebral pathophysiology in certain psychopathically maladjusted children. This statement is correct but is valid for an as yet undetermined percentage of so-called psychopaths. The abnormalities in the electroencephalogram must be correlated with specific patterns of maladjustment. It must not be forgotten furthermore that the majority of individuals with either electroencephalographic or overt manifestations of the convulsive state are not socially maladjusted.

Finally, since psychopathic personality is not a recognizable specific behavioral entity, the evaluation of the importance of hereditary factors in its etiology resolves itself into a general discussion of the importance of hereditary factors in the etiology of maladjustment and personality disorder in general. That subject is treated in another section of this book.

If the concept of psychopathic personality, as ordinarily understood, is as unsatisfactory as has been indicated, it is necessary to consider the reasons why it is still accepted by competent psychiatrists and so widely utilized.

The main reason, in the opinion of the reviewer, is an increasingly definite disagreement on the part of many psychiatrists with those theories which seek to explain almost all psychiatric problems in terms of environmental influences exclusively. The diagnosis of psychopathic personality emphasizes this disagreement. It implies not only that something is wrong with the patient as well as with the environment but also that the chief difficulty lies in the patient's personality make-up. Henderson (1939) has explicitly stated this.

To be consistent, however, those who feel the need for a term to call attention to the liabilities in the personality itself should extend the concept of psychopathic personality to include all personality disorders. Manic-depressive psychosis and schizophrenia are in this broad sense as definite evidence of psychopathy as are the types of maladjustment conventionally diagnosed as psychopathic. Preu (1940) has outlined an approach to psychiatric diagnosis on the basis of this broadened meaning of psychopathic personality, utilizing the general conceptions of Kahn.

There are two other important reasons for the continued acceptance and utilization of the concept of psychopathic personality which may not be so obvious to the nonmedical student of personality disorders. The clinical psychiatrist has to meet many urgent practical problems with which the researcher does not have to concern himself. The clinician finds the label diagnosis of psychopathic personality helpful in facing certain of these problems of everyday clinical work, particularly in institutional practice and in the court.

The diagnosis of psychopathic personality is a convenience in the institutional practice of psychiatry. Many patients voluntarily enter or are committed to psychiatric hospitals who obviously have disabling personality problems or disorders but whose symptoms are not really classified in terms of the more clear-cut established diagnostic categories. Psychopathic personality satisfies the necessity which is felt to give each patient a label diagnosis. The term at least indicates that a psychiatric problem is present. Psychiatrists share with other physicians a reluctance to label a patient "undiagnosed."

The diagnosis of psychopathic personality is also a convenience in court practice where the psychiatrist is asked to express an opinion on the question of responsibility. Psychopathic personality, in the forensic situation, may readily be construed to constitute a mitigating state of affairs, since it indicates that the individual is not fully responsible for his actions although not wholly irresponsible or insane. Whether such diagnostic procedure is jusifiable and socially desirable is open to debate but need not be discussed here. The question has been ably reviewed by Dession (1938).

Other Conceptions of Psychopathic Personality

It has already been mentioned that many individual differences of opinion exist concerning various aspects of the concept of psychopathic personality. It is neither necessary nor practical to consider a large number of these, since most of them deviate only slightly from the consensus with which the discussion has thus far been concerned. Three divergent points of view have been brought forward, however, which deviate sufficiently from the consensus to necessitate separate consideration.

The Contribution of Partridge

Partridge (1930) reviewed the literature on psychopathic personality and concluded that disagreement on all points was so general that the concept was in a state of confusion.

He maintained that the group diagnosed as psychopathic personality or constitutional psychopathic inferiority was both descriptively and etiologically heterogeneous since it included intellectual deficiency and incipient, mild, and atypical neuroses and psychoses as well as the subgroup which he proposed to separate as the sociopathic.

Partridge suggested that a separate diagnostic entity called sociopathic be established, to rank coordinately with the neuroses and (functional) psychoses as a definite, clearly recognizable pattern or kind of maladjustment characterized by difficulty in adapting to the demands of society as the central dominant issue or pathognomonic symptom.

The difficulties in delimiting the sociopathic group were apparent to Partridge. He mentions, for example, the dynamic relationship between the sociopathic (in his sense) and the paranoid. He believes, nevertheless, that if the issue of difficulty in adjusting to society as a whole is made specific for the sociopathic such a diagnostic entity can be established.

Partridge's suggestion is stimulating but its adoption would further confuse the already unsatisfactory official system of psychiatric diagnosis. At the present time two general kinds of diagnosis are made: the descriptive, of which such categories as anxiety, depression, and schizophrenia may be taken as examples, and the so-called etiological diagnoses, such as psychosis with cerebral arteriosclerosis and psychosis with syphilitic meningo-encephalitis, which state the issue in the terminology of internal medicine and mention the personality problem only incidentally. The adoption of the term "sociopathic" would introduce a third kind of diagnosis, the sociologic. This does not seem desirable. Psychiatry has roots both in internal medicine, particularly neurology, and in sociology, but it is not identical with either. The primary concern of psychiatry is the pathology of the individual. Psychiatric diagnosis should therefore be stated in terms of the functioning of the indivdual and not in terms which are primarily either neurologic or sociologic.

The Contribution of Alexander

Alexander (1930) reviewed the question of the neurotic character. This diagnostic term is the psychoanalytic label for the group usually referred to as psychopathic personality. He maintained that the designation neurotic may be as accurately applied to the individual whose difficulties manifest themselves in the form of a typical consistent pattern of social behavior which is clearly a deviation from the normal as to the individual who develops a circumscribed set of symptoms.

He set up four chief groups of psychopathologic reactions differentiated in terms of psychoanalytic dynamics: neurosis, neurotic character, psychosis, and true criminality. These groups are arranged in the order of the decreasing ability of the ego to reject unconscious impulses, the neurotic having the greatest capacity and the true criminal having none. Alexander interpreted the dynamics of the four reactions as follows:

In neurosis, conflict is present. The unconscious impulses are displaced and manifest themselves by means of substitutive gratification.

In neurotic character, conflict is also present but the unconscious impulses manifest themselves by means of neurotic acting out, achieving true but disguised gratification.

In psychosis, conflict is absent, the defenses break down, and the ego organization is destroyed. The unconscious impulses are gratified in an undisguised fashion.

In true criminality conflict is also absent and defense also fails but the ego organization is preserved. The unconscious impulses are unmodified and uninhibited.

Alexander's contention that the behavior of the psychopath is as neurotic as is the behavior of the individuals conventionally diagnosed as neurotic seems to the reviewer to be entirely correct. Whether one accepts his dynamic interpretation depends upon whether one accepts the psychoanalytic system of psychology.

The Contribution of Kahn

Eugen Kahn (1931) reformulated the concept of psychopathic personality. He makes no distinction between psychopathy and neurosis, dealing with both under the general heading of psychopathic personality.

Kahn emphasizes that no sharp distinction can be made between the normal and the psychopathic personality. The psychopath develops symptoms or gets into social difficulty more readily than does the average person. Social maladjustment is the crucial point in the practical diagnosis of psychopathy.

Clinical study of the psychopath reveals no personality components or functions or traits which are not also found in the normal personality. The difference between the two is quantitative. It is observed that in the personality make-up of those individuals classified as psychopathic (on the basis of social maladjustment) certain traits are disproportionately developed in the sense of deficiency or exaggeration. This entails unevenness or disproportion in personality organization which makes smooth functioning and successful environmental adjustment difficult.

The term "psychopathic," as used by Kahn, is therefore descriptive, merely indicating inadequate personality functioning as judged by the occurrence of social maladjustment. It has etiologic implications, however, since maladjustment is dealt with by Kahn essentially as a function of a "pathologic" person and not as the response of a normal person to a difficult environmental situation.

Kahn recognizes the importance of both genetic and environmental influences in shaping the development of personality along psychopathic lines. While warning against rigid etiologic interpretation in individual cases of psychopathy, he leans toward a genetic interpretation of etiology in the psychopathic group as a whole. His discussion of the etiology of psychopathy is sufficiently liberal, however, to leave ample room for difference of opinion concerning causes.

Kahn conceives of the person as an indivisible biologic unit but for purposes of expediency discusses personality in terms of its leading aspects. These he designates as impulse, temperament, and character.

Impulse, in Kahn's sense, means drive, as manifested by the output of energy. Impulse is genetically determined. Kahn discusses total impulse (drive) quantitatively, noting the marked individual variations in output of energy which justify the construction of the abstract types sthenic and asthenic in terms of drive. He also discusses the individual impulses (genetically determined patterns of energy output, drives, instincts), paying particular attention to the sex impulse. He discusses sexual deviations at this point, maintaining that in some instances they are innate impulsive anomalies and in others partly or predominantly determined by social environmental influences.

Temperament is that aspect of personality which refers to the quality of integrated functioning, the way in which behavior is objectively manifested and subjectively experienced. It is concerned with personal functioning in terms of speed of reactivity, tempo, smoothness, and diffuse autonomic participation objectively and in terms of feeling-tone (affect) subjectively. Temperament, like impulse, is genetically determined and not learned.

Kahn discusses temperament in terms of the fundamental mood and the reactive emotionality. The fundamental mood is the state of feeling-tone characteristic of the individual. Outstanding differences may be observed between individuals with respect to fundamental mood, in terms of which abstract temperamental types may be constructed: the cheerful, the gloomy, the anxious, the irritable, the colorless, and so forth. Some individuals, the poikilothymic, are characterized by changeable or fluctuating fundamental mood. The fundamental mood has far-reaching implications for environmental adjustment, since it imparts a specific coloring to the way of experiencing which is characteristic of the individual. The optimism of the cheerful, the pessimism of the gloomy, and the insecurity of the anxious may be taken as examples. A correlation exists between pyknic physique and cheerful, gloomy and poikilothymic fundamental mood, and between leptosomic physique and a fundamental mood of anxiety.

The tendency for the various fundamental moods to be associated with certain other personality traits is noted, with definite implications for social adjustment. Thus there is a tendency for cheerful mood to be associated with vivaciousness, talkativeness, distractibility, and the making of numerous but often superficial social contacts; for gloomy mood to be associated with sluggishness and lack of sociability; for anxious mood to be associated with immaturity and insecurity. The social adjustment of the poikilothymic fluctuates with the swings of mood. Outspoken cheerfulness, marked gloominess, and particularly the cyclic variety of poikilothymic mood predispose to the development of manic-depressive illnesses.

The reactive emotionality is that aspect of temperament which refers to the threshold of affective excitability, the readiness with which affective responses are elicited by appropriate stimuli. Here again antithetical abstract temperamental types may be constructed: the labile and the phlegmatic, each with its implications for social adjustment.

Character is the third leading aspect of personality discussed by Kahn. He uses the term to refer to the "directedness" of personality in the sense of the tendency to strive toward goals. Character is manifested in the complex system of attitudes maintained by the person toward himself and toward other people, particularly as revealed in specific interests and ambitions and other goal-determined patterns of behavior.

The formation of character is the result of the impact of social environmental forces on the person. Since an individual may happen to be born and to grow up in one environment or in another, the direction in which character will develop is to a certain extent a matter of chance, and unpredictable. Kahn stresses, however, that individuals vary considerably on a genetic basis in their potentialities for characterologic development. Impulse and temperament constitute the biologic foundation for character.

The system of attitudes is scrutinized with respect to the relative development of interest in self and of interest in others. The differences which are evident between individuals in this respect permit the construction of antithetical abstract characterologic types: the ego type, characterized by ego-overvaluation, and the environmental type, characterized by ego-undervaluation.

Definite ego-overvaluation may express itself as active autism in which the individual ignores the needs of other people and ruthlessly seeks power. This type of character typifies certain aggressive asocial criminals. Or ego-overvaluation may take the form of egocentricity in which the individual also more or less disregards the needs of others but seeks prestige rather than power. Egocentricity typifies the hysterical individual.

Definite ego-undervaluation likewise may express itself in either of two ways. It may take the form of passive autism in which the individual, feeling insecure in relation to other people, withdraws from contact with them, often with resentment. Paranoid attitudes may be associated. Or ego-undervaluation may express itself in the form of ego-searching in which the individual, here also insecure in relation to others, establishes himself in a dependent, submissive relationship, often seeking sympathy. Hypochondriacal behavior is frequently associated.

Kahn repeatedly emphasizes that the various types schematized in terms of impulse, temperament, and character are pure abstractions which are not to be applied literally to any individual. Various individuals simply show more or less resemblance to these abstractions.

Kahn discusses the various conventional neurotic and psychopathic syndromes in terms of the basic aspects of personality previously outlined. Thus, sexual deviation is discussed chiefly in terms of impulse, emotional-social instability chiefly in terms of impulse and temperament, hypochondriasis chiefly in terms of impulse and character, and hysteria, obsessive-compulsive neurosis, social eccentricity, and schizoid psychopathy chiefly in terms of character. It is continually emphasized, however, that the total personality is involved in every pattern of adjustment and in every clinical syndrome.

Kahn leaves open, in theory, the relative importance of genetic, impersonal environmental factors (infection, trauma, and so forth) and social environmental factors in the shaping of psychopathic personality development. He personally leans toward a predominantly genetic interpretation. He does not discuss intelligence as a fundamental leading aspect of personality.

The general dynamics of psychopathic personality are discussed in quantitative terms. The psychopathic personality is defined as one characterized by quantitative peculiarities in impulse, temperament, and character. These quantitative peculiarities result in a type of personality structure which expresses itself socially in the form of maladjustment.

The point of view expressed by Kahn is an important contribution to psychiatric theory. It puts the concept of psychopathic personality in proper perspective against the background of general personality development and organization. Kahn's approach to the study of personality is biologically oriented and so broadly stated that it leaves ample room for investigation and difference of opinion concerning causal factors and the dynamics of personality development and symptom formation. In the opinion of the reviewer, Kahn has so expanded the meaning of psychopathy that the use of the term itself becomes superfluous. Incidentally, Kahn's terminology does not readily lend itself to use in American institutional and court practice. This practical shortcoming, however, in no way diminishes the usefulness of his general theory in psychiatric research.

Conclusion

The current points of view concerning psychopathic personality have been outlined. The implications of the term, as used by the majority of psychiatrists, have been discussed; and three important divergent points of view have been presented in contrast.

The term "psychopathic personality," as commonly understood, is useless in psychiatric research. It is a diagnosis of convenience arrived at by a process of exclusion. It does not refer to a specific behavioral entity. It serves as a scrap-basket to which is relegated a group of otherwise unclassified personality disorders and problems.

It is felt by some that the label psychopathic serves a useful practical purpose in reminding psychiatrists that personality problems cannot be explained in environmental terms exclusively. This hardly seems necessary, but if it is, then the term should be applied to the neuroses and psychoses as well as to the conditions now designated as psychopathic.

The value of the contributions of Partridge, Alexander, and Kahn is best seen when they are evaluated independently rather than with reference to their bearing on the pseudo-entity psychopathic personality. Partridge indicates the possibilities of a sociologically oriented approach to psychiatric diagnosis. Alexander demonstrates that the kind of behavior now generally referred to as psychopathic can readily be interpreted as neurotic in psychoanalytic terms, thus rounding out the psychoanalytic approach to general psychiatric diagnosis. Kahn offers a biologically oriented approach to general personality development, adjustment, and maladjustment which is the most comprehensive now extant. It is impossible to do justice to these contributions by incidental reference and brief summary; the original literature should be consulted.

The unsatisfactory state of the concept of psychopathic personality illustrates the futility of orienting psychiatric research about the traditional clinical entities as "diseases" of nineteenth century psychiatry. What is needed is a clear description of various problems of behavior expressed in simple unambiguous language. It would thus be possible to undertake a common sense attempt to specify the etiologic factors without preconceived bias. Having done this, one could approach the problems of prevention and treatment in a logical, systematic fashion.

BIBLIOGRAPHY

ALEXANDER, F. 1930. The neurotic character. *Int. J. Psycho-Anal., 2,* 292–311.

DESSION, G. H. 1938. Psychiatry and the conditioning of criminal justice. *Yale Law J., 47,* 319–340.

HENDERSON, D. K. 1939. Psychopathic states. New York: Norton.

HENDERSON, D. K., & GILLESPIE, R. D. 1930. Textbook of psychiatry. (2nd ed.) New York: Oxford Univ. Press.

HENRY, G. W. 1938. Essentials of psychiatry. (3rd ed.) Baltimore: Williams & Wilkins.

JOSEPH, H. H., SOLOMON, P., & BRADLEY, C. 1938. Electroencephalographic analysis of behavior problem children. *Amer. J. Psychiat., 95,* 641–658.

KAHN, E. 1931. Psychopathic personalities. New Haven: Yale University Press.

KOCH, J. L. A. 1891. Die Psychopathischen Minderwertigkeiten. Ravensburg: Maier.

KRAEPELIN, E. 1915. Psychiatrie. Vol. 4. (8th ed.) Part 3. Leipzig: Barth.

MUNCIE, W. 1939. Psychobiology and psychiatry. St. Louis: Mosby.

PARTRIDGE, G. E. 1930. Current conceptions of psychopathic personality. *Amer. J. Psychiat., 10,* 53–99.

PREU, P. W. 1940. Psychopathic personalities. In *Cyclopedia of medicine, surgery and specialties.* Philadelphia: Davis.

PRICHARD, J. C. 1835. Treatise on insanity. London: Gilbert & Piper.
SCHNEIDER, K. 1923. Die psychopathischen Persönlichkeiten. In Aschaffenburg, Handbuch der Psychiatrie. Leipzig-Wien: Deuticke.
STRECKER, E. A., & EBAUGH, F. G. 1940. Practical clinical psychiatry. (5th ed.) Philadelphia: Blakiston.

Chapter 31

SEIZURE STATES

By WILLIAM G. LENNOX, M.D.

IN THE FIELD OF MEDICINE, the logical advance of knowledge is along certain well-recognized lines. First is the accumulation of surface observations and symptoms; second is the task of grouping those manifestations which seem to be related to one another and binding them together by means of a name; third is the finding of the immediate cause or causes of these apparently related phenomena; and fourth is the seemingly visionary search for a final cause, which will explain not only a single symptom complex but many apparently unrelated complexes.

This present discussion will deal mainly with certain seizure states which have been more adequately studied and which have been shown to possess a common constitutional or physiological basis. The attention will be focused on epilepsy, migraine, fainting, and vaso-vagal attacks, but I believe there are other borderland conditions, such as certain types of psychoses, odd behavior, criminology, which future research may show should be classified with the epilepsy-migraine group of seizure states. Older clinicians have not been afraid to link diverse disease processes by means of nomenclature. Thus, according to Liveing (1873), Trousseau called tic douloureux and angina pectoris "epileptiform neuralgia." He said that "mania transitoria" may follow or replace epileptic seizures. Maudsley (1870) speaks of "furor transitorius" lasting a few hours or days and comparable to a fit of epilepsy.

For purposes of orientation I shall first sketch the main features of epilepsy and migraine, without attempting a detailed discussion and documentation, for this will be found in the books by Lennox and Cobb (1928) and by Lennox (1941). Shorter presentations appear in various systems of medicine. Secondly, I shall give in some detail what is known about the personality and behavior of epileptic and migrainous persons.

Epilepsy

Definition.—Epilepsy is a recurrent disturbance in the chemico-electrical activity of the brain which manifests itself in a symptom complex of which impairment of consciousness, perturbation of the autonomic nervous system, convulsive movements or psychic disturbances are the essential components. Definitions may be based on the causes of phenomena or on their manifestations. The above definition attempts to include both. Strictly speaking, there may be asymptomatic as well as symptomatic epilepsy. In the former case the person may have a disturbance of discharging cells which shows itself in an abnormal electroencephalographic tracing only.

Historical.—Epilepsy is referred to in ancient Arabian, Egyptian, and Hebrew writings. The most detailed early discussion of the condition is in the discussion commonly attributed to Hippocrates and dating from about 400 B.C. This is a remarkable document for its common sense and skilful discrediting of the term "sacred disease." The author was a scientific-minded person who explained in detail the mechanism of seizures, namely, the occlusion of the ventricles of the brain by moist humors which interfered with the normal circulation through the brain. In the centuries which surrounded the birth of Christ, Galen, Celsus, Aretaeus of Cappadocia, and Avicenna had a good deal to say about epilepsy. Writers of the middle ages, Guanerius, John of Gaddesden, Bernard of Gordon, and Arnold of Villanova, gave more detailed directions about therapy but added nothing about the cause or mechanism of seizures. Not until the Renaissance did medical writers look at patients subject to seizures with their own eyes and begin to apply the newly discovered facts of anatomy and physiology. Around the year 1700 ideas began to stir. Old explanations of occluded ventricles and mechanical traction on nerves were abandoned. Thomas Willis in England and Hermann Boerhaave in Holland wrote extensively on the subject of epilepsy, reporting cases and autopsy findings. The former likened the seizure to an explosive charge of gunpowder. He stated that the final cause of epilepsy is chemical, a conclusion which is fully upheld by present-day investigators. In the middle of the nineteenth century, physiologists like Fritsch and Hitzig, and clinicians like Hughlings Jackson and Gowers studied the neurological pathways involved in seizures and found at last a drug which had definite value in the control of convulsive seizures. The modern period of investigation and research may be dated from 1920, when an osteopathic practitioner advertised the fact that complete abstinence from food tended to hold seizures in abeyance. Following these observations have come modern studies in blood chemistry and in electroencephalography.

Incidence.—Information derived from the 1917 draft as well as from the questioning of small samples of the population indicates that the incidence of epilepsy in the United States is *approximately* .5%. (Obviously the word "approximately" must be stressed. In many cases seizures are concealed or overlooked. On the other hand, many persons who have had seizures in the past have lost this symptom.) The incidence is much greater among children than adults, because of the fact that either the seizures or the persons who have them tend to disappear. Men and women seem to be about equally affected.

Symptomatology.—The symptoms which were mentioned under Definition may occur in varying proportions in different patients and in the same patients at different times. For purposes of convenience three main types of seizures have been recognized. There is no typical epileptic fit. A seizure may vary all the way from a transient impairment of consciousness which is so slight that it is not recognized either by the patient or by a person observing him, to a convulsion of demoniac fury.

AURA.—A grand mal attack is preceded in about one-half of patients by premonitory symptoms. These are various, consisting perhaps of a sensation of dizziness or of discomfort in the abdomen or, in special cases, a tingling or numbness in an extremity. A symptom which is localized furnishes a valuable means of determining from what part of the brain the seizure arises. The aura, which corresponds to the first gust before a storm, usually lasts but a few seconds and may not even give the patient time for preparing himself against the ensuing attack.

GRAND MAL.—The outstanding phenomenon in this type of seizure is excessive muscular activity. The patient loses consciousness, his muscles become rigid, respiration is suspended, and he falls if not supported. Because of the suspended respiration, the face becomes dusky, the color clearing only with the return of air to the lungs which occurs when movements, instead of being rigid (tonic), become jerking (clonic). After from one to several minutes, jerking movements may cease and the patient gradually regain consciousness. He may have bitten his tongue or have lost control of his sphincters. A convulsion if severe may be succeeded by headache, vomiting, muscular soreness, and depression of spirits. Convulsive attacks occur at variable intervals, some patients having only one or two a year, others having many a day. Very rarely one attack may succeed another without the patient regaining consciousness between. This is called *status epilepticus*.

JACKSONIAN ATTACKS.—A special form of grand mal convulsion begins in an extremity and spreads toward the brain, the patient retaining consciousness, but unable to stop the spasmodic movements. Jacksonian seizures when present point to the corresponding area of the brain, the cells of which are discharging abnormally.

PETIT MAL.—In this form of attack the predominant feature is the loss of consciousness. This is transient, lasting only a few seconds. Unconsciousness begins and ends abruptly. It may not be complete. It is not followed by mental confusion, nor is it attended by more than small twitching motions of the muscles about the eye or face at the rate of approximately three a second. The seizures of petit mal recur with great frequency, often many times a day and every day. They are especially frequent in girls. They appear predominantly at or near puberty, are not usually attended by mental deterioration, and are not easily influenced by drugs.

PSYCHIC EQUIVALENT SEIZURES.—These may be called psychic seizures, psychic variants, or psychomotor seizures. The predominate symptom is amnesia. Consciousness is lost, but activity is not suspended. The person is out of contact with his environment. He may perform purposeful acts, but is not subject to command and after the period of confusion is over has no recollection of what took place. The seizures are longer than petit mal, lasting from a fraction of a minute to hours or even days. Muscular movements if present are tonic and not clonic. The patient's body may rotate or become slightly rigid, but does not go through the violent tonic-clonic sequence of the grand mal. Psychomotor attacks are more frequent in men than in women and in adults than in children.

These three main seizure types may not be pure. A particular seizure may be a combination of two types. Furthermore, nearly one-half of patients have more than one type. Approximately one-half of patients have only grand mal, 8% only petit mal, and 1% only psychic seizures. With or without another type of seizure, grand mal occurs in 90% of patients, petit mal in 45% and psychic in 8%.

Chemical and Physiological Mechanism of Seizures.—Ever since the days of Hippocrates, men have known that seizures arise from a disorder in the brain. Hippocrates was even aware that injury to one side of the brain would cause convulsive movements of the opposite side of the body. Much of the work of persons interested in the study of epilepsy has been concerned with the pathway of transmission of these discharges from the brain. Most profitable has been the electrical stimulation of the brain of animals with observation of the resulting convulsion. This work, initiated by Fritsch and Hitzig (1870), has been elaborated in recent years. Hughlings Jackson made far-reaching conclusions based on close observations of patients who suffered localized convulsions as a result of injury to the brain and who later came to autopsy. In recent years laboratory experiments and clinical observations have been united in the operating room observations of neurosurgeons, especially Penfield and his coworkers (1937). Unfortunately, in patients electrical stimulation of the brain must usually be confined to its surface. The relative strength of current required to produce convulsions when various regions of the brain are stimulated has been studied by Gibbs and Gibbs (1936). Curiously enough, the motor cortex does not have as low a threshold as certain subcortical areas, especially the region anterior to the thalamus. A yet finer means of study is that of Dusser de Barenne and his associates (1937, 1938), who have mapped the functional pathways of the brain not by observing the actions of the animal but by following the spread of electrical patterns through the brain, a procedure made possible by the electroencephalograph.

These studies permit a great extension of our knowledge concerning the nervous pathways which induced impulses follow. They do not disclose the place of origin of seizures which arise spontaneously. Because the clinical manifestations of a seizure in a given individual may vary all the way from transient loss of consciousness to a generalized convulsion, presumably the same area of the brain is not always involved, even though the pathological lesion is constant. If the seizure is a Jacksonian one involving, say, the right hand and arm, with coincident aphasia, the origin and pathway of spread of the discharge is obvious. Seizures which are preceded by hallucinations of sound, taste, or odor are often associated with tumor or other lesion in the temporal lobe.

But what of the petit mal seizures distinguished by only a rhythmic twitching of eyebrows or a fixed upward gaze? Where does the generalized tonic-clonic convulsion arise? The electroencephalogram indicates that in a great majority of cases abnormal discharges appear simultaneously over the whole surface of the brain. Whether the discharge is initiated simultaneously over the cortex or whether it spreads to the cortex from a subcortical center cannot be told until someone has the boldness to place electrodes in subcortical areas of the brain of patients having frequent seizures.

Recent work has supported the contention of Hughlings Jackson that epilepsy is an abnormal discharge of neurones of the brain. A far more subtle and significant question is, what causes this abnormal discharge? The solution of this question will involve knowledge of the electrochemical activity of discharging nervous cells. This peculiar type of discharge which results in cortical dysrhythmia may be due to heredity or environment or both. The fact that epilepsy may be hereditary has long been recognized, but that disturbed electrical activity of the brain may also be hereditary has been shown only recently by Lennox, Gibbs, and Gibbs (1940). Presumably this disturbed activity is based on a peculiar chemical make-up or reaction of nerve cells which is a transmissible characteristic. Given some basic, constitutional and therefore continuous abnormality, discontinuous environmental factors must also be postulated, chemical changes which precipitate the unusual discharge which displays itself in the form of clinical symptoms.

Electroencephalographic Findings.—The results of electrical studies are of great significance for epilepsy and presumably for other conditions associated with alterations of personality. A résumé of the whole subject of electroencephalography, with illustrative tracings and with a complete bibliography of some 600 articles, is presented in the *Atlas* recently written by Gibbs and Gibbs (1941). Electroencephalography also is discussed in this book (Chapter 33 by Lindsley) so that only aspects which bear directly on the subject of seizures will be dealt with here.

1. Electroencephalographic records were made of patients at the time they were having seizures by Berger (1929), who found a great commotion of waves at the time of attacks. Berger's observations with epilepsy went little beyond this point, since his apparatus and his opportunities, as judged by present standards, were limited. Further observations reported by Gibbs, Davis, and Lennox (1935) showed additional

striking features, namely that during petit mal attacks the abnormality consists of a high voltage alternate wave and spike occurring at the rate of approximately three a second, the spike coinciding with the twitching of facial muscles. Grand mal attacks are attended by an increase in the speed and voltage of waves. Later on, Gibbs, Gibbs, and Lennox (1938) observed that during psychomotor seizures characteristic waves were also observed, these being abnormally large voltage slow waves at the rate of from four to eight a second (see Fig. 1).

2. Gibbs, Davis, and Lennox (1935) discovered that abnormalities might be present when patients were not displaying any symptoms. Petit mal patients might show disturbances of rhythm which were in reality very short or low voltage seizure discharges. Later it was found that about 85% of patients with a history of seizures showed abnormalities of rhythm in an interparoxysmal period, during a 20-minute period of observation. (Patients with normal records are usually those having rare seizures.) Dysrhythmia when present consists usually of bursts of waves which are of increased voltage and either abnormally fast or slow. If bursts of fast, spiky waves are present or there is the telltale alternate wave and spike of petit mal, the patient usually has a history of grand mal or of petit mal.

3. A certain proportion of normal persons, approximately 10% in samples so far taken by Gibbs and Gibbs (1941), exhibit abnormalities which are similar to those encountered in patients who have a history of seizures or a related condition. These persons might be called asymptomatic or potential epileptics. Such a condition is not peculiar. Many persons who have no cardiac symptoms can be shown by laboratory methods to have disturbances in the rhythm of the heart. Many persons who are not diabetic have a high blood sugar curve. Individuals with asymptomatic dysrhythmia outnumber those with seizures approximately twenty to one. Presumably they form the reservoir out of which persons with symptoms are recruited.

4. In some persons the electroencephalographic tracing if repeated daily is of barometric value. An increase of abnormal waves may precede a seizure by many hours. Immediately before a grand mal attack there is usually a speed-up of cortical activity with a decrease of voltage.

5. In most patients abnormal activity is present over all accessible surfaces of the cerebrum. In a minority of patients the dysrhythmia begins in one area and seems to spread to others. This is especially likely to occur with patients who have a lesion of the brain in that area, but characteristically persons who have no lesion (so-called idiopathic epilepsy) display great variability from time to time. On one occasion the abnormal waves may be more prominent in one area and on another occasion in another area.

6. The effect of various drugs and changes of body physiology can be shown in the electrical record. Sedatives used in the treatment of patients—bromides and phenobarbital—cause a slowing of the cortical frequencies. Opening or closing the eyes, going to sleep, changes in

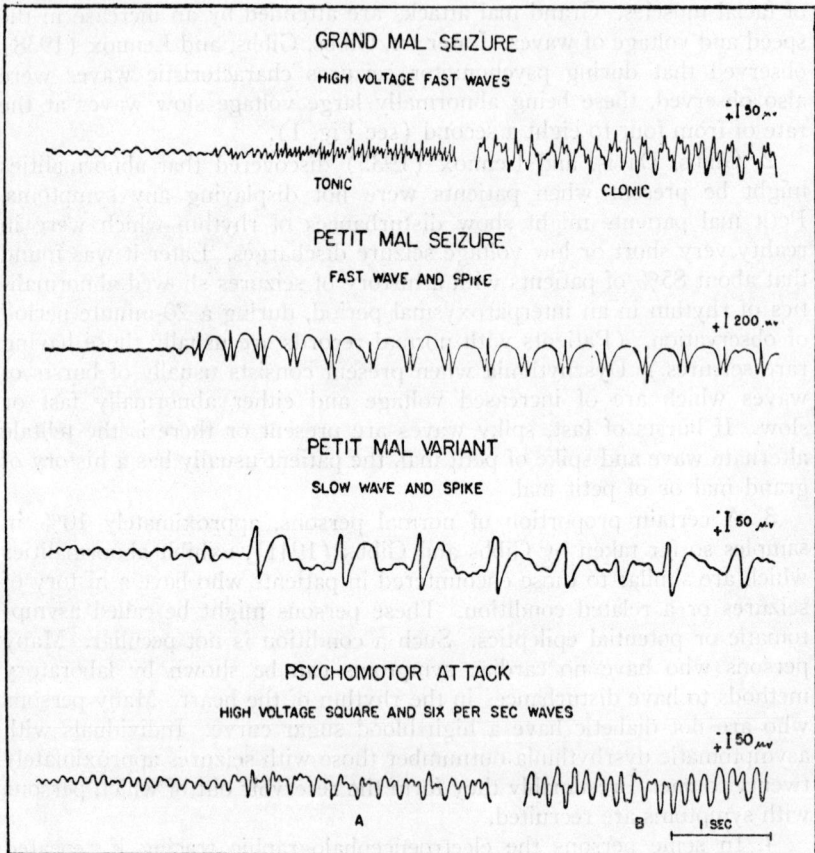

Figure 1

Representative electroencephalograms of four patients to show records taken before, and during, four different types of seizures, viz., grand mal, two forms of petit mal, and psychic variant (psychomotor). At the right is the perpendicular deflection made by a 50-millionth or 200-millionth volt current, and at the bottom the time marked by one second. The left of each tracing is a portion of the person's normal record. The rest of the tracing was made during a seizure. Four different types of seizures are depicted. Uppermost is the tonic and then, after an interval, the clonic phase of a grand mal convulsion. The second tracing is the three a second alternate wave and spike of a petit mal. The third tracing is of the relatively rare slow (two a second) wave and spike called petit mal variant. This is not usually accompanied by symptoms. The fourth tracing was taken during two phases of a psychomotor seizure. The tracings are about one-third their natural size. (F. A. Gibbs, E. L. Gibbs, and W. G. Lennox, *Archives of Neurology and Psychiatry, Chicago,* June, 1939, p. 1112) mental activity influence abnormal as well as normal rhythms. The alternate wave and spike formation of petit mal is especially susceptible to changes in the concentration of carbon dioxide or sugar in the blood, being precipitated by low concentrations and suppressed by high concentrations. Anoxemia if profound enough to cause unconsciousness results in slowing.

7. In addition to the presence of dysrhythmia in a certain proportion of normal individuals, a much larger proportion of persons who have symptoms which are not ordinarily classed as epileptic may show dysrhythmia. Many problem children, as well as adults who show anti-social tendencies, have abnormal records. This subject is discussed by Lindsley (see Chapter 33). Also patients with psychosis may show disturbances of rhythm. Davis and Davis (1939) reported that many manic-depressive and schizophrenic patients have dysrhythmia, although others have records grossly similar to those of normal individuals. Other workers have reported somewhat similar findings.

8. The form of the brain wave seems to be a constitutional characteristic of an individual. Observations on twins made by Davis and Davis (1936) opened the door to a study of the heredity of dysrhythmia. Lennox, Gibbs, and Gibbs (1940 and unpublished observations) have made electrical records of 70 pairs of twins and of 262 close relatives of epileptic patients. Although the pattern of cortical brain waves is a fluid and not a fixed characteristic, it is, these authors believe, an hereditary trait. Of the 262 relatives, 53% had dysrhythmia. In 78 families records were obtained of both parents. In 27% both parents had abnormal records, in 53% only one was definitely abnormal, in 10% one parent's record was borderline, and in only 10% were the records of both parents entirely normal. Confirmatory evidence has been supplied by other workers.

There are 20 persons with cortical dysrhythmia for each person with epilepsy. Presumably the great majority of these normal but dysrhythmic individuals carry a predisposition towards epilepsy or an allied disorder.

A question of moment is, "What are these allied dysrhythmic disorders and can their heredity be traced by means of the electroencephalogram?" Thoughts go immediately to behavior disorders in both children and adults, criminals, especially those committing unreasoned crimes of violence, alcoholics, and psychotic individuals. The presence of a significant dysrhythmia in these groups has not been established. If and when it is, electroencephalography both in diagnosis and in eugenics will have a far-reaching career.

Clinical Data Bearing on Etiology.—Although laboratory studies must be the final authority for determining the ultimate etiology of seizures, much can be learned from the study of patients. Several groups of conditions have long been associated with the appearance of epilepsy.

HEREDITY.—The subject of heredity has already been mentioned. Statistical studies have shown that epilepsy occurs among the near relatives of epileptic patients about five times more frequently than it occurs in the general population (Lennox, 1941). This incidence is greater if seizures began early in life, if the person shows mental deterioration, if the patient is a female, and if the brain was not injured prior to onset of seizures, so-called essential epilepsy.

Less than one-fifth of patients have a family history of epilepsy. Hence seizures are not inherited, but only the tendency to seizures, a predisposition which can be visualized as an hereditary dysrhythmia. Presumably this dysrhythmia is present in all patients who are subject to seizures, but it does not need to be so pronounced in patients who also have received an injury to the brain. This conception is supported by statistical evidence, which shows that persons having epilepsy subsequent to a brain injury have only half as many relatives with epilepsy as patients who have had no injury. Incidence in the injured group is still two or three times greater than in the general population. For practical purposes, epileptics are often divided into groups of so-called essential, or idiopathic, and the so-called symptomatic, or traumatic. Much confusion has been created by this classification. In my opinion idiopathic is synonymous with hereditary. I believe nearly all cases are of hereditary origin, but the importance of the hereditary factor varies, being much smaller in certain patients than in others. Epilepsy may be genetic or acquired, but it is most often of mixed origin.

STRUCTURAL ABNORMALITIES OF BRAIN AND BODY.—Given a predisposition to seizures, almost any abnormality of the brain seems to be a precipitating factor. Changes which occur early in life in association with intra-uterine or birth injuries, asphyxia, excessive sedation, and so forth, seem to be particularly significant because the brain in early life is unusually poorly protected and unusually sensitive to injury. However, infections later in life, especially those involving the brain or its coverings, trauma, tumors, and in later years degenerative change in blood vessels of the brain, provoke seizures in predisposed persons. Some injuries are much more important than others. Thus, gunshot wound of the head is followed by seizures in from 5% to 20% of cases, whereas tumors of certain areas of the brain are accompanied by seizures in the majority of cases.

The brain may suffer injury not only directly but as a result of irritative substances carried to the brain from other parts of the body. Thus disorders of metabolism which produce very low levels of sugar in the blood result in convulsions, as does inadequate activity of the parathyroid glands, which results in an insufficient concentration of calcium.

EMOTIONAL COMPONENTS.—As a gun may be fired by a very slight pressure on the trigger, convulsions may be set off by emotional disturbances which would produce only a storm of tears in an ordinary individual. Some persons who are strong believers in the force of emotional conflicts, especially those of the Freudian persuasion, attribute convulsions wholly to unconscious conflicts. The point might be argued at length. Perhaps the most significant piece of evidence is the lack of reports of successful treatment of epileptic seizures by means of psycho-analytical methods.

Differential Diagnosis Between Epilepsy and Borderline Conditions.—Patients and doctors are often put to it to distinguish between symptoms due to epilepsy and those due to other conditions, principally hysteria, syncope, and carotid sinus reflex. This problem is less acute since the electroencephalogram has come into use. If records can be obtained during a person's paroxysm and the record is normal, a categorical statement can be made that this is not epilepsy. If the record is abnormal, the patient may possibly be one of those normal individuals with an abnormal record or the dysrhythmia may be due to an injury of the brain. However, when dysrhythmia and seizures are present in the same individual, they are probably causally related.

HYSTERIA.—A person having a hysterical seizure does not show more abnormality of brain waves than he had before, and his convulsion can usually be distinguished from that of the epileptic convulsion. However, the borderline is a broad one and physicians commonly make the mistake of calling epilepsy hysteria. A history of emotional conflicts can usually be elicited from a person who has hysteria. Seizures occur in the presence of others; the patient has something to gain by his attack, and feels better for the experience after it is over. A person may have both epilepsy and hysteria.

SYNCOPE.—Fainting is due to an insufficient supply of blood to the brain. The person becomes pale, falls limply, does not have convulsive movements, and comes to in a few minutes. Syncope takes place when the patient is upright, and does not occur when lying in bed. Recurrent fainting episodes, especially if causative factors seem inadequate, need to be looked on with suspicion.

CAROTID SINUS REFLEX.—Rarely an individual, especially one who is elderly with hardened arteries, will faint without apparent cause. If the sinus reflex is at fault, fainting can be induced by pressure on the carotid sinus, which lies at the bifurcation of the carotid artery in the neck.

Means of Altering the Frequency of Seizures.—

PHYSICO-CHEMICAL CHANGES.—Induction of acidosis tends to inhibit seizures, particularly those of the petit mal type. Acidosis can be induced by fasting, by the use of a ketogenic diet, by the ingestion of acids or acid forming salts, by breathing high concentrations of carbon dioxide, and most easily of all by strenuous muscular exercise or work. The opposite condition of alkalosis induced by overventilation or ingestion of large amounts of bicarbonate tends to increase seizures.

Dehydration of body tissues through abstinence in the use of fluids tends to reduce seizures, and flooding the body with water tends to increase them. In the laboratory, petit mal seizures can be decreased by breathing high concentrations of oxygen and can be increased by reducing the oxygen content of the blood. Alteration of chemical constituents of the blood, particularly sugar, calcium, and possibly cholesterol, also modifies seizures.

DRUGS.—Convulsive drugs will produce seizures more readily in epileptic patients than in others. Curiously enough, some clinicians have induced convulsions in patients with the hope of thereby "discharging" the brain and preventing the occurrence of spontaneous seizures. Reports are not in agreement as to whether the induced attacks are the same pattern as spontaneous ones. Drugs are of course used principally to prevent seizures, a subject which will be discussed under treatment.

PROPHYLAXIS.—Efforts to prevent seizures may be either communal or individual. Public efforts consist of the prevention of birth injuries and of head injuries, and the reduction of infectious diseases which play a part in precipitating attacks. More important than these would be the limitation of offspring of persons who are either subject to seizures or have pronounced congenital cerebral dysrhythmia.

Individual prophylaxis consists in the avoidance of head injuries or of infections which attack the brain and in extra care given to persons who may be predisposed, presumably those individuals who show cortical dysrhythmia. The efficacy of drugs in the correction of asymptomatic dysrhythmia has not yet been demonstrated. Certain symptoms such as unexplained night terrors, fainting, attacks of sleep, or outbursts of temper may be premonitory or disguised symptoms of epilepsy, and presumably if treatment is started early, frank seizures might be avoided.

Treatment.—

PHYSICAL.—Most patients think only of the necessity of being rid of the seizures. But in many a patient the elimination of seizures is but half the battle. With this accomplished, he may be so fearful of their return or so out of gear with his environment that he requires psychological care.

Treatment must be individual, for the causes of seizures vary in different individuals. The first and most important consideration is the elimination of the responsible factors. The fundamental, hereditary, cause cannot of course be treated, but numerous contributing causes can be. If there is evidence of a focal cortical lesion, surgery may be required for removal of the scar or of the tumor which is responsible. Abnormalities of physique need to be corrected even though they may play a very small part. Very rarely a glandular disorder or a state of allergy can be remedied with benefit. Aside from individual abnormalities which possibly are directly responsible for seizures, many patients can be helped indirectly through improvement of habits of living and of general physique. Specifically, the induction of a state of acidosis by means of the ketogenic diet has relieved about a third of children who have been given this treatment. Institution of dehydration by means of extreme limitation of fluid intake has been found helpful by some doctors. Therapeutic results are difficult to evaluate, because of the natural tendency to remissions, sometimes of considerable duration, without apparent cause.

PHARMACOLOGICAL.—In 1857 Sir Charles Locock reported good results from the use of bromide; in 1912 Hauptmann first reported the use of phenobarbital; and in 1937 Putnam and Merritt gave the favorable results of experiments with dilantin sodium (sodium diphenyl hydantoinate). Each of these drugs has proved to be more valuable than its predecessor. At the present time, phenobarbital is used most. The daily dose is from one to two grains, but as much as six grains a day may be used in some patients without apparent harm and without producing the disfiguring skin lesions or the drowsiness caused by heavy dosage of bromide. Dilantin is probably the drug of choice, although many patients are not benefited or suffer toxic symptoms. In any case the administration of dilantin requires much more careful supervision than the other two drugs. The beginning dose for adults is one and a half grains three times a day. If toxic symptoms do not appear and if attacks are not controlled, the amount may be increased gradually by steps until therapeutic results are obtained or until a maximum of nine grains a day are taken. The most frequent toxic symptoms are instability of gait, tremor, gastric upsets, eruptions of the skin, swelling of the gums, or, in rare instances, overactivity and psychic disturbance. The appearance of any of these symptoms necessitates reduction of the dose or, if they are alarming, its discontinuance. All three of these drugs are most effective with grand mal attacks. Petit mal attacks are little influenced; in the case of dilantin they are often made worse. On the other hand, dilantin is particularly effective in cases of psychomotor seizures, which are not usually helped by the other two. Dilantin has a great advantage over the other two in that it is not a hypnotic and therefore its use does not result in a slowing of mental activity.

Public Responsibility.—The public has assumed direct responsibility for the care and treatment of that considerable group of patients who cannot readily be cared for at home. For the most part these are the patients who are seriously deteriorated or whose behavior is a trouble or menace to others. In most states of the Union these patients are sent to a mental hospital. This disposition is especially unfortunate if the person's mentality is not impaired. Even if it is, patients subject to seizures require different handling from those who are psychotic. Recognizing the peculiar needs of the epileptic patients, ten states have established hospitals or colonies which are exclusively for the care of epileptic patients. Altogether, these hospitals contain some 13,000 patients, out of the 50,000 or so who are in public charge. There are only two or three small private institutions designed for epileptic patients. The problem of care for an epileptic outside of the home and outside of a state institution at a moderate cost is not adequately met.

Education of the Public.—The public stands in need of education concerning both the medical and the social aspects of epilepsy. Many opinions are widespread which stem from a century ago. Especially is this true with regard to questions about heredity and mental deterioration. Books designed especially to correct this condition are *Science and Seizures* (Lennox, 1941) and *Convulsive Disorders* (Putnam, 1943). The only organization is the Laymen's League against Epilepsy. Members receive educational bulletins and are expected to spread authoritative information and through their dues to contribute towards research.

A Program for Investigation.—The fruitfulness of work done in the last five years with electroencephalography and with dilantin demonstrates what can be done by intensive effort. Further research should be productive of even greater results because the main problems of epilepsy are now laid bare. They are physico-chemical in nature. Because the abnormal discharges can be recorded, the conditions and chemicals which influence these discharges can be studied. This work of course requires expert investigators and expenditure of considerable amounts of money. Many obscure points can be cleared up by clinicians who are in contact with patients and who really are interested in contributing to knowledge. The American League against Epilepsy is a branch of an international organization whose members are, many of them, engaged in research.

Migraine

This symptom complex resembles epilepsy in the fact of recurrence. Like an epileptic seizure, an attack may come only once in a lifetime or may occur several times a week or even become almost continuous.

History.—Aretaeus, who lived in the second century A.D., describes recurrent headaches which are unmistakably migrainous. Writers in the middle ages make frequent reference to it. A long case history which is startlingly clear is by Thomas Willis, whose first complete works were published in 1684.

Incidence.—No exact statistics are available. Samples from small groups vary tremendously with the age, sex, and social condition of the groups tested. About two-thirds of patients who consult physicians are women. A moderate estimate based on samples of the population is 5%.

Relationship to Epilepsy.—Aside from the fact of recurrence, epilepsy and migraine seem to be genetically related in that the incidence of epilepsy and migraine in the same person is greater than the incidence of either in the general population. More significant is the fact that the incidence of migraine is unduly high among the relatives of epileptic patients and an unusual number of relatives of migraine patients have epilepsy (Lennox, 1941).

Symptomatology.—The symptom of greatest importance to the patient is a pain in the head which is usually so severe as to be incapacitating. It is usually localized and characteristically is confined to one side of the head, hence the old term "hemicrania." The pain, however, has a tendency to wander during an attack and to be present in different parts of the head with different headaches. Nausea, usually accompanied by vomiting, and sympathetic disturbances, pallor, chilliness, gooseflesh, changes in pulse rate, are usually present. Some patients experience visual symptoms, blind spots, a blurring of vision or zigzag colors. Headaches are relieved with difficulty by ordinary sedative drugs, but in the great majority of cases are relieved promptly by the nonsedative ergotamine tartrate.

Mechanism of Seizures.—The symptoms which have been named indicate a primary disturbance in the autonomic nervous system. The site of pain is probably in the arteries which supply the meninges and is due to an undue relaxation of arterial walls. The nausea, and vomiting, and the scotoma or, when they occur, the hemiparasthesias or hemiparesis, presumably indicate disturbance of cortical cells, which may be due to alteration of vascular supply.

Etiological Factors.—Heredity is outstanding and a positive history of affected relatives is obtained in three-fourths or more of patients who have the characteristic symptoms. The mothers are of course more often affected than fathers.

Endocrine influences are more prominent than in the case of epilepsy. This is especially observable in women. Headaches are prone first to manifest themselves at the time of puberty and in association with menstruation. Many women are free of attacks during pregnancy and seizures tend to disappear with menopause.

Emotional factors are also more prominent than with epilepsy. The majority of patients relate attacks to periods of emotional stress.

Prophylaxis.—Obviously the most important point is choice of parents who have no personal or family history of migraine or epilepsy. In a person who is predisposed the manifestation of seizures might possibly be minimized or averted by avoidance of conditions such as emotional or physical fatigue, eye strain, or undue sensory stimuli which seem to precipitate attacks.

Treatment.—As with epilepsy, treatment is individual, based on whatever abnormalities can be uncovered as a result of careful examination. The body must be brought into as perfect a state of health as possible and the method of living regulated to avoid undue stresses, internal as well as external.

PHARMACOLOGY.—Ergotamine tartrate, given by subcutaneous injection in .5 mg. doses, is effective in aborting individual attacks of headache in about 90% of persons so treated. It stops not only the headache but also the other symptoms, although nausea and vomiting are at first accentuated. Apparently the pain from sensory stimulation by relaxed arteries is overcome by an increased tonicity of the arterial system. Presumably the fact that arteries of the head are alone involved is due to the autonomic nervous system supply and control of these arteries. Very rarely a patient will be encountered whose pain is not in the head but in the abdomen.

Program for Investigation.—More needs to be known about the chemical influence of hormones, the relationship of emotional disturbances to the action of the sympathetic nervous system, and a much larger collection needs to be made of statistical data.

Personality and Seizure States

This is an interesting subject which has received too little unbiased attention. Neither Gowers (1901) nor Liveing (1873) in their exhaustive books on epilepsy and on migraine mention the subject. In epilepsy the problem of personality and behavior is intertwined with that of mentality. In migraine this difficulty does not arise.

Mentality in Epilepsy.—We must first clarify the subject of mental impairment in epilepsy. Emphatically, poor mentality is not necessarily a feature of epilepsy. Of 1,640 clinic and private patients who had "essential" epilepsy, 67% were classed as mentally normal, 23% as slightly subnormal, 9% as definitely deteriorated and 1% as markedly deteriorated (Lennox, 1941). Thus only one patient in ten would be immediately recognized as subnormal. Of course the proportion is necessarily higher in institutional patients, for the patient's defective mentality is a prime reason for taking the patient from the home. Of patients entering New York's Craig Colony only 11% are mentally normal.

Defective mentality when it occurs may be blamed on one (or more) of five causes:

CONSTITUTION—HEREDITARY.—Congenital physical defects are more common among deteriorated than among mentally normal epileptics (Paskind and Brown, 1936). Patients who are mentally defective at birth have twice as many relatives with epilepsy, and four times as many relatives with psychosis as epileptic patients who are normal at birth (Lennox, 1941).

INJURY TO THE BRAIN BEFORE THE ONSET OF EPILEPSY.—Such an injury may be a principal cause of both seizures and mental defect. Of patients who had a preexisting brain injury 54% were mentally normal, against 67% who had no brain injury.

DEFECTIVE MENTALITY A RESULT OF SEIZURES.—Factors which play a role are the duration of the disease, the type of seizures and their number, and the type and frequency of brain dysrhythmias. The passage of time is especially influential in the first fifteen years of the disorder. In the group studied by Lennox (1941) 24% were found to be abnormal during the first years of the disorder and 54% abnormal if the disease had persisted more than 25 years. There is progressive decrease in mentality with the total number of attacks, especially if these are psychomotor or grand mal, or a combination of these. Cases with pure petit mal may go unscathed. Also the three-a-second wave and spike dysrhythmia of petit mal epilepsy when it occurs without clinical manifestations seems innocuous. Chronic epileptics who are seriously deteriorated very often show abnormally slow waves on the electroencephalogram. Presumably this slowness accompanies the downward progress of the disease. Feebleminded persons without a history of seizures do not have this slowness. Whether this type of dysrhythmia is prognostically significant in incipient epilepsy has not been determined.

Again, intermittent mental sluggishness may be but the expression of continuous stretches of dysrhythmia. A condition of petit mal status may produce a foggy mental state which clears when the brain waves become composed (Putnam and Merritt, 1941).

THE EFFECT OF DRUG THERAPY.—The sedative drugs, bromides, and phenobarbital, if given in large enough quantities may either induce a state of mental sluggishness or in certain patients may induce psychotic states.

PSYCHOLOGICAL STATES SIMULATING DETERIORATION.—Apparent mental sluggishness may be only profound discouragement and self-centered interest brought on by psychological and social mistreatment.

More than one of these factors may be at work in a given individual. The last two are susceptible to direct treatment and improvement.

More certain light is shed on this question by mental testing of groups of patients, especially if continued over a period of years. This has been done for small groups of clinic patients by Wallin (1923), Fox (1924), Branham (1925), Patterson and Fonner (1928), Dawson and Conn (1929), Abadie (1932), Doolittle (1932), Wooster-Drought (1934), Bridge (1934), Fetterman and Barnes (1934), Sullivan and Gahagan (1935), Collins, Atwell, and Moore (1938), Kugelmass, Poull, and Rudnick (1938), Somerfeld-Ziskind and Ziskind (1940), and Collins (1941). Unfortunately the results are distorted by the fact that not all the original patients are followed throughout the period. Some of these authors also studied the defects of mentality which were most consistently displayed by their patients. Memory is the principal loser.

Personality Disorders in Epilepsy.—Gowers (1901) may have failed to mention personality changes in epilepsy because he dealt with clinic and private patients. Spratling (1904), superintendent of Craig

Colony, spoke of mental peculiarities, emotional instability, impulsiveness, moral anergia, and incapacity for productive occupation involving initiative and consecutive activity. In about three-fourths of patients an approaching convulsion was heralded by querulousness, fault finding, and the dominance of trifles.

In this country L. Pierce Clark was the most prolific advocate of the epileptic personality, his articles appearing between 1914 and 1933. His principal contact was with patients in Craig Colony at Sonyea, New York, where for years he was a member of the staff.

Clark states that Kraepelin, Turner, Bianchi, and Vogt had recognized a peculiar personality in epileptics. The characteristics which Clark principally emphasizes are four: eccentricity, supersensitiveness, emotional poverty, and rigidity. Contrary to general opinion, these characteristics, says Clark, are not the result of continued seizures, but are encountered in the history obtained of the patients before seizures began. They become accentuated, however, during the progress of the disease. He estimates that 60% to 70% of all persons subject to seizures have the described personality. These patients he defines as essential, and others as symptomatic epileptics. He admits that some normal persons may have the same characteristics in an attenuated form. Clark (1918a) secured information about 50 private patients by means of a blank containing 121 questions, an amended Hoch-Amsden guide to personality. He found that only two or three had been normal as babies. The majority had evidence of frequent irritability, excessive crying, peevishness, excitability, lability of mood, short-lived interest, tantrums, hypersensitivity, and insistence on having their own way. During the period of school age, three-fifths of the patients were average in their studies, although there were fluctuations in mood and interest, and two-fifths had difficulty in keeping pace. They were inattentive, restless, irritable, and unable to follow school routine. Their voices were harsh and unmelodic, without the normal up and down rhythm. Children were inclined to be turbulent, argumentative, quarrelsome, had no sense of inferiority, and little imagination. Movements were slow, clumsy, and oftentimes grossly incoordinate. Children resented correction, were stubborn and selfish. Many showed abnormal personal attachment to the mother, were conceited, egotistical, their clothes and personal possessions must be just so. Although lenient with themselves, they were punctilious in their demands on others, looked down on servants, and demanded a keen sense of honor in others. Inclined to excuse their own faults, they had no forgiveness for the failings of others. Unlike the psychoneurotic, who is preoccupied with his own body, the epileptic is more solicitous about his ego.

In social relationships, said Clark, the person predisposed to epilepsy has no intimate friends and makes no effort to be popular. He is solitary, except with persons either older or younger than himself. Unlike the feebleminded, he is not gregarious. He has little tact, and gets his own way by persistence or by a fixed attitude of noncooperation. Because he resents correction, the family is inclined to adopt a let-alone attitude toward him. He demands precision and order, is committed to routine, is easily hurt, carries grudges, is resentful, jealous, envious, and resents discipline and exact rules laid down for his conduct. A first attack is sometimes precipitated because of the stress caused by rigid demands made upon him. He is sensitive because he has no rich emotional feelings to impart. In this respect also he is unlike the psychoneurotic, who is daydreaming of his own aggrandizement. He has periods of depression, is stoical in bereavement, in religion superficial, pietistic, perfunctory. Dr. Clark gives examples of these religious characteristics in the founders of Shakerism, of Mormonism, and of Mohammedanism. In the adult, emotional life is not developed beyond that of puberty. Sexual life is perfunctory. An epileptic has no deep love motive. He is ill at ease with the opposite sex and has no desire for children. He is not ordinarily antisocial or criminal, nor is he cruel to animals. He has no tenacity of purpose, although his verbal ambitions are boundless. Work is poorly performed, without precision. To keep him at work requires constant change of occupation, emotional enthusiasm, and praise.

Every case of essential epilepsy, says Clark, shows some of these traits to a marked degree. This observation rather begs the question because Clark diagnosed essential epilepsy only if specific personality traits were present.

As for the observations of other authors, Notkin (1928) observed the epileptic "make-up" in 17% of 150 nondeteriorated clinic patients, these being cases whose epilepsy began before the age of twelve. He believed the "make-up" was the result of seizures and not their cause. The personality was pure schizoid in 8% of cases, and became schizoid in the course of the disease in another 8%. Personality disorders were variable rather than specific. Dawson and Conn (1929) blamed personality disorders on the lowered mental state of their patients, which causes a disintegration of control over the lower, more instinctive reactions. Eyrich (1932) stressed three elements: first, retarded mental processes (apperception, thought, activity, reaction time, a "general vacuity"); second, explosive excitability; and third, motor restlessness without a goal. Doolittle (1932) noted the progressive nature of the disorder in institutional patients. Sullivan and Gahagan (1935) made mental tests and listed personality or conduct disorders in 103 children referred to a psychological clinic. Fourteen were feebleminded. Intelligence quotients ranged from 11 to 141. The median was 92, against 105 for a large group of school children and 103 for a small group of allergic patients. Among the epileptics, approximately one-half had serious personality difficulties or conduct disorders. The mean IQ of problem cases was 75 and of nonproblem cases 88. Early onset of seizures was associated both with a lowered IQ and an increased proportion with personality disorders. Like delinquency in nonepileptic children, such disturbances were greater when the home environment was poor. The disorders of these children were divided almost equally between hyperkinetic behavior (overactivity, fidgety, "constantly into things," ill at ease), emotional disturbances (temper tantrums, cruelty to children and animals, fighting, destructive, high strung, mischievous, teasing, truancy, negativistic, rebellious, moody, stubborn, self-centered), and conduct disorders (bad sex habits, lying, stealing, disobedient, naughty).

Diethelm (1934) found personality features ordinarily associated with epilepsy among relatives of epileptic patients indicating that such features are a constitutional characteristic, but believes that the issue is not the presence of disorders but their evaluation in the whole personality setting. In a study of 54 patients with "essential" epilepsy, Fleck (1934) listed the following characteristics: moroseness, indifference, circumstantial and stereotyped manner of speaking, and limited content of speech, egocentricity, irascibility, hypersociability, and religious devotion. He attributes many of these symptoms to brain injury, since they appear also in nonepileptic persons with brain pathology. In their study of the cortical electrical records of behavior problem children, Strauss, Rahm, and Barrera (1940) used three categories: (1) assaultive, destructive, disobedient, with constant irritability and hostility to their environment; (2) runaway type with fugue-like states; (3) episodic temper outbursts with relatively normal type of behavior between outbursts.

Significance and Causes.—These various contributors to the subject have given a long list of attributes, all of them undesirable from the point of view of society and of the patient himself. In justice, it should be pointed out that many epileptics have very agreeable personalities and a considerable number occupy permanent positions of fame. In my experience, the majority of persons subject to seizures who are encountered in office and clinic do not exhibit the undesirable traits which have been named. Obviously much depends on the bias of the reporter. No "control" observations have been conducted with the aim of ascertaining whether, for example, egocentricity, emotional poverty, or rigidity is more common in a group of epileptics than in a group of artists, of psychologists, or of doctors. Granted that the described traits are unusually common in epileptics the question arises as to their significance. A number of possibilities exist.

1. The traits may be nonspecific. Certainly egocentricity, irritability, moroseness, and so forth occur in the victims of many other chronic and disabling diseases, such as heart disease, arthritis, and alcoholism.

2. The personality traits may be constitutional and the direct cause of seizures. This is the thesis of Clark, Stekel, and others and deserves examination. If the traits are constitutional and hereditary, then they will be found in many of the nonepileptic relatives of the patient. Clark declares this is true. Though he depicts only one family tree (1916), he states that Kraepelin found the epileptic traits in 87% of the families of epileptics (Clark, 1931). If peculiar traits are diagnostic of epilepsy, or if they are regularly present before seizures appear, or are constantly present in the family trees of epileptics, then they might be considered

a constitutional characteristic of essential epilepsy similar to distorted anthropomorphic measurements.

Clark believed that the seizures of epilepsy are psychological in origin. The adult epileptic is only prolonging the fantasies of youth. His attacks represent efforts to regain the intra-uterine state, or they represent reaction to unconscious repressed desires. The epileptic's emotional life is defective because of mental infantilism. The essential nucleus of this defect is a too intense and prolonged fixation of the libido. His egocentric tendencies are due to the self-centered strength of his sexual energies. The severity of the fit is in direct proportion to the outlet demands of the unconscious libido. Clark and Cushing (1931) say the epileptic attack is a return to the Nirvana of the womb. In the epileptic, (1) the death instinct may be stronger, the exaggerated pull of it resulting in the attack; (2) he may need more libido to be fused with the death instinct in order to bring about the destructive (sadistic) force of mastery which would take the person further into reality; (3) in the fusion between libido and death instinct, the proportion of self-destructive forces is stronger; the desire then to be humbled may be greater (masochism) and may show in the annihilation of the ego, represented by the attack.

Because the epileptic fit is accompanied by unconsciousness, MacRobert (1916) says the patient's nonconscious mentality is saying, "I wish I had never been born, and could return to a state of prenatal unconsciousness." He further believed that dreams could precipitate seizures. Göttke (1934) in a 45-page article on the subject of dreams found little evidence of this. Seizures could not be induced by hypnotic suggestion. Unlike narcolepsy, the periods of the seizures and the subsequent sleep are dreamless. Deteriorated patients apparently dream little; Jelliffe (1935) agrees that the epileptic personality is a manifestation of sadistic and aggressive drives, while the fit itself represents the triumph of the death instinct, destroying itself and the future. Both the paroxysms of whooping cough and the epileptic fit are symbolic reactions to an agency which has threatened the life instinct. Cronin (1933) psychoanalyzed a pair of identical twins, one of whom had a convulsion as a result of an emotional impasse. Symbolically he had been castrated and had sadistically attacked his castrators but failed. Stekel, quoted by Karpman (1934), says the epileptic is distrustful, egotistic, sly, a strong hater, and liable to transfer this hatred to the analyst. The hate is carried into action in the uninhibited, and to a convulsion in the inhibited.

3. A peculiar personality and a tendency to seizures may be hereditary traits which are linked together but not causally connected. An undue proportion of parents and siblings of the patient should show similar personality traits, but like the bizarre anthropomorphic measurements described by Paskind and Brown (1939) the traits are concomitants and not causes of seizures. If seizures and personality are linked genetically, peculiar personalities should be more prominent among the relatives of epileptic patients who belong to those groups in which heredity is more pronounced, the "essential" patients, the females, those whose seizures

began early in life, and those who are mentally deteriorated. If personality and the predisposition to seizures are linked genetically, and if, as I believe, a predisposition to seizures is accompanied by cerebral dysrhythmia, then those relatives of patients who have cortical dysrhythmia should also have a peculiar personality. This possibility is suggested also by the fact that a large proportion of children with behavior disorders exhibit cortical dysrhythmia. However, our experience with 150 relatives of epileptics who have abnormal brain waves indicates that dysrhythmia is not usually accompanied by an epileptic personality.

An excellent means of separating hereditary from other influences is the study of identical twins, only one of whom has epilepsy. Freeman (1935) reported such a case. I have seen seven such pairs. The nonepileptic twin always had dysrhythmia, but peculiarities of personality, if present, were more pronounced in the affected twin, an indication that factors other than heredity were mainly responsible.

4. Personality disorders in the epileptic may be simply a special kind of seizure. When bad behavior and grand or petit mal seizures occur in the same patient, the possibility is patent. Yet even without the presence of classical seizures, the abnormal behavior may be suspicious. Maudsley (1870) expressed the matter clearly: "Children of three or four are sometimes seized with attacks of violent shrieking, desperate stubbornness or furious rage, when they bite, kick and do all the destruction they can; these seizures, which are a sort of vicarious epilepsy, come on periodically, and either may pass in the course of a few months into regular epilepsy, or may alternate with it." This is as true for adults as for children. Maudsley quotes Morel in saying that epileptic neuroses may exist in an undeveloped or masked form showing itself not by convulsions, but by periodic attacks of mania or by manifestations of moral perversion deemed wilful viciousness. But, says Morel, no moral influence can touch them for they depend on a morbid physical condition which can only have a physical cure. They get their explanation afterwards when epilepsy occurs. Maudsley speaks of a "convulsive idea" which is strictly comparable with an epileptic convulsion. A murderer butchered a child, wrote in his diary "Killed a little girl; it was fine and hot," and when questioned could give no reason for his crime. Says Maudsley, "Whenever a murder has been committed suddenly, without premeditation, without malice, without motive, openly, and in a way quite different from the way in which murders are commonly done, we ought to look carefully for evidence of previous epilepsy, and other symptoms allied to epilepsy." The Flemish painter Van Gogh had similar periods, except that the violence was inflicted upon himself. He cut off one of his ears, and finally shot himself in the abdomen.

Other episodic incidents may also be classed as epileptic. Brickner and Rosner (1939) described a patient with five- or six-second periods of alternate depression and elation without loss of consciousness. Davidoff's (1939) patient, after a head injury, had paroxysmal, uncontrollable ideas and cerebral dysrhythmia. In our laboratory we have found hereditary cerebral dysrhythmia in a number of patients whose psychomotor seizures were only peculiar or abnormal behavior. As Lindsley points out in another section, a considerable proportion of behavior problem children have cortical dysrhythmia.

An investigation of obvious importance, social as well as scientific, will be the electroencephalographic examination of a sample of our prison population, men and women who are incarcerated because of deeds of violence. If a considerable proportion of these have cortical dysrhythmia, this fact would give backing to Maudsley's contention that their treatment should be physical rather than moral. The legal aspects of epileptic amnesia are discussed elsewhere (Lennox, 1943).

A convulsion, a nasty word, and/or a habit of perseveration may each be an expression of cortical dysrhythmia. This possibility is a demonstrable fact in the case of certain patients and certain reactions. A psychomotor seizure may be an acute period of bad behavior accompanied by a prolonged sequence of slow high voltage cortical waves. Again on a day when a patient is negativistic or surly, his brain wave record will be more abnormal than on a day when he is sweet-tempered. In such instances the abnormal personality is not the result nor the accompaniment of epilepsy, nor an epileptic equivalent: it *is* epilepsy. The case for the significance of coincidentally fluctuating abnormality in brain waves and behavior seems proven. High barometer, fine weather; low barometer, stormy weather.

Not so evident is the case of the person who has an abnormal electrical record and traits of personality which are constantly present, such as a limited range of ideas and of interests. Abnormal records are not confined to persons who have clinical symptoms. Perhaps 15% of "normal" persons have dysrhythmia. To demonstrate a relationship of brain rhythms to behavior, determination should be made of the incidence of dysrhythmia in groups of persons who show, and do not show, disorders of personality. We have the material for such a study in the electrical records of the nonepileptic relatives of epileptic patients. A little more than one-half of these relatives have cortical dysrhythmia. If one of two parents has abnormality of rhythm, he is more likely to be the one who is "flighty," excessively apprehensive, uncooperative, or inflexible. However, some of the most normal of relatives have the worst-looking tracings. In fact it is entirely possible that unusual waves, too glibly called abnormal, may be associated with unusual brilliance or with supernormal personality. As Lombroso pointed out, genius and eccentricity, epilepsy and high achievement may reside in the same individual. Gross dysrhythmia is consistent with normal personality. Pursuit of the subject may require a more explicit technique for studying both personality and brain waves. Gallagher and Gibbs (1942) have placed the results of electrically analyzed records of brain waves against the evaluation of the personality and performance of adolescent boy students. Boys with poor personality tend to have slow waves, and those with good personality fast waves. This promising field is ripe for the harvest.

5. Brain pathology may be responsible for both epilepsy and bad behavior, or repeated seizures may cause brain damage and this in turn cause changes in character. The behavior would then be secondary or even tertiary. Personality changes after brain trauma and encephalitis are dealt with in the chapter by Cobb. Study of the effect on personality of the severe convulsions of "shock therapy" for schizophrenia should help in the evaluation of this factor. Study of identical twins only one of whom has brain damage and epilepsy has been mentioned.

6. Personality changes may result from the altered social environment in which the epileptic finds himself. This environment may be oversoft and yielding, making for bad behavior and selfishness, or more often, openly cruel and hostile. Persons with chronic incapacitating diseases of all sorts, cardiac or joint cripples, the blind and hard of hearing, tend to become suspicious, querulous, and self-centered. Even a normal person if shut out of schools and employment and shunned by companions would in time develop unpleasant traits. In order to evaluate the influence of both physical and psychological injury, more information is needed about the degree of abnormality present in the period before seizures began in comparison with afterwards. Also the influence of the type of seizure is important. In my experience, patients who have only petit mal, a seizure which carries little stigma and does no brain injury, display relatively little evidence of the epileptic personality.

7. Overdosage with sedative drugs may cause temporary periods of surliness or even psychosis. In fact many of the features of the "epileptic personality" could be reproduced by feeding excessive amounts of bromide or phenobarbital over prolonged periods. This possibility has received little attention in the studies of Clark and others which have been mentioned. The decreased emphasis on the epileptic personality in recent years may be due to the fading popularity of bromides. Only a rare neurologist like Pollock (1938) sticks to this 85-year-old drug.

8. The personality disorders may not be a result of the epilepsy nor yet a distinct quality or characteristic of patients, but an expression of mental retardation. In Sullivan's series, problem children constituted 36% of those with an IQ above 70 and 74% of those with an IQ below 70. Defects of mentality and of personality often overlap.

In a given patient, more than one of these eight causes might be operative, or some might be responsible in patient A and others in patient B. Also, of the various traits mentioned, some might be due to one cause and some to another cause. For example, rigidity might be due to heredity, perseveration to impaired mentality, negativism to subclinical dysrhythmia, moroseness to drug therapy, and egocentricity to social ostracism.

The Rorschach Test.—As mentioned on a previous page, a difficulty in studying personality in epileptics has been the lack of objective measurements of traits which do not express themselves in conduct. One possible method is the ink-blot test devised by Rorschach. The purpose and application of this test is described by White (Chapter 6). A number of authors have described a peculiar type of response to the test given by epileptics. The largest number of cases is found in the monograph by Stauder (1939). He agrees with Rorschach that epileptics give a typical response. The characteristics of epileptics which the test reveals in- directly are disturbances of perception, of judgment and of memory; thought which shows poverty of content, retardation, stickiness, circum- stantiability, pedantry, and good-natured dullness; and action which may be explosive or denote irritability. The outstanding symptom of epilepsy is perseveration.

These abnormalities of personality, says Stauder, are inherent in epilepsy and are not the result of seizures, for they are as prominent in patients with few as with many attacks. The relatives of epileptics may show the characteristic Rorschach syndrome. The progressive person- ality change of epilepsy is an indispensable symptom of hereditary epilepsy. Genuine epileptics without signs of epileptic personality change do not exist. Stauder therefore defines epilepsy as a tendency both to seizures and to specific personality changes. Three conditions accentuate the epileptic personality: an athletic constitution (found in 16% of 600 epileptics), the use of phenobarbital, and a certain type of seizure. Any condition which disturbs normal consciousness is a determining factor in the production of the Rorschach syndrome and the epileptic personality. The Rorschach epileptic syndrome is present in normal persons who had received large doses of phenobarbital. Epileptics whose Rorschach test was normal would present the epileptic syndrome if given pheno- barbital or if in a cloudy mental state following a seizure. Stauder be- lieves that phenobarbital accentuates the abnormal personality and psy- chopathology of patients. Seizures which involve prolonged clouding of consciousness are the hardest on personality. Petit mal seizures do less harm.

Mental deterioration, says Stauder, is distinct from these personality disorders, and is not distinguishable from the dementia of other diseases. Unlike personality disorders, the degree of dementia is related to the number of seizures. Severe dementia blurs the typical epileptic Rorschach syndrome.

Stauder reserves the term "genuine epilepsy" for patients with an in- herited tendency to seizures and personality disorder. Of traumatic or symptomatic epileptics, about four-fifths have some elements of the Rorschach syndrome and are called "provoked" epileptics. About one- fifth have abnormal Rorschach response and are termed "exogenous" epileptics. Then there is a small group, 31 out of the hundreds tested, who have few seizures and symptoms and would be called genuine except that they are normal mentally and by Rorschach test. These, called func- tional epileptics, have no relationship to genuine hereditary epilepsy. Then there are the persons (relatives of patients) without seizures but giving the Rorschach response, the epileptoids.

Though written in cumbersome, repetitious German manner this monograph is a definite contribution to the psychological study of epilepsy, and is a challenge to workers in this field. The issue is clear-cut and can be easily decided. If the personality of the patient which shows itself in a specific type of response is synonymous with hereditary epilepsy, and if, as I believe, the hereditary predisposition to epilepsy can be demonstrated by the electroencephalograph, those relatives of epileptics who have abnormal brain waves should give the Rorschach response associated with epilepsy and those with normal brain waves should not. Harrower-Erickson (1941) finds no consistent Rorschach response in patients of normal intelligence, and believes that brain injury or adverse environment is chiefly to blame for whatever personality difficulties are present. The fact that normal individuals give a typical Rorschach response when under the dulling influence of sedative drugs is against the specificity of the response. Also against the value of the Rorschach test in judgment of hereditary traits are the observations of Troup (1938). From a study of ten identical twins she concluded that cultural influences are a greater influence in Rorschach responses than hereditary influences.

Summary.—The divergent factors involved and views expressed make it difficult to summarize the subject of personality in epilepsy. It would seem that the subject of a specific epileptic personality has been overemphasized, because most of the contributors to the subject have dealt with institutional patients. In these patients both mental deterioration and personality disorders predominate and are probably associated. Thinking of the 90% of patients who are outside of institutions, the following statements may be made:

1. The majority of such patients show no gross evidence of a peculiar personality or of unusual behavior, at least no more than samples of the general population.

2. Of the minority group who show peculiarities, these traits for the most part are a result of the seizure state, either of the associated pathology of the brain, the mental deterioration, the action of sedative drugs, or the effect of ostracism.

3. A very small minority of patients displayed peculiar personality traits before seizures began. These cases may possibly be looked on as hereditary and linked with the tendency to seizures or with the hereditary cerebral dysrhythmia. This possibility will become positive if it can be demonstrated that the epileptic personality is associated with hereditary dysrhythmia, and is present in those nonepileptic relatives who have abnormal brain waves.

4. In many cases peculiar traits are expressions of a cortical dysrhythmia. The bad behavior is a seizure.

5. If future research demonstrates that a significant number of persons who have disturbance of personality also have distortion of brain

waves, then epilepsy, which is a cerebral dysrhythmia, would have an intimate relationship to the whole problem of personality and behavior disorders.

Personality in Migraine.—Although migraine has been recognized by medical writers almost as long as epilepsy, little has been said about a peculiar personality. Liveing (1873) and other authors emphasize the importance of emotion in the precipitation of attacks, but apparently the first claims that persons subject to migraine seizures possessed a peculiar personality make-up was advanced by Touraine and Draper (1934). A more detailed analysis of 64 cases has been made also by Wolff (1937, 1940). These workers are in substantial agreement as to the outlines of the characteristics noted, although Touraine and Draper give them a greater significance from the psychoanalytical point of view.

Wolff says that the majority of migraine patients as children were delicate, or treated as such, shy, obedient, sober, pliant, and well-mannered. School work was done conscientiously. They might be both docile and stubborn. Some were obstinate, argumentative, and disobedient, and even sullen. Temper tantrums were met with occasionally. Attachment to the mother was often noted.

Among adults, nine-tenths were unusually ambitious and preoccupied with achievement; they attempted to dominate their environment. Almost all were conscientious, perfectionist, persistent and exacting, meticulous, fastidious, and at the same time efficient. They dressed neatly; they were hard working, endowed with energy and push, and inclined to accumulate responsibilities. They allocated responsibility poorly; they must see a thing through personally, which meant intense application and long hours. Wolff ascribed headaches which occurred during vacations to loss of satisfaction of achievement. As a rule they loved order and a system of classification. Punctuality brought satisfaction, but occasionally patients were afflicted with procrastination and had difficulty in making a judgment. Inflexibility was another prominent characteristic. Although they were themselves creators of plans and systems, they found difficulty in adapting themselves to systems imposed on them by others. They found it difficult to forgive or accept the foibles of others.

As to their attitude toward seizures, they were inclined to disregard common sense limits and rules when free of headache, but during the seizure, they tyrannized their family with their distress and needs. They disregarded the body so long as it functioned properly, but resented bodily interference with the attainment of their ends. Social relations were usually cautious and circumscribed, aloof and politic. Many were thrown into headaches by the anticipation of social intercourse. Sexual dissatisfaction, usually in the direction of distaste, existed in more than four-fifths of the women.

It will be seen that these characteristics are qualitatively different and socially much more acceptable than the personality characteristics which have been claimed for the epileptic. The migrainous person has many of

the characteristics which make for worldly success. As for the significance of these characteristics, Wolff states the personality features mentioned are in no sense pathognomonic of migraine, nor are they associated
with migraine alone. These personality traits in certain life situations
are prone to precipitate attacks in persons predisposed to migraine.

The personality make-up emphasized by Wolff represents a certain
type of soil in which the seeds of migraine readily take root. Apparently
this soil is favorable also to the growth of disorders such as gastric
ulcers, hypertension, and asthma, in persons predisposed to them. The
characteristics which have been named might, when exaggerated, be
classified separately as psychoneuroses. Whether migraine therefore
should be called a psychoneurosis or a disorder which is symbiotic with
psychoneurosis is a fine distinction.

The relationship of personality to migraine is not complicated by some
of the factors suggested for epilepsy—for brain pathology, social ostracism, continuous use of sedative drugs, and mental deterioration do not
complicate the problem of migraine. The constitutional aspect of personality is certainly important but has been too little studied. I have
seen four identical twins in which both twins had migraine and both
had similar personalities. A survey needs to be made of the siblings of
migrainous individuals to determine the degree of their infection with
the traits which have been named. Because migraine headaches are not
associated with striking alterations of the electroencephalogram this technique is not available for comparative studies. Occasionally a person
subject to migraine will experience sharp changes of mood, behavior,
or of personality which seem to substitute for a headache seizure. Some
of these occupy a no-man's-land between psychomotor epilepsy and
migraine.

In the realm of treatment, Wolff proves that much can be attained by
correction of emotional disturbances which lead to headache seizures.
Over 10% of his 64 patients failed to secure any improvement; 28% had
no attacks or only rare ones; an additional 36% were much improved.
Unless the patient has adopted a suitable new pattern of life, headaches
will recur with new provocation. Both the frequency and intensity of the
attacks can be reduced if patients learn to understand themselves better
and exercise a more intelligent management of themselves. Modification
of the inherited personality make-up is not easy, but with intelligence and
cooperation even inherited characteristics can be modified.

BIBLIOGRAPHY

ABADIE, J. 1932. L'Epilepsie psychique. *Rev. neurol.*
BERGER, H. 1929. Ueber das Elektrenkephalogramm des Menschen. *Arch. Psychiat. Nervenkr., 87,* 527–570.
BRANHAM, V. C. 1925. Epileptic reactions in children. *Amer. J. Psychiat., 42,*
423–479.
BRICKNER, R. M., & ROSNER, A. 1939. A brief manic-depressive cycle as an epileptic process. *J. nerv. ment. Dis., 89,* 698–705.
BRIDGE, E. M. 1934. Mental state of the epileptic patient. *Arch. Neurol. Psychiat., Chicago, 32,* 723–736.

CLARK, L. P. 1913. A clinical contribution to the irregular and unusual forms of status epilepticus. *Amer. J. Insan., 70,* 336–410.

—— 1914a. A personality study of the epileptic constitution. *Amer. J. med. Sci., 148,* 729–738.

—— 1914b. A clinical contribution to the diagnosis of epilepsy. *J. Amer. med. Assn., 63,* 1652–1656.

—— 1915. The nature and pathogenesis of epilepsy. *N. Y. med. J.,* February 27, March 6, 13, 20, and 27.

—— 1917a. Clinical studies in epilepsy. Utica, N. Y.: State Hospitals Press.

—— 1917b. The diagnostic importance of recognizing the absence of the epileptic make-up in states simulating idiopathic epilepsy. *Boston med. surg. J., 177,* 915–916.

—— 1918a. The true epileptic. *N. Y. med. J.,* May 4.

—— 1918b. Treatment of the epileptic, based on a study of the fundamental make-up. *J. Amer. med. Assn., 70,* 357–362.

—— 1918c. A character study of the hemiplegic epileptic. *Amer. J. med. Sci., 155,* 796–802.

—— 1931. The psychobiologic concept of essential epilepsy. *Res. Publ. Assn. Res. nerv. ment. Dis., 7,* 65–79.

—— 1933. What is the psychology of organic epilepsy? *Psychoanal. Rev., 20,* 79–85.

CLARK, L. P., & CUSHING, K. 1931. Study in epilepsy. *Med. J. Rec., 133,* 27–31.

COLLINS, A. L. 1941. Psychometric records of institutionalized epileptics. *J. Psychol., 11,* 359–370.

COLLINS, A. L., ATWELL, C. R., & MOORE, M. 1938. Stanford-Binet response patterns in epileptics. *Amer. J. Orthopsychiat., 8,* 51–63.

CRONIN, H. J. 1933. An analysis of the neuroses of identical twins. *Psychoanal. Rev., 20,* 375–387.

DAVIDOFF, L. M. 1939. Psychic seizures as focal manifestations in post-traumatic brain disease. *Yale J. Biol. Med., 11,* 557–559.

DAVIS, H., & DAVIS, P. A. 1936. Action potentials of the brain in normal persons and in normal states of cerebral activity. *Arch. Neurol. Psychiat., Chicago, 36,* 1214–1224.

DAVIS, P. A., & DAVIS, H. 1939. The electroencephalograms of psychotic patients. *Amer. J. Psychiat., 95,* 1007–1025.

DAWSON, S., & CONN, J. C. M. 1929. The intelligence of epileptic children. *Arch. Dis. Childh., 4,* 142–151.

DIETHELM, O. 1934. Epileptic convulsions and the personality setting. *Arch. Neurol. Psychiat., 31,* 755–767.

DOOLITTLE, G. J. 1932. The epileptic personality. *Psychiat. Quart., 6,* 89–96.

DUSSER DE BARENNE, J. G., GREGORIUS, J., McCULLOCH, W. S., & NIMS, L. F. 1937. Functional activity and pH of the cerebral cortex. *J. cell. comp. Physiol., 10,* 277–289.

DUSSER DE BARENNE, J. G., & McCULLOCH, W. S. 1937. Local stimulatory inactivation within the cerebral cortex, the factor for extinction. *Amer. J. Physiol., 118,* 510–524.

—— 1938. Functional organization in the sensory cortex of the monkey. *J. Neurophysiol., 1,* 69–85.

EYRICH, M. 1932. Ueber Charakter und Charakteränderung bei kindlichen und Jugendlichen Epileptikern. *Z. ges. Neurol. Psychiat., 141,* 640–645.

FETTERMAN, J., & BARNES, M. P. 1934. Serial studies of patients with epilepsy. *Arch. Neurol. Psychiat., Chicago, 32,* 798–807.

FLECK, U. 1934. Ueber das Epileptoid und den epileptischen Charakter. *Arch. Psychiat. Nervenkr., 102,* 383–429.

FOX, J. T. 1924. Response of epileptic children to mental and educational tests. *Brit. J. med. Psychol., 4,* 235–248.

FREEMAN, W. 1935. Symptomatic epilepsy in one of identical twins, study of epileptic character. *J. Neurol. Psychopath., 15,* 210–218.

FRITSCH, G., & HITZIG, E. 1870. Ueber die elektrische Erregbarkeit des Grosshirns. *Arch. Anat. Physiol., Lpz.,* pp. 300–332.

GALLAGHER, J. R., & GIBBS, F. A. 1942. Relation between electrical activity of cortex and personality of adolescent boys. *Psychosom. Med., 4,* 134–139.

GIBBS, F. A. 1939. Cortical frequency spectra of schizophrenic, epileptic and normal individuals. *Trans. Amer. neurol. Assn., 65,* 141–144.

GIBBS, F. A., DAVIS, H., & LENNOX, W. G. 1935. The electroencephalogram in epilepsy and in conditions of impaired consciousness. *Arch. Neurol. Psychiat., Chicago, 34,* 1133–1148.

GIBBS, F. A., & GIBBS, E. L. 1936. The convulsion threshold of various parts of the cat's brain. *Arch. Neurol. Psychiat., Chicago, 35,* 109–116.

—— 1941. Atlas of electroencephalography. Boston: F. A. Gibbs, Boston City Hospital.

GÖTTKE, L. 1934. Ueber das Traumleben bei Epileptikern. *Arch. Psychiat. Nervenkr., 101,* 137–163.

GOWERS, W. R. 1901. Epilepsy and other chronic convulsive diseases; their causes, symptoms and treatment. London: Churchill.

HARROWER-ERICKSON, M. R. 1941. Psychological studies of patients with epileptic seizures. In Penfield, W., & Erickson, T. C., *Epilepsy and cerebral localization.* Springfield, Ill.: Thomas. Pp. 546–574.

JELLIFFE, S. E. 1935. Dynamic concepts and the epileptic attack. *Amer. J. Psychiat., 92,* 565–574.

KARPMAN, B. 1934. The obsessive paraphilias (perversions). *Arch. Neurol. Psychiat., Chicago, 32,* 577–584.

KUGELMASS, N., POULL, L. E., & RUDNICK, J. 1938. Mental growth of epileptic children. *Amer. J. Dis. Child., 55,* 295–303.

LENNOX, W. G. 1941. Science and seizures. New York: Harper.

LENNOX, W. G. 1943. Amnesia, real and feigned. *Amer. J. Psychiat., 99,* 732–743.

LENNOX, W. G., & COBB, S. 1928. Epilepsy. *Medicine Monogr.,* Vol. 14.

LENNOX, W. G., GIBBS, E. L., & GIBBS, F. A. 1940. Inheritance of cerebral dysrhythmia and epilepsy. *Arch. Neurol. Psychiat., Chicago, 44,* 1155–1183.

LIVEING, E. 1873. On megrim, sick-headache and some allied disorders. London: Churchill.

MACROBERT, R. G. 1916. The role of the wish in the manifestations of the epileptic type of nervous constitution. *Med. Rec., N. Y.,* May 13.

MAUDSLEY, H. 1870. Body and mind. New York: Appleton-Century.

NOTKIN, J. 1928. Is there an epileptic personality make-up? *Arch. Neurol. Psychiat., Chicago, 20,* 799–803.

PASKIND, H. A., & BROWN, M. 1936. Constitutional differences between deteriorated and non-deteriorated patients with epilepsy: I. Stigmas of degeneracy. *Arch. Neurol. Psychiat., Chicago, 36,* 1037–1044.

—— 1939. Constitutional differences between deteriorated and non-deteriorated patients with epilepsy: II. Anthropometric measurements. *Amer. J. Psychiat., 95,* 901–921.

PATTERSON, H. A., & FONNER, D. 1928. Some observations on the intelligence quotient in epileptics. *Psychiat. Quart., 2,* 542–548.

PENFIELD, W., & BOLDREY, E. 1937. Somatic motor and sensory representation in the cerebral cortex of man as studied by electrical stimulation. *Brain, 60,* 389–443.

POLLOCK, L. J. 1938. Remissions of attacks in epilepsy with sodium bromide. *J. Amer. med. Assn., 110,* 632–634.

PUTNAM, T. J. 1943. Convulsive seizures. New York: Lippincott.

PUTNAM, T. J., & MERRITT, H. H. 1941. Dulness as an epileptic equivalent. *Arch. Neurol. Psychiat., Chicago, 45,* 797–813.

SOMERFELD-ZISKIND, E., & ZISKIND, E. 1940. Effects of phenobarbital on the mentality of epileptic patients. *Arch. Neurol. Psychiat., Chicago, 43,* 70–79.

SPRATLING, W. P. 1904. Epilepsy and its treatment. Philadelphia: Saunders.

STAUDER, K. H. 1939. Konstitution und Wesenänderung der Epileptiker. Leipzig: Georg Thieme.

STRAUSS, H., RAHM, W. E., JR., & BARRERA, S. E. 1940. Studies on group of children with psychiatric disorders; electroencephalographic studies. *Psychosom. Med., 2,* 34–42.

SULLIVAN, E. B., & GAHAGAN, L. 1935. On intelligence of epileptic children. *Genet. Psychol. Monogr., 17,* 309–376.

TOURAINE, G. A., & DRAPER, G. 1934. The migrainous patient. *J. nerv. ment. Dis., 80,* 1–23, 183–204.

TROUP, E. 1938. A comparative study by means of the Rorschach method of personality development in twenty pairs of identical twins. *Genet. Psychol. Monogr., 20,* 461–556.

WALLIN, J. E. W. 1923. The measurement of mental traits in normal and epileptic school children. *Miami Univ. Bull., 21,* 8.
WOLFF, H. G. 1937. Personality features and reactions of subjects with migraine.
Arch. Neurol. Psychiat., Chicago, 37, 895–921.
—— 1940. Migraine. In *Modern medical therapy in general practice.* Baltimore: Williams & Wilkins.
WOOSTER-DROUGHT, C. 1934. Hystero-epilepsy. *Brit. J. med. Psychol., 14,* 50–82.

PART VII

SOME INVESTIGATED CORRELATES OF BEHAVIOR DISORDER

Chapter 32

PSYCHOLOGICAL DEFICIT

By J. McV. Hunt, Ph.D., and C. N. Cofer, Ph.D.

SOME LOSS OF EFFICIENCY is one of the commonest manifestations of disorder or cerebral injury in the human being. This fact is implied in the allusion to the psychotic as one who has "lost his mind," still common in popular speech. It is also recognized by such descriptive terms of psychiatry as *dementia* and *deterioration,* and by the interpretative concept of *regression.* Loss of efficiency also occurs in the aged. With the recognized prevalence of this loss, it is not surprising that a large proportion of the experimental effort devoted to these conditions has been concerned with various aspects of the efficiency of affected individuals. The results of this effort have significant implications for both the nature of these conditions and for the nature of intelligent behavior. To summarize these results and to show these implications are the tasks of this chapter.

We have chosen the term *deficit* to designate this loss of efficiency because it is a neutral term. *Dementia, deterioration,* and *regression,* although more prevalent, have become associated with various beliefs about the nature of the loss. By *dementia* Kraepelin (1919) meant a permanent, irreversible loss of intellectual capacity. By *deterioration* he meant a progressive change in the direction of less and less efficiency. For the majority of workers in this field, these definitions prevail today. *Regression* has been used in several theoretical systems with different implications in each. Since we propose to test these various conceptions with the results of investigation, we prefer a neutral term. *Deficit* has not been associated with any such implications. As used here, it is an operational concept. When any person performs in some situation at a level of efficiency below that expected from comparison with typical individuals or from some indicator in his own present or past behavior, that person manifests a deficit.

Unfortunately for the expositor, the studies in this field are not held together with any single purpose or theory. The methods vary tremendously. Rarely has any investigator carried out a consistent program, or even used a single technique, on the whole gamut of clinical conditions. These facts make it impossible to generalize with certainty. The implications we shall derive from these studies must be regarded as tentative. We hope, nevertheless, that this chapter will clarify the picture to some extent, that it will serve as an object-lesson concerning the pitfalls of the field, and that it will stimulate research in certain promising directions.

We have organized the studies of deficit around the methods employed and the aspects of function concerned, and we have attempted to bring the results to bear upon the main problems in the field. We shall consider first those studies using the standard tests of intelligence; secondly, the studies of specific aspects of behavior, and thirdly, we shall draw certain conclusions concerning the nature of the deficit in the various sorts of conditions and the nature of intelligence.[1]

Results from Standard Tests of Intelligence and of Deficit [2]

Measuring Deficit.—To measure the effects of any condition on efficiency, whether it be disorder, cerebral injury, or age, should require on logical grounds that an individual's efficiency be measured before and after the onset of the condition. In practice this nice logical requirement has not been feasible. Only very recently has any considerable proportion of the population been given the standard tests of intelligence, and no investigator, to our knowledge, has been able to obtain predisorder or preinjury test results from the patients in his sample. For this reason substitute controls have been devised.

In one of the substitutes, the investigator compares the central tendency (mean or median) of scores or mental ages and the measure of variability (standard deviation or interquartile range or range) derived from his sample of patients with similar statistical measures derived from a sample of "normal" individuals. A second of these substitutes consists of using the vocabulary of the damaged individual as an index of his original efficiency. His present efficiency on some other sort of test is then compared with his vocabulary score to determine the extent of his particular deficit (Babcock, 1930). A third substitute, devised by Rylander (1939) to measure the deficit caused by surgical injuries to the frontal lobes, consists of matching each patient with a control of the same age, same educational record, and same cultural level and occupation.[3]

---

[1] Limits of space make it impossible to include everything. Deficit in the epilepsies is omitted because Lennox covers the material in Chapter 31. Results from the feebleminded appear only incidentally for purposes of comparison. Results from the Rorschach test are included only where they are directly related to those from other methods because they appear in White's chapter (6) on the projective methods.

[2] Reviews of this work appear in several sources: Hunt (1936a), Rouvroy (1936), Wechsler (1939), Kendig and Richmond (1940), Roe and Shakow (1942). Since this chapter was written, Brody (1942) has brought out a review in England which has special significance because it contains a section specifically devoted to deficit in old age. We are indebted to Roe and Shakow for the use of their monograph in manuscript form, and to Klebanoff (1944) for the use of his manuscript which reviews the studies of deficit in patients with frontal lobe injuries.

[3] In one instance, Roe and Shakow (1942) used also the mental age equivalent of the educational status of their group of patients.

DEFICIT IN TERMS OF MENTAL AGE.—Measuring deficit with intelligence tests began with the First World War when the modest contributions of Binet and Simon were turned into a social movement. Of the various tests, the Yerkes Point Scale and Terman's 1916 revision of the Binet scale have been used most commonly. Recently, studies employing the Wechsler-Bellevue scale, the first ever standardized on adults, have begun to appear (Wechsler, 1939). These tests yield immediately the relative efficiency of patients, and means of results yield the relative efficiency of the various diagnostic groups. The deficit appears as the difference between the mean mental age of each of the various diagnostic groups and mean mental age of some control group.

Before 1935, investigators were content to compare the mental ages of their patients with the norms derived from the groups of children on which the Point-Scale and the Stanford-Binet were standardized. This introduced age as an uncontrolled variable because the patients were always adults. In recent studies the investigators have recognized the necessity for adult control groups. One sample obtained from the white draft of the First World War yielded an average of 161.04 months of mental age (Yerkes, 1921).[4] It is large (653), but overloaded with young men. Kendig and Richmond (1940) utilized a sample of 217 nurses (median M.A. = 181 months) and a sample of 129 hospital employees (median M.A. = 156 months). Although these samples are better than no adult controls, the nurses averaged younger than patients, and neither group could be considered a random or a representative sample of the population. Roe and Shakow (1942) used a sample of 65 surgical and orthopedic patients (mean M.A. = 163.6 months) collected by Weisenburg, Roe, and McBride (1936). Although this group is small, it was chosen carefully and is satisfyingly representative of the social, economic, and adult-age categories of our population. Furthermore, it serves to hold the factor of living-in-a-hospital relatively constant. The normal average of mental age appears to be in the interval 160–164 months. Because the various disorders have different age ranges (see Landis and Page, 1938, p. 37), what is still needed is a sample of Stanford-Binets from normal adults large enough to allow fractionation for each of the age decades. For Wechsler's (1939) test, the standardization group supplies just this sort of control.

Measuring deficit by comparing the averages of groups of patients with the averages of adult control groups would logically require that the samples of patients and controls be random selections from the groups represented. Actually a number of selective factors affect these samples and much of the variation among the averages reported for every diagnostic group (see Table I) may be attributed to them. For samples of paretics the averages range from 128 months of mental age (Wells and Kelley, 1920) to 152 months (Schott, 1930). For samples of schizo-

---

[4] For purposes of comparison, we have converted the results from all the studies to months of mental age as they appear in Table I.

TABLE I
MENTAL AGE IN THE VARIOUS DIAGNOSTIC GROUPS

Diagnostic Group	Number Cases	M.A. in Months Mean	M.A. in Months Median	Variability S.D.	Variability Range	Investigator
Control groups						
White draft	653	161.0	160	34.01	66–234	Yerkes (1921)
Nurses	217		181		122–224	Kendig & Richmond (1940)
Hospital employees	129		156		94–222	" "
Surgical and orthopedic patients	65	163.6		25.00	96–234	Roe & Shakow (1942)
Psychoses considered primarily "organic"						
Psychosis with alcoholism:						
Chronic	25	126.0				Pressey (1917)
	24		129			Kendig & Richmond (1940)
	30 (R)[5]	145.9		29.2		Roe & Shakow (1942)
Acute	15		150			Jastak (1937)
	17	154.2				Roe & Shakow (1942)
General paralysis (paresis)	12	128.0				Wells & Kelley (1920)
	16	152.5				Schott (1930)
	7	135.0				Jastak (1937)
	69		132			Kendig & Richmond (1940)
	35 (R)	132.1		31.2	68–206	Roe & Shakow (1942)
	24 (n-R)	113.4		24.3	62–160	" "
Other organic psychoses..	9	136.8				Michaels & Schilling (1936)
	14	115.6				Jastak (1937)
Psychoses considered primarily functional						
Schizophrenia:						
All types	50	126.0				Pressey (1917)
	22	167.0				Wells & Kelley (1920)
	50		135			Cornell & Lowden (1923)
	200	125				Wentworth (1923)
	36	180				Michaels & Schilling (1936)
	16	132				Jastak (1937)
	500	138	137		74–221	Kendig & Richmond (1940)
White only	429		143		74–221	" "
Colored	66		101		76–192	" "
	300 (all)	140.6			36–234	Roe & Shakow (1942)
	181 (R)	149.8		34.5	61–234	" "
	119 (n-R)	126.7			36–202	" "
Sub-types:						
Catatonic	51		144			Kendig & Richmond (1940)
	31 (R)	164.8		29.1	96–117	Roe & Shakow (1942)
	28 (n-R)	140.1		35.7	56–202	" "
Hebephrenic	11	148.0				Trapp & James (1937)
	32		138			Kendig & Richmond (1940)
	32 (R)	129.4		30.0	72–197	Roe & Shakow (1942)
	28 (n-R)	105.1		36.0	36–173	" "
Paranoid	16	130.0				Rawlings (1921)
	38	171.0				Trapp & James (1937)
	41		148			Kendig & Richmond (1940)
	58 (R)	154.8		33.5	82–234	Roe & Shakow (1942)
	31 (n-R)	135.7		32.0	80–190	" "
Unclassified	38 (R)	144.0		35.6		" "
	25 (n-R)	131.6		34.4		" "
Manic-depressive psychosis	43	171				Wells & Kelley (1920)
	23	169				Michaels & Schilling (1936)
	23	149				Jastak (1937)
	65		148			Kendig & Richmond (1940)
	19 (R)	166.4		32.0	114–222	Roe & Shakow (1942)
	18 (n-R)	144.6		34.0	84–203	" "

TABLE I—*Continued*

Diagnostic Group	Number Cases	M.A. in Months Mean	M.A. in Months Median	Variability S.D.	Variability Range	Investigator
Paranoia	15	156				Michaels & Schilling (1936)
	41		161			Kendig & Richmond (1940)
	22 (R)	164.7		25.1	122–211	Roe & Shakow (1942)
	9 (n-R)	143.8			80–203	" "
Psychopathic personality..	50	159.0				Cornell & Lowden (1923)
	38	164.0				Michaels & Schilling (1936)
	67		147			Kendig & Richmond (1940)
	22 (R)	156.1		29.4	109–234	Roe & Shakow (1942)
	14 (n-R)	138.8		23.4	101–193	" "
Psychoneuroses						
All types	114	143.0				Hollingworth (1920)
	70		144			Tendler (1923)
	39	180				Michaels & Schilling (1936)
	7	176.0				Jastak (1937)
	26		169			Kendig & Richmond (1940)
	36 (R)	169.1		28.5	106–234	Roe & Shakow (1942)
	12 (n-R)	153.1		33.5	108–196	" "
	256	174.6				Malamud & Gottlieb (1944)
Anxiety neurosis ......unstated		172.0				" "
Hysteria	177	142.8				Hollingworth (1920)
	unstated		162			Tendler (1923)
	16	171.0				Roe & Shakow (1942)
	unstated	177.0				Malamud & Gottlieb (1944)
Neurasthenia	83	156.0				Hollingworth (1920)
	unstated		127			Tendler (1923)
	8	147.0				Roe & Shakow (1942)
	unstated	169.0				Malamud & Gottlieb (1944)
Psychasthenia	10	178.8				Hollingworth (1920)
	unstated		145			Tendler (1923)
	3	177.0				Roe & Shakow (1942)
	unstated	177.0				Malamud & Gottlieb (1944)

[5] Roe & Shakow distinguished between "representative" (R) and "nonrepresentative" (n-R) examinations, and we give both sets of figures here.

phrenics, they range from 125 months (Wentworth, 1923) to 180 months (Michaels and Schilling, 1936), and this range particularly is greater than could be expected from chance fluctuation. The most obvious selective factors are: nature of the institution, care and aim of the investigator, variations in diagnostic practices, and the accessibility of patients at the time of test. Excepting the samples of psychotics reported by Wells and Kelley (1920), and Schott (1930), and the sample of psychoneurotics by Malamud and Gottlieb (1943) which were out-patients, these samples came from state hospitals. Several of these samples made no pretense of being random or representative. Wells and Kelley, and Jastak were primarily interested in the patterns of success and failure to be reported below, and Schott in the retest variability of paretics. Diagnostic practices influence primarily the averages of the subtypes of schizophrenia. Probably the most important selective factor is the degree of cooperativeness required at the time of the test. Practices have differed considerably. Roe and Shakow (1942) have made an honest attempt to deal directly with this factor by dividing their samples from the various diagnostic groups into "representative" and "nonrepresentative" examinations. Their criteria were several. "Representative" performances were characterized by willingness to take the test, interest in the specific tasks, and freedom from factors of a temporary kind like a psychotic episode or an emotional upset. Averages are given for both types of performance, and the deleterious effects of uncooperativeness on mental age are clearly demonstrated. But which average should represent the diagnostic group? We should not agree with the implied assumption that the tests measure any fundamental capacity, and in so far as the psychosis affects cooperativeness, it affects efficiency. In spite of these variations, the averages reported by Kendig and Richmond (1940) and Roe and Shakow (1942), the two most adequate in this group, agree well for most of the diagnostic groups; e.g., for schizophrenics they are respectively 138 months and 140.6 months for "representative" and "nonrepresentative" performances combined.

With these limitations in view, consider the deficits in the various diagnostic groups (see Table I). If we consider the interval of 160–164 months as the average mental age of the general population, every psychotic group shows a deficit. The results from the Yerkes Point Scale and the Stanford-Binet, coupled with those from the Wechsler-Bellevue (Wechsler, 1939, Ch. 6), permit the over-all generalization that the deficit is largest for the "organic" psychoses, next largest for the "functional" psychoses, and that deficit is probably absent in the psychoneuroses.

Among the "organic" psychoses, the deficit is largest for senile dementia and those disorders involving diffuse cortical degeneration such as Alzheimer's disease and Pick's disease, next largest, approximately 30 months, in paretics, and smallest in psychosis with alcoholism. The samples of alcoholics vary considerably and overlap with schizophrenia. Alcoholics with Korsakoff's syndrome (Wechsler, 1939) show great loss; chronic groups average from 126 months (Pressey, 1917) to 146 months (Roe and Shakow, 1942), while acute groups average around 150 months.

Among the "functional" psychoses, schizophrenia shows the greatest average deficit, approximately 20 months, with considerable variation among the subtypes. Paranoia and psychopathic personality are second with averages approximately 10 months below the control average. The averages for the manic-depressive group vary from 148 months (Kendig and Richmond, 1940) to 171 (Wells and Kelley, 1920), and these variations probably reflect variations of psychometric practice. In some hospitals patients are often tested while psychotic behavior is prominent, while in others they are tested only when psychotic behavior has reached a minimum. Roe and Shakow obtained the high average of 166 months from tests given when patients were quiescent, and therefore, the figures of Jastak (148 months) and Kendig and Richmond (149 months) probably reflect the effects of this psychosis more adequately.

The variation among the averages reported for each of the subtypes of schizophrenia may well reflect differences in diagnostic practice. Hebephrenics, however, consistently show the largest deficit which is approximately as great as that found in general paralysis. The "unclassified" group at Worcester (Roe and Shakow) is a close second. The catatonic and paranoid subtypes show the least deficit. Agreement is poorest for the simple subtype. Most of the averages reported for psychoneurotics, on the other hand, are above the norm. Those reported more recently, especially those from Malamud and Gottlieb (1944) who had a sample of 256 patients, contradict the conclusion that psychoneuroses develop in persons of subnormal intelligence. This latter conclusion derives from the older work of Hollingworth (1920) and Tendler (1923) whose averages are exceptionally low.

The effects on mental age of having parts of the brain removed surgically are somewhat equivocal. When we converted the results from the Stanford-Binet (1916 or 1937 revisions), or from related tests, to mental age in months for nineteen cases reported in the American literature, we obtained the remarkably high average mental age of 202 months, range 153 to 251 months.[6] Of these nineteen, fourteen operations concerned the frontal lobe, four the temporal, and one the occipital lobe. Moreover, T. Hunt's psychometric studies with the Stanford-Binet of psychotic cases treated by prefrontal lobotomy yielded no evidence of post-operative deficit (Freeman and Watts, 1942, Ch. 14). From such evidence, Hebb and Penfield (1940) have argued that the excessive deficit found in the "organic" disorders, commonly attributed to cerebral damage, is probably more a matter of diseased cerebral tissue than of the absence of tissue. This may be true, but on the other hand, one should not conclude from these data that these operated cases suffered no deficit. For instance, one reported by Nichols and Hunt (1940) had a consistent IQ of 120, in four tests, but he failed at double alternation, showed great "rigidity of abstract attitude" on the Vigotsky test and exhibited other deficiencies. Such tests as the Stanford-Binet are inadequate to uncover deficit in many of these cases following brain operation. Nevertheless, Rylander (1939) did find reduced mental ages with Hellstrom's Swedish translation of the Stanford-Binet in 32 cases whose frontal lobes had been surgically damaged. His technique of matching each patient with a control from the same environment of about the same age, occupation and education is superior to comparing group averages. Where "large" excisions from the left frontal lobe were involved, the average difference was 16 points of IQ; for "small" excisions from this lobe, 4.3 points (p. 289). A conversion of his reported IQ's to mental age in months yields an average of 168 months for controls and an average of 151 months for operated cases, range 110 to 195 months. This average loss of 17 months contrasts sharply with the results from

---

[6] These figures were computed from the test results in case-studies reported by Ackerly (1933), Brickner (1936), Rowe (1937), Halstead (1940), Hebb (1939a, 1939b, 1941), Hebb and Penfield (1940), Nichols and Hunt (1940).

the American studies. The original mental ages of the American patients were probably much above average.

Inferring deficit from comparing the averages of diagnostic groups with those of control groups representative of the normal population assumes that the various diagnostic groups select victims randomly from the population. Indirect evidence from rate-studies argues against this assumption. Terman (1940) found the proportion of disorders in his group of gifted children, restudied after sixteen years, lower than that for others of their age. Rosanoff (1938) has reported psychoses to be three times as common in illiterates as in literates. Faris and Dunham (1939) found the highest rates of incidence for all the diagnostic groups, excepting the manic-depressive psychosis, in those urban areas where one would expect test-performance to be below average. Babcock (1933), and Kendig and Richmond (1940) considered their samples of schizophrenics below average in education, but they appear to have failed to consider the factor of age in determining the years of education to be expected. On the other hand, Roe and Shakow (1942) point out that in the 723 schizophrenics (mean age 38.1 years) admitted to Massachusetts hospitals in 1935, the educational distribution was 66% grammar school, 29% high school, and 6% college. This corresponds closely to the distribution of 65% grammar school, 25% high school, and 10% college reported for normal individuals in the thirties by Shakow and Goldman (1938). Simmins (1933) found the vocabulary scores of her cross-section of 200 psychotics distributed similarly about an average approximating that for normal adults. Wiersma (1930) has claimed that the prepsychotic intelligence of paretics is normal. The fact that the manic-depressive patients in these studies have approximately a normal average mental age refutes Duncan's (1936) argument that mental deficiency is an important etiological factor in this disorder.

A decline in mental age with age after the twenties argues against attributing entirely to these disorders the larger deficits shown from the "organic" groups where the patients are older. Yerkes (1921) found that officers in the sixth decade averaged about 18 months of mental age below those aged 20 to 25 years. The parents of Willoughby's (1927, 1929) sample of 110 children showed a decline to a "pubertal or prepubertal level" of mental age at age 60. Jones and Conrad (1933) found the peak of mental age in the group aged 18 to 21 years and a gradual decline to 168 months by age 55. Weisenburg, Roe, and McBride (1936) found low negative correlations between test-scores and age in their carefully selected sample of adults. When Wechsler (1939) standardized the Wechsler-Bellevue test on a sample of several thousand subjects he found that mental age declined about 12 months a decade. For this reason he condemned the calculation of an adult IQ with the same basal denominator for all ages, and presented a table of denominators which descends from 15.5 years of mental age for ages 20 to 24 to 12.0 years for ages 50 to 59. Since the "organic" groups average considerably older than the "functional" groups, some of the difference in the size of deficit shown by the tests is attributable to processes of aging.

THE BABCOCK METHOD.—The clever but questionable technique of using the vocabulary score as an index of original "capacity" was originally devised by Babcock (1930) and later revised (1941). Studies of passes and failures on the test items in the Stanford-Binet scale (see review by Harris and Shakow, 1937) had shown that vocabulary scores remain consistently high for patients suffering from nearly all the disorders. The common occurrence of the loss of recent memory in various diseases affecting brain tissue coupled with the findings of Franz that the ablation of cerebral tissue damages primarily new habits in animals had led to the conclusion that cerebral insults damage primarily habits recently acquired. With these two lines of evidence and this conclusion in view, Babcock devised a series of tests, emphasizing information, speed of performance, and ability to learn, to measure efficiency. These she standardized on *normal* individuals and so arranged the scoring that the average discrepancy between their actual scores on the efficiency tests and those predicted from vocabulary scores approximated zero. Thus, in a *disordered* individual, this discrepancy, which she termed an "efficiency index," would serve as a measure of the deficit. If the assumptions are valid, this method enables one to estimate not only the average deficit of a diagnostic group but also the deficit in any individual, and therefore, to determine also the variability of the deficits incurred in any disorder.

The results obtained by investigators who have employed the Babcock test appear in Table II. From top to bottom in the table are the averages and variabilities of the efficiency indices for groups of normal individuals, to serve as a statistical standard, and for the various diagnostic groups for which results have been reported.

Numerically adequate samples are available of normal individuals, of aged normal individuals, and for the diagnostic groups: paresis, schizophrenia, psychosis with alcoholism, and drug addiction. On the whole the averages from the available samples of patients in any diagnostic group agree well. Wittman's exceptionally high average from a small sample of schizophrenics may well be disregarded. Again by this method the deficits average larger for the "organic" groups, excepting the alcoholics and the drug addicts who are not psychotic, than they do for schizophrenia. On the other hand, the deficits of individuals with schizophrenia vary more than do those of any other diagnostic group save possibly the epileptics (Wittman, 1933). Thus, in the data available, the largest individual deficits, measured in terms of the efficiency index, appear in schizophrenics. The variability among the average efficiency indices for normal groups is attributable to age. Gilbert (1935) found an average index of zero in her sample of normal individuals in the twenties, which agrees with Babcock's standardization, but her sample of normal individuals in the sixties shows an average index of —4.8, a

TABLE II

Deficit in Various Diagnostic Groups in Terms of Averages of Babcock's "Efficiency Indices"

Diagnostic Groups	Number Subjects	Efficiency Indices Mean	Median	Variability S.D.	Range	Investigator
Control groups						
	264	0.00	+0.1	1.18		Babcock (1930)
	228		+0.5		— 3.4 to +3.2	Babcock (1933)
	26	—1.20			— 5.2 to +2.1	Wittman (1933)
Age 20–29	185	0.00				Gilbert (1935)
Age 60–69	175	—4.80				Gilbert (1935)
Psychoses considered primarily organic						
General Paralysis (paresis):						
All	75	—4.68	—4.8	2.02		Babcock (1930)
Improving	42	—4.12	—4.0	2.01	— 5.8 to —2.5	Babcock (1930)
Not Improving	33	—5.40	—5.3	1.79	— 6.7 to —4.0	Babcock (1930)
All	98	—5.10			— 9.0 to +0.3	Wittman (1933)
Psychoses with organic brain disease	4	—3.3			— 5.2 to —1.7	Wittman (1933)
Psychoses with cerebral arteriosclerosis	4	—4.9			— 6.1 to —3.7	Wittman (1933)
Psychoses with alcoholism...	66	—2.3			— 4.2 to +1.4	Wittman (1933)
Psychoses with epilepsy.....	26	—5.4			—10.2 to +1.1	Wittman (1933)
Psychoses considered primarily functional						
Dementia praecox (schizophrenia)	124		—3.5		—13.1 to +0.5	Babcock (1933)
	24	—0.8			— 7.3 to +1.7	Wittman (1933)
	110	—3.4			— 8.3 to ?	Schwarz (1932)
Hospitalized drug addicts (abstinent for 6 months)	156	—2.28		1.64		Partington (1940)

deficit as large as that shown by Babcock's paretic group. Still further evidence from this association between increasing age and decreasing efficiency indices on the Babcock test appears in the work of Roe and Shakow (1942) where the size of the average negative indices in psychotic groups correlated —.59 with their mean age. At least part of the low efficiency of the "organic" groups must be attributed to aging rather than to the disorders as such. Age selectivity may account for the low average index of Wittman's (1933) sample of controls, and perhaps for the relatively high average index for her small group of schizophrenics. Babcock's (1930) finding that persons with indices below —2.0 had adjustive difficulties, and her conclusion, that an index below —3.5 is pathological, can be applicable only to young adults.

Since Babcock initiated the use of vocabulary to estimate original capacity, a number of investigators have reported discrepancies between vocabulary scores and scores on various sorts of other tests. The average discrepancies between months of mental age on the Stanford-Binet without vocabulary and on Terman's vocabulary reported for various normal and disordered groups appear in Table III. Considerable variation marks the averages reported for most of the groups. Age selectivity probably accounts for the variation from —11 months (Roe and Shakow, 1942) to +10 months (Kendig and Richmond, 1940) in the samples of normals. This discrepancy has been shown to increase with age by Shakow and Goldman (1938) and by Roe and Shakow (1942) who found it increasing from an average of —4 months for controls in their twenties to —27 for those in their fifties. The variation from a mean of —30.4 (Davidson, 1937) to a median of —2 months (Kendig and Richmond, 1940) in the results from schizophrenic groups is probably a statistical artifact, because the extremely large negative discrepancies do not affect the median as they do the mean. The interesting facts brought out by Kendig and Richmond are that large positive discrepancies may appear for individual schizophrenics and that half this group shows no discrepancy at all. Except for the psychoneurotics whose average discrepancies are normal, all the diagnostic groups show some evidence of deficit. But by this method the deficit in the "organic" groups appears little larger than that in the "functional" groups.

Vocabulary scores have been compared with scores on a battery of the "visual-perception-tests," like those Spearman has used to measure general ability (g), by Simmins (1933) to measure what she termed "g-deterioration" in psychotics. She found the discrepancies between these scores correlated with the judged severity of disorder, but she reported no averages for the various diagnostic groups. Harbinson (1936) has extended Simmins' work and found little evidence of deficit in 36 patients from a hospital treating only the acutely disordered.

Shipley (1940) has recently devised a test that measures deficit in terms of a discrepancy between scores on vocabulary and tests of "abstract" ability which require the subject to discern and to continue a system in a series of items. The discrepancy is expressed as a "conceptual quotient" (CQ) which is virtually "abstraction age" divided by "vocabulary age" (Shipley and Burlingame, 1941). The CQ's of psychoneurotics approached those of normal subjects. Those of patients with "functional" psychoses were lower, and of these, schizophrenics fell below manic-depressive patients. Those of patients with "organic" psychoses were lowest of all. The median of those in private hospitals (N-85) was 20 points above the median of those in state hospitals. This test is recommended by the fact that the self-administering procedure is used for both vocabulary and "abstract" ability, but unfortunately the control group on which it was standardized contained only children and young adults. The age factor undoubtedly complicates the results from both Simmins's and Shipley's variations of the Babcock method.

Despite the comparative advantages of the Babcock method mentioned above, several factors besides age complicate the significance of these discrepancy scores as measures of deficit. First, vocabulary performance is an imperfect indicator of ability as is shown: by the fact that the discrepancy between mental age on Terman's vocabulary and mental age on the other tests of the Stanford correlate negatively with mental age (Altman and Shakow, 1937), and by the fact that feebleminded individuals exhibit an "unquestionable tendency toward lower CQ's" (Ship-

TABLE III

Discrepancy Between Mental Age Equivalents for the Terman Vocabulary Test and Mental Age on the Other Stanford-Binet Tests in Various Diagnostic Groups

Group	Number	Discrepancy (mo.) Mean	Median	Variability S.D.	Range	Investigator
Control groups						
Unselected	200	— 3.6		17.3		Davidson (1937)
	86	— 5.0				Altman & Shakow (1937)
Nurses	217	+ 3			—42 to +43	Kendig & Richmond (1940)
Employees	128	+10			—44 to +49	" "
Surgical cases	65	—11.0				Roe & Shakow (1942)
Delinquent groups						
Prisoners	308	—15.0				Fry (1930)
Delinquents	150	—19.0				Shakow & Millard (1935)
	56	—12.0				Altman & Shakow (1937)
Psychoses considered primarily organic						
Paresis	7	—34.4				Jastak (1937)
	35	—27.0				Roe & Shakow (1942)
With alcoholism ...	15	— 3.7				Jastak (1937)
Chronic	30	—19.0				Roe & Shakow (1942)
Acute	17	—22.0				" "
Other organic psychoses	14	—25.6				Jastak (1937)
Psychoses considered primarily functional						
Dementia praecox (schizophrenia) ..	71	—30.4		24.4		Davidson (1937)
	16	—19.0				Jastak (1937)
	477		— 2		—76 to +51	Kendig & Richmond (1940)
	181	—19.4 (R)[5]				Roe & Shakow (1942)
Manic - depressive psychosis	23	—19.0				Jastak (1937)
	19	—18.0 (R)				Roe & Shakow (1942)
Paranoid condition..	41	—12			—66 to +26	Kendig & Richmond (1940)
	22	—19.0				Roe & Shakow (1942)
Psychoneuroses						
	7	— 2.4				Jastak (1937)
	36	— 4.0				Roe & Shakow (1942)

5 See footnote on page 975.

ley and Burlingame, 1941). Secondly, the vocabulary-performance may suffer as a consequence of disorder as shown: by the fact that mental age on vocabulary tests in paretics and hebephrenic schizophrenics falls considerably below mental age derived from educational level (Roe and Shakow, 1942), and by the fact that vocabulary scores themselves correlate positively with clinical estimates of deterioration (Capps, 1939). Thirdly, the verbal administration of vocabulary tests, involved in all but Shipley's test, requires less in the way of self-direction from the subject than is required in the other modes of administration. Yacorzynski (1941) has pointed out that oral presentation allows for a number of methods of defining a word or item passably that are of unequal difficulty. Further evidence for this criticism derives from the fact that psychotic patients consistently do better on Kent's Oral Emergency Test than they do on the Stanford-Binet (Elwood, Burchard, and Teagarden, 1937), and from Hunt's unpublished finding that schizophrenic patients particularly can be prodded into several times their customary output when the experimenter supplies direction.

While these quantitative test results demonstrate the existence of deficit in most of the psychoses, in aged people, and in individuals who have suffered surgical brain injury, the quantitative results themselves are relatively uninformative. Even as measuring instruments, the tests are only pseudo-quantitative. Such pseudo-units as "months of mental age" or points of "efficiency index" have no clear equality, and no zero for intelligence exists. A rigorous quantitative approach to intelligence and deficit still remains for the future. The "speed" factor might readily be quantified by measuring time required to do various kinds of tasks. For the "power" aspect the way is not so evident. In connection with the studies on "thinking" in the "organic" disorders, we shall suggest utilizing the number of "lines of activity" that an individual can synthesize into a coordinated performance as one possibility for exploration.

Qualitative Results from Intelligence Tests: Is Deficit General or Specific?—

"SCATTER."—Considerable attention has been given to the scattering of successes or failures over the year-levels of the Yerkes Point Scale and the Stanford-Binet. Nine different measures of this "scatter" have been devised. Harris and Shakow (1937) have classified these into three types. The simplest type, range of "scatter," consists in counting the year-levels over which both successes and failures occur (Wells, 1927; Shipley, 1934). A second type emphasizes area and consists in the number of months of credit earned above the basal year (Wallin, 1922). The third type takes both into account, and the most successful of these consists of multiplying failures below and passes above the mental age by the number of year-levels separating each test from the mental age (Pressey & Cole, 1919). Several investigators have reported greater scatter in the performances of psychotic patients than in the performances of normal or feebleminded children, and the greatest scatter appeared in those of "organic" groups.[7] Some of them have suggested that excessive scatter is a useful diagnostic sign, but the use of children for controls, and failure to hold mental age constant, vitiated their results. Kendig and Richmond (1940) have shown, for instance, that many of the tests in the 1916 revision of the Binet show a different degree of difficulty for adults than for children. Harris and Shakow (1938) compared the scatter, measured by four different methods, of matched groups of 154 schizophrenic, 133 normal, and 138 delinquent adults. Only mental age was related significantly to scatter. When mental age was held constant, any differences between the groups disappeared. Kendig and Richmond (1940) found the median of scatter (Pressey's measure) approximately the same in their schizophrenics as in their controls, but

---

[7] See: Pressey (1917), Curtis (1918), Pressey and Cole (1919), Wells and Kelley (1920), Wallin (1922, 1927), Porteus (1922), Malamud and Palmer (1938).

the range was considerably greater in the schizophrenics than in any of the other groups. They also found scatter related to mental age; the largest scatter occurred in the middle range of mental ages, and the feebleminded with low mental ages showed less scatter than schizophrenics. Unfortunately, neither of these investigations included patients with "organic" disorders where the earlier investigators found the greatest scatter. If they really existed, large scatter scores would imply that the deficits of psychotic patients were selective for particular kinds of performance, but the scatter approach appears now to be a blind alley.

KINDS OF TESTS SELECTIVELY FAILED.—The early work on scatter and interest in the nature of deficit have led to item-analyses of psychotic test-failures with the aim of inducing the qualitative characteristics of deficit from an inspection of the nature of the tests failed. The method has usually consisted in comparing the percentage of failures on each test in the psychotic groups and the control groups. When mental age is not controlled, more psychotics than normal subjects fail all the tests, but the differential is smallest for vocabulary (Kendig and Richmond, 1940). Only these results agree with the conclusion of Hart and Spearman (1914), derived from a correlation analysis of psychotic test results, that the deficit in all psychotic groups is of diffuse character, involves all types of activity, and yields a result essentially like feeblemindedness. When mental age is held constant, selectivity appears. We have tabulated the results obtained from ten investigations using the Yerkes Point Scale or the 1916 revision of the Stanford-Binet on schizophrenics, for whom the most data are available, and found a majority agreement concerning selective failure on twelve of the tests. In the Stanford-Binet these tests are: social comprehension (VIII-3 and X-5), finding similarities (VIII-4), giving date (IX-1), arranging blocks in order of weight (IX-2), digits backwards (IX-4), absurdities (X-2), drawing designs from memory (X-3), defining abstract words (XII-2), interpreting fables (XII-5, XVI-2), problem questions (XIV-4).[8] Schizophrenics are consistently superior to nonpsychotics of similar mental age on vocabulary tests, and they are usually superior on such tests of information as distinguishing between president and king (XIV-3). Rabin (1941), using the Wechsler-Bellevue, found schizophrenics much superior to nurses of the same mental age on tests of information and arithmetic, while nurses were much superior on "digit-symbol substitution" and "object assembly."

Interpretations of the nature of the abilities involved in these tests selectively failed and passed by schizophrenics, and also by "organic" patients, have varied considerably. The failures have sometimes been

---

[8] These ten investigations are: Pressey (1917), Wells and Kelley (1920), Rawlings (1921), Wentworth (1924), Altman and Shakow (1937), Piotrowski (1937), Collins, Atwell, and Moore (1938), Malamud and Palmer (1938), Kendig and Richmond (1940), and Roe and Shakow (1942). Methods of comparing and the nature of the control groups differ considerably in these studies, but these differences only add to the validity of the results where agreement occurs.

explained by assuming the loss of fundamental capacities: [9] the capacity to generalize and to conceptualize (Rawlings, 1921; Wentworth, 1924; Moore, 1930; Roe and Shakow, 1942), the capacity to work rapidly, and that to form new associations and acquire new skills (Babcock, 1930, 1933, 1941). Others have emphasized capacity less and have emphasized more the role of "control" and motivation.[10] This emphasis is implied in such concepts as "defective directional control of thought," egocentric preoccupations, and "failure to draw upon information beyond that in the directions given" (Piotrowski, 1937a). As do many of the writers in this latter group (footnote 10), we incline toward assuming a loss of capacity in "organic" patients, particularly in those with cerebral lesions; and for schizophrenics and for the other "functional" psychoses, we incline toward assuming defective motivation and control of performance. The selective superiorities of psychotics have been explained as old habits, acquired when capacity was intact, that are undamaged by lesions because of their age. They are also explained as being the kinds of tasks that require little in the way of sustained voluntary effort. Again we incline toward the former view for "organics" and toward the latter view for schizophrenics. We shall present evidence for these inclinations below.

We might expect patterns of selective failure and success to differentiate to some extent patients with "organic" disorders from those with schizophrenia. Damage to cerebral structure should reduce fundamental capacity, while the "withdrawal" of schizophrenics should leave basic capacities untouched but alter such functions as judgment. Differences in performance are actually relatively few, but those few tend somewhat to corroborate this hypothesis. Common to both types of patients are: superiority over nonpsychotics of similar mental age on vocabulary and information, and inferiority on such conceptual tests as interpreting fables (XII-5 and XVI-2), noticing absurdities (X-2)[11] and finding

---

[9] We would argue that no intelligence test measures any fundamental capacity. Into the determination of test-performance goes a complex of factors: capacity, past experience, present motivation, etc. Ideally one can abstract capacity from this complex, but to do it operationally is very difficult. To show the absence, or the loss, of the capacity for a given performance, it is necessary to show that the organism concerned cannot learn, or relearn, the performance with the best of motivation. The conclusion here mentioned derives from classifying the tests on the Binet scale according to the apparent nature of the processes involved. The majority of the tests failed fall into the following categories of Roe and Shakow: "conceptual thinking," "sustained associative thinking," and with a few in the class of "immediately learned." Kendig and Richmond attempted to use Spearman's dichotomy of eductive and noneductive tests, but they discarded it when they found vocabulary and information, on which patients are selectively superior, in the former group. If this conclusion is accepted, capacity must be considered synonymous with performance. In spite of the difficulties involved, we prefer to maintain a distinction between these concepts.

[10] See: Gatewood (1908), Wiersma (1930), Jastak (1934), Line and Griffin (1935), Malamud and Palmer (1938), Kendig and Richmond (1940), Rabin (1941), Yacorzynski (1941), and Brody (1942).

[11] Paretics do discern absurdities, however, even without the instruction to look for them, if they are clearly based on past experience, as are "fir trees with leaves" and "harvesting in March," and do not involve abstractions. They usually miss, for

similarities, and on tests of sustained associative thinking. Common to both types also is the general pattern: highest scores on vocabulary, next on verbal tests, and lowest on performance tests (Jastak, 1937; Piotrowski, 1937b). Roe and Shakow found no significant difference between paretics and hebephrenics on any of the tests in the Stanford-Binet. On the other hand, others have found differential patterns (Wiersma, 1930; Wechsler, 1939, p. 68; Rabin, 1941). Malamud and Palmer, in a direct search for differences, have shown that "organic" patients are differentially and selectively inferior to feebleminded subjects of the same mental age range on counting from 20 to 1 (VIII-2) and four digits backward (IX-4), while schizophrenics are inferior on social comprehension (VIII-3 and X-5), interpreting pictures (XII-7) and problem questions (XIV-4). They considered that pathological perseveration and disturbances of memory underlay the differential failures of the "organic" group, and that schizophrenics fail differentially on tests "most heavily dependent on practical judgment." If these results are reproducible, they constitute an important finding, for the responses on these particular tests failed by schizophrenics are clearly scored in terms of social standards. There is no intrinsic "rightness" to the answers demanded in the standardization. In so far as schizophrenia consists in an active withdrawal from social interaction, such are precisely the sort of tests schizophrenics should fail differentially. "Organic" patients should not fail them, for these tests appear to require relatively little conceptual capacity or new learning, and the old social habits upon which the correct responses are based are relatively untouched by cerebral damage (see also Font, 1940). The common successes and failures of these two groups of patients may be explained by assuming that reduction of fundamental capacity and reduction of motivation have similar effects on many performances. Roe and Shakow's finding that uncooperativeness affects primarily tests involving conceptual thinking and sustained associative thinking tends to corroborate this assumption.

Several sorts of test-results argue against the loss of fundamental capacity in most schizophrenics. Malamud and Palmer found a differential superiority of schizophrenics on arithmetic reasoning. They considered this superiority illusory, but schizophrenics have also been shown clearly superior to paretics on arithmetic progressions (Hunt, 1935), and Rabin (1941) and Magaret (1942) found that performance on arithmetic tests held up better in schizophrenics than in Wechsler's old-age group. Piotrowski's (1933, 1937a) finding that even schizophrenic children, aged four to ten, earn better vocabulary scores than feebleminded children of the same mental age argues indirectly against such loss, for it would appear that vocabulary building goes on in spite of the disorder. His finding that schizophrenic children improve more on re-

---

instance, "Since the rabbit ran faster than I did, I could overtake it only slowly and finally caught it." Schizophrenics do not note absurdities without instruction to look for them, and then they note the more abstract ones like the latter (Hunt, 1935, and unpublished data). See section on thinking below.

testing than do the feebleminded argues the same way. Kendig and
Richmond found that as schizophrenics recovered their test-performance
improved, and only 43% of a group selected because they had been hospitalized more than five years (average of ten years) retained their
original level of performance or improved when retested. Stephenson
(1932b) has shown scores on g-tests to be correlated with p-scores in
schizophrenics but not in "organic" patients, the higher the p-scores the
lower the g-scores. Muhl's (1930) success in getting schizophrenics who
appeared utterly confused to give accurate answers to questions about
time in the hospital and names of attendants and doctors by means of
automatic writing, and the common clinical observation that catatonics
after some recovery can relate incidents that occurred during a stuporous
phase of the psychosis both argue against any loss of impressionability.
Although gross figures from the recent studies of shock-therapy on test-
performance are confusing (Shipley and Kant, 1940), certain specific
findings are suggestive. Wechsler, Halpern and Jaros (1940) found
that patients showed the greatest improvement in the following: number
of vocational interests indicated, counting by threes (1, 4, 7, etc.), finding similarities, and a directions-test. They considered these tests of
interest in the external world, of sustained effort, and of thought control, respectively. Wittman and Russel (1941) found a high positive
correlation between improvement in efficiency and "attitude" changes.
Thus the tentative generalization can be made that if interest and attitude improve, test-performance improves.[12]

The pattern of deficit in the aged, and in cases of adult brain injury
that does not strike the speech areas, resembles generally the pattern
found in the "organic" psychoses. This is Wechsler's (1939, Ch. 6)
conclusion from finding that the aged show the greatest decline on: repeating digits forward or backward, arithmetic reasoning, digit-symbol
substitution, picture arrangement, block-design, and finding similarities;
and the least or no decline on: vocabulary, information, comprehension,
object-assembly, and picture completion. Magaret's results (1942)
agree essentially with these. Jones and Conrad (1933) point out that at

---

[12] In the future, comparisons of the amount of improvement in test performance
in paretics and schizophrenics with fever- and shock-therapy respectively may yield
evidence on this point. Dubois, Mays, and Landis (1934) found a gain in average
score on the Army Alpha from 48 to only 68 in 16 paretics, and attributed part of
this gain to becoming accustomed to the test situation. In the only study of Binet
performance of paretics (N-78) before and after fever-therapy that we know, 22
improved 10 points or more in IQ, 11 decreased 10 points or more, and 45 showed
no significant change. Epstein and Solomon (1939) concluded that paretics are
unlikely to recover their previous level if the IQ is much lower before treatment
than would be expected from their occupational and educational status. Comparable
results are not available for schizophrenics, but Graham (1940) has reported
improvement in total score, decreased scatter, and a slight shift in the Malamud-
Palmer pattern toward the "organic" after insulin-therapy. The fact that Bolles,
Rosen, and Landis (1938) found the more clinical improvement in schizophrenics
showing the better performances on the sorting tests suggests that shock-therapy
is most effective in patients with the "categorical attitude" intact. Whether or not
this indicates a loss of fundamental capacity in schizophrenia depends upon one's
interpretation of the nature of the "categorical attitude."

the sixth decade 40% of the Army Alpha score is derived from "vocabulary" and "general information" which contribute only 10% of the score at age ten. Miles (1933, 1935) found the greatest deficit in the aged in tests involving "speed, organization and recall of unfamiliar material and difficult logical procedures involving a relatively wide memory span." Gilbert's (1935, 1941) results with the Babcock test and others agree with these of Miles. The amount of deficit that occurs with aging, however, appears to be negatively correlated with original ability (Wiersma, 1930; Gilbert, 1935, 1941; Shakow and Goldman, 1938). For cases of adult brain injury outside the speech-areas, Hebb (1942), summarizing the literature and his own results, describes a similar pattern of success and failure on the Stanford, and points out that they also show vocabulary highest, verbal tests intermediate, and performance tests lowest, which is Jastak's (1937) pattern for the "organic" psychoses. On the other hand, in cases of brain injury during infancy, Hebb (1942) has shown that this latter pattern is reversed to one like that in the feeble-minded: performance tests high, verbal tests and Binet low, and mental age on vocabulary considerably below chronological age. From these results he concludes that development and retention of the abilities measured in tests depend upon the brain in different ways, and "more cerebral efficiency or more intellectual power is needed for intellectual development (acquiring intellectual skills) than for later functioning at the same level" (Hebb, 1942, p. 286). Brody (1942) argues in similar fashion, and concludes that the superiority of mature individuals in social and occupational competence is a function of knowledge and habituated skills. We shall develop this point further in the conclusion of this chapter.

INTERRELATIONS AMONG STATISTICAL FACTORS.—Investigators in the English school of factor-analysis have attempted to show the nature of the deficit in various disorders in terms of Spearman's factors: general ability—g, perseveration—p, fluency—f, will—w, and speed. Jones (1928) found perseveration, measured in terms of performances like the rate of turning required for color-fusion or ratio between output on an habituated task (like writing Z's for 30 seconds) and output on an unhabituated modification of the same task (like writing Z's reversed for 30 seconds), abnormally high in both manic and depressed patients. From these data he questioned Wiersma's conclusion that p is abnormally low in manics. Stephenson (1932a) has found p-scores higher than normal in all diagnostic groups, but highest in the depressed. Schizophrenics gave both very high and relatively low p-scores, and the scores changed with variations in the patients' clinical condition. High p-scores were associated with inaccessibility and low g, as measured by visual-perception tests devised by Line (Stephenson, 1932b; Stephenson, et al., 1934). No such correlation appeared in the performances of "organic" patients, so Stephenson questioned whether low g-scores indicate dementia in schizophrenics and argued that the high p-scores might result from Pavlovian inhibition seen as the interference between patterns of response. Tests of "fluency," such as number of words given in 3 minutes or number of things mentioned to be added to an unfinished picture, normally correlated positively with g-tests. But in cases of manic-depressive psychosis, Stephenson, et al. (1934) found that manics low in g were high in f, that cases relatively normal occupied relatively the same position on both g- and f-tests, and that the depressed had f-scores relatively lower than their g-scores. Tests of "fluency" distinguished manics from the depressed better than speed tests. Fluency appeared low in cases of anxiety. From a classification of 77 female patients with "functional" disorders in terms of f- and p-scores combined, cases of hysteria showed consistently low f-scores but either low or high p-scores; manics were characteristically high in f and low in p; and schizophrenics were distributed in all four of the possible combinations. Too little of this sort of work has been done to allow a systematic picture, but the method appears promising.

In Canada, Line and Griffin (1935) (see also Line, Griffin, and Anderson, 1935) have initiated a program to differentiate the abnormal in terms of statistical factors derived from a wide range of performances. They administered a large battery of tests, including those mentioned above, the Rorschach, word-association, and the Bernreuter, to 50 individuals over a range of "stability" from "good students" to psychotics, and made a factor analysis of the results. Two factors appeared. Factor I, indicated by positive loadings with word-association, oscillation, perseveration, and the Bernreuter scored for both neurotic tendency and introversion-extraversion, they called *objectivity*. Factor II, indicated by positive loadings with total number of responses on the Rorschach, speed, and the Bernreuter scored for dominance and self-sufficiency, they called *fluency*. They interpreted these as directional characteristics of function which, theoretically, should manifest themselves in alertness to objective stimulation. The greater the objectivity and the fluency, the greater the personal stability. In the program indicated, their aims are to utilize factor analysis in a systematic search for directional variables, and to apply these to the abnormal, in order to permit objective measurement of developing stability in youth and in therapy.[13]

Deficit in Specific Aspects of Behavior

For both receptive processes and active processes the evidence of deficit becomes more pronounced as performance becomes more complex. This basic principle was pointed out long ago by Hughlings Jackson (Head, 1926, p. 52) in connection with his investigations of aphasic phenomena. It has been reiterated for other disorders by Wells (1919), by Hollingworth (1930), by Conkey (1938), and by Goldstein (1938).

---

[13] Moore (1930, 1933) has also used factor analysis on ratings of psychiatric symptoms in an effort to arrive at empirical syndromes.

Conkey also noted that recovery occurs most rapidly in the more simple types of performance.

Receptive Processes.—

RECEPTOR THRESHOLDS.—Where the patients need report only the presence or absence of stimulation in some receptor, the majority of the little evidence available shows no deficit. Franz (1910) found no evidence of raised tactual thresholds in psychotics that could not be related to momentary inattentiveness. Grabfield (1914) reported raised thresholds to faradic shock in all diagnostic groups excepting psychoneurotics (1917) and manics (1915a). In 51 schizophrenics the average threshold was high, and about 40% were outside the normal range (1915b). But when Huston (1934) repeated Grabfield's work on schizophrenics with a better technique, he found no significant differences between the means, the scatter about the means, or the interval between ascending and descending series for his patients and his control subjects. Morel (1936) found normal audiometer curves in 31 patients with auditory hallucinations. The threshold was raised in occasional series of presentations while the patient was apparently hallucinating, but it returned immediately to normal. The thresholds of schizophrenics, reported by L. E. Travis (1924) and R. C. Travis (1926) in their studies of the effects of reverie on auditory and visual thresholds, averaged no higher than those of their controls, although they showed more variability. Gelb and Goldstein (1920) reported visual acuity to be satisfactory in several cases of brain injury exhibiting marked perceptual defects. On the other hand, Baird (1906) reported contracted color zones in three of five neurasthenics, and Quensel (1931) reports work by Stern indicating that raised thresholds may underlie defects in visual perception. Good sensory studies are needed. With modern techniques they would be feasible.

PERCEIVING.—In receptive processes where patterns of stimulation must be organized and where learned sets or attitudes play a part, both "functional" and "organic" patients frequently show marked deviations from the normal. When she had schizophrenics copy the Wertheimer figures, Bender (1938) found that they separated the parts, got some parts disoriented in relation to others, and changed the orientation of the figures on the page. Manics, when they cooperated, tended to elaborate the designs without showing evidence of disturbance in these "basic Gestalt principles." Greatly depressed patients occasionally showed the patterns of disorganization found in the "organic" confusional states. Those less depressed tended to draw with exceeding care and precision. Bender gives no data concerning the proportions of patients who showed these disturbances. Kraiz (1936) has reported that some schizophrenics see stationary objects as if they were moving away from the eyes; the visual field may become constricted or so disorganized that the size, the spatial relations, and the consistency of objects are changed.

Several investigators have reported the perception of the body to be altered in the "functional" psychoses (Kraiz, 1936; Schilder, 1935;

Angyal, 1935). In a depersonalized schizophrenic who reported the floor as waving, Angyal analyzed the phenomenon as an exteriorization of the pulse in the plantar region. Cupcea (1936) has reported the absence of the size-weight illusion in 30% of 129 psychotics.

Street (1934) found that both schizophrenics and manic-depressive patients perceived partially drawn figures less readily than did normal individuals. Hunt and Guilford (1933) and Cameron (1936) have found that manic-depressive patients, particularly, see the fluctuations in an ambiguous figure with great difficulty. Once the shift in perspective has been seen, the rates of fluctuation reported are distinctly below those reported by either schizophrenics or normal individuals whose rates are approximately the same.

In an interesting study that should be extended, Malamud and Nygard (1931) found that a few schizophrenic and psychoneurotic patients reported a given distance on the skin as greater when subtended by two points of pressure than when subtended by pain. This tendency reverses that found for almost all normal individuals, and Malamud and Nygard argued that the tendency among psychoneurotics particularly to repress and to compensate for their unpleasant states is generalized to every sort of activity.[14]

Hallucinations constitute the most common form of perceptual symptom in the "functional" psychoses. They appear in from 60% to 80% of schizophrenics, and in about 35% of manic-depressive patients, but in only about 20% of patients with "organic" psychoses. Auditory hallucinations are more prevalent than visual (Lind, 1915; Harrison, 1916; Bowman and Raymond, 1931). Recently, Klüver (1942) has organized a large body of observations on hallucinatory phenomena. Hallucinations apparently have a central origin. In psychoanalytic theory they are explained as wish-fulfillment or projections of the super-ego (Fenichel, 1934, p. 331 ff). Where the latter sort of psychoanalytic explanation is applicable, hallucinations may also be considered as conditioned sensory responses. Here perception of the initial stage of a previously punished act should serve as the conditioned cue.

Cerebral damage may disturb pattern perception in several ways. Some of the most informative studies are the intensive investigations of individual cases grounded in Gestalt theory. Gelb and Goldstein (1920) describe a case of occipital injury with normal acuity who could read slowly and recognize most ordinary objects, but only when he followed the outline with head or hand movements. When they prevented these movements either by restricting devices or by shortening the exposure, this patient could neither read nor recognize forms. He could not recognize a cross-hatched word or objects drawn with discontinuous dots. He could not describe the form of after-images or apprehend "seen movement" such as the "phi" phenomenon. Similar but less pronounced de-

---

[14] This argument is akin to that upon which the projective methods are based. See Chapter 6 by White, and for the results of the Rorschach test, see Klopfer and Kelley (1942).

fects of visual perception have appeared in a case of partial bilateral frontal lobectomy. When Nichols and Hunt (1940) presented the first plate of the Ishihara test of color blindness with the unspecific instruction: "What do you see here?" their patient answered: "A big round spot of blue which is made up of small round blue dots, and some red dots." He missed the "12" completely until later when he was asked to report what figure he saw in this plate.

In the traumatic psychoses with confusional states, the perceptual disturbances uncovered by having patients draw the Wertheimer figures (Bender, 1938) appeared as a disintegration of the parts of the figure from the background, and Goldstein (1937) has found a similar disturbance also characteristic of Pick's disease. Acute alcoholics reproduced the Wertheimer figures incompletely and disorted them with perseverative strokes. Paretics showed a number of different disturbances that Bender related to clinical syndromes. Schilder (1934) has found that in the acute confusions following head injuries points are extended as lines, angles are changed to straight lines, orientation on the page is changed, and connected parts of the figures are separated.

Harrower (1939) has found a rigidity of set manifested in the figure-ground perception of 30 patients with cerebral lesions not involving the occipital lobes. She presented Rubin's vase wherein the outlines of two human faces appear nose to nose, three modifications of this figure in which the vase was enhanced, and three modifications in which the profiles were enhanced. Four sorts of deviation from the behavior of her control-group appeared: (1) marked perseveration of the set engendered by the first perception; (2) failure to recognize any meaningful object in the ambiguous figure even after correctly perceiving all the other figures; (3) such rigidity of set that the less dominant figure could not be seen at will despite its having been seen in drawings where it was dominant, and (4) seeing other objects than profiles or vases throughout the series.

Slowing of pattern perception has been reported repeatedly in cases with cerebral damage.[15] In acute confusions following head injuries, Schilder (1934), for instance, demonstrated with tachistoscopic examination that it took from 200 ms. to 500 ms. for these patients to recognize objects normally recognized in 40 ms. Gelb and Goldstein (1920) showed that the slowing in their case of occipital injury was based on the overt movements required for the recognition of objects, but such an explanation cannot be generalized.

Although these few studies give no systematic picture of the receptive processes in either the "functional" psychoses or the various "organic" conditions, and the same patients have not served in both the threshold and the perceptual studies, it appears tentatively that the perceptual processes show the greater evidence of deficit. Furthermore, the deficit appears to reside in the central processes initiated by receptor action,

---

[15] See: Poppelreuter (1917), Liljencrants (1920), Gelb and Goldstein (1920), Schilder (1934).

particularly in the response to patterns and in the alteration of sets or attitudes.

Active Processes.—

REACTION-TIME.—Almost as soon as the early studies of the personal equation had established the measurement of reaction-time in psychological laboratories, the German investigator, Obersteiner (1874), reported lengthened reaction-times in psychotic patients. Since then the reaction-times of psychotics have been measured with various considerations in view, e.g., to get diagnostic criteria, to get an index of changing clinical conditions, and to understand psychotic symptoms.[16] Most of the earlier investigators used too few subjects to establish differences among psychotic groups or between psychotic and normal groups. Although their techniques and aims differ too much to allow specific comparison of statistical constants, certain tendencies have appeared so consistently in their studies that they are undoubtedly reproducible.

All investigators agree that the average reaction-time for every diagnostic group is longer than that for groups of normal individuals. Patients with "organic" disorders apparently react more slowly than those with "functional" disorders (Bevan-Lewis, 1890; Diefendorf and Dodge, 1908; Wells and Kelley, 1922), but this can hardly be considered an established fact. The reaction-times of manic-depressive patients most nearly approximate the normal. Franz (1906b) was originally surprised to find manics slower than his normal subjects.

Individual differences are increased as would be expected from the fact that some patients in every diagnostic group react as quickly as normal subjects while others show considerable slowing. The slowness of response has been found associated with clinically judged severity of disorder in manic-depressive patients tested repeatedly (Franz, 1906b; Lundholm, 1922), and with relative severity in different individuals tested once (Diefendorf and Dodge, 1908; Scripture, 1916; Huston, Shakow, and Riggs, 1937). Failure to find such association has also been reported by Wells and Kelley (1922) and by Saunders and Isaacs (1929).

Intra-individual variability, as measured by the standard deviation of a series of reaction-times from a single subject, is increased in all the diagnostic groups.[17] Whether manics or depressed patients show the greater variability is still an unsettled question; Lundholm (1922) and Wells and Kelley (1922) say manics, but Franz (1906b) and Bevan-Lewis (1890) say depressed patients. Several investigators have reported greater intra-individual variability in the "functional" disorders than in the "organic" (Bevan-Lewis, 1890; Scripture, 1916; Wells and

---

[16] Reviews of the applications of this method in the psychoses are available in several papers: Franz (1906b), Wells and Kelley (1922), J. McV. Hunt (1936), and a comprehensive bibliography to 1929 in a paper by Saunders and Isaacs (1929).

[17] See: Bevan-Lewis (1890), Franz (1906), Scripture (1916), Wells and Kelley (1922), Saunders and Isaacs (1929), Huston, Shakow, and Riggs (1937), and Rodnick and Shakow (1940).

Kelley, 1922), and so far as we know, no one has reported the contrary. This finding, coupled with the discovery of a higher percentage of anticipatory reactions among patients with "functional" disorders in an experiment where the subjects were instructed to press a key the instant two lines coincided (Saunders and Isaacs, 1929), suggests that the long average reaction-times of patients in the "functional" group are more a matter of motivation and attitude, while those of "organic" patients are more a matter of slowed processes.

Partial substantiation of this hypothesis comes from studies in which the reaction-time method has been used to show that schizophrenics have difficulty sustaining the task or set to respond. Huston, Shakow, and Riggs (1937) assumed that the slowness and variability of schizophrenics might be due to failure to maintain a "high state of readiness to respond." To test their hypothesis, they had their subjects respond to both lights and sounds after preparatory intervals varying from .5 to 10 seconds. In one part of the experiment, a series of reactions was measured with each of the preparatory intervals so that the subject could become accustomed to responding after each one. In another part, reaction-times were measured with the preparatory intervals arranged randomly. Normal subjects averaged shorter times and were less variable with the "regular" procedure, but for the longer preparatory intervals their averages increased and approached those of the "irregular" procedure. Schizophrenic reaction-times for the "regular" procedure rose much more sharply as the preparatory interval was prolonged, and reached equality with those of the "irregular" procedure at somewhere between 2 and 3 seconds. For still longer preparatory intervals in the "regular" procedure, schizophrenics had longer reaction-times than they did for the "irregular" procedure. Patients judged "cooperative" performed more nearly like the normal than did others. Rodnick and Shakow (1940) have repeated this experiment with an extended range of preparatory intervals (1 to 25 seconds). The former trends were thus exaggerated, and they were enabled to construct a composite "set index" from their measures that discriminated between their schizophrenics and controls without any overlapping, even though their control subjects were selected for low intelligence and meager ambition.[18] This is the only score known to us that has differentiated any diagnostic group from a normal group without any overlapping. More important, however, than its possible significance for diagnosis, is the fact that it demonstrates clearly that schizophrenics do not sustain the preparation or task to respond for as long a time as do normal subjects.

---

[18] This composite index is expressed in terms of a single number. The formula is as follows:

$$\text{"Set index"} = 1/2 \left(\frac{M_{7.5r}}{M_{7.5i}} + \frac{M_{15r}}{M_{15i}} \right) M_h + \frac{M_{2r}}{M_{4r}} \cdot M_{2r}$$

where: M_h is the longest mean reaction-time for any series of 10 trials
r stands for "regular" procedure
i stands for "irregular" procedure
The numbers stand for the lengths of the preparatory intervals in seconds

It is interesting theoretically to consider the results of these reaction-time studies in relation to the so-called apathy of schizophrenics and to the conception of this disorder as "withdrawal from reality." In work on animal learning, the reaction-time or latency of a response is frequently used as a measure of its strength (Graham and Gagné, 1940). The shorter the latency, the stronger is the response. Frustrating the satisfactions derived through a response consistently weakens the response, i.e., increases its latency (extinction). Furthermore, an individual animal's latencies show great variability during the course of extinction (Hunt and Solomon, 1943). Seen from this standpoint, the slowness and the excessive variability of the reaction-times of schizophrenics and their failure to maintain a set to react might be taken to indicate a partial extinction of their responses to social stimuli. One should remember in this connection that the response used in these studies of reaction-time is motivated by an experimenter's instructions. According to this interpretation, more complete uncooperativeness would represent a more complete extinction of social responses in these patients. Apathy would represent a more generalized extinction or weakening of the interests learned in the course of social interaction. We would regard these interests as acquired drives (see Miller and Dollard, 1941, Ch. 4). Furthermore, the notion that extinction consists of substituting some other response for the one extinguished would allow for the incorporation of the clinically discerned preoccupations characteristic of schizophrenics into this interpretation, for instance, as substitute responses of an implicit sort. The psychoanalytic notion that the schizophrenic's libido is withdrawn from reality as a result of frustration, and redirected toward internal processes or the ego (Fenichel, 1934; Symons, 1941), to us is essentially similar to this hypothesis we have given. An immediate problem arising from this hypothesis is to determine whether the variability of reaction-times and the "set indices" of "organic" patients differ from those of schizophrenics.[19]

LATENCY OF THE PATELLAR-TENDON REFLEX.—Although weakened preparation for response might account for lengthened reaction time in the "functional" psychoses, the question of slowed neural conduction itself has been raised. Franz (1909) measured the latent-periods of the knee jerk in eight paretics. He found it slightly longer than normal, but his technique was inadequate. More recently, L. E. Travis and his collaborators [20] have measured the latency of the patellar reflex in cases of "functional" psychosis with a view to testing the hypothesis of a reciprocal relationship between higher and lower nerve centers. Con-

---

[19] From the point of view expressed here, the term "functional" would mean *based on learning processes*. This does not imply an absence of organic basis. But if this interpretation of schizophrenic symptoms should be correct, the search for their organic basis becomes but a part of the search for the organic basis of all learning.

[20] See: Travis (1928), Travis and Dorsey (1929), Travis and Young (1930), Dorsey and Travis (1932), and Dysinger (1932).

sidering the catalepsy, muteness, stupor, and disorientation of catatonics as evidence of hypo-function of the cortex, decreased latencies were theoretically expected and found. Increased latencies were predicted and found in manics. We shall not attempt to summarize these studies in detail, for when Huston (1935), in a very careful study, measured patellar latencies in 68 male schizophrenics and in a group of 53 normal male adults matched with the schizophrenics for age, education, and the like, significant differences between the groups in neither means nor standard deviations of latency appeared. Huston, whose interest was concerned directly with the possibility of slowed neural conduction as an explanation of the slowness of schizophrenics in reaction-time and tapping, concluded that this slowness of schizophrenics cannot be attributed to neural defect unless this defect has a locus in centers higher than those involved in the patellar reflex-arc.

DEFICIT AND COMPLEXITY OF THE REACTION.—It is interesting to relate the size of the differences in reaction-time found for schizophrenics and controls to the complexity of the task involved. Fortunately for this purpose, the work at Worcester State Hospital was all done on the same basic population of schizophrenics and controls, although the samples in the various experiments were not coextensive. In Figure 1, by considering the origin on the ordinate as the average time for normal reaction, the bars represent the differences in milliseconds between the mean times of schizophrenics and controls for reactivity of three levels of complexity. For reflex-time (Huston, 1935), the simplest level, the means for the two groups are essentially identical. For simple reaction-time (Huston, Shakow, and Riggs, 1937), the differences between the groups are fairly marked and are statistically significant. Although visual times are considerably longer than auditory, the differences between the groups are similar, 190 ms. and 197 ms. respectively, indicating that when complexity of task is held constant the difference between the groups is relatively constant. For the simplest of choice reactions involving a simple visual discrimination (Huston, Shakow, and Riggs, 1937) another marked increment in the difference between the groups appears. The reactions of patients have been found to average much slower than normal for still more complicated activities: for various types of choice-reaction (Wells and Surges, 1918; Mailloux and Newburger, 1941), for word associations (Otis, 1913; Strong, 1913; Wells, 1919a), for reactions on a substitution-test (Wells and Currie, 1923), for many of the standard tests (Babcock, 1930 and 1941). Unfortunately, however, the data for these tasks at still higher levels of complexity are not comparable with those in the Worcester studies. If, on the basis of this other evidence of slowing, we extrapolate the tendency in Figure 1, we have quantitative evidence that the deficit becomes greater as the complexity of the task increases. Evidence necessary to relate this tendency to the various types of disorder is still lacking. We must agree with Babcock's (1941) emphasis on the importance of time in behavioral proc-

esses to the extent that measures of the time required for various types
and complexities of performance should prove a ready quantitative
approach to certain aspects of deficit and also of intelligence.

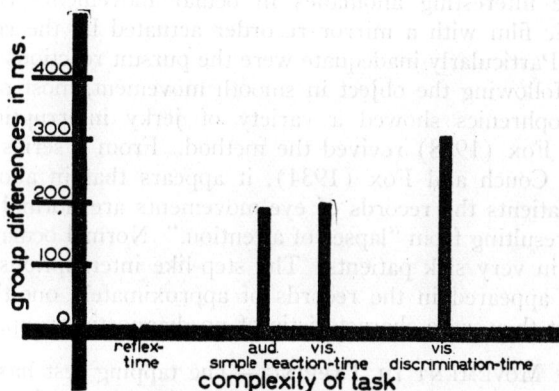

Figure 1

As the complexity of the performance increases, the slowness of schizophrenics,
which is absent at the level of the patellar reflex, becomes progressively more
marked. The origin on the ordinate represents the average time for normal reaction,
and the bars represent the differences in milliseconds between average normal and
average schizophrenic reactions. (From data in papers by Huston, 1935, and
Huston, Shakow, and Riggs, 1937.)

PATELLAR REFLEX.—Changes in the strength of the patellar reflex
in the various organic disorders have been recognized and utilized for
diagnostic purposes for a long time. In one of the early studies of
patellar phenomena, Franz (1909) analyzed the records of 4,199 cases
of paresis and found exaggerated reflexes in 47%, normal reflexes in
24.6%, and reflexes diminished or absent in 21.8%. Diminished reflexes
were associated with fixed pupils, but not with any "mental" phenomena
accessible to Franz. In an investigation of the patellar reflex in the
"functional" psychoses, Strecker and Hughes (1936) found that increasing the stimulating blow brought similar increments of reflex-tension
in schizophrenics and normal subjects, excessive increments of tension
in depressed patients, and no increments in tension in manics and in
agitated involutional patients. When they measured the reinforcing effect
of stretching a spring scale between the hands with 4 kg. of force on
maximally stimulated responses, schizophrenic responses were again like
the normal, but depressed patients showed no reinforcement at all, and
manics showed a typically small and varied amount from moment to
moment. Viewing these results in the light of Sherringtonian theory,
they argue that in depression there must be a great many impulses coming down the cord. These so increase the excitability of the anterior horn
cells that a powerful blow will fire all motor neurones available to the
patellar reflex and leave none to mediate reinforcement. This is an in-

teresting lead. Moreover, it is unusual to find manic-depressive patients differing more than schizophrenics from the normal in any performance.

OCULAR MOVEMENTS.—Years ago Diefendorf and Dodge (1908) found some interesting anomalies in ocular movements recorded on photographic film with a mirror recorder actuated by the corneal protuberance. Particularly inadequate were the pursuit reactions of paretics. Instead of following the object in smooth movement, most paretics and some schizophrenics showed a variety of jerky interruptions. Later Dodge and Fox (1928) revived the method. From a series of studies, the last by Couch and Fox (1934), it appears that in about 50% of psychotic patients the records of eye-movements are normal except for deviations resulting from "lapses of attention." Normal ocular responses may occur in very sick patients. The step-like interruptions of pursuit movements appeared in the records of approximately one-third of the patients, but they were characteristic of no diagnostic group.

RATE OF MOVEMENT IN TAPPING.—The tapping test has been used to investigate the efficiency of psychotic patients ever since Kraepelin (1896) introduced it. The average rate of tapping is probably reduced in all psychotic groups. Of the "functional" disorders, for which the available data are best, schizophrenics average slowest (mean: 19.5 taps in 5 seconds), manic-depressive patients next (24.8), and the controls averaged 28.9 taps. Group differences were all statistically significant (Shakow and Huston, 1936). Investigators have been surprised to discover that this slowing of such performance apparently applies to hyperactive manics as well as to other kinds of psychotics (Franz, 1906).

CONTINUOUS WORK.—Kraepelin (see review, 1925) originally introduced the technique of continuous work because tasks involving but short intervals of performance failed to bring out the deficit evident in everyday life. With various types of tasks schizophrenics work efficiently for a brief period, but performance falls off at an abnormally high rate as they continue. On this kind of observation Kraepelin (1919) appears to have based his judgment that dementia praecox manifests itself largely as a disturbance of volition.[21]

An outstanding exception to this tendency toward rapid reduction of efficiency with continuous performance appears in manic-depressive patients. Using the ergograph, Hoch (1901) found that depressed patients increased the strength of their pulls during a single exhaustion curve before the reduction that comes with exhaustion appeared. Moreover, these patients increased the number of lifts with successive exhaustion curves. This reversal of the fatigue-effect in depressed patients has also been shown for the rate of tapping (Wells, 1919; Strong, 1913), for performance on a substitution test (Wells and Currie, 1923) and on an

---

[21] Incidentally, it is worth noting that weak volition is probably operationally synonymous with weak drive or low motivation. Moreover, all of these terms have much in common with "withdrawal from reality."

addition test (Hull, 1920). Although most investigators have considered this reversal characteristic only of the depressed and retarded and considered it evidence of generalized inhibition (Hoch, 1901; Franz and Hamilton, 1905), Strong (1913) found it more universally among manics than among the depressed. In an unpublished study, Hunt has found similar effects operating with performance on graded arithmetic progressions, and they were just as evident in manics as in depressed patients. Whatever its explanation, here is a clearly reproducible phenomenon, manifesting itself in various sorts of performance, that occurs only in the manic-depressive. No data on the prevalence of the phenomena in manic-depressives are available.

   Association.—Since Galton (1879) first described the process of free-association and suggested its use for "uncovering the uncharted depths of the mind," in various modifications it has become one of the most prominent tools for the study of personality and disorder. Of the four chief modifications, three have been fruitful.

   The least fruitful of these modifications is the classification of verbal responses according to their logical relation to a given list of stimulus-words. This method was brought from Wundt's laboratory by Aschaffenburg (1895, 1899, 1904). Later, Murphy (1920, 1922) continued this approach in America, but he concluded it was fruitless, and agreed with Kraepelin (1919) who had written that "the association-experiment strikes chiefly at the crystallization of the habits of speech, which are for the most part little influenced by the disorders." [22] As Kent and Rosanoff (1910) have pointed out, however, whatever the condition of speech habits in patients, the process of logical grouping is unlikely to uncover anything significant about them, for the significant connections concerned are psychological rather than logical.

   Most famous of the fruitful varieties of associative method is Freud's (1914) continuous free-association, which he appears to have hit upon independently. He developed it as the methodological keystone of psychoanalysis. The fact that the associations of a subject lead backward biographically makes of this method an inverse approach to learning that has taken place within an individual's life history (see Chapter 7 by French). Continuous free-association, however, has been used as an approach to etiology rather than to deficit.

   A second of the fruitful varieties is Jung's (1906) adaptation of the

---

[22] Although the results from vocabulary and information-tests appear to be in line with this view, evidence from the little known study of McDonald (1915) argues that the grammatical structure of speech is considerably altered in the psychoses. He recorded 500 consecutive words from the spontaneous speech of manic-depressive, schizophrenic, and paretic patients, tabulated the parts of speech, and compared these with similar tabulations from the writing of normal adults and children. No patient used as many different words as the child with the poorest vocabulary. Reduced were the proportions of nouns and articles, and increased were the proportions of verbs, pronouns, and adverbs. The patients used a larger proportion of adjectives than did children, but less than did adults. Some differences were also apparent among these diagnostic groups.

method of discrete associations to single stimulus words for psycho-pathological experimentation. From such indicators as delay or blocking of association, repetition of the stimulus word, blushing or embarrassment, and from galvanic reactions and disturbances of breathing correlated with these indicators (Peterson and Jung, 1906), he appears to have inferred the "complex" as a "system of emotionally toned ideas." In this work Jung was attempting to test Freud's generalizations experimentally. He considered his results confirmatory. He found evidence of more complexes in neurotics and psychotics than in normal individuals. Work with word-association was important in leading Jung to his conception of dementia praecox (1909) and to his (1923) division of men into introverts and extraverts and their admixtures. Introverts were individuals who gave associations characterized by subjective or egoistic reference (e.g., table: eating, study, sleep, elegant). Extraverts, on the other hand, gave associations characterized essentially by objective contiguity in space and time (e.g., table: chair, lamp, plate, cover). Because the great majority of the associations of manics were objective, this disorder was considered the extreme of extraversion. Little, we believe, has ever been added to or subtracted from the findings Jung got with his method.[23]

The third fruitful modification of the association-method is that of Kent and Rosanoff (1910). They got the responses of 1,000 normal subjects to a stimulus-list of 100 words, and tabulated them in a frequency table.[24] This standard list enabled them, first, to classify the associations to the stimulus-list from any new subject as "common" (present among the 1,000 responses to this word) or as "individual" (not present), and secondly, to score the degree of commonality of each response in terms of the percentage of the 1,000 subjects who originally gave that response to the stimulus-word concerned. When they gave their stimulus-list to 247 psychotics, the group as a whole gave a higher than average percentage of "individual" responses (26.8%) than did a control group (6.8%). Moreover, schizophrenics gave the highest pro-

---

[23] It seems to us that the methodological kernel of Jung's work has been generally missed. His point that schizophrenics and manics represent the extremes of introversion and extraversion and his recourse to an admixture of intermediate types both imply a measurable variable. This appears to have been the proportion of associations with subjective and with objective reference (see Jung's studies in word-association, 1919). With clinical observation Jung appears to have correlated the relative extremes of such proportions with personal traits. Untrained statistically, he described the trait-correlates of these associative tendencies without their statistical limitations, and cast his findings and his speculations into the mould of a typology. His emphasis on the trait-correlates obscured the essentials of his method. Americans with statistical sophistication, but with probably less psychological sophistication than Jung had, have attacked his problem with questionnaires and ratings for the clinically observed correlates of the basic variable. This mass of American work (for bibliography see Guilford, 1934) has largely by-passed Jung's basic problem. His work should be repeated with a statistical approach.

[24] Copies of this standard list as reprinted from Rosanoff's psychiatry (1938) are available from John Wiley & Co. In view of the changes in our culture which have occurred during the last 30 years, the standardization should probably be repeated.

portion of "individual" responses (38.5%), manic-depressives were second with 21.5%, and approximately 20% appeared for all other types of disorder. Repetitions of this work with schizophrenics (Wells, 1919a; Rawlings, 1921) and with manic-depressives (Wells, 1919a; Strong, 1913) have yielded average percentages of "individual" responses closely approximating those of Kent and Rosanoff. Tendler (1933) found the percentage of "individual" responses for psychoneurotics closer to the normal than to the psychotic average. He found a subgroup, however, whose responses resembled those of children. Wells (1919a) found the percentage of "individual" responses especially high in "deteriorated" schizophrenics, and in manic-depressive patients it reduced as their clinical condition improved.

Although most investigators have disparaged the Kent and Rosanoff method as a diagnostic device because the distributions of "individual" percentages for normal and psychotic groups overlap, the fact that these percentages are exceptionally high in schizophrenia has considerable theoretical interest. If it can be assumed that these verbal associations represent habits inculcated in social interaction, one would expect these high "individual" percentages from the psychoanalytic view that schizophrenia represents a withdrawal from social reality. Moreover, one should not expect them from brain injury not involving the speech areas. Further work with this method is desirable to test this hypothesis.

Emotional Behavior.—A majority of the investigations of emotional behavior in the disorders have been concerned with testing the notion that schizophrenics are apathetic. We shall survey this material from this standpoint, and proceed from simple, basic processes to those more complicated and modifiable.

The startle pattern is a universal and comparatively stable response consisting of blinking the eyes, stereotyped facial movements, head movements, hunching the shoulders, abduction of the upper arms, bending of the elbows, pronation of the lower arms, flexion of the fingers, forward movement of the trunk, contraction of the abdomen, and bending the knees (Landis and Hunt, 1939). When the startle reaction to a pistol shot is recorded by high-speed cinema, it can be analyzed and quantified. With such a technique, Landis, Hunt, and Page (1937) repeated Strauss's (1929) early observations with normal speed photography and found the startle response intensified in schizophrenics, particularly in patients of the catatonic subgroup, and somewhat intensified in the manic-depressive and involutional groups. Paretics and encephalitics responded normally. The response was reduced in epileptics, but the degree of reduction appeared unrelated to any known clinical variables.

From the standpoint of the James-Lange theory, wherein emotions are conceived as the perceptions of the bodily changes aroused by changes in the situation, it has been considered that schizophrenics should exhibit reduced visceral reactions to such exciting stimuli as noises, electrical shocks, and painful pressures. So far as average quantity of reaction is concerned, however, the bulk of results fails to confirm this prediction. Schizophrenics have given breathing changes, measured with the pneumograph, about equal to those of normal subjects.[25] Their changes in blood pressure, as measured by the plethysmograph (DeBruyn, 1909) and the manometer (Gordon, 1930), are about equal to those of the normal. Schizophrenics' changes in pulse-rate following painful stimulations are as great as the normal (Coriat, 1910) or even greater (Cohen and Patterson, 1937). The latter investigators found that increments in heart-rate following painful pressures either increased or failed to decrease with serial presentation in schizophrenics, while they decreased considerably in normal subjects. Results from the galvanic skin-response are inconsistent (see Landis, 1932), but in later studies, schizophrenics' responses averaging as great as the normal have been reported (see Hunt, 1936a).

On the other hand, the expressive records of schizophrenics have shown greater intra-individual variability than is normal (see review by Freeman, 1933). For instance, Forbes and Piotrowski (1934) found greater minute-to-minute variability in the resistance of the skin to small electric flow in 10 catatonics than in the normal, and Richter (1926) has found schizophrenics more variable than any of the "organic" groups on these indicators of autonomic activity. Thus, it appears that variability rather than reduction characterizes the expressive emotional behavior of schizophrenics.

Evidence that "felt emotion" need not disappear in schizophrenia comes from the reports of patients. Lang (1939), writes that "the actual loss of affective strength is considerably less than it seems. For me, external stimuli still retain considerable affective potential even after 9.5 years of the psychosis" (p. 196). On the other hand, we have also heard schizophrenics complain that they "don't feel anything anymore." Whether this felt apathy concerns only particular interests or is truly general is uncertain. Olson (1931) failed to find anything significantly different from the normal on the Pressey X-O test where the subject is to cross out unpleasant words, but Wechsler (1939) did find that schizophrenics expressed an interest in more occupations after insulin-therapy. All one can say is that subjective apathy is not universal among schizophrenics.

Although no reduction of emotional behavior at the reflex or autonomic level appears in schizophrenics, they show marked deviations from the normal and probably from the behavior of patients with "organic" disorder in overt behavior related to emotion. Instead of jerking their hands away quickly, Bender and Schilder (1930) found that stuporous catatonics usually responded to painful electric shocks with tonic squirming in the stimulated hand, tenseness of the whole body, and the visceral reactions mentioned above. Such squirmings were easily

---

[25] See: DeBruyn (1909); Pollock and Dollear (1916); Bender and Schilder (1930).

conditioned to light or touch signals, and furthermore, they generalized to a wider range of conditioned stimuli than did the withdrawals of normal subjects. This squirming response might argue for apathy as Bender and Schilder thought, or it might argue that some other response tendency interfered with hand-withdrawal. Generalization to an excessively broad range of stimuli might argue for "incomplete analysis of the situation" (Bender and Schilder), for a stronger conditioned response, or for a higher degree of "sensitization" in the schizophrenic than in the normal.

From another type of attack at the overt level comes evidence clearly confirming the judgment of apathy in schizophrenia. In a study of the "level of aspiration" with dart-throwing, Hausmann (1933) found that schizophrenics, excepting the paranoid type, indiscriminately raised their "bids" after failure or lowered them after success. The paranoid patients clung to high "bids" regardless of objective scores and in spite of the fact that they were doubly penalized for falling below their predicted scores. This differs markedly from the behavior of manic-depressive patients in this sort of situation. Escalona (1941) found the initial "level of aspiration," measured in terms of predicted scores on a maze-task and a pegboard, highest for manics, next for normal subjects, and lowest for depressed patients. After failure, the order consistently changed to normal subjects highest, depressed patients next, with manics decidedly lowest. Manics either avoided seeing failure or were absurdly afraid of it, while neither success nor failure in the situation affected the initially low predictions of the depressed patients. Stumbar (1934) found that schizophrenics failed to recall more "uncompleted" than "completed" tasks as did Zeigarnik's normal subjects. And Rickers-Ovsiankina (1937b) found that schizophrenics failed to show the normal adult tendency to resume "uncompleted" rather than "completed" tasks. When she (1937a) observed one at a time through a one-way screen the behavior of matched groups of schizophrenics and normal subjects toward a table laden with games and puzzles, no differences between the groups in duration and consistency of response appeared. But the normal subjects consistently played the games and attempted to solve the puzzles, while the schizophrenics, excepting the paranoid patients, aimlessly touched one object after another. Even during this aimless manipulation, they appeared to be thinking about something else. She concluded that "the dynamic conditions prevailing in peripheral regions of the schizophrenic personality are such as to impede the formation of the firm, segregated tension-systems necessary for directed activities" (1937a, p. 176).

Here again the evidence of deficit becomes most pronounced in the more complex and modifiable of the emotional processes. Apparently the apathy of schizophrenics is expressed only at the overt level as lack of interest in the surroundings and activities which typically concern people. Here is evidence that the apathy of schizophrenics consists essentially in a loss of socially acquired drives. Furthermore, this evidence fits our interpretation of schizophrenic symptoms as extinctions of socially learned responses (see above).

IMPROVEMENT WITH REPETITION, INDIVIDUAL VARIABILITY, AND THE QUESTION OF SCHIZOPHRENIC DETERIORATION.—If deterioration is defined as deficit increasing with time (Kraepelin's definition, 1915), the generalization that schizophrenics deteriorate would require (1) that they should show less output with successive repetitions spaced over a relatively prolonged period, and/or (2) that the amount of improvement effected by repetition should be less as the age of the psychosis increases. Although schizophrenics have consistently shown less increase in output with repetition of a performance than is normal, the fact that they do generally increase their output on all sorts of tasks denies the first alternative implication.[26] Of particular significance in this connection is the improvement between sessions, separated by intervals of three months, that Huston (1932) found in performance on Miles' pursuitmeter and that Shakow and Huston (1936) found in the rate of tapping. While normal subjects showed improvement within each session, their scores were poorer on the first trials of a new session than on the last trials of a preceding session. Schizophrenics, on the other hand, improved less within each session, but they actually averaged better for the first trials of a new session than they had on the last trials of preceding sessions. Shakow and Huston considered that this was a manifestation of a slow adjustment of schizophrenics to the general aspects of the experimental situation. The fact that Kendig and Richmond (1940) found a large proportion of schizophrenics improve or maintain their level of performance in retests with the Stanford-Binet after several years of psychosis also argues against this first implication of the generalization that schizophrenics deteriorate.

The evidence available also contradicts the second implication. Kent (1911) actually obtained the greatest improvement in repeated performances from the dilapidated schizophrenics who had been hospitalized for years. The fact that the majority of single measures of output have failed to correlate with the length of time that patients have been hospitalized also argues indirectly against progressing deficit in schizophrenia. Thus, the results of experiments aimed most directly at the crux of the question of schizophrenic deterioration clearly contradict Kraepelin's generalization. It should be noted that many recent psychiatric observations also contradict this generalization (see also Chapter 29 by Cameron).

These same studies have also shown consistently that the output of schizophrenics on tasks repeated is much more variable than is the output of normal subjects. Hunt (1936b) and Wittman (1937) have secured evidence that intra-individual variability in output is greater in schizophrenia than it is in such an "organic" psychosis as paresis. It

---

[26] Both of these facts have been shown in all the studies of repeated performance. See: Gatewood (1909), Kent (1911, 1918), Boring (1913), Huston (1932), Hunt (1936b), and Shakow and Huston (1936).

has also been shown that the ups and downs of output in individual patients is associated with similar ups and downs in psychiatric ratings of "attitude" (Wittman, 1937) and in self-reported attitudes toward the tasks of card-sorting and adding (Hunt, 1936b). Furthermore, Kent (1918) and Hunt (unpublished study) have found that if one takes the effort to gain the confidence and cooperation of schizophrenic patients, one can frequently get large increases in output without what can be considered practice. So far, Hunt has been unable to find any patient with a typical "organic" disorder in whom such a cultivation of co-operation automatically produces marked improvement in output. The training given a case of bilateral frontal lobectomy was effective in increasing output (Nichols and Hunt, 1940), but this consisted of teaching concrete procedures, while getting cooperation consists in giving the patient an impression that he is "understood" and appreciated.[27]

Indirect evidence indicates further that the ups and downs in attitude and in output shown by schizophrenics are associated with the variations in emotional activity at the autonomic level. Gordon (1930) has found variations in blood pressure associated with "distinct modifications of the schizophrenic's attitude, behavior, and his mode of feeling and thinking." And still more indirectly, Sleeper and Jellinek (1936) found the degree of polyuria in schizophrenics correlated significantly only with judged emotional deterioration (negatively) and with IQ (positively). Apparently the excessive water-drinking of these patients was emotionally driven, and so long as the drive remains, they continue to manifest interests and to perform relatively well on tests.

These findings argue that the deficit in schizophrenics is not progressive, and also, that it is one of motivation rather than one of capacity. Furthermore, the excessive variability of schizophrenic output, and the relation of this output to reportable attitude and to cooperativeness constitute more facts which fit our hypothesis that schizophrenic symptoms represent the extinction of socially acquired drives and responses.[28]

Conditioning.—Perhaps the fact that a majority of the few studies of conditioning in patients with "functional" psychoses show them equal or superior to normal individuals is significant in connection with this motivational interpretation of schizophrenic deficit. Pfaffmann and Schlosberg (1935) found that both manic-depressive and schizophrenic patients averaged more conditioned knee jerks than did college students. Grecker

---

[27] Hunt found this possible with only 17 of the 25 schizophrenics in his group. One frequently observes, however, that given schizophrenics will cooperate for one of a staff but not for others. Presumably if one could extend one's range of social manners, one could increase the proportion of schizophrenics whose cooperation one could obtain. It would be interesting to know how large the non-responding proportion is.

[28] These findings would also appear to confirm Kraepelin's (1919) contention that "will" and "attention" are the aspects of "mind" that suffer most in dementia praecox. It is interesting to note in this connection that these faculties are synonymous with "motivation" so far as any operational basis, of which we can think or imagine, is concerned.

(Razran, 1934) found no difference in the rates of acquiring a conditioned tactual response by catatonic and normal subjects. Bender and Schilder (1930) found that schizophrenics showed evidence of conditioning quite as quickly as did normal subjects, but the conditioned responses differed considerably. With a test based on conditioning and extinguishing a response to avoid shock, Gantt (1938) found a high degree of resistance to conditioning in several "organic" disorders. Although he reports no specific results from patients with "functional" disorders, Gantt implies that they may show less resistance by suggesting that the test might be used to distinguish between the "functional" and "organic" disorders. On the other hand, Shipley (1934) found that schizophrenics both acquired and extinguished conditioned-galvanic-skin-responses more slowly than any of his other groups, which in descending order were: manic-depressives, psychoneurotics, and college students. Studies comparing the ease of conditioning various kinds of responses for a cross section of the hospital population would be very valuable.

Memory.—Clinical observers noted long ago that senile patients failed to recall or to utilize recent experiences even when older ones could be recalled. Psychiatric literature describes this retrograde amnesia as common also in general paralysis, psychoses with arteriosclerosis, and Korsakoff's syndrome, but such a deficit is not considered characteristic in the "functional" disorders. Several experimental investigations corroborate these clinical observations. Simmins (1933) has shown that, of the types of patients in her group, only patients with the senile psychoses, general paralysis, and epilepsy performed below normal on her memory tests when general ability (g) was partialed out. Landis and Rechetnick (1934) found good performance on tests of recent memory more closely associated with clinical judgments of improvement in paretics treated with pyrexia or malaria than any other type of performance. When Wells and Martin (1923) gave to 111 patients their memory-test, which involves eight types of impression varying in age from such personal information as birthday and questions concerning standardized school knowledge to recognizing twelve just previously presented postcards in a group of 24, the average of the senile group fell to the 53rd percentile of the normal group and the average of the paretics to the 68th percentile, while that of manic-depressives fell only to the 74th, and that of the schizophrenics only to the 82nd percentile. Even the gross scores show the "organic" groups below the "functional" groups without taking into account the general level of performance. Normal scores on this test correlated +.81 with intelligence.

On the other hand, Rawlings (1921), Foster (1920), and Babcock (1933) have reported test-evidence for memorial defect in the functional disorders. Rawlings even went so far as to consider her findings as indirect evidence of cortical degeneration in schizophrenia. None of these investigators partialed out the general level of performance, however; and none found any memorial deficit as great in the "functional" disorders as in the "organic." Beble's (1925) finding that the average scores of post-encephalitics on Wells' memory test are insignificantly below the normal indicates that cerebral damage need not affect memory. No one, so far as we know, has found any memorial deficit except temporary amnesia in patients following surgical injury to the brain.

The effects of age on memorial function have been shown in a recent study by Shakow, Doekart, and Goldman (1942). When they plotted the scores of 500 normal individuals, aged 15 to 90 and selected to provide a representative sample of the population at each decade, on Wells' memory-test as a function of age, they found evidence of deficit to be drastic after 60 years. Recent material was most affected. When the scores of the various psychotic groups were compared with those of normal individuals in the same decade of age, the effect of the psychoses appeared much less than had previously been supposed. Patients with senile psychoses showed more loss than did psychotics with cerebral arteriosclerosis. In this latter group, vocabulary showed a relatively greater loss than memorial functions, and scores on organized verbal material were much more severely affected than those on such tests as the repetition of digits. As these authors point out, such results raise the question of generalized aphasia in these psychoses with cerebral arteriosclerosis. Moreover, aging appears to have more drastic effects on memory as assessed by Wells' test than do even the "organic" psychoses.

Several investigators [29] have inquired whether the various psychoses affect memory differentially according as its efficiency is tested by the method of recall or the method of recognition. The significance of these studies is unclear to us. Discrepancies between the results of the two methods appear in individual cases, but they are not consistent for any diagnostic group, and as yet they stand unrelated to anything else.

RETENTION AND IMPRESSION.—Several studies tend to show that the memorial deficit in the psychoses consists more of failure to effect an impression than of failure to retain impressions. Of the various tests of memory, those of immediate memory show the greatest loss, especially in the "organic" disorders. Hull (1917, 1920) had patients associate nonsense syllables with twelve Chinese characters to a criterion of one perfect repetition. Patients required longer (av. 102 minutes) than the controls (av. 26 minutes) to reach the criterion. Paretics required considerably more time than did schizophrenics. Retention, measured in terms of proportion of syllables recalled when the Chinese characters were presented a week later, however, was better for the patients than for the controls. But retention measured by the method of savings again showed the controls superior. They could relearn to criterion more rapidly than the patients. Wechsler (1917), using memory tests, also concluded that memorial deficit, at least in Korsakoff's syndrome, consists in an inability at the "fixation stage of memory."

---

[29] See: Achilles (1920), Liljencrants (1922), Moore (1919), and Wylie (1930).

Not all results have agreed with these. When Foster (1920) had schizophrenics draw geometric figures repeatedly from memory, they often elaborated them until they were unrecognizable. When Curran and Schilder (1937) had subjects repeat a narrative over and over, they did it willingly until the "trace appeared organized," then further repetition produced a gradual deterioration of the pattern in both normal individuals and patients. A schizophrenic showed especially marked modifications; by the third repetition, no items of the original narrative persisted. The characteristic failure of schizophrenics to sustain a task would account for these results, however, and the fact that schizophrenics have reported events, occurring while they were stuporous, with considerable accuracy after the stupor argues that their failures of either impression or retention may be an artifact of their uncooperativeness (Lundholm, 1932). When Bender, Curran, and Schilder (1938) had patients with Korsakoff's syndrome draw the Wertheimer figures repeatedly from memory, the tendency toward more primitive types of organization became progressively more pronounced. Gantt (1938) found that two cases of Korsakoff's syndrome retained a conditioned defense reaction but a few minutes, while other patients with "functional" disorders retained the same conditioned response for weeks. When he had senile patients copy one of a pair of figures and draw another from memory, D. E. Cameron (1940) found perseverative tendencies interfering with the process of impression, and compensatory tendencies to elaborate interfered with retention. These results are interesting, but generalizations are impossible at this stage. Deficiencies of impression can hardly account for all memorial defects, however, for every clinical observer has seen cases of paresis and senility who show progressive retrograde loss of memory for the events of their lives. It would appear as if such deteriorative processes damaged the structure carrying the traces of previous behavior.

Language and Thought.—Although disturbances of language and thought have been evident for centuries (Jelliffe, 1930), most experimental studies of them have appeared since the First World War.

Aphasia.—(See also Chapter 18 by Cobb.) Interest in the language disturbances of the aphasias started as a problem in cerebral localization when Gall described the loss of speech with right hemiplegias in 1819. (For the history see Head, 1926, and Weisenburg and McBride, 1935.) Broca further stimulated this interest during the 1860's when he described cases of speech disorder as a result of destruction of the triangular and opercular portions of the inferior frontal gyrus of the left hemisphere demonstrated at necropsy. Trousseau introduced the term "aphasia" in 1864. At about this same time Hughlings Jackson began his now famous observations emphasizing the necessity for an empirical examination of the phenomena of speech-disturbances.[30] He conceived the

---

[30] These papers received little attention until Head had them reprinted (see Jackson, 1915).

aphasias as disturbances of the power to "propositionise" which included "internal speech" or thought and voluntary action as well as spoken or written language. He agreed that the posterior portion of the left frontal convolution is most frequently damaged in persons manifesting these disturbances, but he argued that it was absurd to say that the destroyed tissue "caused" the abnormal utterances. ". . . It has enough to answer for in leaving him unable to speak . . . The positive symptoms arise during the activity of lower centers or lower nervous arrangements which have escaped injury" (Jackson, 1915, pp. 154–155).

The present status of the aphasias may be found in the works of six investigators. The view that the aphasias consist in a list of specific defects of language function, each based on lesions with specific locus in the cerebrum, appears in the writings of Henschen (1921–22) and Kleist (1914–18). On the sensory side, Kleist, for instance, differentiates word-sound-deafness, word-deafness, name-deafness, and sentence-deafness; on the motor side, he differentiates speech-sound-muteness, word-muteness, name-muteness, and sentence-muteness. Each of these special defects is conceived as the result of finely delimited lesions. Henschen believes that even logical thought can be localized. Weisenberg and McBride (1935) point out that Kleist's work suffers because the examinations described were not sufficient to show the actual characteristics of the changes in language and behavior, and further, because the lesions in the brains of his injured soldiers were not so precisely delimited as to justify the conclusion of such nice relations between lesions and behavioral disturbances.

In his famous work on aphasia, Head (1926) carried on the trends initiated by Hughlings Jackson. He assembled a battery of serial tests with standardized procedures which is excellent for analysis of the various aspects of language behavior, but does not sample nonlanguage behavior. From the empirical results of his work, Head concluded that the aphasias were not specific defects of speaking, reading, and writing, nor could they be classified as motor or sensory. He agreed with Jackson that they are disorders of "propositionising" for which he substituted the terms, "symbolic formulation and expression." The more abstract the symbol, the greater the difficulty presented in aphasic patients. Head's purposely loose classification of verbal, syntactical, nominal, and semantic disturbances, which, like his tests, considers only aspects of language behavior, is less valuable than his theory. Although he opposed extreme mechanical views of localization of function like those of Henschen and Kleist, he considered lesions in the lower portion of the pre-central and post-central convolutions associated with verbal aphasia. The association between area of lesion and the nominal and semantic classes of aphasia was less definite. Head argued that intellectual capacity is not primarily affected, but he admitted that in proportion as "symbolic formulation and expression" are necessary for the perfect exercise of psychical aptitudes, general intelligence undoubtedly suffers.

Goldstein (1910) early opposed the classification of the aphasias into specific defects like alexia (inability to read), agraphia (inability to write), aphemia (inability to speak) or amnesic aphasia (loss of memory for words), and he opposed the attempt to localize such specific acts within the cerebrum. He has repeatedly pointed out that, when the examination (1939a) is extended to cover as many aspects of the individual patient's behavior as possible, disturbances of these specific acts never occur alone.[31] His tests include form-perception (Gelb and Goldstein, 1920) and sorting and manipulating (now somewhat standardized, see Goldstein and Sheerer, 1941) as well as language tests and observations of general behavior. He has observed a wide assortment of behavior disorders in patients ordinarily classed as aphasic. They employ "roundabout" methods of action such as tracing a figure with finger or head movements or responding with "that is for drinking" instead of with "cup" when shown a cup and asked what it is. They also show: rigidity of point of view, inability to carry on a simple course of action once it is interrupted, a tendency to become agitated and fearful and more than usually inept when presented with once simple tasks that they can no longer do. This last type of disturbance Goldstein (1939a) terms "catastrophic" behavior, and he interprets such characteristics as fanatical orderliness and avowed disinterest in many situations as methods of escaping this catastrophic embarrassment. For Goldstein (1926, 1927), all these alterations of behavior are manifestations of a single basic change in the total personality of patients with cerebral lesions. He does not deny that the locus of the lesion determines some manifestations of this basic disturbance, but the basic disturbance follows lesions anywhere in the cerebrum. In this Gestalt view he stands at the opposite extreme from Henschen and Kleist.

This single basic change in the total personality is conceived as a loss of capacity to assume the "categorical" or "abstract" attitude which underlies: the voluntary assumption of mental sets, the detachment of the ego from the outer world or from inner experiences, the reflective shifting from one aspect of a situation to another, the holding of several aspects of a situation simultaneously, the formation of hierarchic concepts, the capacity of planning ahead or of thinking and performing symbolically (Goldstein, 1939a, 1940; Goldstein and Sheerer, 1941). Only in the sense that Goldstein's conception of the disturbance in aphasia involves a symbolic process does it agree with Head's. Goldstein's contribution is great, but his emphasis on extensive studies of individual patients affords no statistical information and lends itself to overgeneralization.

Weisenburg and McBride (1935) have made the first study of aphasics that employed a battery of tests involving both language and nonlanguage functions previously standardized on a group of normal individuals comparable to the patients in age, education, and occupational

---

[31] See: Gelb and Goldstein (1920, 1924), Goldstein (1922, 1926, 1927, 1928) and for rapid summaries in English see: Goldstein (1940, Chs. 3 and 4, and 1942) or Goldstein and Sheerer (1941).

status. They also limited the aphasic group to clear-cut cases uncomplicated by any other disorder, and employed a second control group of patients with unilateral cerebral lesions without aphasia. The study was carried out because Weisenburg had found normal individuals who failed some of Head's tests, and because he was dissatisfied with Goldstein's generalizations. From the percentile-profiles of performance, Weisenburg and McBride classified their 60 aphasics into four groups. (1) The predominantly expressive group (which showed defects in articulation and in the formation of words with less pronounced limitations in receptive functions, in the higher language functions, and in the various nonlanguage tests) was largest (43.3%), had the best prognosis, and had lesions localized largely in the anterior or motor part of the dominant hemisphere. (2) The predominantly receptive group (which showed more or less serious disturbances in the perception and understanding of spoken language and printed material with less serious disturbances in the expressive functions) was second largest (28.3%), had an uncertain prognosis depending on the nature of the lesions which were also localized in the anterior portion of the dominant hemisphere but involved the posterior portion to a greater extent. (3) The expressive-receptive group (in which all language functions were severely and equally disturbed) constituted 20% of the sample, had a prognosis definitely poor, and had lesions involving a larger portion of both the anterior and posterior parts of the dominant hemisphere. (4) The amnesic group (where the defects lay primarily in inability to evoke names of objects, conditions, and qualities) constituted only 8.3% of the sample, and the locus of the lesions was indefinite. Contrary to Goldstein's findings, these amnesic patients usually recognized the correct word when they produced it accidentally or when it was suggested to them. They showed defects on nonlanguage tests, but none commensurate with those on language tests. Because the functional defects produced by similar lesions showed great individual variations, Weisenburg and McBride opposed strenuously the theories of specific localization of Henschen and of Kleist. Because these disturbances were never confined to the language functions, they disagreed with Head's interpretation of aphasia as a specific disturbance of language functions. On the other hand, because their aphasics cooperated well, remained socially adjusted to a high degree, and showed the greatest defect in language-tests while the patients with unilateral lesions showed the greatest defects in nonlanguage tests, they found no basis for assuming such a fundamental disturbance as Goldstein described as a universal basis for aphasic phenomena. Unfortunately, however, Weisenburg and McBride, in choosing tests that lent themselves to quantitative scoring, failed to include any of Goldstein's tests of form-perception or of sorting.

While there is considerable agreement among the results and interpretations of Head, of Goldstein, and of Weisenburg and McBride, the disagreements argue that the fundamental nature of aphasic disturbances is still inadequately conceived. Psychologists concerned with learning and

its underlying neural basis should not be surprised at the individual func‹
tional variability produced by similar lesions. The performances, linguistic and nonlinguistic, involved in the various tests must be products
of the individual's past behavior. What *a priori* basis is there for assuming that a given instrumental habit or skill should have the same architectonic organization in the cortex of every individual when it is well
known that different cues and different muscle systems may serve the
same instrumental acts in different individuals and in the same indi‹
vidual at different times?

"Abstract" Behavior in Nonaphasics with Cerebral Lesions.[32]
—Goldstein's generalization that cerebral lesions always produce disturbances of what he calls "abstract" behavior is partially based on the work
of Weigl (1941) and of Nadel (1938). When they gave all tests except
the Vigotsky to patients with cerebral lesions, and included normal subjects which Nadel matched for age and education, defects appeared in all
their patients. Normal subjects often started by sorting objects in such
series as they had seen in concrete situations, but they shifted readily to
the "categorical" approach and usually appeared to prefer it. His generalization, but not necessarily his conception of the deficit as "abstract" behavior, is also supported by the work of Halstead (1940) who gave his
own sorting test to patients after brain-surgery, by the work of Hanfmann and Kasanin (1942) who used the Vigotsky in a study involving
24 patients with "organic" psychoses, by the work of Cleveland (1942)
where the sorting test was given to 20 senile patients, by the work of
Nichols and Hunt (1940) with a case of partial bilateral frontal lobectomy of very superior original ability who failed the Vigotsky and was
unable to do double alternation, and by the work of Hollingworth (1930)
and Conkey (1938) using a hierarchy of tests with cases of traumatic

---

[32] Since we shall refer to them frequently, we give a brief description of the
main performance tests of "abstract" ability (see Goldstein and Sheerer, 1941).
The Goldstein-Sheerer cube-test was designed to determine whether a subject can
analyze a small colored figure well enough to copy it in larger size with Kohs
blocks. Their stick-test was designed to determine whether a subject can copy
figures composed of sticks and reproduce them from memory. Unless the pattern
resembles some commonly experienced object like a roof, such a performance is
assumed to involve an abstract concept of direction in space. The Gelb-Goldstein
color-sorting test was designed to determine whether a subject can sort the Holm-
gren wools according to color concepts. The Weigl color-form test consists of a
dozen blocks in three shapes and four colors. It was designed to determine whether
a subject can shift from one of these categories to the other when told to sort the
objects another way. The Weigl object-sorting test consists of 30 objects which are
randomly arranged on a table. It was designed to determine whether a subject can
sort them according to general concepts, shift these concepts, and discover the principle in groupings presented by the experimenter. The Vigotsky test of concept
formation (Hanfmann and Kasanin, 1942) was originally designed to study schizophrenic thinking (Vigotsky, 1934), but it has been adopted by Goldstein and his
collaborators. This test consists of 22 objects in five geometrical shapes, in five
colors, and in four sizes. The subject has to sort these 22 blocks into four categories, each of which is named with a nonsense syllable. As he sorts, he is corrected
until he has arrived at the definition of the categories (small-tall, small-flat, large-
tall, large-flat), or has had them all placed for him, whence he is asked to formulate
the principle verbally.

head injury. A possible exception to this generalization appears in the work of T. Hunt on the frontal lobotomy patients of Freeman and Watts (1942). Of her psychotics 45% actually improved on the stick test after the operation cutting the pathways between the frontal lobes and the thalamus. Only 10% were poorer. These findings are inconclusive, however, because only the stick test was employed and these patients were already severely psychotic before the operations were performed.

A number of investigators have opposed Goldstein's dichotomy of "abstract" and "concrete" abilities. Halstead (1940), who developed a nice technique of scoring his own sorting test, found patients who sorted into categories like "pictures" or "round things," yet they were distinctly poorer than controls in the percentage of objects spontaneously grouped, and they recalled fewer of the objects after five minutes. Bolles (1937) described four levels of "abstract" ability, and Hanfmann and Kasanin (1942) found at least three levels of performance on the Vigotsky. Cleveland (1942) found individual differences in sorting capacity and followed Wegrocki (1940) in considering a hierarchy of ability for abstracting and generalizing. The case of partial bilateral frontal lobectomy reported by Nichols and Hunt (1940) succeeded with most of Goldstein's tests, but he failed the Vigotsky, double-alternation, and complex arithmetic progressions. It was possible to teach him to do both of the former, but impossible to teach him to do arithmetic progressions that involved sustaining more than two tasks simultaneously. He learned, for instance, to do series like (1–2–4–7–) by writing in the differences between successive numbers. This process yielded two separate series, the main series and that composed of these differences (1, 2, 3, —). These he had to manipulate conjointly in order to comply with the instruction to keep the main series going, and thus the main task appeared to resolve itself into two separate tasks for this patient. On the other hand, this patient did not learn to do a series like (30–29–27–24–) even when the number of items was increased and practice with series after series was given. Keeping the opposed directions of the main series and of the series of differences straight during their conjoint manipulation was more than he could manage. Similarly, complicating the main series so that its breakdown resulted in three separate series, e.g., (1–2–4–8–15–) made it too difficult for him. All these results argue for a hierarchy of "abstract" ability which Goldstein now accepts (Goldstein and Sheerer, 1941).

While Goldstein's theories of "abstract" ability have led to much fruitful work, to us "abstract" ability is still unsatisfying as a concept. We should like to reduce every aspect of deficit to a truly measurable variable. Rate of performance and rate of learning would be readily quantifiable merely by using time as the variable. Rigidity of set or attitude should be readily quantifiable in a similar fashion. The results obtained by Nichols and Hunt (not all of which are given in their paper, 1940) point toward the possibility of defining the "power" aspect of the capacity required for these performances in terms of the number of tasks or lines of activity that a person can sustain simultaneously or synthesize into a single complex operation.

Many concepts appear to involve such a synthesis. For example, learning to count, where the verbal habit of saying numbers in a given order is synthesized with touching objects consecutively. Probably number concepts become "meaningful" only after such a synthesis has become habituated. Inability to learn to count and to form number concepts, as is sometimes seen in the feebleminded,[33] may be attributed to a lack of the fundamental capacity (see definition in footnote above), required for such a synthesis. And in turn, this lack of fundamental capacity may perhaps be attributed to an absence of the necessary neurological substrata. The fact that individuals who receive brain injuries early in life develop vocabularies below their level on the Stanford-Binet and on performance tests (Hebb, 1942) fits this hypothesis. Furthermore, from an introspective analysis, the sorting tests appear to require that one sustain several tasks simultaneously. It is not surprising, in this connection, that performance at the highest level on the Vigotsky is limited almost entirely to college people (Hanfmann and Kasanin, 1942), for college serves both to select the capable and to habituate such syntheses. We would consider the deficit found in patients with cerebral lesions who cannot learn given types of performance as one of fundamental capacity, and tentatively we should like to conceive this deficit in capacity in terms of a rigidity of set and a reduction in the number of tasks or lines of activity that can be sustained simultaneously or synthesized into a single complex operation. Such a conception should stimulate research along another line. The chief defect of the notion lies in defining a "task" or a "line of activity" for experimental work, but this may not prove unfeasible.

For patients with cerebral lesions who can relearn performances, on the other hand, the requisite fundamental capacity cannot be considered destroyed. Aphasics frequently relearn to recognize objects, to name them, and the like, and to what extent other deficits might yield to training is still unknown. When performances reappear, either the healing of tissues or the reorganizing of the skills or habits, e.g., the language habit, over new architectonic arrangements might conceivably account for their reappearance.

THOUGHT IN SCHIZOPHRENIA.—Nearly all work on thought and language in the "functional" psychoses has concerned schizophrenics, and most of the investigations of schizophrenic thinking in controlled situations are very recent. Consider first the basic empirical phenomena.

A number of deficiencies have appeared repeatedly in tasks involving language. The majority of schizophrenics fail to sustain a task or a

---

[33] Based on unpublished work by S. B. Williams who found he could not get many of his feebleminded subjects at Letchworth Village to synthesize the acts of pointing to objects and saying numbers.

topic.[34] This substantiates further the results from the reaction-time studies. They usually fail to see absurdities or to interpret proverbs.[35] A majority of schizophrenics fail in tasks involving the discernment of essential differences or the use of analogies (Wegrocki, 1940; Shipley, 1940). They distort the meaning of words, and these distortions of word-meaning and more especially of topical meaning become more and more pronounced with successive requests for clarification by the experimenter.[36] In these distortions, words take the place of real objects (Katan, 1938); Despert, 1940), or the schizophrenic may use a metaphor but omit the *as though* and then slip from the figurative to the literal meaning of the words used in the metaphor (Muncie, 1937; Woods, 1938). Great individual differences among schizophrenics appear in all these performances and in the tendencies indicated here.

Nonlinguistic tasks have yielded a related series of deficiencies in the performances of schizophrenics. On a picture completion test (Healy PC-II), Hanfmann (1939a) found that most of her schizophrenics responded like normal subjects much of the time, but occasional conspicuous deviations occurred in which they apparently disregarded spatial relationships, used a concrete object to epitomize the situation represented, or transposed the picture into reality. On the Vigotsky test of concept formation, 26 of the 62 schizophrenics in the sample of Hanfmann and Kasanin (1942) got scores below the poorest control, and 14 showed a defect comparable to that found in their patients with "organic" disorders.[37] The poorest of schizophrenics may show no appreciation of the sorting tasks at all, or they may use "concrete" bases such as putting together objects commonly seen in kitchen or bathroom, and be unable to shift to any other like color or shape (Bolles, 1937). On the Vigotsky, Cameron (1939b) found them including the blotter, the pencil, or even the experimenter in the task, asking to have the task altered, and showing incongruities between action and speech such as forming color groups

---

[34] See: Gatewood (1909), Kraepelin (1919), Hunt (1936b), Cameron (1938a, 1939a), and Wegrocki (1940).

[35] See the test studies above and: Hadlich (1931), Zeigarnik (described in Hanfmann and Kasanin, 1942), Hausmann (1933), Hunt (1935), Hanfmann (1939b), Wegrocki (1940).

[36] See: Muncie (1937), Woods (1938), Cameron (1938b), Katan (1939), and Wegrocki (1940).

[37] Hull (1920) appears to have made the first observations of this sort with a technique similar to that of Ach of the Wurzburg school which was also the forerunner of the Vigotsky test, but little attention was paid them until Vigotsky's (1934) results were translated and Bolles (1937) found deteriorated hebephrenics showing a deficit on Goldstein's tests of "abstract" ability. Other studies yielding similar results are: Bolles and Goldstein (1938), Cameron (1939a), and Cleveland (1942). Predicting the outcome of the shock therapies in schizophrenics from performance on the sorting tests has also appeared promising (Bolles, Rosen, and Landis, 1938; Goldstein, 1939b; Zubin and Thompson, 1941). Furthermore, symptoms such as clinically discerned thought disorders, dilapidated personal appearance, and hallucinations, all probably related to poor performance on the sorting tests, have been found associated with poor prognosis in schizophrenics (Terry and Rennie, 1938).

but describing them by enumerating the shapes. On the other hand, eleven of those in the sample of Hanfmann and Kasanin performed at the highest level found among normal subjects with comparable education.

INTERPRETATIONS OF THESE RESULTS HAVE VARIED.—Failure of schizophrenics on absurdities, on proverbs, and on the sorting tests have been seen as the result of a loss of the capacity to generalize (Rawlings, 1921; Wentworth, 1923; Wegrocki, 1940) or its near equivalents: a loss of "abstract" ability (Bolles, 1937; Goldstein, 1939b) or regression from the "categorical" thinking characteristic of adulthood to the "complex" thinking of childhood (Vigotsky, 1934; Zeigarnik; Hanfmann and Kasanin, 1942). Hanfmann (1939b) defended this interpretation by showing that one schizophrenic, whom she studied extensively, did sustain such mechanical tasks as copying words or taking an inventory of surroundings. Such a view makes loss of "abstract" ability basic, and failure to sustain a task becomes a secondary "catastrophic" phenomenon. This interpretation appears to be true for cases of brain injury and the "organic" psychoses, but considerable evidence argues against this view of schizophrenic distractibility and uncooperativeness. Failure of schizophrenics to maintain the "set" to respond appeared clearly in the reaction-time experiments where the task was simple in the extreme. Although he did not emphasize the point, Wegrocki (1940) described schizophrenics as verbalizing analogies correctly but writing wrong answers because their uncontrolled associative processes had carried them on by the time they got pencil to paper. He also reported that a complex task may serve to control some schizophrenics, for patients who performed his tests without error lapsed into the characteristic jargon in voluntary speech. This agrees with Hunt's (1935) finding that schizophrenics who will start usually succeed in doing fairly complex arithmetic progressions. Here the situation continually keeps the task before the subject if he has the capacity to grasp it. On the other hand, in noting absurdities where the instruction to look for them had to be assumed voluntarily or maintained over considerable time while the narrative was being read, they failed miserably. The fact that schizophrenics use metaphor in voluntary speech, even though they slide from figurative to literal meaning of the words, fits this latter interpretation but argues against Hanfmann's. Cameron's (1939a) finding that "deteriorated" schizophrenics used a variety of abstract bases in classifying the Vigotsky blocks also argues against Hanfmann. Furthermore, if "abstract" capacity as such is lost, as is implied in Kraepelin's conception of dementia, recovery of performance on the Vigotsky should not occur automatically with recovery of social interests as Cameron (1938b) observed. A schizophrenic (Lang, 1940), interpreting his own disorder, also argues against the loss of "abstract" capacity.

Several writers (Storch, 1924; White, 1928) have compared schizophrenic thinking to that of primitive peoples because both manifest such characteristics (Stephen, 1935) as not being hampered by a need for consistency, omnipotence of thoughts and wishes, confusion of doing and thinking, and failure to distinguish between things emotionally identified, and argued from these common characteristics that schizophrenia is a regressive disorder. Were the data available, it is likely that marked differences could be shown in the motivation and in other factors controlling the thinking of schizophrenics and of primitive people.

The contention that schizophrenia is a regressive disorder has led to direct comparisons of performances by schizophrenics and children. Vigotsky's (1934) results with the test that now bears his name favors this hypothesis. His generalizations: that "categorical" thinking appears regularly with adolescence, and that "complex" patterns of thinking reappear in adults when the schizophrenic process disturbs the psychological systems that underlie concepts, however, have been modified by other workers using his own method. His dichotomy of thought-forms has been shown inadequate by Thompson (1941) and Hanfmann and Kasanin (1942). Thompson found that the number of hypotheses employed by children increases gradually with age. Hanfmann and Kasanin found that the highest level on the Vigotsky test was limited primarily to college-trained people, and that only 26 of their 62 schizophrenics showed deficit when comparisons were made with controls of comparable education.

Other results show clear differences between the performances of schizophrenics and children. When Cameron (1938b) compared the productions of schizophrenics on incomplete sentences ending in *because* with those of Piaget's children, he found marked differences. Whereas the children had used "motivation" as the causal principle most frequently (83.5%) with progressively fewer instances of "logical justification" (9%) and "cause-and-effect" (7.5%), the schizophrenics used "cause-and-effect" most frequently (45%), "logical justification" more frequently (23%) than did children, and "motivation" in only 32% of their productions. Furthermore, he found severity of disorder unassociated with increased failures to continue incomplete sentences ending in *although* and *even though,* but it was associated with increased failures to continue *because*-sentences, even though the use of *discordance* (although and even though) had appeared much later than the use of *because* in the speech of Piaget's children. In another study, Cameron (1939b) found that children manifested a relative dearth of answers, while schizophrenics had plenty. Schizophrenics and children both showed defective logical organization, but while schizophrenics gave worse distortions with requests to clarify without becoming disturbed, children gave progressively better approximations and did appear distressed by the experimenter's failure to understand. Cameron considered the defective organization of children due to their not yet having learned from social necessity to organize according to adult standards, while those of schizophrenics were attributed to having given up effective social contact.[38]

If one conceives regression as back-tracking over inexorable steps in a developmental process, Cameron has shown that such a conception of schizophrenic thinking fails. On the other hand, if one interprets regression as either the reappearance of older tendencies when newer ones are extinguished (Mowrer, 1939) or the reversion to "simpler levels of creative activity" under the influence of frustration (Barker, Dembo, and Lewin, 1941), the behavior of the immature and the regressed could not be expected to be alike in all aspects, and Cameron's evidence fails to apply. From a speculative standpoint, however, we agree that the past need not supply all schizophrenic symptoms. Many of those substituted for the socially rewarded responses, which we assume are extinguished, are probably entirely new to the schizophrenic's life history.[39]

Several investigators have used the deficiencies on tests of "abstract" ability as indirect evidence of cerebral pathology in schizophrenics because these particular deficiencies appear so characteristically in cases

---

[38] Organic immaturity may also be a factor in these organizational defects in children's thinking. The gradual improvement in organizational performance with age in preadolescents (Thompson, 1941) may argue for the importance of a maturational process, although this fact alone might also be explained by assuming that the skills required for thought-performances are learned slowly. In connection with a study of children's drawings, Cameron (1938a) points out (1) that naming objects drawn follows perceptual isolation of forms, and (2) that the younger child "is unable to fixate the parts and at the same time maintain the original perspective of the whole." Thus such organizing appears to demand that one sustain several tasks simultaneously and synthesize them into a single operation. If it is assumed that this capacity demands certain neural structures, the fact that children live for years with adults without acquiring certain complex types of performance and then acquire them relatively suddenly may perhaps be attributed partly to a maturation process. However, to indicate clearly the limitations of this interpretation, one should not expect primitive peoples to lack the basic capacity to acquire our adult forms of organization. They lack them because these forms did not exist in the cultures that nurtured them. Moreover, they would have great difficulty acquiring ours at adulthood because of the habit interference between their own and ours. It is also possible to interpret these facts of the development of reasoning in children as a consequence of the accumulation of the dynamic effects of habits acquired successively under social motivation. This problem of intellectual development in childhood begs for analysis. Intelligence testing and normative studies of stages in performance have been relatively uninformative, and a strong faith in this latter form of interpretation might produce valuable results if it were properly oriented. We are ready for an experimental attack upon this problem that is oriented in modern behavior theory.

[39] This general argument that we have reiterated may not apply to all schizophrenics. Schizophrenics constitute an extremely heterogeneous population as they are diagnosed now, and one day subgroups with structural or physiological pathology may be differentiated. Cerebral pathology has already been demonstrated in individual patients diagnosed as schizophrenic (see Ch. 29 by Cameron). On the other hand, superficial parallels between schizophrenic behavior and such phenomena as those shown in sleep (Jung, 1908), in normal individuals under low oxygen tension (McFarland, 1932), in aphasia (Tatarenko, 1938), and in "organic" psychoses (Orton, 1930; Krisch, 1932) are only suggestive at best. Moreover, failure to recover need imply no organic involvement other than that which must underlie all learning processes, for recovery could be expected only when the problems producing the schizophrenic reactions have been resolved, as is argued by French and Kasanin (1941).

with cerebral pathology.[40] Such evidence is suggestive, but not crucial, for there are many instances of similar behavior with different determinants. Moreover, Goldstein's basic assumption that "abstract" and "concrete" abilities are not "acquired mental sets" but "capacity levels of the total personality" itself seems dubious to us. Undoubtedly these tests of "abstract" ability require high levels of fundamental capacity, but good performance on these tests would not arise automatically as a consequence of maturation in a person with the greatest fundamental capacity. As must all thought processes like classifying, inducing relations, etc., we should guess that the "abstract" abilities assessed by these tests involve habitual skills which may be either strengthened or weakened by an individual's social experience. These skills probably represent a complex accumulation of habits successively acquired. They appear gradually with age both because the structures upon which fundamental capacity presumably depends mature gradually and because certain basic skills must reach a certain degree of perfection before they can be merged into more complex skills. They may be damaged either by destroying the structures upon which they depend, or by interfering with their reinforcement which is presumably social. We prefer to extend our interpretation of other schizophrenic behavior to schizophrenic thinking, for the schizophrenic withdrawal from social interaction would remove this reinforcement. An argument somewhat resembling this one is presented by Zubin and Thompson (1941), and we should mention that our argument has roots in Adolf Meyer's (1906) interpretation of schizophrenia.

Furthermore, similarities in the performances of schizophrenics and "organic" patients and the aged stand out only so long as one considers success and failure in the tasks presented. When experiments are designed to emphasize factors in the motivation and control of performance, striking differences appear. The parallels that Kraepelin saw between the behavior of schizophrenics and patients with senile psychoses are opposed by Cameron's (1938) finding that senile patients give a considerably higher percentage of logically cogent responses to incomplete statements ending in *because* than do schizophrenics. And more important in this context, seniles maintain an attitude of anticipating criticism and retain the social amenities to a greater extent than do schizophrenics. We have already noted that when schizophrenics and "organic" patients perform repeatedly on the same tasks, the "organic" patients show less variability in both attitude and output than schizophrenics. The contrast found by Hunt (1935) in the performances of schizophrenics and paretics on arithmetic progressions and a narrative containing absurdities is also significant. Although the schizophrenics were slow, if they cooperated at all, they succeeded in continuing fairly complex progressions, but paretics failed all but the simplest progressions with the best of cooperation. Hunt attributed the success of schizophrenics in sustaining the tasks in-

---

[40] See: Vigotsky (1934), Bychowski (1935), Bolles and Goldstein (1938), and Goldstein (1939b).

volved in these arithmetic progressions to the fact that the process of doing progressions continuously instructs the subject if he is capable. Squires (1936) has added that the schizophrenic may succeed because these arithmetic tasks are unrelated to the schizophrenic's "diseased feelings and emotions." It appears, thus, that the differences in this performance are attributable to differences in fundamental capacity. On the other hand, schizophrenics failed invariably to note absurdities in the narrative during the first reading with only the instruction to read it, or during a second reading with the instruction to make improvements in the narrative; and only about half of them noted absurdities at the third reading when instructed explicitly to look for them. Moreover, those who failed at this stage usually attempted to explain away the absurdities.[41] But paretics, if they could continue any progressions beyond the highly practiced multiplication tables, objected to absurdities when they first read the narrative with such statements as: "Fir trees don't have leaves," or "You don't harvest in March." It appeared that schizophrenics were distracted from the content of the narrative or from sustaining the task of looking for absurdities by possible preoccupations, or even that they actively resisted finding absurdities. This "withdrawal" of the schizophrenic could sometimes be overcome with pressure from verbal instructions. The paretics needed no such pressure. Their marked readiness to discern absurdities is perhaps another manifestation of the "extratensive" tendency of patients with brain pathology uncovered by the Rorschach (Piotrowski, 1937; T. Hunt in Freeman and Watts, 1942). Studies designed to emphasize the various factors controlling performance are too few to be more than suggestive, but they argue clearly for different bases for the deficits in schizophrenia and in the "organic" conditions. More of such studies are needed, and they should be based on adequate samples of patients from all diagnostic groups.

Summary and Conclusion Concerning the Nature of Deficit

1. Pseudo-measurements of deficit with standard tests have shown some degree of deficit in all the disorders except, possibly, the psychoneuroses, in the aged, and in patients with surgical brain injury. The deficit is largest in the "organic" psychoses, but some schizophrenics, particularly those of the hebephrenic subgroup, show deficits as large as those in the "organic" disorders. The present tests of intelligence and deficit are not so well adapted as the tests of "abstract" ability to uncover the deficit following surgical brain injury, but the latter are still not well standardized nor have they been well adapted for scoring.

2. Tests of vocabulary and information are failed least often, and tests

---

[41] Unpublished extensions of this work have shown similar tendencies in manic-depressive patients. They have also indicated that schizophrenics tend to note "logical" absurdities ("Because the rabbit ran faster than I did, I could overtake it only slowly and finally caught it"), while "organic" patients note those "based on experience" ("fir trees with leaves" or "harvesting in March") which the schizophrenics sometimes attempt to explain away.

involving conceptual thinking, sustained associative thinking and speed are most regularly failed. In the feebleminded and in cases of brain injury in infancy the pattern of success and failure differs considerably from that in the disorders and that following adult brain injury. Although the patterns in "functional" and "organic" disorders show many similarities, there are some interesting differences.

3. In studies of specific aspects of behavior the evidence of deficit consistently becomes more pronounced as either receptive or expressive performances become more complex.

4. Although schizophrenics show excessive variability in the expressive indicators of emotion, they show no evidence of "apathy" on these indicators, and schizophrenic startle reactions are exaggerated. Evidence of "apathy" shows clearly, however, in the overt behavior of these patients and appears as a loss of interests.

5. Reversal of the "fatigue effect" with continuous work, slowness of perceived fluctuations in ambiguous figures, and possibly certain alterations of the patellar reflex appear specifically characteristic of manic-depressive patients.

6. Evidence of retrograde amnesia in the "organic" psychoses confirms clinical observation. Deficit in memorial efficiency appears to be more a function of aging than psychosis, however, and some evidence indicates that this deficit is more a matter of impressionability or modifiability than of retention.

7. While the deficit in the aphasias is greatest in performance involving language, it is certainly not limited to language performances.

8. Studies of the thought processes, especially those using the sorting tests and the other tests of "abstract" ability, have brought out marked deficiencies in patients with "organic" psychoses, with aphasia, with brain injuries outside the speech-areas, and with schizophrenia.

9. So long as one looks only at the success of patients on these thought tasks, the deficiencies in schizophrenics appear similar to those in the "organic" conditions, but differences appear when experiments are designed to bring out motivation and other factors controlling performance.

10. In reviewing these investigations of deficit, we have developed the hypothesis that intelligent behavior and thinking are dependent upon both fundamental capacities and learned skills. These fundamental capacities we conceive to be based somehow on neural structures and to consist behaviorally of ready modifiability of response and of capacity to sustain several attitudes or tasks simultaneously, to shift readily from one to another, and to synthesize them into a single complex operation. In order for such capacities to be manifest in test-situations, the skills involving them must have been learned. We conceive these skills as higher-order habits acquired through and continually reinforced by the individual's social living. We admit that knowledge of these thought skills and of how to teach them constitutes a hiatus in the field of psychology. The deficit shown in the "organic" psychoses, in the aged, and

in cases of adult brain injury we should attribute largely to damage to the neural structures underlying these performances. Such a deficit may show as reduced modifiability, as inability in performances where many attitudes or tasks must be sustained simultaneously or in performances that involve shifting readily from one attitude to another. Those deficits from which the structurally damaged individual recovers with training may be conceived as resulting from damage to the architectonic arrangements through which these particular performances are organized. The fundamental capacity upon which they depend is not ruined so long as the performances can be relearned, which presumably must involve either healing of tissue or new architectonic arrangements. The deficit in the "functional" psychoses, and particularly in schizophrenia, we conceive as an extinction of standards for performance and of thought skills that have been socially rewarded. The deficit in these disorders is also complicated by conflicts between response tendencies and by distraction from idiosyncratic preoccupations which arise as substitutes for the socially rewarded skills and responses.

11. In the future, we should like to see more experiments to bring out differences in the factors controlling performance, and we should like to see every technique applied to representative samples of the whole gamut of disorders and conditions. Only then can the conclusions of today be denied, or verified or amplified.

BIBLIOGRAPHY

ACHILLES, E. M. 1920. Experimental studies in recall and recognition. *Arch. Psychol., N. Y., 6,* No. 44.

ACKERLY, S. 1935. Instinctive, emotional, and mental changes following prefrontal lobe extirpation. *Amer. J. Psychiat., 92,* 717–729.

ALTMAN, C. H., & SHAKOW, D. 1937. A comparison of the performance of matched groups of schizophrenic patients, normal subjects, and delinquent subjects on some aspects of the Stanford-Binet. *J. educ. Psychol., 28,* 519–529.

ANGYAL, A. 1935. The perceptual basis of somatic delusions in a case of schizophrenia. *Arch. Neurol. Psychiat., Chicago, 34,* 270–279.

ASCHAFFENBURG, G. 1895. Experimentelle Studien über Associationen. *Psychol. Arb., 1,* 209–296.

—— 1899. Experimentelle Studien über Associationen: II. Die Associationen in der Erschöpfung. *Psychol. Arb., 2,* 1–83.

—— 1904. Experimentelle Studien über Associationen: III. Die Ideenflucht. *Psychol. Arb., 4,* 235–373.

BABCOCK, H. 1930. An experiment in the measurement of mental deterioration. *Arch. Psychol., N. Y., 18,* No. 117.

—— 1933. Dementia praecox, a psychological study. Lancaster, Pa.: Science Press.

—— 1941. Time and the mind: personal tempo the key to normal and pathological mental conditions. Cambridge: Sci-Art.

BAIRD, J. W. 1906. Contraction of the color zones in hysteria and neurasthenia. *Psychol. Bull., 3,* 249–254.

BALL, R. J. 1929. An objective measure of emotional instability. *J. appl. Psychol., 13,* 226–256.

BARKER, R., DEMBO, T., & LEWIN, K. 1941. Frustration and regression: an experiment with young children. *Univ. Ia Stud. Child Welf., 18,* No. 1.

BARNES, G. 1924. A comparison of the results of tests in the Terman scale between cases of manic-depressive and dementia praecox psychoses. *J. nerv. ment. Dis., 60,* 584–589.

BEBLE, G. L. 1925. A study of memory deterioration in encephalitis lethargica. *J. nerv. ment. Dis., 61,* 356–364.

BENDER, L. 1938. A visual motor Gestalt test and its clinical use. *Res. Monogr. Amer. Orthopsychiat. Assn.,* No. 3.

BENDER, L., & SCHILDER, P. 1930. Unconditioned and conditioned reactions to pain in schizophrenia. *Amer. J. Psychiat., 10,* 365–384.

BEVAN-LEWIS, W. 1890. Text book of mental diseases. London: Blakiston.

BIRD, C. 1939. Suggestion and suggestibility, a bibliography. *Psychol. Bull., 36,* 264–283.

BOLLES, M. M. 1937. The basis of pertinence; a study of the test performance of aments, dements, and normal children of the same mental age. *Arch. Psychol., N. Y.,* No. 212.

BOLLES, M. M., & GOLDSTEIN, K. 1938. A study of the impairment of "abstract behavior" in schizophrenic patients. *Psychiat. Quart., 12,* 42–66.

BOLLES, M. M., ROSEN, G. P., & LANDIS, C. 1938. Psychological performance tests as prognostic agents for the efficacy of insulin therapy in schizophrenia. *Psychiat. Quart., 12,* 733–737.

BORING, E. G. 1913. Learning in dementia praecox. *Psychol. Monogr., 15,* No. 63.

BOWMAN, K. M., & RAYMOND, A. F. 1931. A statistical study of hallucinations in the manic-depressive psychoses. *Amer. J. Psychiat., 11,* 299–310.

BRICKNER, R. N. 1936. The intellectual functions of the frontal lobes. New York: Macmillan.

BRODY, M. B. 1942. A survey of the results of intelligence tests in psychosis. *Brit. J. med. Psychol., 19,* 215–257.

BROWN, J. F. 1940. Psychodynamics of abnormal behavior. New York: Mc-Graw-Hill.

BYCHOWSKI, G. 1935. Certain problems of schizophrenia in the light of cerebral pathology. (Trans. by W. H. Wegrocki.) *J. nerv. ment. Dis., 81,* 280–298.

CAMERON, D. E. 1936. Studies in depression. *J. ment. Sci., 82,* 148–161.

—— 1940. Certain aspects of defects of recent memory occurring in psychoses of the senium. *Arch. Neurol. Psychiat., Chicago, 43,* 987–992.

CAMERON, N. 1938a. Individual and social factors in the development of graphic symbolization. *J. Psychol., 5,* 165–184.

—— 1938b. Reasoning, regression and communication in schizophrenics. *Psychol. Monogr., 50,* 1–34.

—— 1939a. Schizophrenic thinking in a problem-solving situation. *J. ment. Sci., 85,* 1–24.

—— 1939b. Deterioration and regression in schizophrenic thinking. *J. abnorm. soc. Psychol., 34,* 265–270.

—— 1938c. A study of thinking in senile deterioration and schizophrenic disorganization. *Amer. J. Psychol., 51,* 650–665.

CAPPS, H. M. 1939. Vocabulary changes in mental deterioration. *Arch. Psychol., N. Y.,* No. 242.

CLEVELAND, S. E. 1942. A study of mental deterioration in senile psychosis. Lincoln, Nebr.: Thesis, University Nebraska.

COHEN, L. H., & PATTERSON, M. 1937. Effect of pain on the heart rate of normal and schizophrenic individuals. *J. gen. Psychol., 17,* 273–289.

CORIAT, I. H. 1910. Certain pulse reactions as a measure of emotions. *J. abnorm. Psychol., 4,* 261–279.

CORNELL, E. L., & LOWDEN, G. L. 1923. A comparison of the Stanford and Porteus tests in several types of social inadequacy. *J. abnorm. soc. Psychol., 18,* 33–42.

COUCH, F. H., & FOX, J. C. 1934. Photographic study of ocular movements in mental disease. *Arch. Neurol. Psychiat., Chicago, 31,* 556–578.

CUPCEA, S. 1936. The weight's illusion—Demoor sign—in insane persons. *Bul. Spital. Bolimint. nerv. Sibiu,* pp. 63–65. From: *Psychol. Abstr.,* 1936, *10,* No. 4475.

CURRAN, F. J., & SCHILDER, P. 1937. Experiments in repetition and recall. *J. genet. Psychol., 51,* 163–187.

CURTIS, J. N. 1918. Point scale examinations on the high-grade feebleminded and the insane. *J. abnorm. Psychol., 13,* 77–119.

DAHMS, H., & JENNESS, A. 1937. A study of direct suggestibility and social introversion as related to auditory threshold and to reaction-time during reverie. *J. soc. Psychol., 8,* 251–267.

DAVIDSON, M. 1937. A study of schizophrenic performance on the Stanford-Binet scale. *Brit. J. med. Psychol.*, 17, 93–97.

DEARBORN, G. V. N. 1927. The determination of intellectual regression and progression. *Amer. J. Psychiat.*, 6, 725–741.

—— 1931. Intellectual deterioration in manic-depressive psychosis. *U. S. Veterans' Bur. med. Bull.*, 7, 388–392.

DEBRUYN, J. W. 1909. A study of emotional expression in dementia praecox. *J. abnorm. Psychol.*, 3, 378–385.

DESPERT, J. L. 1940. A comparative study of thinking in schizophrenic children and in children of preschool age. *Amer. J. Psychiat.*, 97, 189–213.

DIEFENDORF, A. R., & DODGE, R. 1908. An experimental study of ocular reactions of the insane from photographic records. *Brain*, 31, 451–489.

DODGE, R., & FOX, J. C. 1928. Optic nystagmus: I. Technical introduction with observations in a case with central scotoma in the right eye and external rectus palsy in the left eye. *Arch. Neurol. Psychiat., Chicago*, 20, 812–823.

DORSEY, J. M., & TRAVIS, L. E. 1932. Reflex response latencies in manic and depressive cases of the cyclothymic group and in cases of catatonic stupor of the schizophrenic group. *Arch. Neurol. Psychiat., Chicago*, 27, 687–690.

DUBOIS, P. H., MAYS, L. L., & LANDIS, C. 1934. Changes in psychological functions in paresis. II. *Psychiat. Quart.*, 8, 699–702.

DYSINGER, D. W. 1932. An action current and reflex time study of psychiatric and neurologic cases. *Psychol. Monogr.*, 43, Whole No. 194, 31–52.

ELLIS, W. D. 1938. A source book of Gestalt psychology. London: Kegan Paul.

ELWOOD, M. I., BURCHARD, E. M. L., & TEAGARDEN, F. M. 1937. An evaluation of the Kent Oral Emergency test. *J. appl. Psychol.*, 21, 75–84.

EPSTEIN, S. H., & SOLOMON, H. C. 1939. The effect of treatment on the mental level of patients with general paresis. *Amer. J. Psychiat.*, 95, 1181–1192.

ESCALONA, S. K. 1940. The effect of success and failure upon the level of aspiration and behavior in manic-depressive psychoses. *Univ. Ia Stud. Child Welf.*, 16, No. 3, 197–302.

FARIS, R. E. L., & DUNHAM, H. W. 1939. Mental disorders in urban areas. Chicago: University Chicago Press.

FENICHEL, O. 1934. Outline of clinical psychoanalysis. (Trans. by B. D. Lewin & G. Zilboorg.) New York: Norton.

FORBES, T. W., & PIOTROWSKI, Z. 1934. Studies of catatonia: IV. Electrical skin resistance of catatonics during sleep. *Psychiat. Quart.*, 8, 722–727.

FOSTER, J. C. 1920. Significant responses in certain memory tests. *J. appl. Psychol.*, 4, 142–154.

FRANZ, S. I. 1906. The times of some mental processes in the retardation and excitement of insanity. *Amer. J. Psychol.*, 17, 38–68.

—— 1909. The knee-jerk in paresis. *J. ment. Sci.*, 65, 471–498.

—— 1910. Touch sensations in different bodily segments. *Bull. Govt Hosp. Insane*, No. 2, 60–72.

FRANZ, S. I., & HAMILTON, G. V. 1905. The effects of exercise upon the retardation in conditions of depression. *Amer. J. Insan.*, 62, 239–256.

FREEMAN, H. 1933. The effect of "habituation" on blood pressure in schizophrenia. *Arch. Neurol. Psychiat., Chicago*, 29, 139–147.

FREEMAN, W., & WATTS, J. W. 1942. Psychosurgery. Springfield, Ill.: C. C. Thomas.

FRENCH, T. M., & KASANIN, J. 1941. A psychodynamic study of the recovery of two schizophrenic cases. *Psychoanal. Quart.*, 10, 1–22.

FREUD, S. 1914. History of the psychoanalytic movement. In *The basic writings of Sigmund Freud*. (Trans. and ed. by A. A. Brill.) New York: Modern Library, 1938.

FUCHS, W. 1920. Untersuchung über das Sehen der Hemianopiker und Hemianblyopiker: I. Verlagerungserscheinungen. *Z. Psychol.*, 84, 67–169.

—— 1921. Untersuchung über das Sehen der Hemianopiker und Hemianblyopiker: II. Die totalisierende Gestaltauffassung. *Z. Psychol.*, 86, 1–143.

FRY, F. D. 1930. The correlation of the reverse audito-vocal digit memory span with the general intelligence and other mental abilities of 308 prisoners of the Eastern State Penitentiary of Pennsylvania. *Psychol. Clin.*, 19, 156–164.

GALTON, F. 1879. Psychometric experiments. *Brain*, 2, 149–162.

GANTT, W. H. 1938. A method of testing cortical function and sensitivity of the skin. An aid in differentiating organogenic and psychogenic disturbances. *Arch. Neurol. Psychiat., Chicago, 40,* 79–85.

GARDNER, G. E. 1940. Childhood physical and mental measurements of psychotic patients. *Amer. J. Orthopsychiat., 10,* 327–342.

GATEWOOD, L. C. 1909. An experimental study of dementia praecox. *Psychol. Monogr., 11,* No. 45, p. 87.

GELB, A., & GOLDSTEIN, K. 1920. Psychologische Analysen hirnpathologischer Fälle. Leipzig: Barth.

GILBERT, J. G. 1935. Mental efficiency in senescence. *Arch. Psychol., N. Y.,* No. 188.

—— 1941. Memory loss in senescence. *J. abnorm. soc. Psychol., 36,* 73–86.

GOLDSTEIN, K. 1910. Ueber Aphasie. *Beih. med. Klin., 6,* 1–32.

—— 1922. Ueber den Einfluss von Sprachstörungen auf das Verhalten gegenuber Farben. *Dtsch. Z. Nervenheilk., 74,* 260–262.

—— 1926. Ueber Aphasie. *Schweiz. Arch. Neurol. Psychiat., 19,* 3–38.

—— 1927. Die Lokalisation in der Grosshirnrinde. *Handb. norm. path. Physiol., 10,* 600–842. Berlin: Springer.

—— 1928. Beobachtungen über die Veränderungen des Gesamtverhaltens bei Gehirnschädigung. *Mschr. Psychiat. Neurol., 68,* 217–242.

—— 1936. The significance of the frontal lobes for mental performances. *J. Neurol. Psychopath., 17,* 27–40.

—— 1937. The problem of the meaning of words based upon observation of aphasic patients. *J. Psychol., 2,* 301–316.

—— 1939a. The organism: a holistic approach to biology derived from pathological data in man. New York: American Book.

—— 1939b. The significance of special mental tests for diagnosis and prognosis in schizophrenia. *Amer. J. Psychiat., 96,* 575–588.

—— 1940. Human nature. Cambridge: Harvard University Press.

—— 1942. After-effects of brain injuries in war; their evaluation and treatment. The application of psychologic methods in the clinic. New York: Grune & Stratton.

GOLDSTEIN, K., & GELB, A. 1924. Das Wesen der amnestischen Aphasie. *Schweiz. Arch. Neurol. Psychiat., 15,* 163–175.

GOLDSTEIN, K., & SHEERER, M. 1941. Abstract and concrete behavior. An experimental study with special tests. *Psychol. Monogr., 33,* Whole No. 239.

GORDON, A. 1930. Mental and emotional phenomena of some psychoses in their relation to blood pressure: diagnostic and prognostic significance of latter. *J. nerv. ment. Dis., 72,* 396–404.

GRABFIELD, G. P. 1914. Variations in the sensory threshold for faradic stimulation in psychopathic subjects. *Bost. med. surg. J., 171,* 883–887.

—— 1915a. Variations in the sensory threshold for faradic stimulation in psychopathic subjects: II. The manic depressive insanity. *Bost. med. surg. J., 173,* 198–202.

—— 1915b. Variations in the sensory threshold for faradic stimulation in psychopathic subjects: III. The dementia praecox group. *Bost. med. surg. J., 173,* 202–205.

—— 1917. Variations in the sensory threshold for faradic stimulation in psychopathic subjects. *J. abnorm. Psychol., 11,* 328–336.

GRAHAM, C. H., & GAGNÉ, R. M. 1940. The acquisition, extinction, and spontaneous recovery of a conditioned operant response. *J. exp. Psychol., 26,* 251–280.

GRAHAM, V. T. 1940. Psychological studies of hypoglycemia therapy. *J. Psychol., 10,* 327–358.

GRINGS, W. W. 1942. The verbal summator technique and abnormal mental states. *J. abnorm. soc. Psychol., 37,* 529–545.

GUILFORD, J. P. 1934. Introversion-extraversion. *Psychol. Bull., 31,* 331–354.

HADLICH, H. 1931. Schizophrenie Denkstoerung. *Psychol. Forsch., 15,* 359–373.

HALSTEAD, W. C. 1940. Preliminary analysis of grouping behavior in patients with cerebral injury by the method of equivalent and non-equivalent stimuli. *Amer. J. Psychiat., 96,* 1263–1294.

HANFMANN, E. 1939a. Thought disturbances in schizophrenia as revealed by performance in a picture completion test. *J. abnorm. soc. Psychol., 34,* 249–264.

—— 1939b. Analysis of the thinking disorder in a case of schizophrenia. *Arch. Neurol. Psychiat., Chicago, 41,* 568–579.

HANFMANN, E., & KASANIN, J. 1942. Conceptual thinking in schizophrenia. *Nerv. ment. Dis. Monogr.*, No. 67.

HARBINSON, M. R. 1936. An investigation of deterioration of "general intelligence" or "G" in psychotic patients. *Brit. J. med. Psychol., 16,* 146–148.

HARRIS, A. J., & SHAKOW, D. 1937. The clinical significance of numerical measures of scatter on the Stanford-Binet. *Psychol. Bull., 34,* 134–150.

—— 1938. Scatter on the Stanford-Binet in schizophrenic, normal, and delinquent adults. *J. abnorm. soc. Psychol., 33,* 100–111.

HARRISON, F. M. 1916. The role of hallucinations in the psychoses based upon a statistical study of 514 cases. *J. nerv. ment. Dis., 43,* 231–249.

HARROWER, M. R. 1939. Changes in figure-ground perception in patients with cortical lesions. *Brit. J. Psychol., 30,* 47–51.

HART, B., & SPEARMAN, C. 1914. Mental tests of dementia. *J. abnorm. Psychol., 9,* 217–264.

HAUSMANN, M. F. 1933a. A method to objectively demonstrate thinking difficulties. *Amer. J. Psychiat., 13,* 613–625.

—— 1933b. A test to evaluate some personality traits. *J. gen. Psychol., 9,* 179–189.

HAZLITT, V. 1930. Children's thinking. *Brit. J. Psychol., 20,* 354–361.

HEAD, H. 1926. Aphasia and kindred disorders of speech. (2 Vols.) New York: Macmillan.

HEALY, W., BRONNER, A. F., & BOWERS, A. M. 1930. The structure and meaning of psychoanalysis. New York: Knopf.

HEBB, D. O. 1939a. Intelligence in man after large removals of cerebral tissue: report of four left frontal lobe cases. *J. gen. Psychol., 21,* 73–87.

—— 1939b. Intelligence in man after large removals of cerebral tissue: defects following right temporal lobectomy. *J. gen. Psychol., 21,* 437–446.

—— 1941. Human intelligence after removal of cerebral tissue from the right frontal lobe. *J. gen. Psychol., 25,* 257–265.

—— 1942. The effect of early and late brain injury upon test scores, and the nature of adult intelligence. *Proc. Amer. phil. Soc., 85,* 275–292.

HEBB, D. O., & PENFIELD, W. 1940. Human behavior after extensive bilateral removal from the frontal lobes. *Arch. Neurol. Psychiat., Chicago, 43,* 421–438.

HENSCHEN, S. E. 1921–22. Klinische und anatomische Beiträge zur Pathologie des Gehirns. Vols. 5–7. Stockholm: Nordiska Bokhandeln.

HOCH, A. 1901. On certain studies with the ergograph. *J. nerv. ment. Dis., 28,* 620–628.

HOLLINGWORTH, H. L. 1920. Psychology of functional neuroses. New York: Appleton-Century.

HULL, C. L. 1917. The formation and retention of associations among the insane. *Amer. J. Psychol., 28,* 419–435.

—— 1920. Quantitative aspects of the evolution of concepts. An experimental study. *Psychol. Monogr., 28,* Whole No. 123.

HUNT, J. McV. 1935. Psychological loss in paretics and schizophrenics. *Amer. J. Psychol., 47,* 458–463.

—— 1936a. Psychological experiments with disordered persons. *Psychol. Bull., 33,* 1–58.

—— 1936b. Psychological government and the high variability of schizophrenic patients. *Amer. J. Psychol., 48,* 64–81.

HUNT, J. McV., & GUILFORD, J. P. 1933. Fluctuation of an ambiguous figure in dementia praecox and in manic-depressive patients. *J. abnorm. soc. Psychol., 27,* 443–452.

HUNT, T. 1942. Intelligence. In Freeman, W., & WATTS, J. W., *Psychosurgery.* Springfield, Ill.: C. C. Thomas.

HUSTON, P. E. 1932. Eye-hand coordination in schizophrenic patients and normals as measured by the pursuitmeter. *Psychol. Bull., 29,* 662.

—— 1934. Sensory threshold to direct current stimulation in schizophrenic and normal subjects. *Arch. Neurol. Psychiat., Chicago, 31,* 590–596.

—— 1935. The reflex time of the patellar tendon reflex in normal and schizophrenic subjects. *J. gen. Psychol., 13,* 3–41.

HUSTON, P. E., SHAKOW, D., & RIGGS, L. A. 1937. Studies of motor function in schizophrenia: II. Reaction time. *J. gen. Psychol., 16,* 39–82.

JACKSON, J. H. 1915. Reprint of some of Hughlings Jackson's papers on affections of speech. (Ed. by H. Head.) *Brain, 38,* 28–190.

JASTAK, J. 1934. Variability of psychometric performances in mental diagnosis. New York: Dissertation, Columbia University.

—— 1937. Psychometric patterns of state hospital patients. *Delaware St. med. J., 9,* 7–10.

JELLIFFE, S. E. 1930. Some random notes on the history of psychiatry of the middle ages. *Amer. J. Psychiat., 10,* 275–286.

JOHNSTON, H. M. 1939. A comparison of the time estimations of schizophrenic patients with those of normal individuals. Providence, R. I.: Thesis, Brown University.

JONES, H. E., & CONRAD, H. S. 1933. The growth and decline of intelligence: a study of a homogeneous group between ages of ten and sixty. *Genet. Psychol. Monogr.,* No. 13, 223–298.

JONES, L. W. 1928. An investigation into the significance of perseveration. *J. ment. Sci., 74,* 653–659.

JUNG, C. G. 1906. On psychophysical relations of the associative experiment. *J. abnorm. Psychol., 1,* 249–257.

—— 1908. The psychology of dementia praecox. (Trans. by A. A. Brill.) *Nerv. ment. Dis. Monogr.,* 1936, Ser. 3.

—— 1919. Studies in word-association. (Trans. by M. D. Eder.) New York: Moffat Yard.

—— 1923. Psychological types or the psychology of individualism. (Trans. by H. G. Baynes.) New York: Harcourt, Brace.

KATAN, M. 1939. A contribution to the understanding of schizophrenic speech. *Int. J. Psycho-Anal., 20,* 353–362.

KENDIG, I., & RICHMOND, W. V. 1940. Psychological studies in dementia praecox. Ann Arbor, Mich.: Edwards.

KENT, G. H. 1911. Experiments on habit formation in dementia praecox. *Psychol. Rev., 18,* 375–410.

—— 1918. An experiment on the instruction of insane subjects. *J. nerv. ment. Dis., 48,* 313–324.

KENT, G. H., & ROSANOFF, A. J. 1910. A study of association in insanity. *Amer. J. Insan., 67,* 37–126.

KLEBANOFF, S. G. 1944. Psychological changes in organic brain lesions and ablations. *Psychol. Bull.* (Unpublished)

KLEIST, K. 1923. Wesen und Lokalisation der Paralogie. *Zbl. Neurol. Psychiat., 33,* 82–83.

—— 1930. Zur hirnpathologischen Auffassung der schizophrenen Grundstörung. *Zbl. Neurol. Psychiat., 56,* 457–459.

—— 1933. Gehirnpathologie. In *Handbuch der ärztlichen Erfahrungen im Weltkriege.* Leipzig: Barth.

—— 1939. Störungen des Denkens und ihre hirnpathologischen Grundlagen (paralogische und alogische Denkstörungen.) In Roggenbau, C. H., *Gegenwartsprobleme der psychologisch-neurologischen Forschung.* Stuttgart: Enke. Pp. 72–87.

KLOPFER, B., & KELLEY, D. M. 1942. The Rorschach technique. New York: World Book.

KLÜVER, H. 1942. Mechanisms of hallucinations. In McNemar, Q., & Merrill, M. A., *Studies in personality.* New York: McGraw-Hill.

KRAEPELIN, E. 1896. Der psychologische Versuch in der Psychiatrie. *Psychol. Arb., 1,* 63–65.

—— 1915. Lehrbuch der Psychiatrie. (8th ed.) Leipzig: Barth.

—— 1919. Dementia praecox and paraphrenia. (Trans. by R. M. Barclay.) Edinburgh: Livingstone.

—— 1925. Arbeitspsychologische Ausblicke. *Psychol. Arb., 8,* 431–450.

KRAIZ, S. V. 1936. The psychosensory disorders in schizophrenia. *Nevropat. Psikhiat. Psikhoghig., 5,* 615–640.

KRISCH, H. 1932. Die Interpretation schizophrener Symptome als Funktionsabbau. *Z. ges. Neurol. Psychiat., 138,* 109–121.

LANDIS, C. 1932. Electrical phenomena of the skin. *Psychol. Bull., 29,* 693–752.

LANDIS, C., & HUNT, W. A. 1939. The startle pattern. New York: Farrar & Rinehart.

LANDIS, C., HUNT, W. A., & PAGE, J. D. 1937. Studies of the startle pattern: VII. Abnormals. *J. Psychol., 4,* 199–206.

LANDIS, C., & PAGE, J. D. 1938. Modern society and mental disease. New York: Farrar & Rinehart.

LANDIS, C., & RECHETNICK, J. 1934. Changes in psychological functions in paresis: I. *Psychiat. Quart., 8,* 693–698.

LANG, J. 1939. The other side of the affective aspects of schizophrenia. *Psychiatry, 2,* 195–202.

—— 1940. The other side of the ideological aspects of schizophrenia. *Psychiatry, 3,* 389–393.

LIDZ, T. 1939. A study of the effect of right frontal lobectomy on intelligence and temperament. *J. Neurol. Psychiat., Lond., 2,* 211–222.

LILJENCRANTS, J. 1922. Memory defects in the organic psychoses. *Psychol. Monogr., 32,* Whole No. 143, 76.

LIND, J. E. 1915. Statistical study of hallucinations in the manic-depressive type of psychoses. *J. nerv. ment. Dis., 42,* 727–735.

LINE, W., & GRIFFIN, J. D. M. 1935. The objective determination of factors underlying mental health. *Amer. J. Psychiat., 91,* 833–842.

LINE, W., GRIFFIN, J. D. M., & ANDERSON, G. W. 1935. The objective measurement of mental stability. *J. ment. Sci., 81,* 61–106.

LUNDHOLM, H. 1922. Reaction time as an indicator of emotional disturbances in manic-depressive psychoses. *J. abnorm. Psychol., 17,* 292–318.

—— 1932. Schizophrenia. Durham, N. C.: Duke University Press.

MAGARET, A. 1942. Parallels in the behavior of schizophrenics, paretics, and presenile non-psychotics. *J. abnorm. soc. Psychol., 37,* 511–528.

MAILLOUX, N. M., & NEWBURGER, M. 1941. The work curves of psychotic individuals. *J. abnorm. soc. Psychol., 36,* 110–114.

MALAMUD, W., & GOTTLIEB, J. 1944. Therapeutic results in psychoneurosis. (Unpublished)

MALAMUD, W., & NYGARD, W. J. 1931. The rôle played by the cutaneous senses in spatial perceptions: II. Investigations in mental diseases. *J. nerv. ment. Dis., 73,* 465–477.

MALAMUD, W., & PALMER, E. M. 1938. Intellectual deterioration in the psychoses. *Arch. Neurol. Psychiat., Chicago, 39,* 68–81.

McFARLAND, R. A. 1932. The psychological effects of oxygen deprivation (anoxemia) on human behavior. *Arch. Psychol., N. Y.,* No. 145.

MEYER, A. 1910. The dynamic interpretation of dementia praecox. *Amer. J. Psychol., 21,* 385–403.

MICHAELS, J. J., & SCHILLING, M. E. 1936. The correlations of the intelligence quotients of the Porteus Maze and Binet-Simon tests in 200 neuropsychiatric patients. *Amer. J. Orthopsychiat., 6,* 71–74.

MILES, W. R. 1933. Age and human ability. *Psychol. Rev., 40,* 99–123.

—— 1935. Age and human society. In Murchison, C., *A handbook of social psychology.* Worcester, Mass.: Clark University Press.

MISKOLCZY, D. 1937. Die Wortliche Verteilung der Gehirnveränderungen bei der Schizophrenie. *Psychiat.-neurol. Wschr., 39,* 145–147.

MOORE, T. V. 1919. The correlation between memory and perception in the presence of diffuse cortical degeneration. *Psychol. Monogr., 27,* Whole No. 120.

—— 1930. Empirical determination of certain syndromes underlying praecox and manic-depressive insanity. *Amer. J. Psychiat., 9,* 719–738.

—— 1933. The essential psychoses and their fundamental syndromes. *Stud. Psychiat. Psychol., Catholic Univ. Amer., 3,* No. 3.

MOREL, F. 1936. Examen audiométrique de malades présentant des hallucinations auditive verbales. *Ann. méd.-psychol., 94,* 520–533.

MOWRER, O. H. 1940. An experimental analogue of "regression" with incidental observations on "reaction-formation." *J. abnorm. soc. Psychol., 35,* 56–87.

MÜHL, A. M. 1930. Automatic writing. Dresden: Steinkopff.

MUNCIE, W. 1937. The psychopathology of metaphor. *Arch. Neurol. Psychiat., Chicago, 37,* 796–804.

MURPHY, G. 1920. A comparison of manic-depressive and dementia praecox cases by the free-association method. *Amer. J. Insan., 77,* 545–558.

—— 1922. Types of word-association in dementia praecox, manic-depressives, and normal persons. *Amer. J. Psychiat., 2,* 539–571.

MURSELL, G. 1929. Decrease in intelligence with increase in age among inmates of penal institutions. *J. juven. Res., 13,* 197–203.

NADEL, A. B.   1938.   A qualitative analysis of behavior following cerebral lesions. *Arch. Psychol., N. Y.*, No. 224.

NICHOLS, I. C., & HUNT, J. McV.   1940.   A case of partial bilateral frontal lobectomy. A psychopathological study. *Amer. J. Psychiat., 96*, 1063–1083.

OBERSTEINER, H.   1874.   Ueber eine neue einfache Methode zur Bestimmung der psychischen Leistungsfähigkeit des Gehirnes Geisteskranker. *Virchows Arch., 59*, 427–458.

OLSON, E.   1931.   A study of emotions in psychopathic personalities. *J. appl. Psychol., 15*, 182–198.

ORTON, S. T.   1930.   Some neurological concepts applied to catatonia. *Arch. Neurol. Psychiat., Chicago, 23*, 111–124.

PARTINGTON, J. E.   1940.   The comparative mental efficiency of a drug addict group. *J. appl. Psychol., 24*, 48–57.

PETERSON, F., & JUNG, C. G.   1907.   Psycho-physical investigations with the galvanometer and pneumograph in normal and insane individuals. *Brain, 30*, 153–218.

PFAFFMANN, C., & SCHLOSBERG, H.   1935.   The conditioned knee-jerk in psychotic and normal individuals. *J. Psychol., 1*, 201–208.

PIOTROWSKI, Z. A.   1933.   The test behavior of schizophrenic children. *Proc. Amer. Assn. Stud. ment. Def., 38*, 332–334.

—— 1937a.   A comparison of congenitally defective children with schizophrenic children in regard to personality structure and intelligence type. *Proc. Amer. Assn. Stud. ment. Def., 42*, 78–90.

—— 1937b.   Objective signs of invalidity of Stanford-Binet tests. *Psychiat. Quart., 11*, 623–636.

—— 1937c.   The Rorschach inkblot method in organic disturbances of the central nervous system. *J. nerv. ment. Dis., 86*, 525–537.

POLLOCK, L. J., & DALLEAR, A. H.   1916.   Pneumographic studies of emotional reactions in dementia praecox. *Inst. Quart., Springfield, Ia, 7*, 73–78.

POPPELREUTER, W.   1917.   Die psychischen Schädigungen durch Kopfschuss. (2 Vols.)   Leipzig: Leopold Voss.

PORTEUS, S. D.   1922.   Studies in mental deviations. *Train. Sch. Publ., Vineland, N. J.*, No. 24.

PREDA, G., STOENESCU, T., & CUPCEA, S.   1934.   La memoire de fixation dans les maladies mentales. *Noua Rev. med., 9*, 1–7.

PRESSEY, S. L.   1917.   Distinctive features in psychological test measurements made upon dementia praecox and chronic alcoholic patients. *J. abnorm. Psychol., 12*, 130–139.

PRESSEY, S. L., & COLE, L. W.   1919.   Irregularity in a psychological examination as a measure of mental deterioration. *J. abnorm. Psychol., 13*, 285–294.

PUMPIAN-MINDLIN, E.   1935.   Ueber die Bestimmung der bewussten Zeitschätzung bei normalen und dementen Epileptikern. *Schweiz. Arch. Neurol. Psychiat., 36*, 291–305.

QUENSEL, F.   1931.   Erkrankungen der höheren optischen Zentren. In Kurze, *Handbuch der Ophthalmologie, 6*, 324–475.   Berlin: Springer.

RABIN, A. I.   1941.   Test-score patterns in schizophrenia and non-psychotic states. *J. Psychol., 12*, 91–100.

RAWLINGS, E.   1921.   The intellectual status of patients with paranoid dementia praecox: its relation to the organic brain changes. *Arch. Neurol. Psychiat., Chicago, 5*, 283–295.

RAZRAN, G. H. S.   1934.   Conditioned withdrawal responses with shock as the conditioning stimulus in adult human subjects. *Psychol. Bull., 31*, 111–143.

RICHTER, C. P.   1928.   Electrical skin resistance. Diurnal and daily variation in psychopathic and normal persons. *Arch. Neurol. Psychiat., Chicago, 19*, 488–508.

RICKERS-OVSIANKINA, M.   1937a.   Studies on the personality structure of schizophrenic individuals: I. The accessibility of schizophrenics to environmental influences. *J. gen. Psychol., 16*, 153–178.

—— 1937b.   Studies on the personality structure of schizophrenic individuals: II. Reaction to interrupted tasks. *J. gen. Psychol., 16*, 179–196.

RODNICK, E. H., & SHAKOW, D.   1940.   Set in the schizophrenic as measured by a composite reaction time index. *Amer. J. Psychiat., 97*, 214–225.

ROE, A., & SHAKOW, D.   1942.   Intelligence in mental disorder. *Ann. N. Y. Acad Sci., 42*, 361–490.

ROSANOFF, A. J. 1938. Manual of psychiatry. (7th ed.) New York: Wiley.

ROSANOFF, A. J., MARTIN, H. E., & ROSANOFF, I. 1918. A higher scale of mental measurement and its application to cases of insanity. *Psychol. Monogr.*, 25, Whole No. 109.

ROUVROY, C. 1936. Les études experimentales sur l'intelligence chez les malades mentaux. *J. belge Neurol. Psychiat.*, 8, 479–529.

ROWE, S. N. 1937. Mental changes following the removal of the right cerebral hemisphere for brain tumor. *Amer. J. Psychiat.*, 94, 605–614.

RYLANDER, G. 1939. Personality changes after operations on the frontal lobes. London: Oxford University Press. Also: *Acta psychiat., Kbh.*, Suppl. 20.

SAUNDERS, E. B., & ISAACS, S. 1929. Tests of reaction time and motor inhibition in the psychoses. *Amer. J. Psychiat.*, 9, 79–112.

SCHILDER, P. 1934. Psychic disturbances after head injuries. *Amer. J. Psychiat.*, 91, 155–188.

—— 1935. The image and appearance of the human body. London: Routledge.

SCHOTT, E. L. 1930. Variability of mental ratings in retests of neuropsychiatric cases. *Amer. J. Psychiat.*, 10, 213–227.

—— 1931. Superior intelligence in patients with nervous and mental disease. *J. abnorm. soc. Psychol.*, 26, 94–101.

SCHWARZ, R. 1932. Measurement of mental deterioration in dementia praecox. *Amer. J. Psychiat.*, 12, 555–560.

SCRIPTURE, E. W. 1916. Reaction time in nervous and mental diseases. *J. ment. Sci.*, 62, 698–719.

SHAKOW, D., DOEKART, M. B., & GOLDMAN, R. 1941. The memory function in psychotics. *Dis. nerv. Syst.*, 2, 43–48.

SHAKOW, D., & GOLDMAN, R. 1938. The effect of age on the Stanford-Binet vocabulary score of adults. *J. educ. Psychol.*, 29, 241–256.

SHAKOW, D., & HUSTON, P. E. 1936. Studies of motor function in schizophrenia: I. Speed of tapping. *J. gen. Psychol.*, 15, 63–108.

SHAKOW, D., & MILLARD, M. 1935. A psychometric study of 150 delinquents. *J. soc. Psychol.*, 6, 437–457.

SHIPLEY, W. C. 1934a. Studies of catatonia: VI. Further investigation of the perseverational tendency. *Psychiat. Quart.*, 8, 736–744.

—— 1934b. Stanford-Binet scattering as related to IQ in clinical cases. *Psychol. Bull.*, 31, 684.

—— 1940. A self-administering scale for measuring intellectual impairment and deterioration. *J. Psychol.*, 9, 371–377.

SHIPLEY, W. C., & BURLINGAME, C. C. 1941. A convenient self-administering scale for measuring intellectual impairment in psychotics. *Amer. J. Psychiat.*, 97, 1313–1324.

SHIPLEY, W. C., & KANT, F. 1940. The insulin-shock and metrazol treatments of schizophrenics with emphasis on psychological aspects. *Psychol. Bull.*, 37, 259–284.

SIMMINS, C. 1933. Studies in experimental psychiatry: IV. Deterioration of 'G' in psychotic patients. *J. ment. Sci.*, 79, 704–734.

SLEEPER, F. H., & JELLINEK, E. M. 1936. A comparative physiologic, psychologic, and psychiatric study of polyuric and non-polyuric schizophrenic patients. *J. nerv. ment. Dis.*, 83, 557–563.

SQUIRES, P. C. 1936. Psychological loss in paretics and schizophrenics: a discussion. *Amer. J. Psychol.*, 48, 169–172.

STEPHEN, K. 1935. Psychoanalysis and medicine. New York: Macmillan.

STEPHENSON, W. 1931. Studies in experimental psychiatry: I. A case of general inertia. *J. ment. Sci.*, 77, 723–741.

—— 1932a. Studies in experimental psychiatry: II. Some contact of *p*-factor with psychiatry. *J. ment. Sci.*, 78, 315–330.

—— 1932b. Studies in experimental psychiatry: III. *p*-score and inhibition for high-*p* praecox cases. *J. ment. Sci.*, 78, 774–928.

STEPHENSON, W., MACKENZIE, M., SIMMINS, C. A., KAPP, D. M., & STUDMAN, G. L. 1934. Spearman factors and psychiatry. *Brit. J. med. Psychol.*, 14, 101–135.

STORCH, A. 1924. The primitive archaic forms of inner experience and thought in schizophrenia. *Nerv. ment. Dis. Monogr.*, No. 36.

STRAUSS, H. 1929. Das Zusammenschrecken. *J. Psychol. Neurol., Lpz.*, 39, 111–231.

STRECKER, E. A., & HUGHES, J. 1936. Functional changes in the patellar reflex as seen in the psychoses. *Amer. J. Psychiat., 93*, 547–557.

STREET, R. 1934. The Gestalt Completion Test and mental disorder. *J. abnorm. soc. Psychol., 29*, 141–142.

STRONG, E. K. 1913. Comparison between experimental data and clinical results in manic-depressive insanity. *Amer. J. Psychol., 24*, 66–98.

STUDMAN, L. G. 1935. Studies in experimental psychiatry: V. "W" and "F" factors in relation to traits of personality. *J. ment. Sci., 81*, 107–144.

STUMBUR, E. D. 1934. [The memorizing of finished and unfinished actions in schizophrenia.] *Sovetsk. Nevropatol., 3*, No. 11/12, 261–269.

SUPER, D. E. 1942. The Bernreuter Personality Inventory: a review of research. *Psychol. Bull., 39*, 94–125.

SYMONS, N. J. 1941. On schizophrenia. *Brit. J. med. Psychol., 18*, 285–422.

TATARENKO, N. P. 1938. [Aphasia-like disturbances of speech in schizophrenics.] *Sovetsk. Psikhonevrol., 14*, 65–68.

TENDLER, A. D. 1923. The mental status of psychoneurotics. *Arch. Psychol., N. Y.*, No. 60.

—— 1933. Associative tendencies in psychoneurotics. *Psychol. Clin., 22*, 108–116.

TERMAN, L. M., & ODEN, M. 1940. The significance of deviates: II. Status of the California gifted group at the end of sixteen years; III. Correlates of adult achievement in the California gifted group. *Yearb. nat. Soc. Stud. Educ., 1940, 39*, Part I, 67–74, 74–89.

TERRY, G. C., & RENNIE, T. A. C. 1938. Analysis of parergasia. *Nerv. ment. Dis. Monogr.*, No. 64.

THOMPSON, J. 1941. The ability of children of different grade levels to generalize on sorting tests. *J. Psychol., 11*, 119–126.

TOURO DEL PINO, J. 1939. Estudió experimental de la evolución del pensamiento esquizofrénico en el tratamiento por el cardiazol. *Rev. Neuro-Psiquiat., Lima, 2*, 391–425.

TRAPP, C. E., & JAMES, E. B. 1937. Comparative intelligence ratings in the four types of dementia praecox. *J. nerv. ment. Dis., 86*, 399–404.

TRAVIS, L. E. 1924. Suggestibility and negativism as measured by auditory threshold during reverie. *J. abnorm. soc. Psychol., 18*, 350–368.

—— 1925. A test for distinguishing between schizophrenoses and psychoneuroses. *J. abnorm. soc. Psychol., 19*, 283–298.

—— 1928. Rate of reflex conduction in a cataleptic patient. *Proc. Soc. exp. Biol., N. Y., 25*, 598–599.

TRAVIS, L. E., & DORSEY, J. M. 1929. Patellar tendon reflex time in psychiatric and in neurologic cases. *Arch. Neurol. Psychiat., Chicago, 22*, 99–104.

TRAVIS, L. E., & YOUNG, C. W. 1930. The relations of electromyographically measured reflex time in the patellar and Achilles reflexes to certain physical measurements and to intelligence. *J. gen. Psychol., 3*, 374–400.

TRAVIS, R. C. 1926. The diagnosis of character types by visual and auditory thresholds. *Psychol. Monogr., 36*, Whole No. 168, 18–37.

VIGOTSKY, I. S. 1934. Thought in schizophrenia. *Arch. Neurol. Psychiat., Chicago, 31*, 1063–1077.

WALLIN, J. E. W. 1922. Intelligence irregularity as measured by scattering in the Binet Scale. *J. educ. Psychol., 13*, 140–151.

—— 1927. A further note on scattering in the Binet Scale. *J. appl. Psychol., 11*, 143–154.

WECHSLER, D. 1917. A study of retention in Korsakoff's psychosis. New York: Dissertation, Columbia University.

—— 1929. General intelligence, mental level and the neuroses. In Wechsler, I. S., *The neuroses*. Philadelphia: Saunders.

—— 1939. The measurement of adult intelligence. Baltimore: Williams & Wilkins.

WECHSLER, D., HALPERN, F., & JAROS, E. 1940. Psychometric study of insulin-treated schizophrenics. *Psychiat. Quart., 14*, 466–476.

WEGROCKI, H. 1940. Generalizing ability in schizophrenia. *Arch. Psychol., N. Y.*, No. 254.

WEIGL, E. 1941. On the psychology of the so-called processes of abstraction. (Trans. by M. J. Reoch, and ed. by C. Landis & K. Goldstein.) *J. abnorm. soc. Psychol., 36*, 3–33.

WEISENBURG, T., & McBRIDE, K. E. 1935. Aphasia: a clinical and psychological study. New York: Commonwealth Fund.

WEISENBURG, T., ROE, A., & McBRIDE, K. E. 1936. Adult intelligence. New York: Commonwealth Fund.

WELLS, F. L. 1909. Studies in retardation as given in the fatigue phenomena of the tapping test. *Amer. J. Psychol., 20,* 38–59.

—— 1919a. Autistic mechanisms in association reaction. *Psychol. Rev., 26,* 376–381.

—— 1919b. Psychotic performance in cancellation and direction tests. *Psychol. Rev., 26,* 366–376.

—— 1927. Mental tests in clinical practice. Yonkers, N. Y.: World Book.

—— 1930. Learning functions in an obscure amnesia with implications for re-education. *J. gen. Psychol., 8,* 173–197.

WELLS, F. L., & CURRIE, J. P. 1923. Time factors in the substitution test with psychotic cases. *J. abnorm. Psychol., 17,* 402–404.

WELLS, F. L., & KELLEY, C. M. 1920. Intelligence and psychosis. *Amer. J. Insan., 77,* 17–45.

—— 1922. The simple reaction in psychosis. *Amer. J. Psychiat., 2,* 53–59.

WELLS, F. L., & MARTIN, H. A. 1923. A method of memory examination suitable for psychotic cases. *Amer. J. Psychiat., 8,* 243–258.

WELLS, F. L., & STURGES, H. A. 1918. The pathology of choice reactions. *Amer. J. Insan., 75,* 81–119.

WENTWORTH, M. M. 1924. Two hundred cases of dementia praecox tested by the Stanford Revision. *J. abnorm. soc. Psychol., 18,* 378–384.

WHITE, W. A. 1928. The language of schizophrenia. *Res. Publ. Assn. Res. nerv. ment. Dis., 5,* 323–343.

WIERSMA, E. D. 1930. The psychology of dementia. *J. ment. Sci., 76,* 1–42.

WILLOUGHBY, R. R. 1927. Family similarities in mental test abilities. *Genet. Psychol. Monogr., 2,* No. 4, 235–277.

—— 1929. Age and intelligence. *J. educ. Psychol., 20,* 678.

WITTMAN, M. P. 1933. The Babcock deterioration test in state hospital practice. *J. abnorm. soc. Psychol., 28,* 70–84.

—— 1937. An evaluation of opposed theories concerning the etiology of so-called "dementia" in dementia praecox. *Amer. J. Psychiat., 93,* 1363–1377.

WITTMAN, M. P., & RUSSEL, J. T. 1941. Mental efficiency levels before and after shock therapy. *Elgin Pap., 4,* 70–81.

WOODS, W. L. 1938. Language study in schizophrenia. *J. nerv. ment. Dis., 87,* 290–316.

WORCHEL, P., & LYERLY, J. G. 1941. Effects of prefrontal lobotomy on depressed patients. *J. Neurophysiol., 4,* 62–67.

WYLIE, M. 1930. An experimental study of recognition and recall in abnormal mental cases. *Psychol. Monogr., 39,* Whole No. 180.

YACORZYNSKI, G. K. 1941. An evaluation of the postulates underlying the Babcock deterioration test. *Psychol. Rev., 48,* 261–267.

YERKES, R. M. (Ed.) 1921. Psychological examining in the United States Army. Washington, D. C.: National Academy of Sciences.

ZUBIN, J., & THOMPSON, J. 1941. Sorting tests in relation to drug therapy in schizophrenia. New York: New York State Psychiatric Institute.

ZUKER, K., & HUBERT, W. H. DEB. 1935. A study of the changes in function found in schizophrenic thought disorder. *J. ment. Sci., 81,* 1–45.

Chapter 33

ELECTROENCEPHALOGRAPHY

By Donald B. Lindsley, Ph.D.

Personality, in its broadest sense, may be construed to mean a totality of behavior based upon interdependent structural and functional components of a living organism. Behavior may be defined to include any change or adjustment made by the organism, either in whole or part, to internal and external environmental influences. Therefore the many faceted thing we call personality (see Chapter 1 by MacKinnon), and its disorders, may be approached from many angles. One approach is through the electrical changes which serve as signs of underlying physicochemical conditions associated with metabolic and other processes during relative states of rest as well as during activity induced by stimulation.

All living tissues possess electrical properties which are subject to study in terms of familiar units of electrical measurement, and the brain is no exception. In the study of personality and behavior aberrations the newly developed technique of electroencephalography, which deals with the recording of electrical potentials from the brain, is of importance in the differentiation of individuals and in the measurement and evaluation of response to internal and external environmental influences.

An attempt will be made in this chapter to survey the results of a number of investigations which have utilized the method of electroencephalography to study behavior and its disorders in the human organism. No attempt will be made to review the results of the many animal experiments which have contributed so extensively to the methodology and background of information necessary to the understanding of the results in human studies.

History.—The recording of electrical potentials from the brain of man began in 1924 with the work of Hans Berger, a German neuropsychiatrist. Prior to that time, for a period of 50 years, scattered reports appeared in the literature describing observations of electrical activity in the exposed brains of animals. These early studies (for references see Jasper, 1937; Walter, 1938; and Gibbs and Gibbs, 1941) attracted little attention, partly because electrical phenomena associated with nervous activity were little understood at the time and partly because the potentials were so minute that their details could not be adequately registered by available recording instruments. Berger's interest in these early observations led, after some preliminary experimentation with animals, to the study of human subjects. After five years of work, he published in 1929 the first report of human brain potentials.

Because of his interest in psychiatry and neurology Berger quickly sought to apply his newly discovered technique to the study of pathological conditions in man, but not without first attempting to determine the nature of the phenomenon, the limitations of the technique, and the characteristics of the electrical activity of the brain in normal individuals. He demonstrated that the more or less continuous rhythmic fluctuations of potential recorded from electrodes attached to the scalp at the front and back of the head arose from the brain tissue and were not due to circulatory pulsations, muscle activity, or other extraneous factors. He was able to show that the electrical activity of the brain is modified by sleep, anesthesia, and various forms of sensory stimulation; that the patterns of activity vary with age in young children; and that certain pathological conditions produce abnormal manifestations of the electrical record from the brain. These and other original observations are described in his extensive series of publications (1929 to 1938).

Adrian and Matthews (1934a) in England were the first to publish confirmation of Berger's findings, and Gibbs and Davis (1935), Jasper and Carmichael (1935), and Loomis, et al. (1935a, 1935b) in America soon added further proof. In the meantime information concerning the electrical activity of the central nervous system of animals was rapidly accumulating. Interest in the work spread rapidly to other parts of the world, new apparatus and techniques were developed, and many publications of animal and human investigations appeared.

Early reviews of the subject, dealing principally with results of animal studies have been presented by Fischer (1932), Kornmüller (1935c), and Gozzano (1935). More recent and more extensive reviews, including human electroencephalography, are those by Kornmüller (1937a), Jasper (1937), Berger (1938a), Bremer (1938a), Davis, H. (1938b), Fessard (1938), Liberson (1938), Walter (1938), Rohracher (1938b), Bertrand, et al. (1939), and Gibbs and Gibbs (1941). The last named review is in the form of an Atlas and presents many records illustrative of normal and pathological conditions.

Electroencephalography in pediatrics has been reviewed by Byers (1941) and Brill (1942), and its use in psychological studies has been discussed by Kreezer (1938b) and Knott (1941). Workers in many different lands have published, in several different languages, discussions of technique, method and applications, usually coupled with descriptions of their own preliminary results. Lack of space does not permit the listing of all of these but some of the more representative are: Schäckter (1936), Cucchi (1938), H. Davis (1938a), Godlowski (1938), Newman (1938), Asenjo (1939), Cottenot and Liquier (1939), Davis and Davis (1939), Rohracher (1939), Aguero y Montoro (1940), Caprile and Gascón (1940), Spielberg (1940a), H. Davis (1941), P. A. Davis (1941e), and Carrillo (1941).

Articles dealing particularly with clinical applications are: Baudouin and Fischgold (1938, 1939), Golse (1938), Kornmüller (1938), Balado, *et al.* (1939), Dalsgaard-Nielsen (1939), Goodwin and Hall (1939), Hyland, *et al* (1939), Jung (1939a, 1941), Kornmüller (1939), Schmelvkin (1939), Torrents (1940), Walter (1940a), Pacella and Barrera (1941), Prados y Such (1941), Ramirez Moreno (1941), Serota and Grinker (1941), Yeager and Walsh (1941), and Gibbs (1942b).

Nature of Phenomenon.—Berger's discovery that the human brain during a relative state of rest, in the absence of specific stimulation, has an electrical beat or rhythm of its own was surprising indeed, so much so that his results were looked upon with considerable skepticism until confirmed by others. However, some preparation for understanding the electrical phenomena of the brain had already developed from the results of animal studies. For example, slow, rhythmic potential waves were recorded from isolated ganglia of the caterpillar and water beetle by Adrian (1930, 1931) and in the isolated brain stem of the goldfish by Adrian and Buytendijk (1931). Isolated from other parts of the nervous system and cut off from sources of sensory impulses the brain stem of the goldfish produced slow, rhythmic potentials which were correlated with respiratory movements of the gill slits. Here was evidence in the central nervous system of rhythmic electrical activities of spontaneous and autonomous origin, controlled presumably by metabolic processes, and resembling the automatic regulation of activity in the nonnervous embryonic heart. Further evidence of automaticity in the isolated frog brain has been presented by Libet and Gerard (1938, 1939, 1941).

At the time of Berger's discovery of human brain rhythms considerable was known about the characteristics of electrical potentials associated with the nerve impulse, but this type of activity, associated with discrete events such as the passage of the nerve impulse in response to sensory and reflex stimulation, did not appear to be of immediate significance for the interpretation of the electrical changes emanating from the complex network of axons, dendrites, cell bodies, and supporting structures of the brain. The potentials from the brain consisted of continuous, often sinusoidal, rhythmic variations of different frequencies and patterns. Instead of being initiated by specific stimulation, the rhythms appeared to be of spontaneous and autonomous character and were in fact diminished or abolished temporarily by certain types of sensory stimulation. For a good discussion of the nature of autonomous rhythms of the brain and the factors which affect them, see particularly the papers presented at a symposium by Bishop (1936), Davis (1936), Gerard (1936), Hoagland (1936b), and Jasper (1936b).

It was possible to rule out extraneous sources of electrical activity such as potentials originating in scalp, face and neck muscles, static potentials of the eyeballs, circulatory pulsations, and so forth (Berger, 1929; Adrian and Matthews, 1934; Jasper and Andrews, 1936, 1938a;

Lyman, 1941). However, one must always be on guard against artifacts produced in these ways. The influence of sensory stimulation, sleep, anesthesia, and so forth in modifying the rhythmic potentials served to demonstrate the nervous character of the electrical activity and even suggested a cortical origin. Recording directly from the surface of the brain at time of operation (Berger, 1935a; Foerster and Altenburger, 1935; Walter, 1936; Schwartz and Kerr, 1940; Scarff and Rahm, 1941) furnished more direct proof of the cortical origin of the potentials. These studies showed also that the type of activity recorded from the surface of the scalp was very similar to that recorded from electrodes in direct contact with brain tissue except that on the surface of the skull the patterns of activity were less well localized and were greatly reduced in amplitude. The amount of reduction is of the order of 5 to 1 in the rabbit (Kornmüller and Janzen, 1939b), but in man is considerably more according to Walter (1936) who reports potentials of the order of 1 to 10 millivolts on the surface of the cortex as opposed to 10 to 100 microvolts on the surface of the scalp. This reduction is undoubtedly due to the increased resistance and diffusion caused by the scalp and skull. Some idea of the manner of diffusion or spread of the potentials on the surface of the scalp from a localized source in the brain has been presented by Adrian and Yamagiwa (1935) who experimented with an artificial source of potential in the skull of a cadaver, and by Andrews (1938) who discussed the physical basis of brain potentials from theoretical and applied points of view.

In spite of the clinical and experimental usefulness of the electroencephalogram and the numerous studies which have added to our information concerning it, many questions still remain with respect to the fundamental nature and specific origin of the potentials. For example, do the potentials originate in cell bodies of cortical neurones or do they represent axonal, dendritic or synaptic activity? What gives rise to the rhythms of different frequencies and different patterns? What is the role of the various cortical layers, the cytoarchitectural variations from one part of the cortex to another, or the ascending, descending, and tangential pathways in the cortex? How many neural units are required to produce an electrical disturbance which may be recorded at the surface of the scalp? What determines the combination and apparent synchronicity of cellular discharges? What is the relationship between the apparently autonomous and spontaneous rhythms of the resting cortex and evoked potentials produced by specific afferent stimulation? How are the potential rhythms of the various areas of the cortex related to one another? Are there fixed or shifting centers of control, that is "pacemakers," in the cortex which serve to integrate the activities of the different parts, or are cortical electrical activities regulated principally by thalamic and other subcortical centers?

Partial answers to some of these questions have already been provided by results of animal studies and additional evidence is rapidly accumulating. It is now generally believed that the spontaneous potentials of the cortex originate principally in nerve cell bodies (Bartley and Bishop, 1933; Bishop, 1935; Bremer, 1938b, 1938c; Libet and Gerard, 1938, 1941; Rosenblueth and Cannon, 1942) rather than in the axons. There is evidence from lesions circumscribing certain areas that some spontaneous rhythms of the cortex originate in local regions and are relatively independent of other parts of the cortex (Bartley and Bishop, 1933; Bremer, 1938b, 1938c; Gerard and Libet, 1939, 1940; Rosenblueth and Cannon, 1942). There is also reason to believe that "loop" or "reverberating" circuits between thalamus and cortex are necessary to the maintenance of certain types of spontaneous activity (Bishop, 1936; Bishop and O'Leary, 1936; Dempsey and Morison, 1942; Rosenblueth and Cannon, 1942). In fact the work of Dusser de Barenne and McCulloch (1938) indicates that even more complex circuits are involved, including certain nonthalamic nuclei. Incoming impulses from sensory receptors must be properly integrated at both thalamic and cortical levels with spontaneous rhythms in these circuits in order to be effective and evoke maximal cortical response.

With respect to the role of different cortical layers Dusser de Barenne and McCulloch (1936) have shown that spontaneous potentials of the cortex are practically abolished by thermocoagulation of the outer three layers of the cortex and are completely and permanently abolished by destruction of the four outer layers. Kornmüller (1935c) maintains that there are differences in the bioelectric activity of different parts of the cortex, corresponding to the architectonic fields. Similar gross differences have been pointed out in man (Jasper and Andrews, 1936, 1938a; Laugier and Liberson, 1937; Rubin, 1938a), although the distinction between areas is greatly reduced when the potentials are recorded through the scalp and skull.

Most workers have agreed with Adrian and Matthews (1934a) that summation of discharges of individual neurones is necessary for the production of potentials sufficiently large to be recorded from the surface of the scalp. Adrian and Matthews (1934b) in attempting to record cortical response from individual neurones concluded that the slow, rhythmic cortical waves are summations of temporally dispersed faster components in individual neurones. On the other hand Renshaw, et al. (1940) using microelectrodes to record unit responses from the hippocampus of the cat found both slow and rapid potential fluctuations. On the basis of their data it is not possible to decide whether cortical rhythms are composed of summations of individual neurone discharges of the same slow frequency, or are built up by synchronization of many fast components. An interesting paper on the interaction and integration of neuronal activity has been presented by Gerard (1941).

Despite the lack of a clear understanding of the nature and origin of the potential rhythms recorded from the surface of the scalp, the electroencephalogram possesses certain measurable and discriminable characteristics which may be utilized in clinical and experimental studies. Caution must be urged, however, against too much theorizing before an adequate understanding of causal or underlying factors has been attained. It is highly desirable for those working with the human electroencephalogram to keep in close contact with the results of electrophysiological investigation in the animal field.

Terminology.—The record of the electrical activity from the brain of man was called by Berger (1929) an *Elektrenkephalogramm*. The English equivalent is *electroencephalogram*. The abbreviation is EEG. Other designations used in published studies are *brain potentials* and the more popular rubric, *brain waves*. Berger originally recorded the potentials from across the entire surface of the head, with one electrode attached to the forehead and the other at the back. Investigators have since come to use several electrodes more closely spaced so as to record from relatively localized regions corresponding roughly to the anatomical subdivisions of the brain. Tracings from electrodes placed over different areas of the brain are therefore designated as *occipital EEG, frontal EEG,* and so forth. In order to distinguish between records from the surface of the scalp and those obtained with electrodes in direct contact with exposed portions of the brain, the former are referred to as *electroencephalograms* and the latter as *electrograms*. Thus there may be *cortical electrograms, cerebellar electrograms,* or *thalamic electrograms,* depending upon the part of the exposed brain from which the potentials are derived.

Types of Waves in the EEG and Their Characteristics.—Berger (1929, 1932b) found in the EEG of normal adults two types of waves which were distinguished by their frequency, amplitude and differential response to sensory stimulation. The larger, rhythmic waves averaging about 10 per second and subject to modification by stimulation, he called *alpha waves*. The more rapid, less prominent waves, often superimposed on or forming a background for the alpha rhythm, he called *beta waves*.

ALPHA WAVES.—Berger (1933d, 1935a, 1936, 1938c) held that alpha waves originate in all parts of the cortex, whereas Adrian and Matthews (1934a), and Adrian and Yamagiwa (1935) concluded that the source or focus of the alpha waves was in the neighborhood of area 19 of the occipital lobes. The evidence which follows indicates that Berger's view was more nearly correct, although it is true that in most normal subjects the strongest and most persistent alpha rhythm is found over the occipito-parietal regions. Cortical electrograms in man (Foerster and Altenburger, 1935; Scarff and Rahm, 1941) have revealed alpha rhythms in all regions of the cortex, but predominantly over the various sensory fields. Likewise the distribution of the alpha rhythm over the surface of the scalp has been shown by Liberson (1937), Jasper and Andrews (1938a), Loomis, *et al.* (1938), and Rubin (1938a) to be widespread and to have simultaneously differential features over the occipital, temporal, and frontal areas. Lindsley (1938b), using a phase reversal localization method similar to that employed by Adrian and Yamagiwa.

demonstrated separate foci for the alpha rhythm in occipital, occipito-parietal, parieto-frontal, and temporal regions.

Smith (1939, 1941) has shown that the occipital and precentral alpha rhythms in infants and young children first appear at different times and have different developmental sequences. The alpha rhythm over the sensory-motor regions is present at birth and has a frequency of 7 to 8 per second (Smith, 1938a, 1941), whereas the occipital alpha rhythm first appears in the third or fourth month at a frequency of 3 to 4 per second (Lindsley, 1936, 1938a, 1939; Smith, 1938b, 1939). The frequency of the precentral alpha rhythm increases very little during the first year, but the occipital alpha rhythm increases rapidly; after the first year both rhythms increase at similar rates and attain an adult frequency level at about ten to twelve years of age.

The normal range of frequencies for the alpha rhythm in adults, regardless of the region of the head, is 8 to 13 per second. Occasionally slightly higher or lower frequencies are found, but they are usually considered as suggestive of abnormality. For children below ten years of age a lower range of frequencies must be accepted as normal, due to the change in frequency with age. The voltage level of the alpha waves is difficult to specify since it varies with the position and distance between electrodes, as well as with the use of bipolar and monopolar recording methods.[1] Typical of the relative voltage levels for occipital and precentral alpha rhythms are the following results recently obtained by the author in a group of 20 normal, young adult men. Using a bipolar method, with electrodes 5 centimeters apart, the mean occipital alpha wave voltage was 24 microvolts, the range for individual subjects was 9 to 48; the mean for the precentral alpha rhythm was 13 microvolts with a range from 8 to 23 (unpublished data). Monopolar recording methods result in greater voltages than bipolar (see Figure 1). The voltages given here are in essential agreement with those reported by others (Davis and Davis, 1936; Jasper and Andrews, 1936). The usual limits cited for alpha voltages are from 5 to 100 microvolts; alpha voltages in excess of the upper limit are frequently pathological.

BETA WAVES.—There is a wide diversity of opinion concerning the origin, characteristics and significance of the beta waves. This is partly due to the fact that their voltage is low, the frequency high, and the pattern somewhat irregular. These characteristics lead to difficulty in adequately recording and measuring the beta waves and make them easily confused with action potentials from muscles of the scalp. In addition they are not readily affected by factors which modify the alpha

---

[1] In the case of the monopolar system of recording, one electrode is placed on the scalp over an "active" region of the brain, the other electrode is attached to a supposedly "inactive" or "indifferent" region, such as the lobe of the ear or mastoid process. With the bipolar system both electrodes are attached to the scalp, usually about five centimeters apart, over "active" regions of the brain. There are advantages and disadvantages of both systems; these have been discussed by Tönnies (1934), Jasper and Andrews (1936), Jung (1939a), Kornmüller and Janzen (1939b), Kornmüller (1940a), and Gibbs and Gibbs (1941).

rhythm. As a consequence most investigators have not found it profitable to study them extensively.

Most workers agree with Jasper and Andrews (1936, 1938a) that beta waves are more prominent over the precentral and frontal regions of the brain than elsewhere, although like the alpha waves they are found to some extent over all regions. Recording directly from the cortex at time of operation Scarff and Rahm (1941) found beta waves predominating in the frontal regions of the brain. Berger (1932b, 1936, 1938c) has reported the frequency of beta waves to range from 20 to more than 100 per second, but he does not agree with Rohracher (1935, 1937c) and Gemelli (1937) that they may attain frequencies of 1,000 to 2,000 per second. Since others have failed to observe such high frequencies it seems likely that they are due to some source of artifact.

According to Jasper and Andrews (1938a), who have made the most systematic observations of beta waves, the frequency range is predominantly from 18 to 30 per second with a mean of about 25 per second; the voltage range is from 5 to 20 microvolts. Unlike the occipital alpha rhythm, which is temporarily blocked by visual, and to some extent by other types of sensory stimulation, the beta waves are not markedly affected. Jasper and Andrews (1938a) state that tactual and auditory stimuli may affect the beta waves without producing an effect on the alpha waves. This result does not, however, seem to have been confirmed generally. Strong, sudden, unexpected stimulation of "startle" character may block the beta waves temporarily.

GAMMA WAVES.—Very low amplitude beta-like waves of 35 to 45 per second, noted particularly over the precentral and frontal regions, were tentatively labelled *gamma waves* by Jasper and Andrews (1938a). No special response characteristics have been described for these waves and their significance is not known. The term is not commonly used.

Adrian and Matthews (1934a, 1934b) were of the opinion that beta and alpha waves represent discharge potentials from the same cellular units, the alpha waves representing a more fully synchronized discharge. A number of observations might be interpreted as consistent with this point of view. Of the various cortical regions, beta waves are most prominent and alpha waves least prominent in the precentral and frontal areas. This may be due to the fact that the precentral and frontal regions are more highly differentiated in terms of the variety of functions they subserve and hence less subject to synchronized activity than are the sensory projection fields, where the alpha rhythm is strong and the beta rhythm feeble. Likewise sensory stimulation in blocking or disrupting the alpha rhythm frequently leaves only the smaller, faster beta-like waves. Because of this Adrian and Matthews (1934a) have concluded that sensory stimulation has a desynchronizing effect on groups of cells beating in unison. Also consistent with a common origin of beta and alpha waves might be the observations of Jasper and Andrews (1938a), that the frequency of both types of waves is increased by elevation of body temperature, and by Lindsley (1938a), that alpha and beta waves show essentially parallel increases in frequency as a function of age in young children.

Berger (1938c) does not believe that alpha and beta waves have a common origin. He thinks that they originate in different types of cells in the different cortical layers; the alpha waves coming from the deeper pyramidal cell layers and the beta waves from the superficial layers of the cortex. He cites the results of Bremer as indicating that beta waves arise from the small ganglion cells of the superficial layers. As a consequence of his observations that only the alpha waves are modified or reduced in amplitude by sensory stimulation, shifting of attention, sleep, anesthesia, stupor, and various disease processes, Berger (1930, 1932b) concluded that alpha waves are a reflection of biological activities associated with psychophysical processes and that beta waves are an expression of nutritive and metabolic functions. Precisely the opposite view has been proposed by Rohracher (1938b) and Alberti (1941).

In addition to *alpha, beta,* and *gamma* waves, a number of other frequency components have been observed in the EEG of normal adults, at rest, with the eyes closed. Grass and Gibbs (1938), and Gibbs (1942a) have presented cortical frequency spectra [2] showing some degree of energy represented at each frequency level from 1 to 60 cycles per second. The greatest amount of energy is found at the low frequency end of the spectrum; there are also energy peaks corresponding to the mean frequency level of the alpha and beta waves. Other less prominent peaks indicate the presence of other frequency components; some of these plus other abnormal distributions of energy in the spectrum are useful for detecting pathology and results of this character will be presented later. The application of names to particular rhythms detected by the wave analyzer or by observational analysis of the EEG has not seemed warranted since there are all gradations of voltage and considerable overlapping of frequency bands. As a consequence it is more accurate to describe rhythms in terms of their frequency, amplitude, and patterned characteristics.

DELTA WAVES.—One additional designation, applying particularly to abnormally slow waves found in pathological records, but present also in the records of normal subjects during sleep and certain other physiological states other than the normal waking one, is that of the *delta waves.* This term was used originally by Walter (1937) to designate the abnormal, slow waves of large magnitude, usually of 2 to 3 per second or less, found in the region of brain tumors and serving as a

---

[2] Frequency spectra are distributions of energy at each frequency level from 1 to 60 cycles per second. Known as a Fourier transform, the method has been described by Grass and Gibbs (1938). Briefly, it consists in recording the EEG as a shadowgram, making a belt of one meter of the record and revolving it before a beam of light and a photo-cell. The resulting voltage fluctuations are then passed through a variable electric filter and the output rectified and recorded as energy at each frequency level.

means of localizing the tumor. The name *delta waves* is now commonly applied to all slow waves with a frequency less than about 8 per second, the lower limit of alpha waves in normal adults. A different criterion is necessary in the case of children, whose alpha waves may be slower than 8 per second. Except during sleep and certain other specifiable conditions, delta waves are considered indicative of abnormality. They occur in a variety of pathological conditions of the brain, of both physiological and anatomical nature.

In certain types of pathology the EEG may be characterized by outstanding deviations from normal in the form of single waves of peculiar shape or of waves repeated in rhythmic or nonrhythmic patterns, such as spikes, multiple spikes, spike and slow wave complex, saw-toothed waves, square-topped waves, and so forth. These are usually further qualified, if possible, by measurements of magnitude and duration. Thus abnormality of the EEG may be appraised in terms of a number of independent factors as well as in terms of combinations of these factors. Abnormality may be determined by rhythms that are too fast as well as too slow, by voltages which are too low as well as too high, and by amounts of activity ranging from zero to 100% presence in a given unit of the record.

Methodology.—

Although no two investigators follow precisely the same procedure in recording the human EEG, there has gradually evolved a certain measure of standardization so that general comparability of results is attained. Despite differences in the number of electrodes used and their placement on the head, differences in amplifiers and recording systems, variations in the position and condition of the subject during the recording of the EEG, the results obtained in various laboratories are in fairly close agreement.

ELECTRODES AND THEIR ARRANGEMENT.—The main requirements for electrodes are that they be good conductors, that they make adequate contact with the surface of the scalp through an electrode paste or some other electrolyte solution, that their position may be made secure so that drying of the electrolyte or shifting of contact is prohibited, and that they may be worn by the subject without discomfort. A common type of electrode consists of flattened or cup shaped pellets of solder (Gibbs and Gibbs, 1941), of about 5 to 10 millimeters in diameter, or similar sized silver electrodes which may be chlorided and made relatively nonpolarizable (Jasper and Andrews, 1938a). Polarization is relatively unimportant, however, since current flowing in the circuit is extremely small and alternating. After the locus for the electrodes has been determined by appropriate measurement, a small amount of hair is cut to allow the electrode to fit snugly against the scalp surface and the scalp is cleaned with a solvent, such as acetone, to remove oil and sebaceous secretions. The electrodes are held in place by means of collodion. Flexible, insulated wire of small gauge leads from each electrode to a plug-in board and thence by insulated cable to a switch box where different combinations of electrodes may be selected.

There is no standard system of electrode placement or leads, such as there is in the field of electrocardiography, but most workers have certain criteria, based on measurements with respect to anatomical landmarks of the skull, which enable them to state clearly the location of their leads. There is usually a similarity of arrangement of electrodes on the surface of the scalp so that representative samples of electrical activity may be obtained from the various regions of the head. Systematic arrangements of electrodes for routine clinical examination, or more detailed localization studies have been described by Jasper (1941) and by Gibbs and Gibbs (1941).

LOCALIZATION METHODS.—The first step in localization consists in noting regional deviations from normal expectancy. A comparison of the activity from bilaterally homologous areas is important for detecting unilateral abnormalities. Two specific methods for fairly precise localization within a single hemisphere have been described. One is the *phase reversal technique* (Adrian and Matthews, 1934a). Electrodes are usually closely spaced and arranged in line so that each successive electrode is connected to two different amplifying and recording systems. The leads from each electrode are so oriented with respect to the input connections of the two amplifiers that an electrical disturbance of a given potential sign originating under an electrode common to two amplifying-recording systems produces waves of reversed phase in each tracing. With several electrodes in line and a multiple recording system the focus of a localized abnormal disturbance usually may be readily detected by noting the region under an electrode which is common to two reversed tracings. The *method of triangulation* (Jasper and Hawke, 1938) consists of placing electrodes on the scalp in such a manner as to represent three corners of a triangle; a focus of disturbance near a corner of the triangle is reflected by phase reversal in the tracings from the two amplifying and recording systems connected to the electrode in that region. Differences in the magnitude of the disturbance recorded from electrodes bounding the three sides of the triangle are also useful in localizing the focus of abnormality.

For localizing abnormalities in subcortical regions, particularly at the base of the skull in the region of the hypothalamus, Grinker (1938) introduced a *basal lead*. The basal electrode, consisting of a long pointed wire, insulated except at its tip, is introduced through the nostril until its pointed tip is imbedded in the periosteum of the sphenoid bone at the back of the pharynx. Grinker and Serota (1938), Hoagland, *et al.* (1938b), and Grinker (1939) have used this technique, particularly in the study of emotional states and their apparent hypothalamic correlates. Jasper (1941) described a slight modification of the technique and its application in conjunction with triangulation to points on the surface of the scalp, in the localization of diencephalic abnormalities. A clear description of the various localization methods, with illustrative records and diagrams, has been presented by Jasper (1941).

REQUIREMENTS OF AMPLIFIERS AND RECORDING SYSTEMS.—Since the voltages recorded from the surface of the scalp, except in certain pathological cases, are for the most part less than 100 microvolts, considerable degree of amplification is necessary. This may amount to as much as a millionfold, depending upon the sensitivity of the recording unit. The amplifiers must magnify, without appreciable distortion, potentials varying in duration from more than one second to one-sixtieth of a second or less. The over-all frequency-response characteristics of the amplifying and recording system should be uniform, with a constant input voltage, over a range of frequencies from less than one to at least 60 per second, or more if higher frequencies are to be studied.

The most common amplifier in use is of the push-pull type and resistance-capacity coupled, with large enough coupling condensors to accommodate slow potential changes. Direct coupled amplifiers are ideal from the point of view of fidelity of response, but frequently lack stability. Details concerning required characteristics and amplifier design may be found in the following reference sources: Tönnies (1932, 1938), Garceau and Davis (1934, 1935), Matthews (1934, 1938), Jasper and Andrews (1936), Loomis, et al. (1938), Jung (1939b), Rahm (1939), Torrents (1939) Herrnfeld and Sjaardema (1940), and Goodwin (1941).

A variety of recording units have been used. Berger's early studies were made with a sensitive string galvanometer without amplification. After amplification became available, less sensitive instruments were used. Cathode ray and mirror, or galvanometer type oscillographs are useful but require photographic recording. The more recently developed inkwriting oscillographs, either of the crystal or electromagnetic types, because of their convenience and economy are now most widely used. From one to six or more of these inkwriting units may be arranged to trace records simultaneously, from as many regions of the head, on paper tape moving at a uniform rate.

PROCEDURE.—After the electrodes have been cemented to appropriate regions of the head the subject reclines on a cot, or sits quietly and relaxed in an electrically shielded and relatively sound-proof room so as to be free from external stimulation and distraction. Either the room is darkened or the subject closes his eyes, for visual stimulation disturbs the pattern of activity from the brain. Tracings of electrical activity from different combinations of head regions are obtained during a period of 15 minutes to a half hour or more depending upon the nature of the study and the time available. Ordinarily to make a careful examination of a patient, especially where localization of abnormality is necessary, a period of at least an hour is required, including the time spent in putting on and taking off 10 or more electrodes and in obtaining a systematic series of records. It is desirable to have an observer stay with the subject to note and signal movements and other characteristics of behavior which might introduce artifacts or serve as useful correlates of the electrical changes produced in the record.

EVALUATION OF THE EEG.—For most clinical purposes, the experienced electroencephalographer familiar with normal and abnormal variations of the EEG can readily detect the pathological features of the record. However, for more detailed study and analysis for experimental purposes there are several, quite precise, quantitative measures of the different characteristics of the record which may be made. Among these may be mentioned frequency or the average number of waves per second, amplitude or the average voltage in terms of microvolts, and per-cent-time or the amount of time that certain types of waves are present during a substantial unit of the record. The latter measure when applied to the alpha rhythm is frequently referred to as per-cent-time alpha, or alpha index, but may also be applied in the case of other types of waves, especially the abnormally slow or delta waves.

Hoagland, *et al.* (1937a, 1937b) devised a method, known as the *delta index,* for determining the excess length of one meter of record contributed by the voltage component of waves slower than alpha waves. This was done by running a map measurer over the crest and trough of all waves of greater duration than alpha waves of about 8 per second, but along the linear axis or baseline wherever alpha waves were present. Variations of this method for measuring the slow wave components of the EEG are the *delta excess* (Davis and Sulzbach, 1940), which included the excess length of record contributed by waves slower than 5 per second; the *Wellenindex* or *wave index* (Jung, 1939a), a product of the duration (in tenths of a second) and voltage (in tenths of a millivolt) of the slowest and most prominent waves recurring at least three times in every 10 second unit of record; and the *abnormality index* (Strauss, 1942) derived by the formula: $P \times V/10F,$ where P equals per-cent-time delta, F the lowest delta frequency, and V the highest voltage of F in microvolts. The method devised by Grass and Gibbs (1938) for plotting the energy in various frequency components of the EEG, known as a *cortical frequency spectrum* or *Fourier transform* has already been described.

A method of classifying the patterns of activity of the EEG on a qualitative basis, principally in terms of the prominence, persistence, and regularity of the occipital alpha rhythm, was first described by Davis and Davis (1936). Alpha rhythms present more than 75% of the time were labeled *dominant;* 50 to 75%, *subdominant;* 25 to 50%, *mixed;* and below 25%, *rare.* Voltage and regularity usually decreased with amount, and beta and low voltage slow waves were sometimes observed in the mixed and rare classifications. A further elaboration of this system, giving more weight to quality and types of rhythms than to voltage or per-cent-time, was later presented by P. A. Davis (1941e).

Methods of measuring the phase relationships of alpha waves from bilaterally homologous areas have been described by Travis and Knott (1937c), Jung (1939a), Lindsley (1940a), and Therman (1940).

The Electroencephalogram in Normal Individuals

The EEG of the typical normal adult subject when awake, but at rest and relaxed, in the dark or with eyes closed and in the absence of specific stimulation shows a more or less continuous series of rhythmic waves. These are composed principally of *alpha* and *beta* waves, whose characteristics and limiting features have already been discussed. Since the alpha waves in most subjects and in most areas of the head constitute the outstanding part of the picture, the discussion which follows will be concerned principally with them. Furthermore, since the alpha rhythm is more prominent over the occipital lobes of the brain than elsewhere in most subjects and since the majority of studies deal primarily with the occipital alpha rhythm, most of what follows will have reference to the occipital alpha rhythm unless otherwise specified.

Inter- and Intra-Individual Differences.—As previously stated, the alpha rhythm in different normal adult subjects ranges in frequency from 8 to 13 per second, with a mean of about 10 per second; voltage ranges from 5 microvolts or less to about 100 microvolts, with a mean

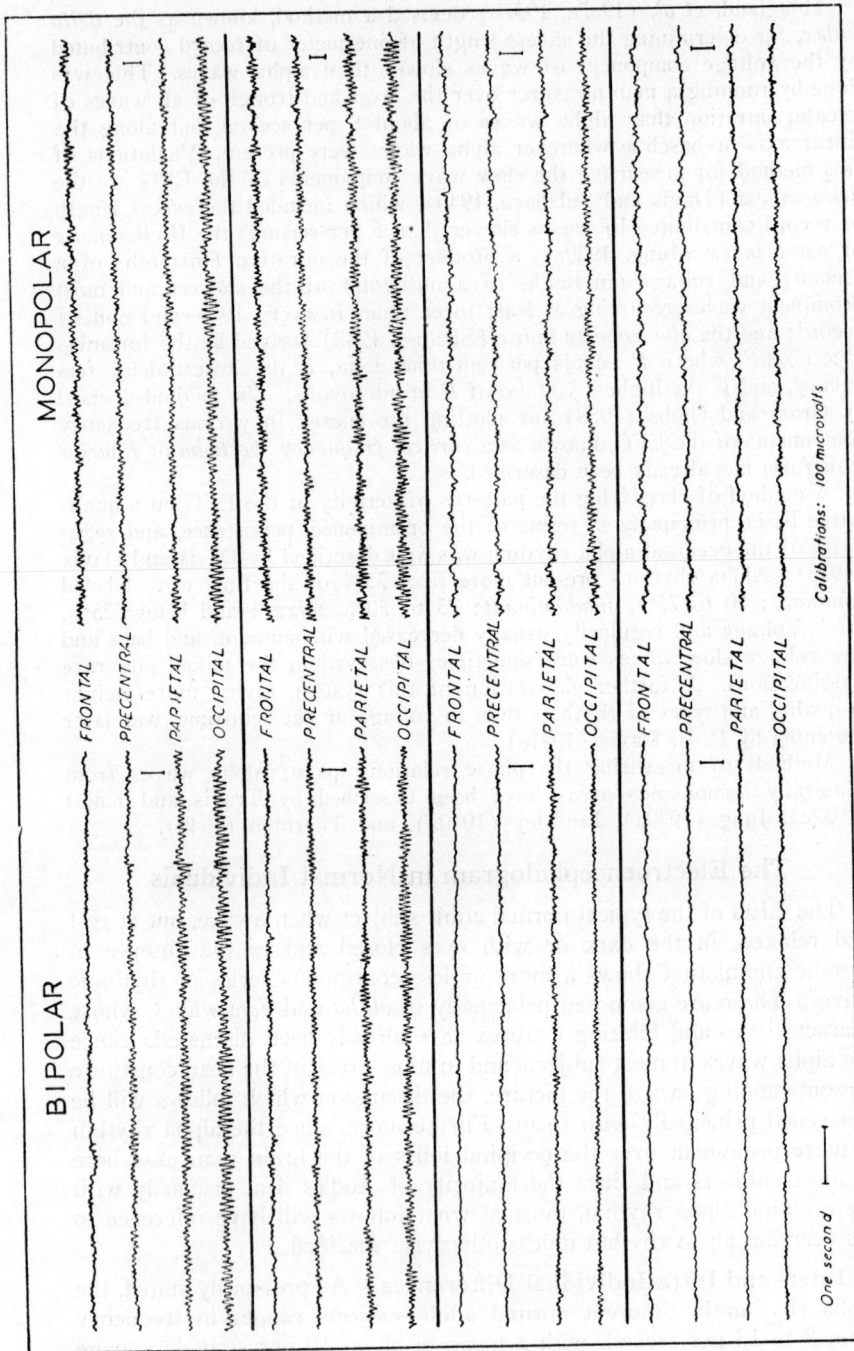

Figure 1

Individual differences in the EEG's of four normal adult subjects.

of about 25 for bipolar methods to perhaps 40 to 50 microvolts by mono-polar methods; the per-cent-time or alpha index varies from almost zero to 100%. From these facts it may be gathered that there is considerable range of individual variability, but in addition there are also variations in the pattern of the waves, ranging from almost complete arrhythmicity consisting of mixtures of alpha and beta waves of irregular dimensions, to extremely rhythmic and regular wave forms. In addition a pattern of rhythmic alpha waves may show variable periods of waxing and waning, sometimes shifting abruptly and in other cases showing a smooth modulation of amplitude. Some of these characteristics are illustrated in the EEG's of different normal adult subjects shown in Figure 1. These individual differences have been confirmed by numer-ous workers who have studied groups of normal adult subjects (Berger, 1930, 1931; Davis and Davis, 1936; Jasper and Andrews, 1936, 1938a; Loomis, et al., 1936b; Lemere, 1936, 1941; Lindsley, 1936, 1938a; Liberson, 1937, 1941; Rubin, 1938a, 1938b; and others).

Whereas interindividual variability among normal subjects is clearly apparent, intraindividual variability tends to be small. The EEG of the individual person during the course of a single recording period shows moment to moment variations in frequency, amplitude, and pattern and no particular section of the record appears precisely like another. Yet as the record streams on and on, one cannot help being impressed with the high degree of similarity all the way through. Averages of fre-quency, amplitude, and per-cent-time from meter to meter of record show very narrow variability. Variability in frequency of the alpha rhythm from day to day, month to month, or even longer intervals seldom exceeds 2 cycles per second and is usually less than 1 cycle per second (Loomis, et al., 1936b; Jasper and Cruickshank, 1937; Jasper and Andrews, 1938a). Lindsley and Rubenstein (1937) recorded EEG's in four young adult women for 32 consecutive days and found that the standard deviation of alpha frequency for any one subject did not exceed .47 per second, which means that daily variations were for the most part less than 1 cycle per second. Liberson (1937) found intra-individual variability of alpha wave amplitude significantly less than interindividual variability among 80 normal subjects. Rubin (1938b) studying the variability of the EEG's in normals and schizophrenics found that both groups show insignificant variations in per-cent-time alpha, number of alpha bursts, and average length of alpha bursts within an experimental session and only slightly greater deviation from day to day.

Travis and Gottlober (1936, 1937), studying the consistency and individuality of EEG's, conclude "that not only can an individual be distinguished from other individuals by his brain potentials, but under relatively constant experimental conditions an individual's brain poten-tials are highly consistent from day to day." Davis and Davis (1936) note that different persons show different patterns of activity and that each tends to reproduce his own characteristics. However, they maintain that the individuality is not as complete as that of a finger-print, due to the dynamic factors involved. They studied the EEG's of 8 pairs of identical twins (18 to 58 years of age) and found the records as similar as those of the same person at different times; also they found certain unique features of a record common to both members of a twin pair. They conclude that the EEG "reveals some inborn feature or pattern of cerebral activity. The pattern is labile, to be sure, but the degree of lability seems to be one of its inborn characteristics." Davis (1936) has suggested that the individuality of the EEG may represent a cortical organization which has an hereditary basis. The similarity of EEG's in twins has also been noted by Loomis, et al. (1936b). Raney (1939) studying 17 pairs of identical twins noted both greater qualitative and quantitative similarity of their EEG's than for those of unrelated children, but stressed the fact that the differences held mainly for groups and that some twin pairs deviated as widely as nontwins. Furthermore, he pointed out that the EEG's recorded from both sides of the head in identical twins show a reversed bilateral asymmetry corresponding to reversed laterality, and that in some twins the bilateral differences exceed those in nontwins.

Further evidence of the expression of heredity in the brain wave pattern has recently been adduced by Lennox, et al. (1942), who studied 70 pairs of twins. Among 53 "normal" pairs were 41 twin pairs said to be monozygotic; 35 of these were judged to have identical EEG's, 5 were doubtful, and 1 pair showed definite dissimilarity. In 5 dizygotic pairs of the same sex, the EEG's were dissimilar in 4 and similar in one. In 7 pairs of opposite sexed twins, the EEG's were obviously dissimilar in all. For the whole group of 53 twins, the EEG similarity or dissimilarity agreed with the correspondence of physical characteristics in 87%, was doubtful in 9%, and disagreed in 4%. Among 17 twins, with a history of epilepsy or brain injury in one or both members of a pair, certain abnormal features of the EEG were common to both members, even though one was clinically "normal." Other evidence that pathological features of the EEG may be inherited has come from studies of epileptics and their relatives (Lennox, et al., 1939, 1940b, 1942; Löwenbach, 1939; Strauss, et al., 1939; Robinson, 1940). Gottlober (1938b), on the other hand, studied the EEG's of the father, mother, and two or more siblings in each of 15 families and found no characteristics of the alpha rhythm which were significantly related within family groups.

With a view of determining whether individual differences in brain wave activity are persistent under differing conditions, and therefore indicative of a fundamental or inborn characteristic, Knott, et al. (1939) studied two groups of subjects with diverse waking patterns under the additional condition of sleep. There was no high relationship between individual differences awake and asleep, and there was a greater similarity of individual records during sleeping than during waking conditions. Henry (1941a), following up this approach, studied 20 subjects with distributed alpha indices, making them a heterogeneous group with respect to amount of alpha activity. He found that the various sleep rhythms they displayed during an all-night sleep period were more nearly alike than their daytime waking records; also that their alpha indices immediately after waking in the morning were not as widely distributed as during daytime records, thus making them a more nearly homogeneous group. Actually the means for the early morning records were approximately the same as for the daytime records, the principal change being one of a tendency of regression toward the mean.

In another study Henry (1941b) used four subjects representing different quartiles of the alpha index distribution and compared their alpha indices during various "psychological activities" such as silent and oral reading, talking, and resting with eyes open and closed. Certain of the "psychological activities" tended to reduce the amount of individuality exhibited in the EEG's. It was concluded that environmental factors, as well as inborn characteristics may determine the amount of alpha activity in the EEG.

Although the results of the Knott and Henry studies are interesting, it may be questioned how much relevance they have for the problem of whether the individuality of the patterns and characteristics of the EEG are rooted in factors of biologic inheritance. It would seem that the physiological states involved in the conditions they studied include too many uncontrolled variables which may directly or indirectly modify the electrical activity of the brain. On the other hand, it would be surprising indeed if the cortical organization, assumed by some to be inborn and accountable for the variations in EEG patterns, were not also modified by numerous secondary factors, which tend to obscure hereditary likenesses. The interdependence of so many anatomical, physiological, and psychological factors as components in the structure and dynamics of personality, makes any single variable difficult to find and to assess in relation to personality. The striking interindividual differences in the EEG, like so many other individual differences in physical and mental characteristics, offer plentiful lure, but so far little substantial bounty, to those seeking personality correlates. The following studies represent attempts to relate the EEG to certain aspects of personality.

Personality and the EEG.—Lemere (1936), assessing EEG's on a qualitative basis, according to whether they showed "good" alpha waves (constant, regular, and over 50 microvolts) or "poor" alpha waves (variable, irregular, and below 50 microvolts), studied 26 normal persons and 40 psychotic patients. Using a psychiatric classification, both patients and normals were separated according to cyclothymic or schizoid make-up. He concluded that "good" alpha waves were associated with the former and "poor" alpha waves with the latter. Apathy or affective deficiency of schizophrenics seemed to him the feature of the illness most clearly related to "poor" alpha wave production; whereas emotional instability and lability manifest in disseminated sclerosis and manic-depressive patients appeared closely related to "good" alpha waves. Similar personality characteristics in normals were said to be associated with either "good" or "poor" alpha wave production, which Lemere assumed was based on constitutional factors. Elsewhere (1939, 1941) he has presented similar results based on larger groups of normals and patients, but has dealt principally with the supposed physiopathological mechanisms of the latter and has said little about the personality and EEG relationships in the former. His explanation for the EEG dichotomy in patients will be discussed later under psychiatric disorders.

Lemere's results in schizophrenic and manic-depressive patients have not been strongly reinforced by others (Berger, 1937c) ; McMahon and Walter, 1938; Davis and Davis, 1939; Jasper, et al., 1939; Davis, 1940b; Finley and Campbell, 1941 ; Walter, 1942), although this is possibly due to different approaches to the problem. Yeager and Baldes (1937), using the Davis EEG classification scheme, reported that a high percentage of their dementia praecox patients had EEG's of the "rare" or "mixed" type of patterns, and that manic-depressives and involutional melancholics had a tendency toward a "dominant" type of pattern. This seems to be in essential agreement with Lemere's results.

In normal persons Gottlober (1938a) studied certain personality traits in relation to the EEG. Of 67 subjects judged by subjective rating and the Nebraska Personality Inventory to be either extraverted or introverted, he found that 82% of the former had a "dominant-subdominant" or high alpha wave type of pattern and 18% had a "mixed-rare" or low alpha pattern; 57% of the introverts had high alphas and 43% low alphas. He concluded that individuals showing a high degree of extraversion tend to show a "dominant-subdominant" alpha rhythm, but indicated that it could not yet be stated that introverts show predominantly a "mixed-rare" type of alpha pattern. Henry and Knott (1941), repeating Gottlober's study with 40 men and 40 women and using the Nebraska Personality Inventory to classify their subjects according to degree of extraversion or introversion, did not obtain the same results. In fact their results showed a tendency to the reverse of Gottlober's. Only 43% of their extraverts had high alphas whereas 60% of the introverts also had high alphas. The relation between introversion and a high alpha index was not statistically significant.

Lindsley (1938a) in the course of another study had data available on three possible aspects of personality, namely, intelligence (Stanford-Binet and Otis tests), dominance or assertiveness (Allport's Ascendance-Submission Test), and emotional stability (Woodworth-Mathews' Personal Data Sheet) for 88 normal children of ten to fourteen years of age. These he correlated with per-cent-time alpha and a qualitative rating of the pattern of the EEG based on a system similar to the Davis classification. No significant relationships were found.

A psychoanalytic approach has been utilized by Saul, et al. (1937), in the search for correlates of the individuality of the EEG pattern. Using the alpha index as a measure of the EEG, 31 individuals undergoing psychoanalysis were retested after an interval of seven months. Twenty-five showed alpha indices on retest agreeing with original indices within 10 points; only two deviated by more than 17 points. All deviations greater than 10 points were in the direction of a lowered alpha index on retest, but there was no relationship between these changes and the clinical changes reported by the analysts. Alpha indices were determined for 66 persons while in process of analysis or just following completion of analysis. The same type of distribution of alpha indices was found as for a group of 200 normals; the indices were evenly distributed from zero to 100%.

These investigators then attempted to correlate alpha index with the emotional and instinctive trends revealed by psychoanalysis. They concluded that two opposing trends correlated with low and high alpha indices. A low alpha index was said to go with a trend toward activity and a high alpha index with a trend toward passivity or inhibition. Behaviorally these trends were revealed by the individual's habitual actions and attitudes toward persons, food, work, sleep, and sex. A *high alpha index* was said to be associated with a passive, dependent, receptive attitude toward other persons. Such a person works to satisfy desires but under protest; desires and requires more than the average amount of sleep; has a dependent attitude toward women, especially the mother; when thwarted may develop temper tantrums or a depression; dreams of inactivity, inhibited activity, or rejected activity and other passive, receptive states. Such individuals are described as solid citizens, and patient workers and planners. A *low alpha index* is associated with consistent, well-directed, freely indulged drives to activity; a "reaction-formation" against passive desires; an active "masculine" trend amounting to nonovert homosexuality in women which expresses itself in dreams, masculine dress, and other forms of competition with men; also dreams of activity are common. An independent, aggressive person, who is a leader in social activities, who is a doer in reality rather than in intellectual sublimation, and who is impatient for gratification of instinctual impulses, is described as the type of individual who might be expected to have a low alpha index. It is pointed out, however, that these "active" and "passive" types are not entirely unmixed or rigidly restricted to high and low alpha indices. The relationship is more in the nature of a trend or tendency.

Following up the approach of Saul and collaborators, Rubin and Bowman (1942) studied a group of 100 peptic ulcer patients. They recorded EEG's from the occipital area and obtained personality data by interview, particularly with reference to such factors as work attitude, parental identification, attitude toward mate and friends, and a childhood history. Using the Davis classification system they found about 70% of their patients fell in the "dominant" EEG category, whereas among a normal population only about 20% are so classified. Twenty per cent of their patients were classified in the "rare" or low alpha group. Since the majority of their patients show a "dominant" pattern they conclude, on the basis of the study by Saul, *et al.* (1937), that there is a relationship between peptic ulcer and a passive, receptive personality structure. In support of this they offer their personality data, which they believe indicates that the peptic ulcer patients are in general a dependent, mother-identifying group as children and adolescents. On approaching maturity the high and low alpha groups develop differently, the former continues to be dependent on a mother surrogate, but the latter manages to achieve independence, through a strong "reaction-formation" to an underlying passivity. It was claimed that more of the high or "dominant" alpha group held their jobs over a prolonged period and more of them were passive toward their mates.

Berger (1938c) states that it is a peculiar fact that the feebleminded frequently have "better" (probably meaning more prominent and more rhythmic and regular) alpha waves than intelligent persons. This he believes is due to a more automatic cortical function, or an undisturbed passive stream of ideas less interfered with by external and internal stimuli. He contrasts a "passive EEG" of this type with an "active" one in a state of attention or mental work where alpha waves are diminished and there is more of a tendency toward beta waves. He states that it is more difficult for an intelligent person to stay "passive" long, and as a consequence there is a tendency for such a person to have a "mixed EEG" composed of "active" and "passive" parts. Hence children, feeble-minded, and primitive people tend to show the best resting alpha waves.

In a study utilizing the EEG for purposes of professional selection, Liberson (1941), using frequency, amplitude, and the Davis classification of pattern as measures of the EEG, compared his results on 168 subjects, ranging from low rank to engineers, with a biometric profile consisting of a variety of physiological and psychological measures. He found that those with EEG's classified in the "mixed" category fell below the average for the group on the biometric profile, whereas those in the "dominant" group fell above, particularly in sensory functions, memory, vital capacity, and voluntary endurance in apnea. In a variety of other psycho-physiological functions, including general intelligence, the two groups were not widely separated. According to Liberson, amplitude and alpha index classification give the best predictions for separating the groups according to biometric differences.

Thorner, et al. (1942), using the Grass-Gibbs spectrum analysis method, have attempted to select aviators for their flying ability on the basis of the EEG. Flying ability was rated by instructor pilots. Fifty-five student pilots and 54 pilots were studied. Three types of EEG spectrums were described. Fifty per cent of the entire group had a type A spectrum with a simple energy peak in the 5 to 15 per second range; 40% had a type B spectrum with a narrow or complex energy peak in the 5 to 15 per second range; and 10% had no definite peak in the 5 to 15 per second range. They conclude that flying ability tends to be high if the center of the energy peak is about 10.5 per second and falls off as the energy peak deviates from this value to either side. Other so-called "abnormal" tendencies were utilized to improve the selection slightly.

Practically all of these studies of the EEG in relation to personality are characterized by several inadequacies. First of all, from the point of view of the EEG. Records from one area of the brain are frequently taken as representative of the whole. More important is the fact that too little analysis and quantification is attempted; usually only one measure is utilized, despite the fact that the individuality of the EEG is contributed by more than one characteristic, at least three of which are subject to fairly precise measurement. From the point of view of personality there is too great a tendency to rely on subjective judgments and ratings, or to attempt to relate the EEG to an isolated dichotomous trait, which often cannot be clearly defined and at best represents only a fragment of the total personality picture. A better approach to the problem would seem to be to take EEG's from all representative head regions, make a detailed analysis of each in terms of the measurable characteristics and then classify or group persons according to the differential features of their EEG's. A search for behavioral and personality characteristics common to the persons in each EEG category could then be made, using various combinations of tests and other methods of evaluation.

Developmental Aspects of the EEG.—

INFANCY AND CHILDHOOD.—Berger (1932c) was the first to note that the EEG of infants and young children differs from that of adults. He concluded that the alpha rhythm is not present until the third or fourth month and that its frequency at onset is low, but increases with age. This was confirmed by Loomis, et al. (1936b) and Lindsley (1936). The latter studied the development of the occipital alpha rhythm in 100 children ranging in age from one month to sixteen years. Below three months of age he found principally nonrhythmic potentials of irregular shape and size, but mainly of low amplitude. Beginning in the third or fourth month a definite occipital alpha rhythm became apparent at a frequency of 3 to 4 per second. The frequency of the rhythm increased rapidly during the first year, being about 5 to 6 per second at one year, but increased somewhat more slowly thereafter and attained an adult frequency level at about eight to ten years. The onset of the rhythm at about three months was thought to be associated with certain developing visual perceptive functions, and the increase in frequency with age to be related to myelinization or other developmental growth processes.

Subsequent studies (Lindsley, 1938a, 1939; Smith, 1937, 1938a, 1938b, 1939; Bernhard and Skoglund, 1939a, 1939b; Brill and Seidemann, 1941), based on large groups of children of all ages, have established age norms for frequency and amplitude, and have noted other developmental characteristics of the EEG. All are in agreement that there is a definite frequency growth curve for the occipital alpha rhythm which has a logarithmic form. Weinbach (1938a) fitted data obtained by Lindsley and Smith on frequency growth of the alpha rhythm in children to equations representing other biologic growth processes. He also pointed out that the decline in time-rate of increase in alpha frequency is a constant, probably a genetic one constant for each species. Weinbach (1938b) and Lindsley (1938a) have called attention to the similarity of the curves of growth of brain weight and the rate of growth of the occipital alpha frequency.

Smith's extensive studies (1938a, 1938b, 1938c, 1939, 1941) of newborn infants have revealed that several distinct rhythms are present over the sensory-motor regions at birth, but only when the activity level of the child is reduced during the initial stages of drowsiness. Prominent among these is the forerunner of the precentral alpha rhythm at a frequency of 6.5 to 7.5 per second, which does not change greatly during the first year of life but thereafter increases parallel to the occipital alpha rhythm. Smith (1941) points out that the earlier development of rhythms in the sensory-motor regions than in other areas of the cortex is in accord with the histological evidence of advanced cellular development there, also that certain aspects of motor behavior seem to be correlated with the development of precentral rhythms.

PRENATAL EEG.—Lindsley (1942), in the course of recording fetal heart potentials from the abdomen of the mother, has recorded, during the seventh month of pregnancy, rhythmic potential waves which he believes originated in the brain of the fetus. These rhythmic potentials could be recorded from the region over the palpable head of the fetus only, and corresponded in frequency to the precentral alpha rhythm observed by Smith in newborn infants. The possibility of recording the EEG prenatally may have some importance for the correlation of physiologic and histologic development of the cortex; furthermore it may be useful for comparison with the EEG shortly after birth in order to determine the nature of the effects of birth injury.

Psychological Variables and the EEG.—

SENSORY STIMULATION.—One of the striking demonstrations which may be made with the EEG is the blocking of the occipital alpha rhythm with *visual stimulation* (see Figure 2). Berger (1930) noted that opening the eyes in a lighted room abolished the alpha waves, and that opening the eyes in a dark room did not, although Jasper and Cruickshank (1937) mention that attempting to see in the dark is sometimes effective. Since Berger found that other types of sensory stimuli had similar effects on the alpha rhythm, he concluded that the focusing of attention rather than special sensory processes is responsible for the blocking of the alpha rhythm. Adrian and Matthews (1934a) believed that some pattern or form in the field of vision was necessary for blocking the occipital alpha rhythm, although they agreed with Berger that attention focused on a problem will block the rhythm even in the absence of visual stimulation.

Latency of blocking or the time from the onset of a visual stimulus to the reduction in amplitude or disappearance of the alpha waves is about .3 second (Berger, 1932b; Jasper and Cruickshank, 1937; Knott, 1938b; and others) but varies with the intensity and duration of the stimulus

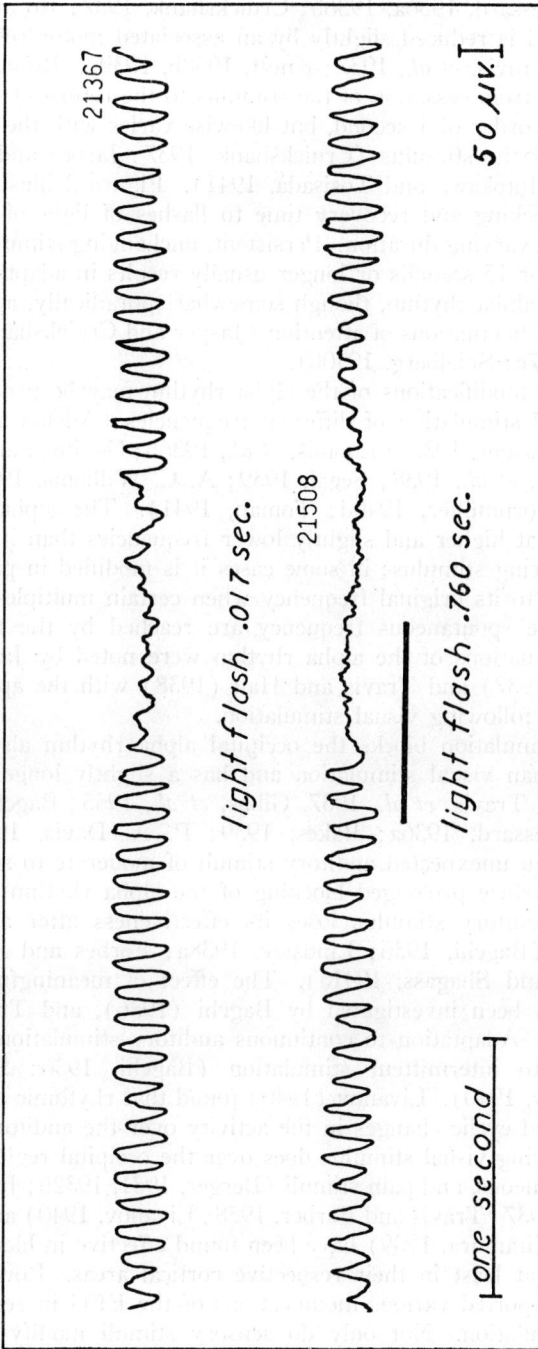

Figure 2

Blocking of the occipital alpha rhythm by light flashes of different durations, but of the same intensity.

(Durup and Fessard, 1936a, 1936b; Cruickshank, 1937; Ito and Kasahara, 1939) and is reduced slightly by an associated motor response to the stimulus (Travis, *et al.*, 1937; Knott, 1938b, 1939). Recovery time or the duration from cessation of the stimulus to the return of the alpha waves is of the order of 1 second, but likewise varies with the intensity and duration of the stimulus (Cruickshank, 1937; Jasper and Cruickshank, 1937; Motokawa and Tosisada, 1941). Figure 2 illustrates the variation in blocking and recovery time to flashes of light of constant intensity, but of varying duration. Persistent, unchanging stimulation for a period of 10 or 15 seconds or longer usually results in adaptation and a return of the alpha rhythm, though somewhat sporadically, apparently depending upon fluctuations of attention (Jasper and Cruickshank, 1937; Rohracher, 1937c; Spielberg, 1940b).

A variety of modifications of the alpha rhythm may be produced by flickering visual stimulation of different frequencies (Adrian and Matthews, 1934a; Jasper, 1936a; Loomis, *et al.*, 1936b; Goldman and Segal, 1938; Goldman, *et al.*, 1938; Segal, 1939; A. C. Williams, 1939; Livanov, 1940; Kornmüller, 1940d; Toman, 1941). The alpha rhythm may be driven at higher and slightly lower frequencies than its normal rate by a flickering stimulus; in some cases it is modified in pattern or may shift back to its original frequency when certain multiples or submultiples of the spontaneous frequency are reached by the flickering stimulus. Fluctuations of the alpha rhythm were noted by Jasper and Cruickshank (1937) and Travis and Hall (1938) with the appearance of after-images following visual stimulation.

Auditory stimulation blocks the occipital alpha rhythm also, but is less effective than visual stimulation and has a slightly longer latency (Berger, 1930; Travis, *et al.*, 1937, Gibbs, *et al.*, 1935; Bagchi, 1936; Durup and Fessard, 1936a; Bakes, 1939; P. A. Davis, 1939; and others). Sudden unexpected auditory stimuli of moderate to strong intensity may produce prolonged blocking of the alpha rhythm (Berger, 1933a). An auditory stimulus loses its effectiveness after a number of repetitions (Bagchi, 1936; Lindsley, 1938a; Forbes and Andrews, 1937; Jasper and Shagass, 1941a). The effect of meaningful, verbal stimulation has been investigated by Bagchi (1936), and Travis and Egan (1938a). Adaptation to continuous auditory stimulation is more marked than to intermittent stimulation (Bagchi, 1936; Spielberg, 1940b; Livanov, 1940). Livanov (1940) found that rhythmic acoustical stimuli produced cyclic changes in the activity over the auditory region just as a flickering visual stimulus does over the occipital region.

Tactile, cutaneous, and pain stimuli (Berger, 1931, 1932b; Jasper and Cruickshank, 1937; Travis and Barber, 1938; Livanov, 1940) and gustatory stimuli (Kitamura, 1939) have been found effective in blocking the alpha rhythm, at least in their respective cortical areas. Lovell, *et al.* (1939) have reported various modifications of the EEG in response to vestibular stimulation. Not only do sensory stimuli modify or block the spontaneous rhythms of the cortex, but in some instances they actually initiate responses, called evoked potentials, with on and off effects. These have been noted for visual stimulation by Jasper (1936b) and Cruickshank (1937) and for auditory stimulation by P. A. Davis (1939). H. Davis, *et al.* (1939a) have noted a multi-phasic response to auditory stimulation during sleep, which they call a "*K*-complex."

ATTENTION AND "MENTAL SET."—Berger (1930, 1932b, 1938c) consistently held to the view that anything which distracted a subject, or tended to focus attention upon a stimulus or a task blocked the alpha rhythm. He interpreted blocking as an inhibitory phenomenon (after Pavlov). Changes in the EEG with attention were in accord, he thought, with the idea that perception may take place through only one sensory channel at a time. Thus energy might be directed into the part of the brain which is active, but the rest of the brain is temporarily inhibited (1930, 1931). The influence of states of attentiveness, or readiness to respond, induced by means of preparatory signals or instructions, was investigated by A. C. Williams (1939, 1940). He found evidence of facilitation of the alpha rhythm in the form of bursts of increased activity during these states. The mobilization of attention or effort directed toward a single task such as silent or oral reading, according to Knott (1938b) reduces the amplitude of the alpha waves. Given an appropriate "mental set" by preliminary instructions to respond to certain stimuli in certain ways led to reduction of blocking time (Knott, 1939). Knott believes that some peripherally maintained process such as afferent impulses from kinesthetic sources alters the electrocortical conditions associated with "mental set." A similar view is held by Freeman (1940), who attempted to show that a "postural substrate" or peripheral excitation level, represented principally by proprioceptive and interoceptive impulses, determines central excitatory tendencies and governs the autonomous rhythms of the brain. Hadley (1940, 1941), proceeding on the basis of this hypothesis, studied cortical and peripheral activity during rest and mental work, but concluded that there were no consistent relationships betwen skeletal muscle or heart activity and the EEG.

It cannot be denied, however, that relaxation and mental repose favor the development of stronger and more persistent spontaneous rhythms of the brain. Many workers have noted that an apprehensive or physically tense subject at the very beginning of a period of study produces an EEG which is not entirely typical of the pattern of activity the EEG may show after the initial tension has been dissipated. Whether the cortical activity is dependent upon the peripheral state or vice versa is not known. There is also a possibility that both are determined by discharges from subcortical centers, especially those from the diencephalic region which may be associated with emotional states.

MENTAL WORK AND EFFORT.—It is well known that answering questions involving mental effort or doing problems in mental arithmetic blocks the alpha rhythm and otherwise modifies the EEG (Berger, 1930, 1932b, 1938c; Gibbs, *et al.*, 1935; Rohracher, 1935, 1937a, 1937b,

1937c; Liberson, 1937; and others). Again, however, it is not known whether these are direct results of cortical activity or are secondary to emotional or affective states created by the situation. Berger (1933a) notes that alpha production during mental work is variable and sporadic, which he interprets as evidence of fluctuation of attention and concentration. Berger (1938c) found a predominance of fast beta waves of 40 to 100 per second during mental work. Rohracher (1937b) and Gemelli (1937) described very high frequency activity (1,000 to 2,000 per second) during mental effort. As previously mentioned, frequencies of this order are probably from some extraneous source, rather than from the brain. In fact there is a possibility that the so-called beta wave activity observed by Berger was at least partially due to muscular tension which is frequently associated with mental effort.

Travis (1937) reported on what he called "the temporal course of consciousness." Occipital EEG's were recorded in eight subjects while lying in a dark room and allowing their "mind to wander." They were interrupted at various times by the word *"Now"* at which time they were to give an introspective report of what stream of thought was interrupted. When changes in the EEG were correlated with the subject's report of the content of consciousness, it was found that visual images, kinesthetic sensations, and mental effort were associated with relatively small brain potentials while mental blankness and abstract thinking were associated with relatively large potentials. A few reports suggested that verbal ideas and anxiety were associated mainly with small waves, usually more rapid than normal 10 per second alpha waves. It was concluded that large, regular brain waves indicate a state of cortical equilibrium represented by general psychic activity, while a dissolution of this collective action into more rapid and irregular waves of lower amplitude represents a high degree of specificity in psychic activity.

THE EEG IN RELATION TO EMOTIONAL AND AUTOMATIC FACTORS. —Berger (1933a) has reported that fright abolishes the alpha rhythm. The unexpected explosion of a firecracker caused in one subject an abolition of alpha waves for 17 seconds, with sporadic appearance and disappearance of the waves for a longer interval. He noted also that after fright the alpha waves may speed up to almost double the original frequency. He states that fear and anxiety are apt to produce more rapid alpha waves than normal. Jasper and Andrews (1938a) also observed that "startle" might block the alpha rhythm for 15 to 20 seconds; beta waves were blocked only momentarily. Loomis, *et al.* (1936b) and A. C. Williams (1939) observed that embarrassment and apprehension practically abolish the alpha waves. By imagining a terrifying situation some subjects could produce a phantasy of fear by which they could stop the alpha waves almost at will.

Obermann (1939) investigated affective states aroused in 33 subjects by artificial lying situations. Lie records were detected with considerably better than chance success by five experienced judges who noted

abolished. In this latter respect their results differ from those of Loomis and collaborators.

Marinesco, et al. (1937b) made observations of a subject who could fall into such a profound state of sleep that he did not awaken when needles were inserted through the scalp. His EEG showed periods of normal alpha waves interspersed with periods of 1 or 2 seconds in duration when no alpha waves were present. During "hypnotic sleep" they observed at first an augmentation of frequency and voltage, but later a reduction in both.

Thomson, et al. (1937) studied an individual who was subject to migraine headaches and who was able voluntarily to induce light trance states in himself. Memory for events during the trance state frequently was absent. During a trance he sat completely relaxed with his head back against a chair and asked and answered questions as three or four different assumed personalities. Drowsiness was common for an hour or more preceding a trance state and the EEG immediately before, during a brief period of dozing, was characteristic of light sleep. During the trance state the alpha index approximated 100%, whereas before or after the trance it ranged from 10 to 50%. They interpret the trance state as one of light sleep.

INTELLIGENCE AND THE EEG.—Relatively little investigation of the relationship between intelligence and the EEG has been carried out with populations of normal subjects. Considerable work has been done in connection with mental deficiency, the results of which will appear farther on. Lindsley (1938a), correlating frequency of occipital alpha waves, per-cent-time alpha, and pattern of waves with intelligence (Stanford-Binet and Otis tests) in 88 normal children of ten to fourteen years of age, found no significant relationships. Knott, et al. (1942) found a correlation of .50 between occipital alpha frequency and intelligence (Stanford-Binet Revision) for a group of 48 eight-year-olds. The relationship between alpha index and intelligence for the same group was not significant and neither were correlations between occipital or precentral alpha frequency and intelligence for another group of 42 twelve-year-olds.

From the preceding results it appears doubtful that there is any very high degree of relationship between intelligence as measured by tests and the EEG; the results in the area of mental deficiency in general confirm this. Although the correlation obtained between intelligence and occipital alpha frequency by Knott and collaborators for a group of eight-year-olds is statistically significant it still does not express a very high degree of relationship. The surprising thing is that it is as high as they found, for in a single age group such as they used in order to partial out the effect of a third variable, chronological age, the dispersion of alpha frequencies is limited to about 3 cycles per second [Lindsley (1938a) found the range of frequencies for eight-year-olds to be 7.3 to 10.3 per second].

Interindividual differences in frequency do not therefore stand in a very high ratio to intraindividual variations which probably range from zero to 1 or more cycles per second from day to day. This would seem to preclude high correlations within a single age group.

A wider dispersion of frequencies could be obtained by including other age groups, especially lower ones, but this brings other factors into the picture. The most important of these is the fact that curves of alpha frequency growth and mental growth are both functions of age. Alpha frequency is a logarithmic function of age, whereas mental growth, measured by an age-scale such as the Stanford-Binet, is arbitrarily made a linear function, with a slope of 1 for the average child. Add to these difficulties of handling and interpreting the data, the variability of measurement of intelligence, and the variety of physiological factors to be described in the next section which influence the EEG, and the problem of establishing a relationship between intelligence and the EEG becomes quite complex, if not indeed meaningless.

Physiological Factors and the EEG.—A variety of effects may be produced in the EEG of a normal individual by modifications in the physiological state of the organism. The changes in physiological state may occur naturally as in sleep or may be produced experimentally. Individuals vary in the amount of physiological stress or change that they are able to undergo before showing behavior aberrations or variations in the EEG. Differentiations of this kind among individuals are often important to a better understanding of personality and behavior disorders. A knowledge of the limits of physiological change which may be tolerated is useful for classifying individuals according to the stability of their reaction systems, for selecting individuals for certain tasks or occupations, and for determining optimal environmental conditions. For these purposes the EEG is frequently a more sensitive indicator than external signs of behavior.

RESPIRATORY REQUIREMENTS.—The effects of *oxygen want* on the EEG were noted by Berger (1934b), who found that, except for a decrease in amplitude of the alpha waves, no marked change occurred until consciousness became impaired. With loss of consciousness the EEG changed suddenly and markedly, developing large slow waves of 1 to 2 per second. After one minute of normal oxygen supply, the slow waves disappeared and consciousness returned. P. A. Davis, *et al.* (1938), found that gas mixtures containing 8 to 11% oxygen produced first an increase and then a decrease in amplitude of the alpha waves; thereafter there was a gradual induction of irregular and sporadic delta waves. It was not until after 10 to 15 minutes of breathing of 8% oxygen, when cyanosis was marked and consciousness impaired, that delta waves of low frequency and high amplitude dominated the record. The delta waves disappeared promptly upon restoration of oxygen, but the EEG did not return to its original state until at least two minutes later.

Gibbs, *et al.* (1935) studied the effects on the EEG of breathing pure nitrogen. First there was an increase in amplitude and a gradual slowing of alpha waves. When the subject became extremely confused or unconscious large delta waves of 2 to 5 per second appeared. Similar changes were noted when *syncope* was produced by tilting or by means of sodium nitrite. Lindsley and Rubenstein (1937) found no significant variation in frequency or amplitude of alpha waves in four normal subjects during the breathing of pure oxygen, or during the breathing of a 10% oxygen mixture to approximate limits of toleration. Lyman, *et al.* (1941) studied the effect of reduced atmospheric pressure (reduction of partial pressure of oxygen) on the EEG. During "ascent" in a pressure chamber an oxygen mask was worn. There was some reduction in the amplitude, amount, and regularity of the alpha waves during the early part of the "ascent," but little change beyond 12,000 feet. The oxygen mask was taken off for 10 minutes at 18,000 feet, but no marked changes in the brain potentials were noted.

From the foregoing results it may be concluded that *reduced oxygen* has no marked effect on the EEG until impairment of consciousness occurs, at which time, or shortly before, the EEG shows a predominance of delta waves. It is important to note, however, that F. A. Gibbs, *et al.* (1942) found that unconsciousness induced in normal subjects by breathing a mixture of 2% oxygen and 5% carbon dioxide was not associated with high voltage delta waves. From the results of this and another study (E. L. Gibbs, *et al.*, 1942), involving determinations of carbon dioxide in arterial and internal jugular blood, it was concluded that slow waves associated with oxygen deficiency are not due to cerebral anoxia, but rather are due to a lowered carbon dioxide tension in the brain.

The effects of voluntary *hyperventilation* or overbreathing, with consequent *reduction of carbon dioxide* in the blood, are well known both clinically and electroencephalographically. In fact hyperventilation has become a standard procedure for producing physiological stress during the recording of the EEG. Deep, regular, and rapid breathing for several minutes may produce dizziness and eventually unconsciousness in a normal subject. However, before this happens there may be, even in the records of otherwise normal individuals, some induction of abnormal slow waves. Ordinarily normal persons do not show abnormal phenomena within a period of 3 minutes of voluntary overbreathing, although persons with epilepsy or even epileptic tendencies only, may develop abnormal patterns of activity within less than 1 minute of hyperventilation and in some instances seizures may occur.

Thus hyperventilation is useful for detecting evidence of physiological instability or inadequacy of homeostasis and in certain disorders, epilepsy particularly, it may elicit latent signs of abnormality in the EEG. Gibbs, *et al.* (1935) described the effect of hyperventilation in producing delta waves in the EEG and in precipitating seizures in epileptics. Davis and Wallace (1942), studying normal subjects, found that delta waves were less easily induced when the respired air contained oxygen in excess of the normal 20%, and also when glucose was administered before hyperventilation. They concluded that hyperventilation facilitates delta wave production by causing cerebral vasoconstriction, which in turn diminishes the supply of oxygen and dextrose available to the brain. E. L. Gibbs, *et al.* (1942) have presented evidence which favors another explanation. The analysis of arterial and internal jugular blood for oxygen and carbon dioxide content at intervals during the recording of the EEG revealed evidence which suggested to them that the principal cause of delta wave development in some individuals during hyperventilation is a failure of homeostatic mechanisms to preserve carbon dioxide tension in the brain. Their evidence seems to indicate that in such individuals there is insufficient cerebral vasoconstriction to compensate for the reduction in carbon dioxide during hyperventilation.

Liberson and Strauss (1941) found that delta wave activity during hyperventilation diminishes with increasing age, being most marked in children below fifteen years of age. This has been confirmed by Brill and Seidemann (1942), who also noted that delta wave discharges during hyperventilation occur among normal and nonepileptic subjects and are not therefore pathognomonic for epilepsy. The latter investigators suggest that an abnormal response to hyperventilation may occur in normal brain tissue when there is a disturbance in the regulatory mechanism for carbon dioxide in the blood, or may arise from damaged brain tissue abnormally responsive to normal shifts of carbon dioxide level.

Cohn and Katzenelbogen (1939) report that in deep sea diving the replacement of nitrogen with helium tends to produce a sedative action. They compared EEG's recorded during the breathing of normal air and a helium-oxygen mixture and found that the latter increased the amount of alpha activity present. They suggest that helium may help to maintain an optimum oxygen supply to the cortex.

HYPO- AND HYPERGLYCEMIA.—Reduction of the blood sugar level below a critical limit will produce coma and unconsciousness, but before this stage is reached there is a slowing of the alpha rhythm and sporadic slow wave components may appear in the EEG (Berger, 1937d; Hoagland, *et al.*, 1937a, 1937b; Marinesco, *et al.*, 1938; F. A. Gibbs, *et al.*, 1939, 1940; Himwich, *et al.*, 1939a, 1939b; P. A. Davis, 1941c). During coma, continuous large slow waves predominate. Slight hypoglycemia may significantly affect results during hyperventilation (Davis and Wallace, 1942; Rubin and Turner, 1942). High concentrations of blood sugar tend to shift the energy in the cortical frequency spectrum toward the higher frequencies (F. A. Gibbs, *et al.*, 1940).

ACID-BASE BALANCE.—Changes in the *pH* of the blood beyond certain limits have been reported by Lennox, *et al.* (1938) and F. A. Gibbs, *et al.* (1940), to slow the electrical activity of the cortex with a shift toward alkalinity and to speed up activity with a shift toward acidity.

TEMPERATURE.—Hoagland (1936b, 1936c, 1936d) has demonstrated that the elevation of body temperature in human subjects by diathermy treatment increases the frequency of the alpha waves. This has been confirmed also by Jasper (1936a). Hoagland believed that the frequency of the rhythm was directly related to metabolic processes and that the increased frequency with temperature elevation was a reflection of the increase in velocity of underlying chemical events.

METABOLISM.—Frequency of the alpha rhythm has been found to be related to metabolism in normal subjects (Lindsley and Rubenstein, 1937) and in patients with thyroid disorders (Ross and Schwab, 1939). Artificial elevation of metabolism by means of thyroid extract has been shown to increase the frequency of the alpha waves (Gerard, 1936; Lindsley and Rubenstein, 1937; Rubin, et al., 1937). There is an obvious difficulty in attempting to correlate metabolism with the EEG, since the former is representative of the activities of the organism as a whole whereas the latter represents only a part of that whole. No doubt if metabolism of a part of the living brain could be determined at the same time that the electrical activity was recorded from that part a much closer correspondence would be revealed. The fact that temperature, blood sugar level, acid-base balance, oxygen consumption, and other physiological variables are known to produce variations in the EEG is strong evidence that characteristics of the EEG are in part controlled by metabolic factors.

DRUGS AND ANESTHETICS.—A number of drugs, if administered in sufficient quantity, have been found to modify the pattern and characteristics of the EEG. However, little is known as yet about the locus of action of the drugs and in many cases it is not clear whether or not the modifications of the EEG produced in this way are secondary to other physiological changes produced by the drugs. In some instances it is possible that a particular drug directly affects the electrical output of cortical cells, whereas in others the effect may be principally upon thalamic or other subcortical centers and thus produce changes in the EEG by modifying cortical and subcortical interrelationships. The blocking of the influx of centripetal impulses from peripheral sources at the thalamic level is no doubt responsible for many of the changes which may be produced in the EEG. A further complication is the fact that some drugs, though depressant in moderate or large doses, have excitant properties in small dosages or in the early stages of the effect.

Only a cursory review of the effects of drugs and anesthetics on the EEG can be given here. Further discussion of the therapeutic use of drugs and their effects on the EEG will be brought out later.

There is a tendency for all anesthetic drugs, given in sufficient amount to induce a state of surgical anesthesia, to produce changes in the EEG similar to those of deep sleep, namely, continuous large slow waves of about 1 or 2 per second. During the initial excitant and subsequent early depressant phases the chief differential effects on the EEG by the different anesthetics are apparent. *Volatile, fat solvent anesthetics* such as *chloroform* and *ether* (Berger, 1931, 1932b; F. A. Gibbs, et al.,

1937a) show initially an increase in size of alpha waves followed by a diminution in frequency, amplitude, and amount of alpha waves, and an increase in the amount of beta activity; ultimately alpha waves disappear and are replaced by slow delta waves. *Anesthetic gases* such as *nitrous oxide* (van der Molen, 1938), and *cyclopropane* (Rubin and Freeman, 1940, 1941) show initially an increase in amplitude of alpha waves and a gradual diminution of frequency and amount; later during deepening anesthesia alpha waves are replaced almost entirely by slow waves of 3 per second or less. During recovery from cyclopropane the pattern of the EEG is more varied and shows considerable shifting from slow to fast frequencies. *Barbiturates* such as evipan (Berger, 1934a), or *evipal* (F. A. Gibbs, *et al.*, 1937a), *phenobarbital* (F. A. Gibbs, *et al.*, 1937a; Cutts and Jasper, 1939; Lindsley and Henry, 1942), and *sodium amytal* (Hughes, *et al.*, 1938; Fowler, 1941; Rubin, *et al.*, 1942; Cohn and Katzenelbogen, 1942) are more differential in their effects on the EEG than other anesthetics and differ among themselves, although there is a distinct tendency for all barbiturates in general to produce prominent fast frequency components in the EEG. This property has been noted most clearly and most consistently for sodium amytal. In the author's experience (unpublished observations) the extremely rhythmic, almost sinusoidal, fast waves of 15 to 20 per second, appearing and disappearing at different intervals of time and in different regions of the head, constitute the outstanding feature of the sodium amytal EEG. *Alkaloids* such as *scopolamine* (Berger, 1931; F. A. Gibbs, *et al.*, 1937a), *morphine* (Berger, 1931, 1937e; F. A. Gibbs, *et al.*, 1937a) ; *cocaine* (Berger, 1937d; Fowler, 1941; Rubin, *et al.*, 1942), *atropine* (Berger, 1937d; F. A. Gibbs, *et al.*, 1937a) ; *caffeine* (F. A. Gibbs, *et al.*, 1937a; Grüttner and Bonkáló, 1940b; Fowler, 1941), and *mescaline* (Chweitzer, *et al.*, 1937a, 1937b; Rubin, *et al.*, 1942), depending upon dosage, produce varied changes in the EEG, consisting of modification of the frequency, amplitude, and amount of the alpha rhythm. With larger doses, these drugs tend to increase the amount of beta activity also. The alpha wave changes are not always consistent from one drug to another, although during the initial excitatory phases of each there is a tendency for accentuation of the alpha waves; subsequently the amount of alpha activity is reduced and there is a tendency to burst-like discharges of alpha waves with intervening beta waves, especially for scopolamine, morphine, and mescaline.

Fowler (1941) and Rubin, *et al.* (1942), have noted in connection with sodium amytal, mescaline, and cocaine that changes in the EEG were accompanied by definite psychological changes in behavior and personality. The latter emphasize that the psychological changes are of two types, those characteristic of a particular drug and those characteristic of the individual, including his personality and behavior disorder or psychosis.

Andrews (1941) made an extensive study of morphine addicts and found that while receiving the drug they show a higher alpha wave output (per cent time alpha) than normals or than addicts who have not had the drug for a year or more. In addicts, during and after withdrawal of the drug the high alpha output may persist for a considerable period of time or may drop suddenly, in spite of the fact that during progressive withdrawal there is a high degree of "emotional tension" present, a factor which frequently greatly diminishes alpha output. In general a single dose in a nonaddict had little effect on the EEG.

Autonomic drugs such as *adrenalin* (F. A. Gibbs, *et al.*, 1937a; Fowler, 1941), *mecholyl* (Fowler, 1941), *atropine* (F. A. Gibbs, *et al.*, 1937a), *ergot* (F. A. Gibbs, *et al.*, 1937a), *benzedrine* (F. A. Gibbs, *et al.*, 1937a; Cutts and Jasper, 1939; Lindsley and Henry, 1942; Rubin, *et al.*, 1942), and others, given in the usual clinical dosages, have not produced marked or consistent changes in the EEG, despite the fact that in some instances behavior may have been definitely altered.

Hoagland, *et al.* (1939), found that *dinitrophenol*, a respiratory and metabolic stimulant, increased the frequency of the alpha waves. Rubin and Freeman (1938) observed that *cyanide*, a respiratory stimulant, increased the amplitude, amount, and regularity of the alpha rhythm in schizophrenic patients. Convulsant drugs such as *cardiazol* or *metrazol* produce striking changes in the EEG associated with convulsions; the EEG changes resemble those seen in actual convulsive seizures and will be discussed further in connection with shock therapy.

Loomis, *et al.* (1936b), noted that alcohol increased the amplitude and decreased the frequency of the alpha rhythm; during the early stages of alcoholic sleep the alpha rhythm persisted and in this respect the EEG was unlike that of sleep. F. A. Gibbs, *et al.* (1937a), found that alcoholic intoxication caused slowing and a reduction of the alpha rhythm, with some increase in beta activity and slow waves. A more extensive study of the effects of alcohol on the EEG was made by P. A. Davis, *et al.* (1941), who found a slowing and a reduction of the alpha rhythm during low concentrations of blood alcohol; but with higher concentrations (125 to 140 mg. per 100 cc.), episodes of 4 to 8 per second slow waves appeared and were associated with clinical signs of slurring of speech, ataxia, emotional changes, and poor performance on psychometric tests.

The EEG seems to be a fairly sensitive indicator of modifications of central nervous system activity induced by certain drugs and there is a definite need for careful and systematic study of such changes in relation to varying amounts of drugs. This information should provide a better understanding of the effects and locus of action of drugs, and in some instances the EEG, in combination with clinical observations of behavior, should be useful in determining the optimal dosage of medication.

FATIGUE.—Grüttner and Bonkáló (1940b) have observed that the EEG of normal persons during fatigued states shows irregularity, slowing, and reduction of the alpha rhythm with some tendency to random slow waves. *Pervitin* (1-Phenyl-2-methylaminopropans) and *caffeine*, after 20 to 30 minutes, alleviated the feeling of fatigue, but only caffeine tended to return the EEG to its normal state.

SLEEP.—The EEG undergoes striking changes during the process of going to sleep. Berger (1932b) noted that there was a marked reduction in the alpha waves. Loomis, *et al.* (1935a, 1935b, 1936a, 1936b), studying all-night sleep records, observed the gradual reduction of the alpha rhythm during the drowsy phase of going to sleep and called attention to a variety of new wave forms and patterns appearing with the onset of sleep, emphasizing particularly the development of 12 to 15 per second spindle formations and the appearance of random slow waves. From the work of several groups of investigators (Loomis, *et al.*, 1937, 1938; Blake and Gerard, 1937; Klaue, 1937; Harvey, *et al.*, 1937; Davis, *et al.*, 1937, 1938; Marinesco, *et al.*, 1937b, 1937c; Blake, *et al.*, 1939; Müller, 1939; Grüttner and Bonkáló, 1940a) there has emerged a fairly consistent and systematic picture of the changes of the EEG during various stages of sleep. Briefly, these stages may be characterized as follows: (1) relaxed and resting, but awake—normal alpha rhythm at start, but with occasional interruptions and diminution of amplitude toward end of stage; (2) distinctly drowsy and beginning of light sleep—alpha rhythm drops out and low voltage slow waves of 4 to 5 per second appear; (3) real sleep—spindle-shaped volleys of 14 per second waves appear, and slow waves increase in magnitude and decrease in frequency; (4) deeper sleep—spindle formations become more prominent and slow waves become larger, slower, and more continuous; (5) very deep sleep —spindles disappear, slow waves become very large and very slow (less than 1 per second and up to 500 microvolts) and more irregular.

During the process of going to sleep there is some tendency for the patterns of the EEG to fluctuate from one stage to another in the *A, B,* and *C* stages; the "onset of sleep" probably occurs at the end of the *B* stage. When the alpha waves disappear during the *B* stage, awareness of external stimulation is lost or greatly depressed. Dreams occur chiefly during the *B* and *C* stages, but are seldom recalled if alpha waves have been completely absent for some time. The transition from sleep to wakefulness follows a similar, though more variable, course. With return of consciousness on waking, alpha waves are present, but continue to be of low voltage for some time (Blake, *et al.*, 1939); hence EEG patterns for different individuals on waking tend to be more homogeneous (Henry, 1941a). Movement of the individual, or stimulation during sleep frequently causes the EEG pattern to revert temporarily to an earlier or lighter stage of sleep.

The Electroencephalogram in Neurologic Disorders.—Clinical application of the EEG began early with the work of Berger. Its usefulness as an adjunct to the clinical, neurologic examination soon became evident, first, in connection with epilepsy and related disorders and subsequently in the discrimination and localization of brain tumors and other types of brain pathology. Not only has the EEG proved useful as a supplementary tool for the neurologist and neurosurgeon, but it has brought forth information which has provoked new conceptions of brain function and new ways of envisaging brain disorders.

EPILEPSY AND RELATED DISORDERS.—During an epileptic attack, or even in the intervals between attacks, the EEG may show unusual patterns of electrical activity consisting of paroxysmal outbursts of waves of abnormal frequency and voltage. Some of the patterns are composed of wave-complexes so unique that they practically constitute a signature for certain types of epileptic disturbances. However, the trend of results of recent studies shows that there may be considerable overlapping of patterns and wave forms among the so-called "epilepsies," and that some of the variations associated with epilepsy may also be found to some extent in certain nonepileptic conditions. Despite this fact, the EEG has proved to be of exceptional value in the diagnosis, experimental study and treatment of epilepsy (see Chapter 31 by Lennox).

Berger (1931, 1932c, 1933b, 1934b, 1935b) was the first to study epileptic states in human subjects by means of the EEG. He noted that the EEG was unusually flat during the epileptic stupor following an attack and that during an "absence" the alpha waves dropped out and were replaced by high amplitude beta waves. He also observed that large 3 per second waves were associated with the rhythmic convulsive movements of a seizure. However, Berger found it difficult to record the EEG satisfactorily during seizures and was unable to give a very systematic description of the electrical events which occur during seizures.

F. A. Gibbs, et al. (1935, 1936) were the first to obtain satisfactory records during seizures and to differentially classify the EEG patterns during petit mal and grand mal attacks. During petit mal seizures they observed large, smooth contoured, 3 per second waves or wave and spike formations of about 3 per second. The latter pattern was considered pathognomonic for petit mal epilepsy by Gibbs and Lennox (1937). Between seizures they frequently found the EEG normal except for occasional, brief groups of waves of a pattern similar to that during a seizure state, but of lower amplitude and less persistent. They called these low amplitude outbursts "larval seizures" since they seemed to be composed of the same elements as the electrical discharge during an actual attack. Later this type of activity became known as a *subclinical seizure* since there were no clinical manifestations associated with the electrical outbursts. During grand mal attacks there was a gradual building up of high amplitude fast waves of about 15 to 25 per second. Shortly after this discharge began, tonic contractions appeared; as the seizure progressed and clonic contractions began, slow waves mixed with fast waves appeared. During the relaxation phase following the cessation of convulsive activity, the EEG was abnormally flat and only slowly returned to its initial state as the patient regained consciousness.

After recording EEG's during seizures in a large number of epileptics of different types, F. A. Gibbs, et al. (1937b, 1938a), concluded that epilepsy can best be defined, in terms of electrocortical events represented in the EEG, as a *paroxysmal cerebral dysrhythmia*. They described three types of EEG's corresponding to different types of seizure patterns and later (Gibbs, *et al.*, 1939) added a fourth. These four general types of seizure patterns are illustrated in Figure 3, but it should be emphasized that there are many additional variations of the EEG in epilepsy. According to these authors the EEG during *petit mal attacks* is characterized by a wave and spike formation which is commonly most prominent in the frontal and precentral regions. *Grand mal attacks* are associated with a crescendo burst of fast waves starting from low amplitude and gradually building up during the tonic phase to high voltage waves which fuse into 3 to 6 per second waves as the clonic phase begins. This type of activity frequently originates in the frontal and precentral regions also. *Psychomotor* or *psychic equivalent attacks*, consisting of apparently conscious acts of impulsive, uncontrolled character, are accompanied by a building up in voltage of 3 to 6 per second waves, often with squared tops. This pattern frequently develops into high voltage 6 per second waves and is most commonly observed over post-central and occipital regions. In the *petit mal variant attack* there is usually no clonic activity as in petit mal and the EEG pattern consists of a slow wave and spike of about 2 per second or less rather than the typical 3 per second pattern of petit mal.

A somewhat different emphasis in the classification of EEG patterns in epilepsy has been proposed by Jasper and Kershman (1941), and Jasper (1941). Studying a group of 494 epileptics, principally during the intervals between attacks, they found that definite abnormalities of a paroxysmal character were present in the EEG's of 95% of the patients. They emphasized two abnormal features of the EEG's of epileptics, *hypersynchrony*, or abnormal voltage, and *dysrhythmia*, or abnormal frequency. The former, they believe, is the more important and they point out that a seizure discharge in some cases may consist of a normal 10 per second rhythm but of paroxysmally high voltage.

Jasper and Kershman report that localization or the distribution of the disturbance provides the most satisfactory basis for classifying the EEG's of epileptics. They describe three principal categories of disturbance: localized unilateral, bilaterally synchronized, and diffuse. About half of their cases showed discrete areas of localization of the EEG disturbance in one hemisphere; 35% showed bilaterally synchronous discharges, usually of bitemporal or bifrontal origin; and 15% showed diffuse or widespread abnormalities. Another important aspect of their classification system is the type of wave form and manner of occurrence of the pattern of disturbance. Some patterns occur as random disturbances whereas others appear as paroxysmal rhythmic sequences. The former are represented as isolated single or multiple spikes, sharp waves, and delta waves; the latter appear in a variety of rhythmic forms, including 3 per second waves, 3 per second wave and spike formations and 6, 10, 14, and 25 per second waves.

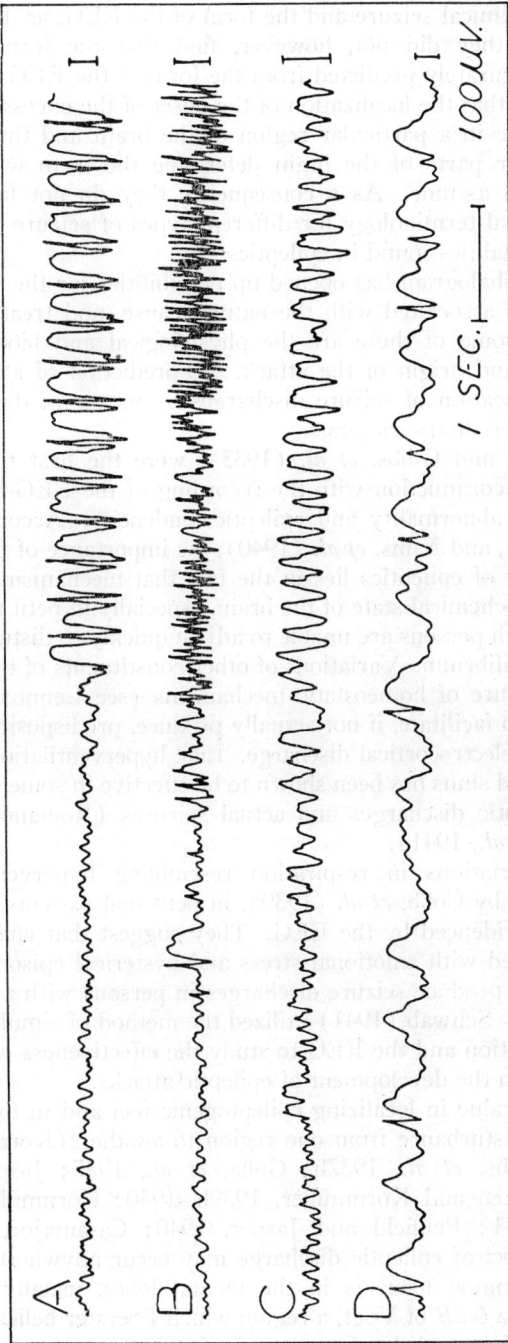

Figure 3

Electrocortical discharges during four varieties of epileptic attack. A. Petit mal attack; B. Grand mal attack; C. Psychomotor discharge; D. Petit mal variant attack. (Illustrations taken from Gibbs and Gibbs (1941), by permission)

Although Jasper and Kershman found some correspondence between the pattern of the clinical seizure and the form of the EEG, as did Gibbs and collaborators, they did not, however, find that the form of the seizure could be accurately predicted from the form of the EEG disturbance. They believe that the localization of the onset of the excessive electrocortical discharge in a particular region of the brain and that area's relations with other parts of the brain determine the form which the clinical seizure will assume. As a consequence they do not favor the application of clinical terminology for different types of seizure patterns to the EEG abnormalities found in epileptics.

The electroencephalogram has opened up possibilities for the study of a variety of factors associated with the nature, cause, and treatment of epilepsy. Among some of these are the physiological and biochemical aspects, the locus and origin of the attack, the prediction of attacks in advance, the modification of seizure discharges by means of drugs and so forth, and the hereditary factors.

Berger (1934b) and Gibbs, et al. (1935), were the first to utilize hyperventilation in conjunction with the recording of the EEG to bring out latent signs of abnormality and epileptic tendencies. According to Gibbs, et al. (1940), and Nims, et al. (1940), the importance of this procedure in the study of epileptics lies in the fact that mechanisms which regulate the physicochemical state of the brain, especially in petit mal, are so impaired that such persons are unable to adjust quickly to disturbances of the acid-base equilibrium. Variations of other constituents of the blood stream and the failure of homeostatic mechanisms (see Lennox, et al., 1938) no doubt also facilitate, if not actually produce, predisposing tendencies to excessive electrocortical discharge. Like hyperventilation, stimulation of the carotid sinus has been shown to be effective in some patients in producing epileptic discharges and actual seizures (Romano, et al., 1940; Margolin, et al., 1941).

Spontaneous variations in respiration resembling hyperventilation have been observed by Cobb, et al. (1939), in petit mal patients preceding an attack, as evidenced by the EEG. They suggest that changes in respiration associated with emotional stress and hysterical episodes may well be sufficient to produce seizure discharges in persons with a predisposition to epilepsy. Schwab (1941) utilized the method of simultaneous recording of respiration and the EEG to study the effectiveness of therapeutic procedures on the development of epileptic attacks.

The EEG is of value in localizing epileptogenic foci and in following the spread of the disturbance from one region to another (Kornmüller, 1935a, 1935b; Gibbs, et al., 1937b; Golla, et al., 1937; Jasper and Hawke, 1938; Janzen and Kornmüller, 1939b, 1940; Kornmüller and Janzen, 1939a, 1941; Penfield and Jasper, 1940; Casamajor, et al., 1941). Although foci of epileptic discharge may occur anywhere in the brain the most common locus is in the frontal lobes, usually in the neighborhood of area 6 aB of Vogt, a region which Foerster believed was important in the origin and development of seizures.

Jung (1939b, 1939d, 1939e) studied vegetative and EEG changes simultaneously during many petit mal seizures. Although he found some differential autonomic responses they were not striking and appeared to be secondary to the seizure itself rather than a cause of the seizure discharge. He found that muscle action potentials during clonic convulsions followed the spike of the wave and spike formation by about 40 to 60 milliseconds. He observed that sensory stimulation, especially auditory and pain, was effective in interrupting and inhibiting a seizure discharge already under way. This has been observed also by Schwab (1941) who found loud sounds more effective than light stimulation in terminating a seizure discharge. Reaction time to stimulation during an attack was greatly prolonged, but variable, depending upon the magnitude and duration of the seizure discharge.

Berger (1934b) believed that his findings in connection with the EEG in epilepsy indicated that seizure phenomena were manifestations of defective thalamic control of the cortex, with marked fluctuations of inhibitory influence giving rise to the pattern of seizure discharge. Kornmüller and Janzen (1941) also emphasize the importance of subcortical control, especially in petit mal seizures, since in some cases they found clinical manifestations of the seizure prior to the onset of the electrocortical discharge and persistence of convulsions after cessation of abnormalities in the EEG. The lack of a cortical focus of the EEG disturbance was also interpreted as evidence of subcortical origin of seizures in some patients. It has been reported (Gibbs, et al., 1937b; Jasper, 1941), however, that removal of an area of focal discharge sometimes eliminates further seizures as well as EEG abnormalities, but permanent relief is not always assured.

In connection with the course and treatment of epilepsy in an individual the EEG is of considerable value as an indicator of changing condition as well as of optimal dosage of anticonvulsant therapy. In addition to surgical intervention, Gibbs, et al. (1938a) point out that anticonvulsant drugs such as phenobarbital tend to limit the spread of the electrical discharge as well as disorganize and reduce it. Lennox (1940) has discussed the value of drugs in the treatment of epilepsy. He states that the ideal drug would be a regulator of the rate of the electrical rhythms of the brain. Since the rate in grand mal is abnormally fast, in psychomotor seizures abnormally slow and in petit mal alternately fast and slow, the commonly used anticonvulsants or sedatives, which tend to slow the rate, are principally of value in the treatment of grand mal. On the other hand, bromides and phenobarbital do have beneficial effects in some petit mal cases; not apparently by suppressing the spike component entirely but by a general reduction and disorganization of the pattern.

Lennox, et al. (1936), and Gibbs, et al. (1937b), found that phenobarbital and bromides increased the interval between seizures and reduced their intensity. Jasper and Nichols (1938) observed a decrease in epileptiform activity in the EEG with luminal, sodium bromide or ketogenic diet. They point out that the EEG is valuable for following the course of treatment with anticonvulsants; they also suggest that it may indicate treatment for those who would not otherwise receive it due to the lack of clinical seizures, but who have EEG evidence of convulsive tendencies. In a group of children with frequent petit mal attacks, Logan and Baldes (1942) found that a ketogenic diet resulted in both clinical and electroencephalographic improvement. There was a reduction in the number of seizures as well as a reduction of the amount of epileptiform activity in the EEG.

Putnam and Merritt (1941) described a form of epileptic equivalent state which they identified as dullness. The principal disturbance is one of intellectual function and the attack may not be appreciated by the patient or by those about him. The attacks are essentially brief "absences" and may occur frequently. The best means of recognizing such patients is by the EEG. Although there is no distinctive EEG abnormality, the patient can frequently correlate brief intellectual lapses with simultaneous EEG abnormalities. Putnam and Merritt found dilantin an effective form of treatment in such cases.

One of the most interesting and at the same time important aspects of the EEG has been its use in detecting hereditary evidences of epileptic tendencies in relatives of epileptic patients. The incidence of abnormality of epileptiform type in the EEG's of relatives (parents, siblings, and children) of epileptics is as follows: Lennox, et al. (1940), 60%; Strauss, et al. (1939), 27%; Löwenbach (1939), 46%; and Robinson (1940), 36%. Only the first two studies were based upon large numbers of subjects. Although there is considerable variation in the percentages, due probably to different criteria of abnormality and different selections of relatives, there is general agreement of the results in showing a significant hereditary component.

Lennox, et al. (1939, 1940) recorded EEG's in 183 relatives of 94 epileptics and in 100 control subjects who had no near relatives with epilepsy. Sixty per cent of the relatives as opposed to 10% of the control group had definitely abnormal EEG's. EEG's were obtained from both parents in 55 families and in 35% records from both parents were abnormal; in only 5% were the EEG's clearly normal. Similar evidence comes from several other sources as was indicated above. The data of Strauss, et al. (1939), were based on the EEG's of 93 relatives of 31 patients with a diagnosis of "idiopathic" epilepsy. They found some families much more highly saturated with epileptiform activity than others.

Lennox, et al. (1940), and Gibbs (1940) believe the evidence indicates that the dysrhythmia of epilepsy is inheritable and that when such dysrhythmia is demonstrable it may represent a predisposition to epilepsy or some related disorder. They feel that dysrhythmia may prove to be a dominant trait since only 2.4% of near relatives of epileptics have clinical evidence of epilepsy, whereas 60% have dysrhythmia. Strauss, et al. (1939), raise the question of what significance epileptiform activity in the EEG's of relatives of epileptics may have when they are free of clinical evidence of seizures. They state that it may indicate a possibility of subsequent development of overt seizures in young siblings, but they feel that only a small number of the adult relatives with abnormalities in the EEG will actually develop overt seizures. They also point out the possibility of such relatives serving as "carriers" of epilepsy. Löwenbach (1939), after raising the question of whether the abnormalities of the EEG's of relatives of epileptics are a symptom of epilepsy still not severe enough to produce clinical evidence of convulsions, or are an expression of a nonspecific functional instability of the central nervous system, concludes in favor of the latter point of view.

Lennox, et al. (1939, 1940), studied 17 pairs of twins, one or both of which had a history of epilepsy in the case of 15 pairs. Among these were nine identical twin pairs; in two pairs both members had epilepsy and abnormal EEG's and in seven other pairs both members had dysrhythmia but only one of each pair had seizures. In five or more of these latter cases, the epileptic member had received an injury of the brain prior to the onset of seizures. In one set of similar twins one member had symptomatic epilepsy due to a head injury and the other member had normal brain waves; in another pair of similar twins one had hysterical seizures and both members of the pair had normal EEG's. Of four dissimilar twin pairs in which one member of each had epilepsy, three of the normal members had normal EEG's. From these data the authors conclude that epilepsy, the plant, is not inherited but that a predisposition, the seed, is inherited in the form of cerebral dysrhythmia. In a person with cerebral dysrhythmia, and thus a predisposition, actual seizures may be facilitated by secondary factors such as brain injury, toxic conditions and the like.

RELATED CONDITIONS.—From time to time certain conditions such as migraine, pyknolepsy, cataplexy, narcolepsy, and certain behavior disorders of children have been likened to epilepsy. From the point of view of the EEG, only pyknolepsy and some behavior disorders of children show abnormalities similar to those of petit mal and psychomotor epilepsy. Golla, et al. (1937), and Kornmüller and Janzen (1941) have found large amplitude 3 to 6 per second waves in children with pyknolepsy. A diffuse representation of abnormality is frequently present with the most marked disturbance localized in the posterior head regions, especially in the occipital areas. Golla and collaborators found these patterns unaffected by luminal, but benzedrine abolished both the EEG abnormalities and the seizures after a few days of treatment. Jasper and Nichols (1938) and Jasper, et al. (1938), were the first to liken the slow waves of the EEG's of behavior problem children to those of epileptics and they pointed out that the behavior was also similar, inasmuch as such children had what they called an "epileptoid" personality, characterized by impulsive and variable behavior. The EEG in behavior problem children will be described more fully elsewhere.

There is uniform agreement on the fact that the EEG presents no pathognomonic picture for *narcolepsy* (Gibbs, *et al.,* 1935; Janzen, 1939; Blake, *et al.,* 1939; Janzen and Behnsen, 1940; Dynes, 1941; Dynes and Finley, 1941). During a narcoleptic attack the EEG shows patterns of activity characteristic of physiologic sleep, although the stages or normal sleep are somewhat foreshortened in the narcoleptic state. Accordingly, from the point of view of the EEG, narcolepsy appears to be a pathological extension of a normal physiologic mechanism. Likewise there is no evidence that the EEG is characterized by any specific abnormality during *migraine headaches* (Lemere, 1937).

BRAIN LESIONS.—The EEG has been used extensively in the detection and localization of a variety of forms of brain lesions. For these purposes it has proved to be an exceptionally useful adjunct to the usual clinical neurologic examination and has become a distinct aid to the neurosurgeon. In some cases where no obvious clinical signs of localization are present the EEG may reveal evidences of pathology and thus give direction to further search by clinical examination and X-ray methods, in other cases it has provided valuable confirmatory evidence of localized pathology.

Brain tumors and *abscesses* are most readily detected when they directly involve or impinge upon the cortex, although the EEG may also reveal evidence of subcortical tumors by their indirect effect upon the electrical activity of the cortex. Tumor tissue itself is not active electrically (Foerster and Altenburger, 1935; Scarff and Rahm, 1941), but the adjacent regions of brain tissue in process of invasion or otherwise interfered with by toxic conditions, circulatory inadequacy, or pressure effects give rise to a variety of abnormalities. These may take the form of a reduction of the alpha rhythm as noted by Berger (1931, 1933b) or of large slow delta waves of less than 1 to 3 per second (Walter, 1936, 1937). Walter called the concentration of such waves of increased amplitude over the area of the tumor a "delta wave focus." The focus of a tumor may be more precisely determined by phase reversal and triangulation methods. In addition to the large random or rhythmic slow waves, Case and Bucy (1938) have noted that there may be isolated spikes and "saw-tooth" wave forms arising from the region of a tumor or other pathological process. Frequently a tumor or other pathology may be detected by the bilateral differences in the electrical activity on the two sides of the head (Kornmüller, 1904b). Figure 4 illustrates the localization of a tumor by means of the EEG.

A number of techniques and methods of localization have been described (Kornmüller, 1938, 1939, 1940a, 1940b, 1940c; Kornmüller and Janzen, 1939a, 1939b; Williams and Gibbs, 1938a, 1938b, 1939; Gibbs, Munro, and Wegner, 1941; and others). The accuracy of localization, particularly for tumors involving the cortex, has been shown to compare very favorably with other more time consuming or more rigorous methods, including the neurologic examination, pnuemoencephalography and ventriculography (Yeager, *et al.,* 1940; Gibbs,

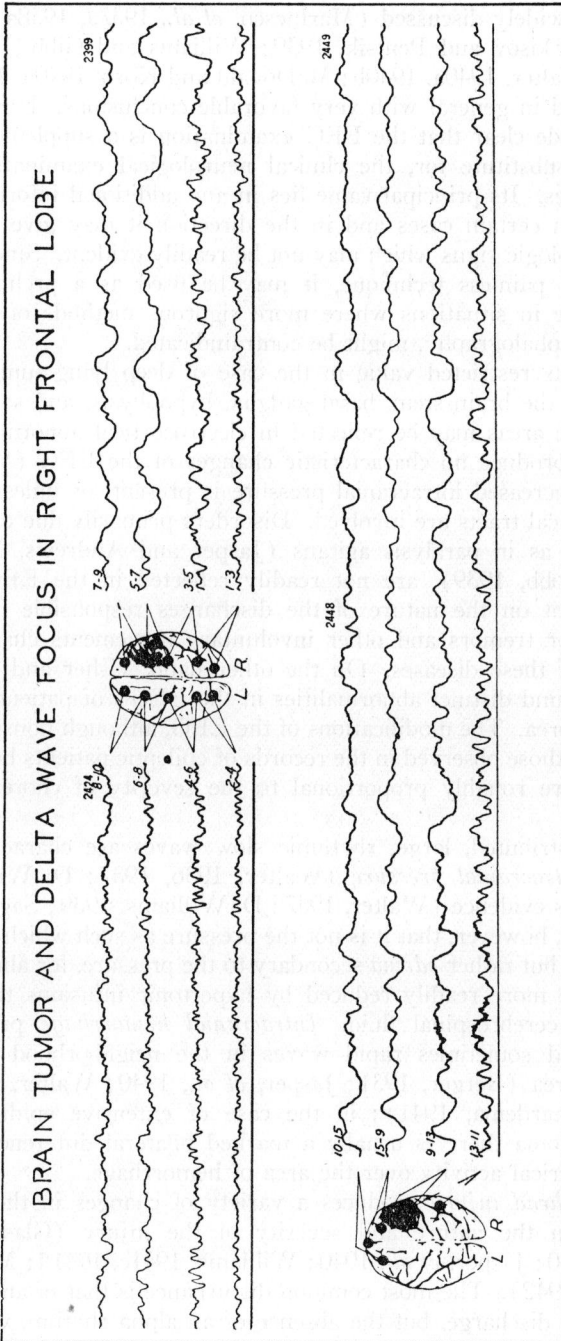

Figure 4

Localization of a brain tumor by electroencephalography. Large, random delta waves over the right frontal lobe; relative quiescence over left frontal lobe. Lower record shows phase reversal of delta waves from leads on either side of tumor.

Munro, and Wegner, 1941). The diagnostic and surgical value of the EEG has been widely discussed (Marinesco, *et al.*, 1937a, 1938a; Torrents, 1940; Sarkisov and Pentsik, 1939; Williams and Gibbs, 1938a, 1938b, 1939; Walter, 1940a, 1940b; McDonald and Korb, 1940a, 1940b; and others), and in general with very favorable conclusions. However, it should be made clear that the EEG examination is a supplement to, rather than a substitute for, the clinical neurological examination or X-ray procedures. Its principal value lies in any additional information it may reveal in certain cases and in the direction it may give to the search for neurologic signs which may not be readily evident. Since it is a harmless and painless technique, it may be used as a preliminary searching device in situations where more rigorous methods of study, such as air encephalography, might be contraindicated.

The EEG has restricted value in the case of deep lying tumors or other lesions of the brain stem, basal ganglia, hypophysis, and so forth. Lesions in these areas may be reflected in electrocortical abnormalities, but in general produce no characteristic changes of the EEG (Walter, 1937), unless increased intracranial pressure is present, or unless optic or thalamo-cortical tracts are involved. Disorders primarily due to basal ganglia lesions, as in paralysis agitans (Jasper and Andrews, 1938b; Schwab and Cobb, 1939), are not readily reflected in the EEG and throw little light on the nature of the discharges responsible for the peripheral motor tremors and other involuntary movements characteristic of some of these diseases. On the other hand, Usher and Jasper (1941) have found distinct abnormalities in the EEG's of patients with Sydenham's chorea. The modifications of the EEG, although nonspecific, were similar to those observed in the records of epileptic patients between attacks and were roughly proportional to the severity of chorea clinically.

Diffusely distributed, large, rhythmic slow waves are characteristic of *increased intracranial pressure* (Walter, 1936, 1937; D. Williams, 1939). There is evidence (Walter, 1937; D. Williams, 1939; Sager and Herman, 1939), however, that it is not the pressure as such which causes the slow waves, but rather *edema* secondary to the pressure, for abnormal slow waves are more readily reduced by hypertonic infusions than by withdrawal of cerebrospinal fluid. *Intracranial hemorrhage* produces slow waves and sometimes rapid waves in the neighborhood of the hemorrhaged area (Berger, 1931; Jasper, *et al.*, 1940; Walter, 1940c; Glaser and Sjaardema, 1941); in the case of extensive epidural or subdural hematoma there is usually a marked bilateral difference with absence of electrical activity over the area of hemorrhage.

Trauma or *head injury* produces a variety of changes in the EEG depending upon the nature and severity of the injury (Glaser and Sjaardema, 1940; Jasper, *et al.*, 1940; Williams, 1941c, 1941d; Marmor and Savitsky, 1942). The most common disturbance is that of an excessive delta wave discharge, but the absence of an alpha rhythm, variable alpha rhythms with sudden sharp wave discharges or actual epileptiform activity may be the chief indication of an acute or chronic disturbance resulting from a brain injury. In general the more acute and the more severe the injury, the slower and more prominent the delta wave activity. According to Williams (1941d), abnormality of the EEG following head injury is usually indicative of organic cerebral damage. He found that abnormality of the EEG may persist in about 50% of the patients with a chronic post-traumatic syndrome. Although there is a close relationship between clinical improvement and the return of the EEG to a normal state, abnormality may persist in the EEG for some time after clinical recovery appears to be complete; consequently it furnishes a more sensitive index of cerebral dysfunction than does the clinical state as revealed by the usual methods of examination. A normal EEG following a head injury is substantial evidence that cerebral damage has not occurred. Therefore the EEG is useful for detecting malingering, hysteria, and the presence of other psychogenic factors which frequently follow accidents.

The abolition, reduction, or other modification of the occipital alpha rhythm has been noted in patients with *defects of the peripheral visual mechanism* or with *lesions of the optic tracts* (Lemere, 1937; Baudouin, Halbron, *et al.*, 1939; Postelli and Seidenari, 1939; Seidenari, 1940; Bucy and Case, 1940). Lemere (1942) has pointed out that this fact makes the EEG useful for distinguishing hysterical from real blindness. Bilateral differences in the frequency, amplitude, and amount of alpha rhythm have been observed in simultaneous recording from homologous areas of the two hemispheres in patients with *aphasia* (Marinesco, *et al.*, 1936b, 1936c, 1938a). Rubin (1939b) reported that areal and bilateral differences in amount of alpha rhythm constitute valuable cues for detecting *cerebral atrophy.*

INFECTIOUS CONDITIONS.—Diseases involving the meninges and cortex in a somewhat diffuse, though spotty distribution, usually produce, during the acute stages of irritation and early degeneration, a widespread disturbance of the EEG. In patients with *general paresis* (Berger, 1931, 1932c, 1933b; Bennett, *et al.*, 1940; Finley, *et al.*, 1942), the EEG has shown marked irregularity of the alpha rhythm and numerous widespread slow waves; frequently also the beta rhythms, especially of the anterior head regions, are accentuated. Finley, *et al.* (1942), studying a large number of patients with various types of neurosyphilis, found a variety of patterns of abnormality but no consistent differential features for the various types. General paresis patients showing clinical remissions following treatment frequently show a marked reduction in the abnormality of their EEG's and in some cases a complete return of the records to a normal state (Bennett, *et al.*, 1940, 1942; Finley, *et al.*, 1942). Hoagland (1936a), investigating the pacemaker aspects of cellular respiration as reflected by variations in frequency of the alpha rhythm in normals and general paretics subjected to hyperpyrexia treatments, concluded that there are definite changes in cellular respiration with advancing stages of spirochete infection.

Lindsley and Cutts (1941) made periodic electroencephalographic examinations of a boy during recovery from acute *encephalitis.* Three months after the acute phase of the attack the EEG showed gross slow wave disturbances, widely distributed over the surface of the head. Associated with these diffuse electrocortical abnormalities were occasional convulsions and extremely disturbed and variable behavior. During the course of one and one-half years there was complete clinical recovery and associated with the changes in behavior were distinct improvements in the EEG, which eventually also became completely normal.

It appears that all forms of brain tissue-destroying processes, whether produced by infections, toxic agents, intra-cranial pressure, circulatory failure, or direct injury, are usually characterized by delta wave activity as long as the active process of infringement or deterioration persists. When the active process of destruction ceases and degeneration of certain cells or cell groups is complete, there is frequently a return of the EEG to a normal pattern of activity, providing of course that the area of destruction is not too large and not too concentrated.

ENDOCRINE AND METABOLIC DISORDERS.—Endocrine disturbances, with or without abnormalities of metabolic rate, are capable of greatly modifying the activity of the EEG. *Hypo-* and *hyperthyroidism* tend to produce opposite effects; in the case of the former alpha frequencies are slowed and in the latter alpha rhythms tend to be abnormally fast (Ross and Schwab, 1939). *Congenitally myxedematous patients,* who also were idiots, showed a number of EEG anomalies including reduction of amplitude or even absence of alpha rhythm, lack of responsiveness of alpha rhythm to sensory stimulation, and presence of delta waves of 3 to 4 per second (Bertrand, *et al.,* 1938; Guillain, 1938). Hoffman, *et al.* (1942), found definite abnormalities of the EEG in 18 of 25 patients with *Addison's disease,* consisting of slower than normal alpha waves especially over the frontal cortex, unusual sensitivity to hyperventilation with marked slow wave production, and a considerable reduction of normal beta waves. These workers found that the abnormalities of the resting records were not modified by hormone treatment, vitamin B complex, intravenous infusions of glucose, or a diet rich in carbohydrates. On the other hand, Engel and Margolin (1941a) described a patient with Addison's disease who had marked personality changes and severe disturbances of carbohydrate metabolism, although the basal metabolic rate was normal. This patient's EEG showed diffuse and continuous delta wave activity. Both the patient's symptoms and EEG disturbances were alleviated by a high carbohydrate diet and adrenal cortex extract.

Engel and Margolin (1941b) studied two groups of patients representing what they called exogenous and endogenous deficiency states. The former was represented by patients with vitamin deficiencies and abnormal dietary habits; the latter was composed of patients with adrenal insufficiency. Both groups showed neuropsychiatric disturbances, hypoglycemia, and cerebral dysrhythmias. After administration of dextrose the abnormal slow waves of the EEG disappeared, but reappeared when the blood sugar level fell again, at which time unfavorable personality reactions also developed. Engel and Margolin conclude that the EEG furnishes a satisfactory quantitative method of studying the effects of variations in carbohydrate metabolism on cortical activity, and that it is a useful correlate of the personality changes resulting from defective carbohydrate metabolism.

The Electroencephalogram in Psychiatric and Psychologic Disorders.—Although numerous studies have been made of psychiatric disorders, especially of the classical psychoses, no distinctive abnormality of the EEG has been found which could be said to be pathognomonic of a particular type of disorder. Various deviations from normal have been noted but consistency has been lacking and the overlapping of patterns of activity with those in normals and epileptics has left the results in a somewhat inconclusive state. This may be due in part to the difficulty of differential clinical diagnosis or possibly to insufficient detailed analysis of the electrical records, but it seems more likely that the pathological basis of the psychoses, whatever that may be, is of such a nature that it is not readily reflected in the over-all picture of cortical activity provided by the EEG.

SCHIZOPHRENIA.—Berger (1931, 1933b, 1937c) recorded EEG's in schizophrenic patients but found no characteristic deviations from normal, except during states of excitement or hallucinatory experiences. He did note that there was some tendency toward a reduced amplitude of alpha waves and sometimes a tendency toward low amplitude fast waves such as are observed in tense normal subjects. As previously mentioned, Lemere (1936, 1938, 1939, 1941) has consistently held the view that there is a sharp contrast between the EEG's of schizophrenic and manic-depressive patients, and that this contrast may also be observed in the records of normals who may be classed as of schizoid or cyclothymic make-up. He believes that a feeble, irregular alpha rhythm is characteristic of the schizophrenic, whereas a strong, rhythmic alpha wave pattern is characteristic of the manic-depressive patient.

Lemere (1941) holds that the low amplitude alpha rhythm in schizophrenia is "due to a low activity cortex that permits irrelevant ideas to exist side by side without the energy necessary for proper segregation and rational correlation." Elsewhere (1939) he postulated that the lack of cortical energy production in schizophrenia is due principally to a constitutionally inadequate diencephalon. He states (1941) that clinical observation supports this notion since in schizophrenia there is an inadequate, poorly sustained affect (thalamus) and a defective, labile homeostasis (hypothalamus), coupled with normal or superior intelligence (cortex). He cites as further evidence the fact that insulin, metrazol, and total-push therapy, which influence the schizophrenic process, also strengthen the alpha rhythm; these effects are presumably accomplished by the action of the agents on the diencephalon.

Grinker and Serota (1941) also conclude that there is a deficiency of hypothalamic function in schizophrenia. Their conclusions are based upon results obtained by recording from the "hypothalamus" and the cortex. They found that schizophrenics, in contrast to normals and neurotics, show little electrical reaction of the hypothalamus and cortex to external cold. Whereas an intramuscular injection of adrenalin causes a marked effect in normals and neurotics, schizophrenics show little subjective and usually no objective effect through electrical responses of the hypothalamus and cortex. Electrical stimulation of the hypothalamus in schizophrenics produces little or no electrical response in the hypothalamus or cortex, although in normals and neurotics there was a marked response from both structures accompanied by subjective effects as well. Verbal stimulation produced no significant hypothalamic or cortical response in schizophrenics, but did in neurotic subjects.

Hoagland, Cameron, and Rubin (1937a, 1937b) and Hoagland, Rubin, and Cameron (1936, 1937), using the "delta index" as a measure of slow wave activity, found higher values in schizophrenics than in normals, although there was some overlapping of range values. McMahon and Walter (1938) criticize Hoagland's delta index as a measure of disturbance in the EEG of schizophrenics and state that they were unable to confirm Lemere's results. In fact in contrast to Lemere's results they report that some schizophrenics show an unusually persistent and prominent alpha rhythm, especially in the post-central regions. They observed in others a pathological delta wave discharge, principally in the frontal regions. Neither of these variations was considered diagnostic nor especially helpful in formulating a theory of the pathology of the disease.

Rubin (1938b) found that schizophrenics and normals show no significant differences in frequency, amplitude and amount of alpha rhythm, although schizophrenics show more variability from day to day. Rubin and Cohen (1939) analyzed the EEG's of schizophrenics and normals with respect to imagery-type. Whereas auditory and visual imagery types predominate in normal subjects, schizophrenics are said to be principally of kinesthetic, tactual and temperature imagery-types. There were, however, no very significant differences between normals and schizophrenics in the amount of alpha rhythm present, although again there was more day-to-day variability.

Comparisons of the EEG's of schizophrenics and epileptics have been made by Gibbs, et al. (1938b), and by Jasper, et al. (1939); the former found likenesses between the EEG's of schizophrenia and psychomotor epilepsy, the latter also found that about one quarter of their schizophrenics showed evidence of epileptiform activity. In general, however,

Jasper and collaborators found that epileptics and schizophrenics were represented on opposite extremes of a scale of the amount of alpha wave activity present in the EEG, with normals holding an intermediate position. There were wide individual differences among the schizophrenics and a wide variety of abnormalities in their EEG's, such as dissociation of activity in homologous areas on the two sides of the head, poor regulation of frequency and amplitude of alpha waves, abnormal grouping of potentials and random slow waves of epileptiform type. None of these abnormalities could be said to be characteristic or diagnostic of schizophrenia.

Davis and Davis (1939) point out that psychotics cannot be recognized by their EEG's, although as a group they show more abnormalities than a group of normal subjects. With respect to alpha index they found no significant differences between schizophrenics and manic-depressive patients, and considerable overlapping by both groups with the ranges for normal subjects. Elsewhere P. A. Davis (1940, 1942) characterized the EEG's of schizophrenics as "choppy" and irregular and with a tendency to low amplitude fast waves; manic-depressive patients were observed to have more prominent and more regular alpha wave patterns. Similar observations have been made by Yeager and Baldes (1937).

Finley and Campbell (1941) found a greater percentage of borderline and abnormal EEG's among a group of 500 schizophrenics than among a group of 215 normals. There was a higher percentage of abnormal records among catatonic-hebephrenics than among other subgroups. These authors conclude that there is nothing consistent or diagnostic about the EEG's of schizophrenics, since a considerable variety of patterns were found. Although low amplitude fast activity was common, this type of activity was also observed in the records of other neuropsychiatric patients, especially manic-depressives. Gibbs (1939a, 1940) in analyzing the cortical frequency spectra of schizophrenic patients and normals found that schizophrenics show a disproportionate amount of energy in the frequency ranges above the normal alpha frequency. Clardy, et al. (1941), recorded EEG's in a small group of children showing schizophrenic-like reactions. They stress the importance of slow waves of about 7 per second and bilateral differences in pattern.

From the foregoing reports it may be seen that there is no characteristic picture presented by the EEG in schizophrenia and nothing to clearly differentiate the EEG's of schizophrenics from those of normals or from those of other psychotic patients. As a group, however, schizophrenics seem to show a variety of abnormalities, mainly of the low amplitude, irregular, high frequency rhythms. There is also some evidence of slow dysrhythmias and in some cases patterns of epileptiform type.

MANIC-DEPRESSIVE PSYCHOSIS.—Lemere (1936, 1939, 1941) reports that the EEG's of manic-depressive patients tend to be characterized by a strong, rhythmic alpha activity, except in the more severely disturbed and depressed patients, whose records also show some delta activity. He explains (1941) the overproduction of cortical energy in manic-depressives as due to an overactive diencephalon and a secondarily over-active cortex; the clinical counterparts of these processes are an excessive affect and intellectual distortions. P. A. Davis (1942) reported that the EEG's of manic-depressives are more rhythmic and regular and present a stronger alpha rhythm than those of schizophrenics. In another study P. A. Davis (1941c) observed that manic-depressive depressed patients have a tendency toward good alpha wave production with some slow wave components whereas manic-depressive manic patients show faster and less regular alpha rhythms mixed with beta rhythms. No marked change in the EEG occurred, however, when patients passed from a manic to a depressed phase or vice versa.

ORGANIC PSYCHOSES.—Psychoses associated with general paresis, senility, arteriosclerosis and chronic alcoholism have been studied by Hoch and Kubis (1941). They found that there was some correlation between the EEG findings and the clinical status, although there was by no means an absolute relationship. Abnormality of the EEG was more common among acute cases where marked mental symptoms developed rapidly; however, in some cases, both acute and chronic, with decided psychotic manifestations, the EEG was normal. In the most deteriorated chronic cases slow waves were frequently observed. They conclude that the EEG in organic psychoses is most significant when delta waves are present, for in such cases mental impairment is usually demonstrable.

NEUROSES.—Only scattered observations on the EEG's of psycho-neurotics have been made and these for the most part present no characteristic picture. The only feature of note is a tendency for instability of the pattern of activity. In patients with marked tensions and anxieties there is frequently a suppression of the alpha rhythm and a tendency to low amplitude beta-like waves. This is also characteristic of some normal subjects who are unusually apprehensive about the recording procedure, but usually the effect disappears with reassurances and a better state of relaxation.

HYSTERIA.—Titeca (1938) observed in two cases of hysterical anesthesia that normal reductions of alpha rhythm could not be produced by stimulation of the affected parts. He concluded that this indicated a functional isolation of certain nerve centers due to hysteria. In a patient deaf and dumb from a fright, Paulian, et al. (1939), observed an absence of alpha waves and numerous beta waves over the frontal and frontal-parietal regions with attempts by the patient to speak and hear. After a cure by "torpedoing" the patient with electric shocks on the neck, head and larynx the alpha waves returned.

BEHAVIOR DISORDERS IN CHILDREN.—Electroencephalographic studies have thrown new light on the possible causes of behavior problems and delinquency among children. In the absence of physical and neurologic signs in children presenting behavior disorders of this character the causes for misbehavior have been sought principally in environmental factors. All too frequently, however, children exposed to the same types of unfavorable environment and even members of the same family have presented striking contrasts. in behavior. The first evidence that disturbances of cortical function might play a significant role in such disorders was presented by Jasper, et al. (1938). These investigators found in a group of 71 behavior problem children that the EEG's showed abnormalities in 73% of the cases. In addition to disturbances of the pattern of the alpha rhythm numerous evidences of slow waves ranging in frequency from 2 to 7 per second were observed. Some of the abnormalities were suggestive of epileptiform activity. Other workers (Lindsley and Cutts, 1940; Strauss, et al., 1940; Brill, et al., 1942; Brown and Solomon, 1942; Secunda and Finley, 1942) studying groups of problem children have observed abnormalities of various types in from 70 to 90% of the cases.

Not only do the EEG's of such children show a significant amount of slow activity of 3 and 6 per second, but additional latent signs of electrocortical disturbances are revealed by a brief period of hyperventilation. This suggests that there is an underlying physiological instability. Drugs such as benzedrine, phenobarbital and dilantin, which have been used to control hyperactive and impulsive behavior with some success, have not on the whole produced significant changes in the EEG's of behavior problem children (Cutts and Jasper, 1939; Lindsley and Henry, 1942). This does not necessarily mean, however, that the electrical disturbances revealed by the EEG in such children are not in some way partially responsible for the deviant behavior manifestations.

So far no close relationship between the type of behavior disturbance and the EEG abnormality has been established, but this may be due to the fact that behavior disorders are unusually labile and subject to secondary modification by numerous environmental factors. In some cases the EEG abnormalities have led to closer search for neurologic factors and have revealed localized cortical defects, but the chief cause of abnormalities of the EEG in problem children seems to reside in physiopathologic mechanisms, the precise nature of which is as yet unknown. There is some evidence that growth and maturational factors play a part in the physiologic disturbances, for Secunda and Finley (1942) have reported that the abnormality of the EEG in such cases decreases with age.

MENTAL DEFICIENCY.—Berger (1932c) reported that the EEG's of feebleminded persons resemble those of normal persons, except for some reduction in amplitude and frequency of the alpha rhythm in the lowest grades of feeblemindedness. Later (1938c) he stated that the EEG of the adult feebleminded person shows a better resting alpha rhythm than in normal healthy adults. This he believed was due to their relatively undisturbed, passive mental make-up. The most extensive studies of mentally deficient persons have been made by Kreezer (1936, 1937, 1939a, 1939b). By dealing with adult subjects he has in effect been able to hold chronological age constant, at least in so far as it might affect the frequency and pattern of the alpha rhythm, and has compared the EEG's at different mental age levels. In general, he has found in mongolian and hereditary types of mental deficiency a tendency for frequency, amplitude, and amount of alpha rhythm to increase with increasing mental age. The increase was not a continuous function of mental age, but was most evident in the region of six to eight years of mental age. The changes with increasing mental age, though statistically significant, were not striking and marked individual differences were noted within a particular mental age level.

SHOCK THERAPY.—Finally, one of the uses to which the EEG has been put is the study of the nature, and effects upon the nervous system, of convulsive shock therapy. Numerous EEG studies have been made during, and for varying periods of time after, *metrazol shock* (Cook and Walter, 1938; Rubin and Wall, 1939; Strauss and Rahm, 1940; Davis and Sulzbach, 1940; Levy, *et al.,* 1942), and *electroshock* (Levy, *et al.,* 1942; Pacella and Barrera, 1942; Pacella, *et al.,* 1942; Fleming, *et al.,* 1939). The electrocortical discharges during the convulsive shock period are similar in both cases and resemble the activity recorded in epileptics during a grand mal attack, except when a subconvulsive dose is given with resulting patterns of activity more nearly resembling petit mal attacks. After the first few shock periods there is frequently evidence of cortical disturbance in the form of spontaneous slow wave discharges. These usually persist throughout the course of the shock series and for varying periods of time after the termination of the series. In some cases delta wave discharges have been present as long as six months after the period of shock therapy, although for the most part such cortical disturbances have disappeared within two months. In some patients making clinical recovery from a previous psychiatric condition, following shock therapy, there is evidence of a restoration of the EEG to a more normal type of picture, whereas in others little or no change occurs.

From the foregoing account of the use of the EEG in the study of neurologic and psychiatric conditions it is evident that the most important applications have been in the field of the former. With further refinement of the technique and better standards of classification of EEG data in terms of the range of characteristics observed in the records of normal individuals there is a possibility that the more subtle personality and behavior distortions observed in psychiatric disorders may be illuminated by analysis of the EEG.

BIBLIOGRAPHY

ADRIAN, E. D. 1930. The activity of the nervous system of the caterpillar. *J. Physiol., 70,* 34–36.

—— 1931. Potential changes in the isolated nervous system of the Dysticus marginalis. *J. Physiol., 72,* 132–151.

——· 1934. Electrical activity of the nervous system. *Arch. Neurol. Psychiat., Chicago, 32,* 1125–1136.

ADRIAN, E. D., & BUYTENDIJK, F. J. J. 1931. Potential changes in the isolated brain stem of the goldfish. *J. Physiol., 71,* 121–135.

ADRIAN, E. D., & MATTHEWS, B. H. C. 1934a. The Berger rhythm: Potential changes from the occipital lobes of man. *Brain, 57,* 355–385.

—— 1934b. The interpretation of potential waves in the cortex. *J. Physiol., 81,* 440–471.

ADRIAN, E. D., & YAMAGIWA, K. 1935. The origin of the Berger rhythm. *Brain, 58,* 322–351.

AGÜERO Y MONTORO, H. 1940. (Electro-encephalography and its psychophysiologic possibilities.) *Vida nueva, 45,* 221–225.

ALBERTI, J. L. 1941. Fenómenos psicoeléctricos: electroencefalogramas. Nuevas interpretaciones de las ondas "alfa" y "beta." *Ann. Inst. Psicol., Univ. B. Aires, 3,* 521–541.

ANDREWS, H. L. 1938. The physical basis of brain potential recording. *Sth. med. J., Bgham, 31,* 315–320.

—— 1941. Brain potentials and morphine addiction. *Psychosom. Med., 3,* 399–409.

ASENJO, A. 1939. Estado actual de las investigaciones bioeléctricas en el cerebro humano. *Rev. méd. Chile, 67,* 1015–1022.

BAGCHI, B. K. 1936. The adaptation and variability of response of the human brain rhythm. *J. Psychol., 3,* 463–485.

—— 1939. The origin and nature of the brain rhythm. *Calcutta med. J., 36,* 334–345.

BAKES, F. P. 1939. Effect of response to auditory stimulation on the latent time of blocking of the Berger rhythm. *J. exp. Psychol., 24,* 406–418.

BALADO, M., & ORIBE, M. F. 1940. La encefalografía en el diagnóstico de las lesiones quiasmáticas e hipofarias. *Sem. méd., B. Aires, 1,* 1173–1187.

BALADO, M., & ROMERO, L. F. 1940a. (Conditions of appearance and propagation of cortical tangential tracings in electroencephalogram.) *Arch. argent. Neurol., 23,* 9–29.

—— 1940b. (Direction of electric currents of cortex; electroencephalographic study of case of cystic astrocytoma.) *Sem. méd., B. Aires, 1,* 545–553.

—— 1940c. Sobre la dirección de las corrientes eléctricas de la corteza cerebral. *Arch. argent. Neurol., 22,* 7–20.

BALADO, M., ROMERO, L. F., & NOISEAUX, P. J. 1939. Electroencefalograma humana; sus aplicaciones a la fisiología y patología cerebrales. *Arch. argent. Neurol., 20,* 215–380.

BARNETT, A. 1941. Techniques for obtaining electroencephalograms using ocular and intranasal electrodes. *J. Lab. clin. Med., 26,* 1659–1663.

BARTLEY, S. H., & BISHOP, G. H. 1933. The cortical response to stimulation of the optic nerve of the rabbit. *Amer. J. Physiol., 103,* 159–172.

BAUDOUIN, A., & FISCHGOLD, H. 1938. Les phénomènes bio-électriques du système nerveux et leurs applications possibles à la médecine. *J. Radiol. Electrol., 22,* 401–428.

—— 1939a. Les phénomènes bio-électriques du système nerveux et leurs applications à la médecine. *J. Radiol. Electrol., 23,* 296–303.

—— 1939b. L'électroencéphalogramme humain et son utilization clinique. *Biol. méd., Paris, 29,* 617–664.

BAUDOUIN, A., FISCHGOLD, H., & LERIQUE, J. 1939. L'électro-encéphalogramme multiple de l'homme normal. *Bull. Acad. Méd. Paris, 121,* 89–100.

BAUDOUIN, A., FISCHGOLD, H., WELTI, J., & LERIQUE, J. 1938. L'électro-encéphalographie dans l'épilepsie. *Bull. Soc. méd. Hôp. Paris, 54,* 1324–1336.

BAUDOUIN, A., HALBRON, P., FISCHGOLD, H., & MION, R. J. 1939. L'examen électrique de la région occipitale dans les lésions des voies optiques. *Bull. Soc. ophthal. Paris, 51,* 176–182.

BENNETT, A. E. 1942. The value of electroencephalography in neurology. *Dis. nerv. Syst., 3*, 185–197.

BENNETT, A. E., CASH, P. T., & HOEKSTRA, C. S. 1940. Artificial fever therapy in general paretics with electroencephalographic studies. *Psychiat. Quart., 15,* 750–771.

—— 1942. Artificial fever therapy for dementia paralytica with electroencephalographic studies. *Arch. Neurol. Psychiat., Chicago, 47,* 167–169.

BERGER, H. 1929. Über das Elektrenkephalogramm des Menschen. I. *Arch. Psychiat. Nervenkr., 87,* 527–570.

—— 1930. Über das Elektrenkephalogramm des Menschen. II. *J. Psychol. Neurol., Lpz., 40,* 160–179.

—— 1931. Über das Elektrenkephalogramm des Menschen. III. *Arch. Psychiat. Nervenkr., 94,* 16–60.

—— 1932a. Das Elektrenkephalogramm des Menschen und seine Bedeutung für die Psychophysiologie. *Z. Psychol., 126,* 1–13.

—— 1932b. Über das Elektrenkephalogramm des Menschen. IV. *Arch. Psychiat. Nervenkr., 97,* 6–26.

—— 1932c. Über das Elektrenkephalogramm des Menschen. V. *Arch. Psychiat. Nervenkr., 98,* 231–257.

—— 1933a. Über das Elektrenkephalogramm des Menschen. VI. *Arch. Psychiat. Nervenkr., 99,* 555–574.

—— 1933b. Über das Elektrenkephalogramm des Menschen. VII. *Arch. Psychiat. Nervenkr., 100,* 301–320.

—— 1933c. Über das Elektrenkephalogramm des Menschen. VIII. *Arch. Psychiat. Nervenkr., 101,* 452–469.

—— 1933d. Über die Tätigheit des menschlichen Grosshirns. *Münch. med. Wschr., 80,* 844–864.

—— 1934a. Die physiologischen Bedingungen der Bewusstseinserscheinungen. *Z. Psychol., 132,* 360–370.

—— 1934b. Über das Elektrenkephalogramm des Menschen. IX. *Arch Psychiat Nervenkr., 102,* 538–557.

—— 1934c. Über das Elektrenkephalogramm des Menschen. *Dtsch. med. Wschr., 51,* 1947–1954.

—— 1935a. Über das Elektrenkephalogramm des Menschen. X. *Arch. Psychiat. Nervenkr., 103,* 444–454.

—— 1935b. Über die Entstehung der Erscheinungen des grossen epileptischen Anfalls. *Klin. Wschr., 14,* 217–219.

—— 1936. Über das Elektrenkephalogramm des Menschen. XI. *Arch. Psychiat. Nervenkr., 104,* 678–689.

—— 1937a. Das Elektrenkephalogramm des Menschen und seine psycho-physiologische Deutung. *XI Congr. int. Psychol., 1,* 220–226.

—— 1937b. Das Elektrenkephalogramm des Menschen und seine psycho-physiologische Deutung. *Industr. Psychotech., 7–8,* 222–227.

—— 1937c. Über das Elektrenkephalogramm des Menschen. XII. *Arch. Psychiat. Nervenkr., 106,* 165–187.

—— 1937d. Über das Elektrenkephalogramm des Menschen. XIII. *Arch. Psychiat. Nervenkr., 106,* 577–584.

—— 1938a. Das Elektrenkephalogramm des Menschen. *Nova Acta Leopoldina, 6,* 173–309.

—— 1938b. Über das Elektrenkephalogramm des Menschen. *Allg. Z. Psychiat., 108,* 254–273.

—— 1938c. Über das Elektrenkephalogramm des Menschen. XIV. *Arch. Psychiat. Nervenkr., 108,* 407–431.

BERNHARD, C. G., & SKOGLUND, C. R. 1939a. (Alpha frequency of human brain potentials as functions of age.) *Skand. Arch. Physiol., 82,* 178–184.

—— 1939b. Recherches sur la fréquence alpha de l'électro-encéphalogramme chez l'enfant. *Acta psychiat., Kbh., 14,* 223–231.

BERTRAND, I., DELAY, J., & GUILLAIN, J. 1938. L'électro-encéphalogramme dans le myxoedème. *C. R. Soc. Biol., Paris, 129,* 395–398.

—— 1939. L'électro-encéphalogramme normal et pathologique. Paris: Masson.

BISHOP, G. H. 1935. Electrical responses accompanying activity of the optic pathway. *Arch. Ophthal., Chicago, 14,* 992–1019.

—— 1936. The interpretation of cortical potentials. *Cold Spr. Harb. Symp. quant. Biol., 4,* 305–319.

BISHOP, G. H., & O'LEARY, J. 1936. Components of the electrical response of the optic cortex of the rabbit. *Amer. J. Physiol., 117, 292–308.*

BLAKE, H., & GERARD, R. W. 1937. Brain potentials during sleep. *Amer. J. Physiol., 119, 692–703.*

BLAKE, H., GERARD, R. W., & KLEITMAN, N. 1939. Factors influencing brain potentials during sleep. *J. Neurophysiol., 2, 48–60.*

BREMER, F. 1938a. L'activité électrique de l'écorce cérébral. Paris: Hermann & Cie.

—— 1938b. Parente des diverses ondes électrique de l'écorce cérébrale. *C. R. Soc. Biol., Paris, 128, 544–550.*

—— 1938c. Ondes électriques de l'écorce cérébrale et influx nerveux corticifuges. *C. R. Soc. Biol., Paris, 128, 550–555.*

BRILL, N. Q. 1942. Electroencephalography. In *Advances in Pediatrics.* New York: Interscience Publisher. Pp. 127–149.

BRILL, N. Q., & SEIDEMANN, H. 1941. The electroencephalogram of normal children. *Amer. J. Psychiat., 98, 250–256.*

—— 1942. Electroencephalographic changes during hyperventilation in epileptic and non-epileptic disorders. *Ann. intern. Med., 16, 451–461.*

BRILL, N. Q., SEIDEMANN, H., MONTAGUE, H., & BALSER, B. H. 1942. Electroencephalographic studies in delinquent behavior problem children. *Amer. J. Psychiat., 98, 494–498.*

BROWN, W. T., & SOLOMON, C. I. 1942. Delinquency and the electroencephalograph. *Amer. J. Psychiat., 98, 499–503.*

BUCY, P. C., & CASE, T. J. 1940. An association between homonymous hemianopsia and unilateral absence of alpha waves. *Trans. Amer. neurol. Assn., 66, 17–20.*

BYERS, R. K. 1941. Electroencephalography. *J. Pediat., 18, 811–833.*

CAPRILE, A. M. A., & GASCÓN, A. 1940. (Human electroencephalogram.) *Prensa méd. argent., 27, 2249–2260.*

CARRILLO, R. 1941. Introducción al estudio del electroencefalograma. *Index Neurol. Psiquiat., B. Aires, 2, 179–191.*

CASAMAJOR, L., SMITH, J. R., CONSTABLE, K., & WALTER, C. W. P. 1941. The electroencephalogram of children with focal convulsive seizures. *Arch. Neurol. Psychiat., 45, 834–847.*

CASE, T. J. 1938. Electroencephalograpy in the diagnosis and localization of intracranial conditions. *J. nerv. ment. Dis., 87, 598–602.*

—— 1940. Association of homonymous hemianopsia and unilateral absence of alpha waves. *Arch. Neurol. Psychiat., Chicago, 43, 1273–1274.*

CASE, T. J., & BUCY, P. C. 1938. Localization of cerebral lesions by electroencephalography. *J. Neurophysiol., 1, 245–261.*

CHWEITZER, A., GEBLEWICZ, E., & LIBERSON, W. 1937a. Action de la mescaline sur les ondes alpha (rythme de Berger) chez l'homme. *C. R. Soc. Biol., Paris, 124, 1296–1299.*

—— 1937b. Étude de l'électrencéphalogramme humain dans un cas d'intoxication mescalinique. *Année psychol., 37, 94–119.*

CLARDY, E. R., GOLDENSOHN, L. N., & LEVINE, K. 1941. Schizophrenic-like reactions in children; preliminary report; studies by electroencephalography. *Psychiat. Quart., 15, 100–116.*

COBB, S., SARGANT, W. W., & SCHWAB, R. S. 1939. Simultaneous respiratory and electro-encephalographic recording in cases of petit mal. *Arch. Neurol. Psychiat., Chicago, 42, 1189–1191.*

COHN, R., & KATZENELBOGEN, S. 1939. Electroencephalographic studies, after inhalation of helium-oxygen mixtures. *U. S. Nav. med. Bull., 37, 596–599.*

—— 1942. Electroencephalographic changes induced by intravenous sodium amytal. *Proc. Soc. exp. Biol., N. Y., 40, 560–563.*

COOK, L. C., & WALTER, W. G. 1938. The electro-encephalogram in convulsions induced by cardiazol. *J. Neurol. Psychiat., 1, 180–186.*

COTTENOT, P., & LIQUIER, A. 1939. L'électroencéphalogramme humain. *Médecine, Paris, 20, 707–709.*

CRUICKSHANK, R. M. 1937. Human occipital brain potentials as affected by intensity-duration variables of visual stimulation. *J. exp. Psychol., 21, 625–641.*

CUCCHI, A. 1938. (The bio-electrical phenomena in the cerebral cortex.) *Riv. sper. Freniat., 62, 233–240.*

CUTTS, K. K., & JASPER, H. H. 1939. Effect of benzedrine sulfate and phenobarbital on behavior problem children with abnormal electroencephalograms. *Arch. Neurol. Psychiat., Chicago, 41,* 1138–1145.

DALSGAARD-NIELSEN, T. 1939. Om electroencephalografien og dens anvendelse i neurologien. *Ugeskr. Laeg., 101,* 947–960.

DARROW, C. W., JOST, H., SOLOMON, A. P., & MERGENER, J. C. 1942. Autonomic indications of excitatory and homeostatic effects on the electroencephalogram. *J. Psychol., 14,* 115–130.

DAVIS, H. 1936. Some aspects of the electrical activity of the cerebral cortex. *Cold Spr. Harb. Symp. quant. Biol., 4,* 285–291.

—— 1938a. Interpretations of the electrical activity of the brain. *Amer. J. Psychiat., 94,* 825–834.

—— 1938b. The electroencephalogram. *Tabul. biol., Berl., 16,* 116–131.

—— 1941. Electroencephalography. *J. Amer. med. Assn., 117,* 983–987.

DAVIS, H., & DAVIS, P. A. 1936. Action potentials of the brain in normal states of cerebral activity. *Arch. Neurol. Psychiat., Chicago, 36,* 1214–1224.

—— 1939. The electrical activity of the brain: Its relation to physiological states of impaired consciousness. *Res. Publ. Assn. Res. nerv. ment. Dis., 19,* 50–80.

DAVIS, H., DAVIS, P. A., LOOMIS, A. L., HARVEY, E. N., & HOBERT, G. 1937. Changes in human brain potentials during the onset of sleep. *Science, 86,* 448–450.

—— 1938. Human brain potentials during the onset of sleep. *J. Neurophysiol., 1,* 24–38.

—— 1939a. Electrical reactions of the human brain to auditory stimulation during sleep. *J. Neurophysiol., 2,* 500–514.

—— 1939b. A search for changes in direct-current potentials of the head during sleep. *J. Neurophysiol., 2,* 129–135.

DAVIS, H., & WALLACE, W. M. 1942. Factors affecting changes produced in electroencephalogram by standardized hyperventilation. *Arch. Neurol. Psychiat., Chicago, 47,* 971–1008.

DAVIS, P. A. 1939. The electrical response of the human brain to auditory stimuli. *Amer. J. Physiol., 126,* 455–476.

—— 1940. Evaluation of the electroencephalogram of schizophrenic patients. *Amer. J. Psychiat., 96,* 851–860.

—— 1941a. Electroencephalographic studies on three cases of frontal lobotomy. *Psychosom. Med., 3,* 38–50.

—— 1941b. Effect on electroencephalogram of alterations of blood sugar levels. *Amer. J. Physiol., 133,* 259–260.

—— 1941c. Electroencephalograms of manic-depressive patients. *Amer. J. Psychiat., 98,* 430–433.

—— 1941d. Technique and evaluation of the electroencephalogram. *J. Neurophysiol., 4,* 92–114.

—— 1942. A comparative study of the EEGs of schizophrenic and manic-depressive patients. *Amer. J. Psychiat., 99,* 210–217.

DAVIS, P. A., & DAVIS, H. 1939. The electroencephalograms of psychotic patients. *Amer. J. Psychiat., 95,* 1007–1025.

DAVIS, J. A., DAVIS, H., & THOMPSON, J. W. 1938. Progressive changes in the human electroencephalogram under low oxygen tension. *Amer. J. Physiol., 123,* 51–52.

DAVIS, P. A., GIBBS, F. A., DAVIS, H., JETTER, W. W., & TROWBRIDGE. 1941. The effects of alcohol upon the electroencephalogram. *Quart. J. Stud. Alcohol, 1,* 626–637.

DAVIS, P. A., & SULZBACH, W. 1940. Changes in the electroencephalogram during metrazol therapy. *Arch. Neurol. Psychiat., Chicago, 43,* 341–353.

DEMPSEY, E. W., & MORISON, R. S. 1942. The interaction of certain spontaneous and induced cortical potentials. *Amer. J. Physiol., 135,* 301–308.

DURUP, G., & FESSARD, A. 1936a. L'électrencéphalogramme de l'homme. Observations psychophysiologiques relatives à l'action des stimuli visuels et auditifs. *Année psychol., 36,* 1–32.

—— 1936b. L'électrencéphalogramme de l'homme. Données quantitatives sur l'arrêt provoqué par des stimuli visuels ou auditifs. *C. R. Soc. Biol., Paris, 122,* 756–758.

DUSSER DE BARENNE, J. G., & McCULLOCH, W. S. 1936. Some effects of laminar thermocoagulation upon the local action potentials of the cerebral cortex of the monkey. *Amer. J. Physiol., 114,* 692–694.

DUSSER DE BARENNE, J. G., & McCULLOCH, W. S. 1938. Sensorimotor cortex, nucleus caudatus and thalamus opticus. *J. Neurophysiol., 1,* 364–377.

DYNES, J. B. 1941. Narcolepsy and cataplexy (with electroencephalographic studies). *Lahey Clin. Bull., 2,* 83–90.

DYNES, J. B., & FINLEY, K. H. 1941. The electroencephalograph as an aid in the study of narcolepsy. *Arch. Neurol. Psychiat., Chicago, 46,* 598–612.

ECHLIN, F. A. 1942. The electroencephalogram in epilepsy. *J. nerv. ment. Dis., 96,* 565–567.

ENGEL, G. L., & MARGOLIN, S. G. 1941a. Neuropsychiatric disturbances in Addison's disease and role of impaired carbohydrate metabolism in production of abnormal cerebral function. *Arch. Neurol. Psychiat., Chicago, 45,* 881–883.

—— 1941b. Clinical correlation of the electroencephalogram with carbohydrate metabolism. *Arch. Neurol. Psychiat., Chicago, 45,* 890–892.

FESSARD, A. 1938. Signes électriques de l'activité cérébrale chez l'homme. *Paris méd., 1,* 301–312.

FINLEY, K. H., & CAMPBELL, M. C. 1941. Electroencephalography in schizophrenia. *Amer. J. Psychiat., 98,* 374–381.

FINLEY, K. H., & LESKO, J. M. 1941. EEG studies of nine cases with major psychoses receiving metrazol. *Amer. J. Psychiat., 98,* 185–191.

FINLEY, K. H., ROSE, A., & SOLOMON, H. C. 1942. The electroencephalogram in neurosyphilis. *Dis. nerv. Syst., 3.*

FISCHER, M. H. 1932. Elektrobiologische Erscheinungen an der Hirnrinde. *Pflüg. Arch. ges. Physiol., 230,* 161–178.

FLEMING, G. W. T. H., GOLLA, F. L., & WALTER, W. G. 1939. Electro-convulsion therapy in schizophrenia. *Lancet,* Part 2, 1353.

FOERSTER, O., & ALTENBURGER, H. 1935. Elektrobiologische Vorgänge an der menschlichen Hirnrinde. *Dtsch. Z. Nervenheilk., 135,* 277–288.

FORBES, T. W., & ANDREWS, H. L. 1937. Independent control of alpha rhythm and "psychogalvanic" response. *Science, 86,* 474–476.

FOWLER, O. D. 1941. Neurophysiological and psychological changes induced by certain drugs: II. Electrocortical changes. *J. exp. Psychol., 28,* 37–52.

FRANKE, L. J. 1938. (Anatomicophysiologic basis of hysteria in connection with electro-encephalographic examination during auto-hypnosis.) *Ned. Tijdschr. Geneesk., 82,* 1428–1431.

FRANKE, L. J., & KOOPMAN, L. J. 1938. (The parallelism of electro-biological processes in the cortex with pathopsychological and parapsychological phenomena.) *Z. ges. Neurol. Psychiat., 162,* 259–288.

FREEMAN, G. L. 1940. Cortical autonomous rhythms and excitation levels of other bodily tissues. *J. exp. Psychol., 27,* 160–171.

FREEMAN, W., & WATTS, J. W. 1942. Psychosurgery. Springfield, Ill.: Thomas. Ch. 16.

FREY, T. 1938. The electro-encephalogram in epilepsy. *Acta psychiat., Kbh., 13,* 433–446.

GARCEAU, E. L., & DAVIS, H. 1934. An amplifier, recording system, and stimulating devices for the study of cerebral action currents. *Amer. J. Physiol., 107,* 305–310.

—— 1935. An ink-writing electro-encephalograph. *Arch. Neurol. Psychiat., Chicago, 34,* 1292–1294.

GEMELLI, A. 1937. Nuove ricerche sui processi elettrici del cervello umano. *Boll. Soc. ital. Biol. sper., 12,* 204–205.

GERARD, R. W. 1936. Factors controlling brain potentials. *Cold Spr. Harb. Sympos. quant. Biol., 4,* 292–298.

—— 1941. The interaction of neurones. *Ohio J. Sci., 41,* 160–172.

GERARD, R. W., & LIBET, B. 1939. On the unison of neurone beats. In *Livro de Homenagem aos Professores Alvaro e Miguel Ozorio de Almeida.* Rio de Janeiro: Instituto Oswaldo Cruz. Pp. 288–294.

—— 1940. The control of normal and "convulsive" brain potentials. *Amer. J. Psychiat., 1940, 96,* 1125–1151.

GIBBS, E. L., GIBBS, F. A., LENNOX, W. G., & NIMS, L. G. 1942. Regulation of cerebral carbon dioxide. *Arch. Neurol. Psychiat., Chicago, 47,* 879–889.

GIBBS, E. L., LENNOX, W. G., & GIBBS, F. A. 1940. Variations in the carbon dioxide content of the blood in epilepsy. *Arch. Neurol. Psychiat., Chicago, 43,* 223–239.

GIBBS, F. A. 1937. Interpretation of the electro-encephalogram. *J. Psychol., 4,* 365–382.

—— 1939a. Cortical frequency of schizophrenic, epileptic and normal individuals. *Trans. Amer. neurol. Assn., 65,* 141–144.

—— 1939b. Electroencephalography in epilepsy. *J. Pediat., 15,* 749–762.

—— 1940. Spectra from eight cortical areas of normal adults, epileptic, parents of epileptic and schizophrenic patients. *Trans. Amer. neurol. Assn., 66,* 211–212.

—— 1942a. Cortical frequency spectra of healthy adults. *J. nerv. ment. Dis., 95,* 417–426.

—— 1942b. Diagnostic and prognostic value of the electroencephalogram. *J. Amer. med. Assn., 118,* 216–218.

GIBBS, F. A., & DAVIS, H. 1935. Changes in the human electroencephalogram associated with loss of consciousness. *Amer. J. Physiol., 113,* 49–50.

GIBBS, F. A., DAVIS, H., & LENNOX, W. G. 1935. The electro-encephalogram in epilepsy and in conditions of impaired consciousness. *Arch. Neurol. Psychiat., Chicago, 34,* 1133–1148.

GIBBS, F. A., & GIBBS, E. L. 1941. Atlas of electroencephalography. Boston: F. A. Gibbs, Boston City Hospital.

GIBBS, F. A., GIBBS, E. L., & LENNOX, W. G. 1937a. Effect on the electro-encephalogram of certain drugs which influence nervous activity. *Arch. intern. Med., 60,* 154–166.

—— 1937b. Epilepsy: a paroxysmal cerebral dysrhythmia. *Brain, 60,* 377–388.

—— 1938a. Cerebral dysrhythmias of epilepsy: measures for their control. *Arch. Neurol. Psychiat., Chicago, 39,* 298–314.

—— 1938b. The likeness of the cortical dysrhythmias of schizophrenic and psychomotor epilepsy. *Amer. J. Psychiat., 95,* 255–269.

—— 1939. The influence of the blood sugar level on the wave and spike formation in petit mal epilepsy. *Arch. Neurol. Psychiat., Chicago, 41,* 1111–1116.

GIBBS, F. A., & LENNOX, W. G. 1937. The electrical activity of the brain in epilepsy. *New Engl. J. Med., 216,* 98–99.

GIBBS, F. A., LENNOX, W. G., & GIBBS, E. L. 1936. The electro-encephalogram in diagnosis and in localization of epileptic seizures. *Arch. Neurol. Psychiat., Chicago, 36,* 1225–1235.

—— 1941. The cortical frequency spectrum in epilepsy. *Arch. Neurol. Psychiat., Chicago, 46,* 613–620.

GIBBS, F. A., LENNOX, W. G., NIMS, L. F., & GIBBS, E. L. 1942. Differentiation of the effects of low oxygen and low carbon dioxide on the electrical activity of the cortex. *Fed. Proc. Amer. Soc. exp. Biol., 1,* No. 1, Part II, 29.

GIBBS, F. A., MUNRO, D., & WEGNER, W. R. 1941. A standard electroencephalographic technic for the localization of gross intra-cranial lesions. *New Engl. J. Med., 225,* 279–282.

GIBBS, F. A., WILLIAMS, D., & GIBBS, E. L. 1940. Modification of the cortical frequency spectrum by changes in carbon dioxide, blood sugar and oxygen. *J. Neurophysiol., 3,* 49–58.

GLASER, M. A., & SJAARDEMA, H. 1940. The value of the electroencephalogram in craniocerebral injuries. *West. J. Surg. Obstet. Gynec., 48,* 689–696.

—— 1941. Electro-encephalographic diagnosis of extradural and subdural hemorrhage. *Proc. Soc. exp. Biol., N. Y., 47,* 138–140.

GODLOWSKI, W. 1938. (Bioelectric phenomena in cortex of man.) *Nowiny lek., 50,* 73–83.

GOLDENSOHN, L. N., MARMOR, J., & MEYER, B. C. 1940. Pneumo-encephalographic and electro-encephalographic localization of an epileptogenic focus. *J. Amer. Med. Assn., 20,* 429–431.

GOLDMAN, G., & SEGAL, J. 1938. Les interférences induites par des stimuli intermittents dans l'électrencéphalogramme de l'homme. *Année psychol., 38,* 178–185.

GOLDMAN, G., SEGAL, J., & SEGALIS, M. 1938. L'action d'une excitation intermittente sur le rhythme de Berger. *C. R. Soc. Biol., Paris, 127,* 1217–1220.

GOLLA, F., GRAHAM, S., & WALTER, W. G. 1937. The electro-encephalogram in epilepsy. *J. ment. Sci., 83,* 137–155.

GOLSE, J. 1938. L'électro-encéphalographie clinique; technique et résultats du Central Pathological Laboratory du Maudsley Hospital de Londres. *Encéphale, 33,* 244–253.

GOODWIN, C. W. 1941. A differential amplifier for resting and action potentials of biological systems. *Yale J. Biol. Med., 14,* 101–106.

GOODWIN, J. E., & HALL, G. E. 1939. The human electroencephalogram and its clinical significance. *Canad. med. Assn. J., 41,* 146–151.

GOODWIN, J. E., KERR, W. K., & LAWSON, F. L. 1940. Bioelectric responses in metrazol and insulin shock. *Amer. J. Psychiat., 96,* 1390–1405.

GOTTLOBER, A. B. 1938a. The relationship between brain potentials and personality. *J. exp. Psychol., 22,* 67–74.

—— 1938b. Inheritance of brain potential patterns. *J. exp. Psychol., 22,* 193–200.

GOZZANO, M. 1935. Ricerche sui fenomeni elettrici della corteccis cerebrale. *Riv. neurol., 3,* 212–261.

—— 1936. Bioelektrische Erscheinungen bei der Reflexepilepsie. *J. Psychol. Neurol., Lpz., 47,* 24–39.

GRASS, A. M., & GIBBS, F. A. 1938. A Fourier transform of the electroencephalogram. *J. Neurophysiol., 1,* 521–526.

GRINKER, R. R. 1938. Method for studying and influencing cortico-hypothalamic relations. *Science, 87,* 73–74.

—— 1939. Hypothalamic functions in psychosomatic interrelations. *Psychosom. Med., 1,* 19–47.

GRINKER, R. R., & SEROTA, H. M. 1938. Studies on corticohypothalamic relations in cat and man. *J. Neurophysiol., 1,* 573–589.

—— 1941. Electroencephalographic studies of cortico-hypothalamic relations in schizophrenia. *Amer. J. Psychiat., 98,* 385–392.

GRINKER, R. R., SEROTA, H., & STEIN, S. I. 1938. Myoclonic epilepsy. *Arch. Neurol. Psychiat., Chicago, 40,* 968–980.

GRÜTTNER, R., & BONKÁLÓ, A. 1940a. Über Ermüdung und Schlaf auf Grund hirnbioelektrischer Untersuchungen. *Arch. Psychiat. Nervenkr., 111,* 652–665.

—— 1940b. Hirnbioelektrische Untersuchungen über die Wirkung des Pervitin und des Coffein bei Ermüdungszuständen. *Psychiat. neurol. Wschr., 42,* 1–6.

GUILLAIN, G., BERTRAND, I., DELAY, J., & GUILLAIN, J. 1938. Les anomalies de l'électroencéphalogramme dans le myxodème. *Bull. Soc. méd. Hôp. Paris, 54,* 1610–1617.

HADLEY, J. M. 1940. Some relationships between electrical signs of central and peripheral activity: I. During rest. *J. exp. Psychol., 27,* 640–656.

—— 1941. Some relationships between electrical signs of central and peripheral activity: II. During "mental work." *J. exp. Psychol., 28,* 53–62.

HALL, G. E., *et al.* 1938. Physiological studies in experimental insulin and metrazol shock. *Amer. J. Psychiat., 95,* 553–556.

HARVEY, E. N., LOOMIS, A. L., & HOBART, G. A. 1937. Cerebral processes during sleep as studied by human brain potentials. *Science, 85,* 443–444.

HENRY, C. E. 1941a. Electroencephalographic individual differences and their constancy. I. During sleep. *J. exp. Psychol., 29,* 117–132.

—— 1941b. Electroencephalographic individual differences and their constancy. II. During waking. *J. exp. Psychol., 29,* 236–247.

HENRY, C. E., & KNOTT, J. R. 1941. A note on the relationship between "personality" and the alpha rhythm of the electroencephalogram. *J. exp. Psychol., 28,* 362–366.

HERRNFELD, F. P., & SJAARDEMA, H. 1940. An improved amplifier for electroencephalography. *J. exp. Psychol., 27,* 208–215.

HIMWICH, H. E., FROSTIG, J. P., FAZEKAS, J. F., HOAGLAND, H., & HADIDIAN, Z. 1939. Clinical electro-encephalographic and biochemical changes during insulin hypoglycemia. *Proc. Soc. exp. Biol., N. Y., 40,* 401–402.

HIMWICH, H. E., HADIDIAN, Z., FAZEKAS, J. F., & HOAGLAND, H. 1939. Cerebral metabolism and electrical activity during hypoglycemia. *Amer. J. Physiol., 125,* 578–585.

HOAGLAND, H. 1936a. Pacemakers of human brain waves in normals and general paretics. *Amer. J. Physiol., 116,* 604–615.

—— 1936b. Some pacemaker aspects of rhythmic activity in the nervous system. *Cold Spr. Harb. Symp. quant. Biol., 4,* 267–284.

—— 1936c. Electrical brain waves and temperature. *Science, 84,* 139–140.

—— 1936d. Temperature characteristics of the "Berger rhythm" in man. *Science, 83,* 84–85.

HOAGLAND, H., CAMERON, D. E., & RUBIN, M. A. 1937a. The electroencephalograms of schizophrenics during insulin treatments. *Amer. J. Psychiat., 94,* 183–208.

—— 1937b. The "delta index" of the electroencephalogram in relation to insulin treatments of schizophrenia. *Psychol. Rec., 1,* 196–202.

—— 1938. Emotion in man as tested by the delta index of the electroencephalogram. I. *J. gen. Psychol., 19,* 227–245.

HOAGLAND, H., CAMERON, D. E., RUBIN, M. A., & TEGELBERG, J. J. 1938. Emotion in man as tested by the delta index of the electroencephalogram: II. Simultaneous records from cortex and from a region near the hypothalamus. *J. gen. Psychol., 19,* 247–261.

HOAGLAND, H., RUBIN, M. A., & CAMERON, D. E. 1936. Electrical brain waves in schizophrenia during insulin treatment. *J. Psychol., 3,* 513–519.

—— 1937. The electroencephalogram of schizophrenics during insulin hypoglycemia and recovery. *Amer. J. Physiol., 120,* 559–570.

—— 1939. Brain wave frequencies and cellular metabolism. Effects of dinitrophenol. *J. Neurophysiol., 2,* 170–172.

HOCH, P., & KUBIS, J. 1941. Electroencephalographic studies in organic psychoses. *Amer. J. Psychiat., 98,* 404–408.

HOFFMAN, W. C., LEWIS, R. A., & THORN, G. W. 1942. The electroencephalogram in Addison's disease. *Johns Hopk. Hosp. Bull., 70,* 335–361.

HUGHES, J., STRECKER, E. A., & APPEL, K. E. 1938. Some clinical and physiological aspects of the brain potentials. *Amer. J. Psychiat., 94,* 1179–1186.

HUGHES, J., & WIGTON, R. 1941. EEG studies on patients receiving electric shock treatment. *Arch. Neurol. Psychiat., Chicago, 46,* 747.

HYLAND, H. H., GOODWIN, J. E., & HALL, G. E. 1939. Clinical applications of electroencephalography. *Canad. med. Assn. J., 41,* 239–246.

ITO, G., & KASAHARA, Y. 1939. Über das Grundproblem der spontanen Schwankungen des Grosshirnstromes. *Tohoku psychol. Fol., 7,* 13–32.

JANZEN, R. 1939. Hirnbioelektrische Untersuchungen über den physiologischen Schlaf und den Schlafanfall bei Kranken mit genuiner Narkolepsie. *Dtsch. Z. Nervenheilk., 149,* 93–106.

JANZEN, R., & BEHNSEN, G. 1940. Beitrag zur Pathophysiologie des Anfallsgeschehens insbesondere des kataplektischen Anfalls beim Narkolepsiesyndrom. Klinische und hirnbioelektrische Untersuchung. *Arch. Psychiat. Nervenkr., 111,* 178–189.

JANZEN, R., & KORNMÜLLER, A. E. 1939a. Örtliche Unterschiede hirnbioelektrischer Erscheinungen von kranken Menschen bei Ableitung durch die Kopfschwarte. *Arch. Psychiat. Nervenkr., 109,* 247–263.

—— 1939b. Hirnbioelektrische Erscheinungen bei Änderungen der Bewusstseinslage. *Dtsch. Z. Nervenheilk., 149,* 74–92.

—— 1939c. Einige Erfahrungen über die Anwendung der hirnbioelektrischen Lokaldiagnose kortikaler Prozesse bei Ableitung durch die Kopfschwarte des Menschen. *Psychiat.-neurol. Wschr., 41,* 5–7.

—— 1940. Hirnbioelektrische Untersuchungen an Kranken mit symptomatischer Epilepsie. *Dtsch. Z. Nervenheilk., 150,* 283–295.

JASPER, H. H. 1936a. Cortical excitatory state and variability of human brain rhythms. *Science, 83,* 259–260.

—— 1936b. Cortical excitatory state and synchronism in the control of bioelectric autonomous rhythms. *Cold Spr. Harb. Symp. quant. Biol., 4,* 320–338.

—— 1937. Electrical signs of cortical activity. *Psychol. Bull., 34,* 411–481.

—— 1941. Electroencephalography. In Penfield, W., & Erickson, T. C., *Epilepsy and cerebral localization.* Springfield, Ill.: Thomas. Pp. 380–454.

JASPER, H. H., & ANDREWS, H. L. 1936. Human brain rhythms: I. Recording techniques and preliminary results. *J. gen. Psychol., 14,* 98–126.

—— 1938a. Electro-encephalography: III. Normal differentiation of occipital and precentral regions in man. *Arch. Neurol. Psychiat., Chicago, 39,* 96–115.

—— 1938b. Brain potentials and voluntary muscle activity in man. *J. Neurophysiol., 1,* 87–100.

JASPER, H. H., & CARMICHAEL, L. 1935. Electrical potentials from the intact human brain. *Science, 81,* 51–53.

JASPER, H. H., & CRUICKSHANK, R. M. 1937. Electro-encephalography: II. Visual stimulation and the after-image as affecting the occipital alpha rhythm. *J. gen. Psychol., 17,* 29–48.

JASPER, H. H., FITZPATRICK, C. P., & SOLOMON, P. 1939. Analogies and opposites in schizophrenia and epilepsy. *Amer. J. Psychiat., 95,* 835–851.
JASPER, H. H., & HAWKE, W. A. 1938. Electro-encephalography. IV. Localization of seizure waves in epilepsy. *Arch. Neurol. Psychiat., Chicago, 39,* 885–901.
JASPER, H. H., & KERSCHMAN, J. 1941. Electroencephalographic classification of the epilepsies. *Arch. Neurol. Psychiat., Chicago, 45,* 903–943.
JASPER, H. H., KERSCHMAN, J., & ELVIDGE, A. 1940. Electroencephalographic studies of injury to the head. *Arch. Neurol. Psychiat., Chicago, 44,* 328–348.
JASPER, H. H., & NICHOLS, I. C. 1938. Electrical signs of cortical function in epilepsy and allied disorders. *Amer. J. Psychiat., 94,* 835–850.
JASPER, H. H., & SHAGASS, C. 1941a. Conditioning the occipital alpha rhythm in man. *J. exp. Psychol., 28,* 373–388.
—— 1941b. Conscious time judgments related to conditioned time intervals and voluntary control of the alpha rhythm. *J. exp. Psychol., 28,* 503–508.
JASPER, H. H., SOLOMON, P., & BRADLEY, C. 1938. Electroencephalographic analyses of behavior problem children. *Amer. J. Psychiat., 95,* 641–658.
JONESCO-SISESTI, N., SAGER, O., & KREINDLER, A. 1940. L'électroencéphalogramme pendant le coma et après la mort. *Acad. Roum. Bull., Sect. Sci., 22,* 391–395.
JOST, H. 1941. Some physiological changes during frustration. *Child Develpm., 12,* 9–15.
JUNG, R. 1939a. Das Elektrencephalogramm und seine klinische Anwendung: Methodik der Ableitung, Registrierung und Deutung des EEG. *Nervenarzt, 12,* 569–591.
—— 1939b. Ein Apparat zur mehrfachen Registrierung von Tätigkeit und Funktionen des animalen und vegetativen Nervensystems. (Elektrenkephalogramm, EKG, Muskulationsströme, Augenbewegungen, Galvanischer Hautreflex, Plethysmogramm, Liquordruck und Atmung.) *Z. ges. Neurol. Psychiat., 165,* 374–397.
—— 1939c. Elektrencephalographische Befunde bei der Epilepsie und ihren Grenzgebieten. *Arch. Psychiat. Nervenkr., 109,* 335–338.
—— 1939d. Über vegetative Reaktionen und Hemmungswirkung von Sinnesreizen im kleinen epileptischen Anfall. *Nervenarzt, 12,* 169–185.
—— 1939e. Epilepsie und vasomatorische Reaktionen: Elektrencephalogramm, vegetative Vorgänge und Liquordruck beim kleinen epileptischen Anfall. *Z. ges. Neurol. Psychiat., 167,* 601–605.
—— 1939f. Physiologische Untersuchungen bei der familiären paroxysmalen Lähmung. *III Congr. Neurol. int., Copenhagen.* Pp. 291–294.
—— 1941. Das Elektrencephalogramm und seine klinische Anwendung. *Nervenarzt, 14,* 57–70.
JURGENS, B. 1940. Über vegetative Reaktionen beim Menschen in ihrer Abhängigkeit von verschiedenen Reizen. *Arch. Psychiat. Nervenkr., 111,* 88–114.
KITAMURA, K. 1939. Die elektrencephalographische Untersuchung der Geschmacksempfindlichkeit. *Tohoku psychol. Fol., 7,* 13–32.
KLAUE, R. 1937. Die bioelektrische Tätigkeit der Grosshirnrinde im normalen Schlaf und in der Narkose durch Schlafmittel. *J. Psychol. Neurol., Lpz., 47,* 510–531.
KNOTT, J. R. 1938a. Brain potentials during silent and oral reading. *J. gen. Psychol., 18,* 57–62.
—— 1938b. Reduced latent time of blocking of the Berger rhythm to light stimuli. *Proc. Soc. exp. Biol., N. Y., 38,* 216–217.
—— 1939. Some effects of "mental set" upon the electrophysiological processes of the human cerebral cortex. *J. exp. Psychol., 24,* 384–405.
—— 1941. Electroencephalography and physiological psychology: evaluation and statement of problem. *Psychol. Bull., 38,* 944–975.
KNOTT, J. R., FRIEDMAN, H., & BARDSLEY, R. 1942. Some electroencephalographic correlates of intelligence in eight-year- and twelve-year-old children. *J. exp. Psychol., 30,* 380–391.
KNOTT, J. R., & HENRY, C. E. 1941. The conditioning of the blocking of the alpha rhythm of the human electroencephalogram. *J. exp. Psychol., 28,* 134–144.
KNOTT, J. R., HENRY, C. E., & HADLEY, J. M. 1939. Brain potentials during sleep: a comparative study of the dominant and non-dominant alpha groups. *J. exp. Psychol., 24,* 157–168.
KNOTT, J. R., & TRAVIS, L. E. 1937. A note on the relationship between duration and amplitude of cortical potentials. *J. Psychol., 3,* 169–172.

KORNMÜLLER, A. E. 1935a. Der Mechanismus des epileptischen Anfalles auf Grund bioelektrischer Untersuchungen am Zentralnervensystem. *Fortschr. Neurol. Psychiat., 7, 2–30.*

—— 1935b. Der Mechanismus des epileptischen Anfalls auf Grund biolektrischer Untersuchungen am Zentralnervensystem. *Fortschr. Neurol. Psychiat., 7, 391–400.*

—— 1935c. Die bioelektrischen Erscheinungen architektonischer Felder der Grosshirnrinde. *Biol. Rev., 10, 383–426.*

—— 1936. Bioelektrische Untersuchungen über den Pathomechanismus des Zentralnervensystems. *Dtsch. Z. Nervenheilk., 139, 81–89.*

—— 1937a. Die bioelektrischen Erscheinungen der Hirnrindenfelder mit allgemeinen Ergebnissen zur Physiologie und Pathophysiologie des zentralnervösen Griseum. Leipzig: Thieme.

—— 1937b. Über feinere bioelektrische Reaktionen der "optischen" Hirnrinde und zur Frage ihrer Zuordnung zu Wahrnehmungen. *Arch. Pyschiat. Nervenkr., 107, 93–105.*

—— 1938. Die Untersuchungen über die bioelektrischen Potentialschwankungen der Hirnrindenfelder im Dienste der Klinik. *Münch. med. Wschr., 85, 1956–1960.*

—— 1939. Einige Voraussetzungen der hirnbioelektrischen Untersuchung des Menschen. *Dtsch. med. Wschr., 65, 1601–1605.*

—— 1940a. Weitere Ergebnisse über die normalen hirnbioelektrischen Erscheinungen des Menschen bei Ableitung durch die Kopfschwarte. Einblicke in den Mechanismus der corticalen Erregungsabläufe und in die regionale Gliederung der Hirnrinde. *Z. ges. Neurol. Psychiat., 168, 248–268.*

—— 1940b. Einige weitere Erfahrungen über die Lokalisation von Tumoren und anderen herdförmigen Erkrankungen des Gehirns mittles der hirnbioelektrischen Lokalisationsmethodik. *Zbl. Neurochir., 5, 75–85.*

—— 1940c. Die hirnbioelektrische Untersuchung des Menschen. I. Die Grundlagen der Methodik und das Verhalten des Gesunden. *Fortschr. Neurol. Psychiat., 12, 193–209.*

—— 1940d. Über einige bei Killkürbewegungen und auf Sinnesreize auftretende bioelektrische Erscheinungen der Hirnrinde des Menschen. *Z. Sinnesphysiol., 68, 119–150.*

KORNMÜLLER, A. E., & JANZEN, R. 1939a. Über lokalisierte hirnbioelektrische Erscheinungen bei Kranken, insbesondere Epileptikern. *Z. ges. Neurol. Psychiat. 165, 372–374.*

—— 1939b. Die Methodik der lokalisierten Ableitungen hirnbioelektrischer Erscheinungen von der Kopfschwarte des Menschen, ihre Begründung und Begrenzung. *Z. ges. Neurol. Psychiat., 166, 287–308.*

—— 1939c. Über die normalen bioelektrischen Erscheinungen des menschlichen Gehirns. *Arch. Psychiat. Nervenkr., 110, 224–252.*

—— 1941. Hirnbioelektrische Untersuchungen bei genuiner Epilepsie. *Dtsch. Z. Nervenheilk., 152, 78–104.*

KREEZER, G. 1936. Electric potentials of the brain in certain types of mental deficiency. *Arch. Neurol. Psychiat., Chicago, 36, 1206–1213.*

—— 1937. Electrical phenomena of the brain among the feeble-minded. *Proc. Amer. Assn. ment. Def., 42, 130–141.*

—— 1938. The electro-encephalogram and its use in psychology. *Amer. J. Psychol., 51, 737–750.*

—— 1939a. Intelligence level and occipital alpha rhythm in the Mongolian type of mental deficiency. *Amer. J. Psychol., 52, 503–532.*

—— 1939b. Research in progress upon the electro-encephalogram in mental deficiency. *Proc. Amer. Assn. ment. Def., 44, 120–124.*

LAUGIER, H., & LIBERSON, W. 1937. Contribution à l'étude de l'éctro-encéphalogramme humain. *C. R. Soc. Biol., Paris, 125, 13–17.*

LEMERE, F. 1936. The significance of individual differences in the Berger rhythm. *Brain, 59, 366–375.*

—— 1937. Berger's alpha rhythm in organic lesions of the brain. *Brain, 60, 118–125.*

—— 1938. Effects on electroencephalogram of various agents used in treating schizophrenia. *J. Neurophysiol., 1, 590–595.*

—— 1939. Electroencephalography. *Psychiat. Quart., 13, 5–15.*

LEMERE, F. 1941. Cortical energy production in the psychoses. *Psychosom. Med.*, *3*, 152–156.

—— 1942. Electroencephalography: as a method of distinguishing true from false blindness. *J. Amer. med. Assn.*, *118*, 884–885.

LENNOX, W. G., GIBBS, E. L., & GIBBS, F. A. 1939. The inheritance of epilepsy as revealed by the electroencephalograph. *J. Amer. med. Assn.*, *113*, 1002–1003.

—— 1940. Inheritance of cerebral dysrhythmia and epilepsy. *Arch. Neurol. Psychiat., Chicago, 44*, 1155–1183.

—— 1942. Twins, brain waves and epilepsy. *J. nerv. ment. Dis.*, *95*, 353–355.

LENNOX, W. G., GIBBS, F. A., & GIBBS, E. L. 1936. Effect on the electroencephalogram of drugs and conditions which influence seizures. *Arch. Neurol. Psychiat., Chicago, 36*, 1236–1245.

—— 1938. The relationship in man of cerebral activity to blood flow and to blood constituents. *J. Neurol. Psychiat., 1*, 211–225.

LEVY, N. A., SEROTA, H. M., & GRINKER, R. R. 1942. Disturbance in brain function following convulsive shock therapy: Electroencephalographic and clinical studies. *Arch. Neurol. Psychiat., Chicago, 47*, 1009–1029.

LIBERSON, W. 1936. Électrencéphalographie transcranienne chez l'homme. *Travail hum., 4*, 303–320.

—— 1937. Recherches sur les électroencéphalogrammes transcraniens de l'homme. *Travail hum., 5*, 431–463.

—— 1938. Les données récentes de l'électrencéphalographic chez l'homme. *Biotypologie, 2*, 98–134.

—— 1941. Recherches biométriques sur les électroencéphalogrammes individuels. *Contr. Inst. Biol. Univ. Montreal, No. 9*, 1–19.

LIBERSON, W. T., & STRAUSS, H. 1941. Electroencephalographic studies: slow activity during hyperventilation in relation to age. *Proc. Soc. exp. Biol., N. Y., 48*, 674–676.

LIBET, B., & GERARD, R. D. 1938. Automaticity of central neurones after synaptic block by nicotine. *Proc. Soc. exp. Biol., N. Y., 38*, 886–888.

—— 1939. Control of the potentials of the isolated frog brain. *J. Neurophysiol., 2*, 153–169.

—— 1941. Steady potential fields and neurone activity. *J. Neurophysiol., 4*, 438–455.

LINDSLEY, D. B. 1936. Brain potentials in children and adults. *Science, 84*, 354.

—— 1938a. Electrical potentials of the brain in children and adults. *J. gen. Psychol., 19*, 285–306.

—— 1938b. Foci of activity of the alpha rhythm in the human electroencephalogram. *J. exp. Psychol., 23*, 159–171.

—— 1939. A longitudinal study of the occipital alpha rhythm in normal children: frequency and amplitude standards. *J. genet. Psychol., 55*, 197–213.

—— 1940. Bilateral differences in brain potentials from the two cerebral hemispheres in relation to laterality and stuttering. *J. exp. Psychol., 26*, 211–225.

—— 1942. Heart and brain potentials of human fetuses in utero. *Amer. J. Psychol., 55*, 412–416.

LINDSLEY, D. B., & BRADLEY, C. 1939. Electroencephalography as an aid to understanding certain behavior disorders of childhood. *Z. Kinderpsychiat., 6*, 33–37.

LINDSLEY, D. B., & CUTTS, K. K. 1940. The electroencephalograms of "constitutionally inferior" and behavior problem children: comparison with normal children and adults. *Arch. Neurol. Psychiat., Chicago, 44*, 1199–1212.

—— 1941. Clinical and electroencephalographic changes in a child during recovery from encephalitis. *Arch. Neurol. Psychiat., Chicago, 45*, 156–161.

LINDSLEY, D. B., & HENRY, C. E. 1942. The effect of drugs on behavior and the electroencephalograms of children with behavior disorders. *Psychosom. Med., 4*, 140–149.

LINDSLEY, D. B., & RUBENSTEIN, B. B. 1937. Relationship between brain potentials and some other physiological variables. *Proc. Soc. exp. Biol., N. Y., 35*, 558–563.

LINDSLEY, D. B., & SASSAMAN, W. H. 1938. Autonomic activity and brain potentials associated with "voluntary" control of the pilomotors (Mm. arrectores pilorum). *J. Neurophysiol., 1*, 342–349.

LIVANOV, M. N. 1940. (Rhythmical stimuli and the interrelation between the areas of the cerebral cortex.) *J. Physiol., U.S.S.R., 28*, 172–182, 183–194.

LOGAN, G. B., & BALDES, E. J. 1942. Parallel clinical and electro-encephalographic improvement in epilepsy: a study of children treated by the ketogenic diet. *Proc. Mayo Clin., 17,* 345–352.

LOOMIS, A. L., HARVEY, E. N., & HOBART, G. 1935a. Potential rhythms of the cerebral cortex during sleep. *Science, 81,* 597–598.

——— 1935b. Further observations on the potential rhythms of the cerebral cortex during sleep. *Science, 82,* 198–200.

——— 1936a. Brain potentials during hypnosis. *Science, 83,* 239–241.

——— 1936b. Electrical potentials of the human brain. *J. exp. Psychol., 19,* 249–279.

——— 1937. Cerebral states during sleep, as studied by human brain potentials. *J. exp. Psychol., 21,* 127–144.

——— 1938. Distribution of disturbance-patterns in the human electroencephalogram, with special reference to sleep. *J. Neurophysiol., 1,* 413–430.

LOVELL, H. W., CZARSKI, T. J., & LYMAN, R. S. 1939. The effect of vestibular stimulation on brain waves. *Chin. J. Physiol., 14,* 389–410.

LÖWENBACH, H. 1939. The electroencephalogram in healthy relatives of epileptics: constitutional elements in "idiopathic epilepsy." *Johns Hopk. Hosp. Bull., 65,* 125–137.

LÖWENBACH, H., & LYMAN, R. S. 1940. The electroencephalogram in electrically induced convulsions in rabbits. *J. Neurol. Psychiat., 3,* 336–342.

LYMAN, R. S. 1941. Eye movements in the electroencephalogram. *Johns Hopk. Hosp. Bull., 68,* 1–31.

LYMAN, R. S., CARLSON, W. A., & BENSON, O. O., JR. 1941. Effects of reduced atmospheric pressures on the electroencephalogram. *J. Aviat. Med., 12,* 115–125.

MARGOLIN, S. G., STRAUSS, H., & ENGEL, G. L. 1941. Electroencephalographic changes associated with hypersensitivity of the carotid sinus. *Arch. Neurol. Psychiat., Chicago, 45,* 889–890.

MARINESCO, G., SAGER, O., & KREINDLER, A. 1936a. Études électroencéphalographiques. Electroencéphalogramme chez une malade avec extirpation du lobe frontal. *Bull. Acad. Méd. Paris, 115,* 873–877.

——— 1936b. Études électroencéphalographiques sur l'aphasie; phénomène de restitution et de compensation dans les lésions du cerveau. *Bull. Acad. Méd. Paris, 116,* 383–385.

——— 1936c. Études électroencéphalographiques. L'électroencéphalogramme dans l'aphasie. *Bull. Acad. Méd. Paris, 116,* 182–186.

——— 1937a. Études électroencéphalographiques. VI. L'électroencéphalogramme de l'homme et sa valeur localisatrice. *Bull. Acad. Méd. Roumanie, 2,* 439–454.

——— 1937b. Études électroencéphalographiques. Le sommeil naturel et le sommeil hypnotique. *Bull. Acad. Méd. Paris, 117,* 273–276.

——— 1937c. Études électroencéphalographiques. VII. Le sommeil et le coma. *Bull. Acad. Méd. Roumanie, 4,* 17–24.

——— 1938a. L'électroencéphalogramme dans certains états pathologiques. *Pr. méd., 46,* 650–654.

——— 1938b. L'encéphalogramme de la région précentrale chez l'homme a l'état normal et pathologique. *Bull. Acad. Méd. Paris, 119,* 593–598.

MARMOR, J., & SAVITSKY, N. 1942. Electro-encephalography in cases of head injury. *J. nerv. ment. Dis., 95,* 285–298.

MARTINSON, B. M. 1939. A study of brain potentials during mental blocking. *J. exp. Psychol., 24,* 143–156.

MATTHEWS, B. H. C. 1934. A special purpose amplifier. *J. Physiol., 81,* 28–29P.

——— 1938. A simple universal amplifier. *J. Physiol., 93,* 25–27P.

McDONALD, C. A., & KORB, M. 1940a. Brain abscess with brain potentials. *R. I. med. J., 23,* 81–84.

——— 1940b. Brain tumor with normal brain potentials. *R. I. med. J., 23,* 111–113.

McMAHON, J. F., & WALTER, W. G. 1938. Electro-encephalogram in schizophrenia. *J. ment. Sci., 84,* 781–787.

McNEEL, B. H., DEWAN, J. G., MYERS, C. R., PROCTOR, L. D., & GOODWIN, J. E. 1941. Parallel psychological, psychiatric and physiological findings in schizophrenic patients under insulin shock treatment. *Amer. J. Psychiat., 98,* 422–429.

MOTOKAWA, K., & TOSISADA, M. 1941. Die elektrenkephalographische Untersuchung über den Adaptationsmechanismus des Zentralnervensystems. *Jap. J. med. Sci., Biophys., 7,* 213–233.

MUFSON, J. A., & CHODOFF, P. 1942. Convulsions in Paget's disease; electro-encephalographic observations. *Ann. intern. Med., 16,* 762–771.

MÜLLER, L. R. 1939. Über bioelektrische Vorgänge im Grosshirn während des Wachens und des Schlafens. *Klin. Wschr., 18,* 1589–1592.

MURPHY, W. F. 1941. Narcolepsy; a review and presentation of seven cases. *Amer. J. Psychiat., 98,* 334–339.

NEWMAN, H. W. 1938. Electro-encephalography. *Amer. J. med. Sci., 196,* 882–888.

NIMS, L. F., GIBBS, E. L., LENNOX, W. G., GIBBS, F. A., & WILLIAMS, D. 1940. Adjustment of acid-base balance of patients with petit mal epilepsy to over-ventilation. *Arch. Neurol. Psychiat., Chicago, 43,* 262–269.

OBERMANN, C. E. 1939. The effect on the Berger rhythm of mild affective states. *J. abnorm. soc. Psychol., 34,* 84–95.

OMBREDANE, A. 1941. L'agnosie acoustique. *Rev. Neurol. Psiquiat. S. Paulo, 7,* 37–55.

PACELLA, B. L., & BARRERA, S. E. 1941. Electroencephalography: its applications in neurology and psychiatry. *Psychiat. Quart., 15,* 407–437.

—— 1942. Some considerations of the electroencephalogram in the "convulsive state" (electrically induced seizures). *J. nerv. ment. Dis., 96,* 125–129.

PACELLA, B. L., BARRERA, S. E., & KALINOWSKY, L. 1942. Variations in electro-encephalogram associated with electric shock therapy of patients with mental disorders. *Arch. Neurol. Psychiat., Chicago, 47,* 367–384.

PAGNIEZ, P. 1937. Application de l'électroencéphalographie à l'étude de l'épilepsie. *Pr. méd., 45,* 780–782.

PAGNIEZ, P., LIBERSON, W., & PLICHET, A. 1938a. Contribution à l'étude électro-encéphalographique des épileptiques. *Pr. méd., 46,* 1465–1468.

—— 1938b. Contribution a l'étude des électroencéphalogrammes des épileptiques. *C. R. Soc. Biol., Paris, 128,* 1084–1088.

—— 1939. Renseignements fournis par l'électroencéphalographie dans l'épilepsie. *Médecine, Paris, 20,* 105.

PAULIAN, D., TUDOR, M., & CONSTANTINESCO, G. 1939. L'électro-encéphalo-gramme dans un cas de mutisme et surdité hystériques. *Rev. neurol., 71,* 738–741.

PENFIELD, W., & JASPER, H. 1940. Electroencephalography in focal epilepsy. *Trans. Amer. neurol. Assn., 66,* 26–30.

POLATIN, P., STRAUSS, H., & ALTMANN, L. L. 1940. Transient organic reactions during shock therapy of psychoses; clinical study with electroencephalographic and psychologic performance correlates. *Psychiat. Quart., 14,* 457–465.

POSTELI, T., & COLOMBATI, S. 1940. L'elettroencefalogramma nei tumori cerebrali e in altra malattie organische del cervello. *Riv. oto-neuro-oftal., 17,* 28–36.

POSTELI, T., & SEIDENARI, R. 1939. Contributo all' applicazione clinica dell' elet-troencefalografia: reerti encefalografici in alcune cerebro-e oftalmopatie. *Riv. oto-neuro-oftal., 16,* 1–14.

PRADOS Y SUCH, M. 1941. Valor clínico del electroencefalograma. *Ciencia, Méx., 2,* 1–13.

PUTNAM, T. J., & MERRITT, H. H. 1941. Dulness as an epileptic equivalent. *Arch. Neurol. Psychiat., Chicago, 45,* 797, 813.

RAHM, W. E., JR. 1939. A new bio-electronic application: electroencephalography. *Electronics, 12,* 11–13.

RAHM, W. E., JR., & WILLIAMS, A. C. 1938. Aspects of electro-encephalogram in epilepsy and feeblemindedness. *Psychiat. Quart., 12,* 230–235.

RAMIREZ MORENO, S. 1941. Estudios sobre electroencefalografía. *Rev. méx. Psiquiat. Neurol., 8,* 11–41.

RANEY, E. T. 1939. Brain potentials and lateral dominance in identical twins. *J. exp. Psychol., 24,* 21–39.

RENSHAW, B., FORBES, A., & MORISON, B. R. 1940. Activity of isocortex and hippocampus: Electrical studies with microelectrodes. *J. Neurophysiol., 3,* 74–105.

RHEINBERGER, M. B., & SIRIS, J. 1940. Resorption of intracranial gumma under electroencephalographic control. *Arch. Neurol. Psychiat., Chicago, 44,* 879–885.

ROBINSON, L. J. 1940. Cerebral dysrhythmias in relatives of epileptic persons. *Arch. Neurol. Psychiat., Chicago, 44,* 1109–1111.

—— 1941. Incidence of abnormal electroencephalograms in epileptic persons over forty years of age. *Dis. nerv. Syst., 2,* 55–58.

ROHRACHER, H. 1935. Die gehirnelektrischen Erscheinungen bei geistiger Arbeit. *Z. Psychol., 136,* 308–324.

—— 1937a. Die gehirnelektrischen Erscheinungen bei verschiedenen psychischen Vorgängen. *Comment. pontif. Acad. Sci., 1,* 89–133.

—— 1937b. I fenomeni elettrici del cervello concomitanti ai processi psichici. *Arch. ital. Psicol., 15,* 113–158.

—— 1937c. Die gehirnelektrischen Erscheinungen bei Sinnesreizen. *Z. Psychol., 140,* 274–308.

—— 1938a. Weitere Untersuchungen über die Kurvenform cerebraler Potential-schwankungen. *Pflüg. Arch. ges. Physiol., 240,* 191–196.

—— 1938b. Experimentelle und theoretische Untersuchungen über die gehirn-elektrischen Vorgänge. *Comment. pontif. Acad. Sci., 2,* 225–273.

—— 1939. Fehlerquellen und Kontrollmethoden bei gehirnelektrischen Unter-suchungen. *Pflüg. Arch. ges. Physiol., 242,* 389–402.

—— 1940. Die elektrischen Vorgänge im menschlichen Gehirn. *Z. Psychol., 149,* 209–281.

ROMANO, J., STEAD, E. A., JR., & TAYLOR, Z. E. 1940. Clinical and electroen-cephalographic changes produced by a sensitive carotid sinus of the cerebral type. *New Engl. J. Med., 223,* 708–712.

ROSENBLUETH, A., & CANNON, W. B. 1942. Cortical responses to electric stimu-lation. *Amer. J. Physiol., 135,* 690–741.

ROSS, D. A., & SCHWAB, R. S. 1939. The cortical alpha rhythm in thyroid dis-orders. *Endocrinology, 25,* 75–79.

RUBIN, M. A. 1938a. The distribution of the alpha rhythm over the cerebral cortex of normal man. *J. Neurophysiol., 1,* 313–323.

—— 1938b. A variability study of the normal and schizophrenic occipital alpha rhythm. I. *J. Psychol., 6,* 325–334.

—— 1939a. Electro-encephalogram of schizophrenic patients during administra-tion of vitamin B₁. *Proc. Soc. exp. Biol., N. Y., 42,* 440–441.

—— 1939b. Electro-encephalographic localization of atrophy in the cerebral cor-tex of man. *Proc. Soc. exp. Biol., N. Y., 40,* 153–154.

—— 1940. Electroencephalography in the psychoses. *Amer. J. Psychiat., 96,* 862–873.

RUBIN, M. A., & COHEN, L. H. 1938. The electroencephalogram in bromide in-toxication. *Arch. Neurol. Psychiat., Chicago, 40,* 922–927.

—— 1939. A variability study of the normal and schizophrenic occipital alpha rhythm. II. The electro-encephalogram and imagery type. *J. ment. Sci., 85,* 779–783.

RUBIN, M. A., COHEN, L. H., & HOAGLAND, H. 1937. The effect of artificially raised metabolic rate on the electro-encephalogram of schizophrenic patients. *Endocrinology, 21,* 536–540.

RUBIN, M. A., & FREEMAN, H. 1938. The influence of cyanide on brain poten-tials in man. *J. Neurophysiol., 1,* 527–532.

—— 1940. Brain potential changes in man during cyclopropane anesthesia. *J. Neurophysiol., 3,* 33–42.

—— 1941. Brain potential changes and skin temperature during cyclopropane anesthesia. *Anesth. Analges., 20,* 45–49.

RUBIN, M. A., MALAMUD, W., & HOPE, J. M. 1942. The electroencephalogram and psychopathological manifestations in schizophrenia as influenced by drugs. *Psychosom. Med., 4,* 355–361.

RUBIN, M. A., & TURNER, E. 1942. Blood sugar level and influence of hyper-ventilation on slow activity in electroencephalogram. *Proc. Soc. exp. Biol., N. Y., 50,* 270–272.

RUBIN, M. A., & WALL, C. 1939. Brain potential changes in man induced by metrazol. *J. Neurol. Psychiat., 2,* 107–114.

RUBIN, S., & BOWMAN, K. M. 1942. Electroencephalographic and personality correlates in peptic ulcer. *Psychosom. Med., 4,* 309–318.

SAGER, O., & KREINDLER, A. 1939. Études électroencéphalographiques dans l'épi-lepsie. *J. belge Neurol. Psychiat., 39,* 265–275.

SARKISOV, S. A., & LIVANOV, M. N. 1941. (Characteristics of Berger's rhythm in normal and pathological states.) *Nevropat. Psikhiat., 10,* 28–35.

SARKISOV, S. A., & PENTSIK, A. S. 1939. (Electro-encephalogram in cases of cerebral tumors.) *Acta med. USSR, 2,* 185–190.

SAUL, L. J., DAVIS, H., & DAVIS, P. A. 1937. Correlations between electroencephalograms and the psychological organization of the individual. *Trans. Amer. neurol. Assn., 63,* 167–169.

SAVITSKY, N., & MARMOR, J. 1940. Electroencephalography in cases of head injury. *Trans. Amer. neurol. Assn., 66,* 30–34.

SCARFF, J. E., & RAHM, W. E., JR. 1941. The human electro-corticogram: a report of spontaneous electrical potentials obtained from the exposed human brain. *J. Neurophysiol., 4,* 418–426.

SCHÄCKTER, M. 1936. L'activité électrique du cerveau humain. *Ann. Fac. franc. méd. pharm. Beyrouth, 8,* 183–196.

SCHMELVKIN, D. G. 1939. (Electro-encephalogram and its clinical significance; disturbance of alpha-rhythm in certain unilateral lesions.) *Sovetsk. psikhonevrol., 15,* 45–53.

SCHWAB, R. S. 1941. The influence of visual and auditory stimuli on the electroencephalographic tracing of petit mal. *Amer. J. Psychiat., 97,* 1301–1310.

SCHWAB, R. S., & COBB, S. 1939. Simultaneous electromyograms and electroencephalograms in paralysis agitans. *J. Neurophysiol., 2,* 36–41.

SCHWAB, R. S., GRUNWALD, A., & SARGANT, W. W. 1941. Regulation of epilepsy by synchronized recording of respiration and brain waves. *Arch. Neurol. Psychiat., Chicago, 46,* 1017–1034.

SCHWARTZ, H. G., & KERR, A. S. 1940. Electrical activity of exposed human brain, description of technic and report of observation. *Arch. Neurol. Psychiat., Chicago, 43,* 547–559.

SECUNDA, L., & FINLEY, K. H. 1942. Electroencephalographic studies in children presenting behavior disorders. *New Engl. J. Med., 226,* 850–854.

SEGAL, J. 1939. Le mécanisme de la vision en lumière intermittente. *J. Psychol. norm. path., 36,* 451–539.

SEIDENARI, R. 1940. Applicazione dell'elettrencefalogramma in derivazione occipitooculare nallo studio di alcune affezioni oculari. *Riv. oto-neuro-oftal, 17,* 1–17.

SEROTA, H. M., & GRINKER, R. R. 1941. The present status of electroencephalography in clinical diagnosis. *Dis. nerv. Syst., 2,* 276–288.

SHERMAN, M., & JOST, H. 1942. Frustration reactions of normal and neurotic persons. *J. Psychol., 13,* 3–19.

SMITH, J. R. 1937. The electroencephalogram during infancy and childhood. *Proc. Soc. exp. Biol., N. Y., 36,* 384–386.

—— 1938a. The electroencephalogram during normal infancy and childhood: I. Rhythmic activities present in the neonate and their subsequent development. *J. genet. Psychol., 53,* 431–453.

—— 1938b. The electroencephalogram during normal infancy and childhood: II. The nature of the growth of the alpha waves. *J. genet. Psychol., 53,* 455–469.

—— 1938c. The electroencephalogram during normal infancy and childhood: III. Preliminary observations on the pattern sequence during sleep. *J. genet. Psychol., 53,* 471–482.

—— 1939. The "occipital" and "pre-central" alpha rhythms during the first two years. *J. Psychol., 7,* 223–226.

—— 1941. The frequency growth of the human alpha rhythms during normal infancy and childhood. *J. Psychol., 11,* 177–198.

SMITH, J. R., WALTER, C. W. P., & LAIDLAW, R. W. 1940. The electroencephalogram in cases of neoplasms of the posterior fossa. *Arch. Neurol. Psychiat., Chicago, 43,* 472–486.

SOTO ROMAY, R. 1938. (Ossification (osteoma) of falx cerebri resulting in traumatic epilepsy; importance of electro-encephalogram for locating localization of lesion.) *Sem. méd., B. Aires, 2,* 1473–1480.

SPEILBERG, P. I. 1940a. (The human electroencephalogram.) *J. Physiol., U.S.S.R., 28,* 195–202.

—— 1940b. (The adaptation of the human cerebral cortex to permanent stimulation and after depression rhythms.) *J. Physiol., U.S.R.R., 28,* 203–210.

STEWART, W. B. 1941. Electroencephalographic changes associated with different forms of experimentally produced increased intracranial pressure *Johns Hopk. Hosp. Bull., 69,* 240–265.

STRAUSS, H. 1942. Electroencephalographic studies: a method for differential diagnosis of abnormal electroencephalograms. *J. Mt Sinai Hosp., N. Y., 9,* 17–22.

STRAUSS, H., & RAHM, W. E., JR. 1940. Effect of metrazol injections on the electroencephalogram. *Psychiat. Quart., 14*, 43–48.

STRAUSS, H., RAHM, W. E., JR., & BARRERA, S. E. 1939. Electroencephalographic studies in relatives of epileptics. *Proc. Soc. exp. Biol., N. Y., 42*, 207–212.

—— 1940. Studies on a group of children with psychiatric disorders. I. Electroencephalographic studies. *Psychosom. Med., 2*, 34–42.

THERMAN, O. 1940. Bilateral synchronization in the human electroencephalogram. *Amer. J. Physiol., 129*, 479–480.

THOMSON, M. M., FORBES, T. W., & BOLLES, M. M. 1937. Brain potential rhythms in a case showing self-induced apparent trance states. *Amer. J. Psychiat., 93*, 1313–1314.

THORNER, M., GIBBS, F. A., & GIBBS, E. L. 1942. Relation between the electroencephalogram and flying ability. *War Med., Chicago, 2*, 255–262.

TITECA, J. 1938. Étude électrencéphalographique de deux cas d'anesthesie hystérique. *J. belge Neurol. Psychiat., 38*, 442–478.

TOMAN, J. 1941. Flicker potentials and the alpha rhythm in man. *J. Neurophysiol., 4*, 51–61.

TÖNNIES, J. F. 1932. Der Neurograph, ein Apparat zur Aufzeichnung bioelektrischer Vorgänge unter Ausschaltung der photographischen Kurvendarstellung. *Naturwissenschaften, 41*, 653–658.

—— 1934. Die unipolare Ableitung elektrischer Spannung vom menschlichen Gehirn. *Naturwissenschaften, 22*, 411–414.

—— 1938. Differential amplifier. *Rev. sci. Instrum., 9*, 95–97.

TORRENTS, E. 1939a. (Introduction to new field of investigation; normal and pathological electrical activity of human brain; electroencephalography.) *Arch. urug. Med., 14*, 248–264.

—— 1939b. (Electro-encephalography; compensating symmetric amplifier.) *Arch. Soc. biol. Montevideo, 9*, 185–189.

—— 1940. El electro-encephalograma patologico. *Arch. urug. Med., 17*, 265–278.

TRAVIS, L. E. 1937. Brain potentials and the temporal course of consciousness. *J. exp. Psychol., 21*, 302–309.

TRAVIS, L. E., & BARBER, V. 1938. The effect of tactile stimulation upon the Berger rhythm. *J. exp. Psychol., 22*, 269–272.

TRAVIS, L. E., & COFER, C. N. 1937. The temporal relationship between brain potentials and certain neuro-muscular rhythms. *J. exp. Psychol., 21*, 565–569.

TRAVIS, L. E., & EGAN, J. P. 1938a. Increase in frequency of alpha rhythm by verbal stimulation. *J. exp. Psychol., 23*, 384–393.

—— 1938b. Conditioning of the electrical response of the cortex. *J. exp. Psychol., 22*, 524–531.

TRAVIS, L. E., & GOTTLOBER, A. 1936. Do brain waves have individuality? *Arch. Soc. Biol. Montevideo, 9*, 190–193.

—— 1937. How consistent are an individual's brain potentials from day to day? *Science, 85*, 233–234.

TRAVIS, L. E., & HALL, M. E. 1938. Effect of visual after-sensations upon brain potential patterning under different degrees of attention. *J. exp. Psychol., 22*, 472–479.

TRAVIS, L. E., & KNOTT, J. R. 1936. Brain potentials from normal speakers and stutterers. *J. Psychol., 2*, 137–150.

—— 1937a. Brain potential studies of perseveration: I. Perseveration time to light. *J. Psychol., 3*, 97–100.

—— 1937b. Brain potential studies of perseveration: II. Perseveration time to visually presented words. *J. exp. Psychol., 21*, 353–358.

—— 1937c. Bilaterally recorded brain potentials from normal speakers and stutterers. *J. Speech Disorders, 2*, 239–241.

TRAVIS, L. E., KNOTT, J. R., & GRIFFITH, P. E. 1937. Effect of response on the latency and frequency of the Berger rhythm. *J. gen. Psychol., 16*, 391–401.

TRAVIS, L. E., & MALAMUD, W. 1937. Brain potentials from normal subjects, stutterers and schizophrenic patients. *Amer. J. Psychiat., 93*, 929–932.

TROWBRIDGE, E. H., JR., & FINLEY, K. H. 1942. The electroencephalogram and pneumoencephalogram in non-focal neurological disorders. *Amer. J. Roentgenol., 47*, 699–702.

USHER, S. J., & HASPER, H. H. 1941. The etiology of Sydenham's chorea: electroencephalographic studies. *Canad. med. Assn. J., 44*, 365–371.

VAN DER MOLEN, H. R. 1938. (Electro-encephalogram during nitrous oxide anesthesia in labor.) *Ned Tijdschr. Geneesk., 82*, 379–382.

—— 1939. (Electro-encephalograms of patients with epilepsy; explanation.) *Ned. Tijdschr. Geneesk., 83*, 1599–1605.

WALTER, W. G. 1936. The location of cerebral tumours by electro-encephalography. *Lancet*, Part 2, 305–308.

—— 1937. The electro-encephalogram in cases of cerebral tumour. *Proc. R. Soc. Med., 30*, 579–598.

—— 1938. Critical review: The technique and application of electroencephalography. *J. Neurol. Psychiat., 1*, 359–385.

—— 1940a. Electroencephalography: aid to diagnosis. *Bristol med.-chir. J., 57*, 1–8.

—— 1940b. Electroencephalography in diagnosis of cerebral tumor and abscess. *Pract. oto-rhinolaryng., 3*, 17–26.

—— 1940c. Traumatic extradural hemorrhage; clinical application of electroencephalography. *Bristol med.-chir. J., 57*, 86–90.

—— 1942. Electro-encephalography in cases of mental disorder. *J. ment. Sci., 88*, 110–121.

WALTER, W. G., GRIFFITHS, G. M., & NEVIN, S. 1939. The electro-encephalogram in a case of pathological sleep due to hypothalamic tumour. *Brit. med. J.*, Part 1, 107–109.

WEINBACH, A. P. 1938a. Some physiological phenomena fitted to growth equations. II. Brain potentials. *Hum. Biol., 10*, 145–150.

—— 1938b. Some physiological phenomena fitted to growth equations. III. Rate of growth of brain potentials (alpha frequency) compared with rate of growth of the brain. *Growth, 2*, 247–251.

WILLIAMS, A. C., JR. 1939. Some psychological correlates of the electroencephalogram. *Arch. Psychol., N. Y.*, No. 240, 5–48.

—— 1940. Facilitation of the alpha rhythm of the electroencephalogram. *J. exp. Psychol., 26*, 413–422.

WILLIAMS, D. 1939. The abnormal cortical potentials associated with high intracranial pressure. *Brain, 62*, 321–334.

—— 1941a. The effect of choline-like substances on the cerebral electrical discharges in epilepsy. *J. Neurol. Psychiat., 4*, 32–48.

—— 1941b. The significance of an abnormal electroencephalogram. *J. Neurol. Psychiat., 4*, 257–268.

—— 1941c. The electro-encephalogram in acute head injuries. *J. Neurol. Psychiat., 4*, 107–130.

—— 1941d. The electro-encephalogram in chronic post-traumatic states. *J. Neurol. Psychiat., 4*, 131 ff.

WILLIAMS, D., & GIBBS, F. A. 1938a. Localization of cerebral lesions by electroencephalography. *Trans. Amer. neurol. Assn., 64*, 130–134.

—— 1938b. The localization of intracranial lesions by electroencephalography. *New Engl. J. Med., 218*, 998–1002.

—— 1939. Electroencephalography in clinical neurology. *Arch. Neurol. Psychiat., Chicago, 41*, 519–534.

WOLTMAN, H. W., & CRAIG, W. M. 1941. Altered behavior caused by removable tumor of brain; site suggested by electroencephalogram. *Proc. Mayo Clin., 16*, 49–51.

YEAGER, C. L. 1938. Electroencephalography as aid in localizing organic lesions. *Proc. Mayo Clin., 13*, 422–426.

YEAGER, C. L., & BALDES, E. J. 1937. The electro-encephalogram in organic and non-organic mental disorders. *Proc. Mayo Clin., 12*, 705–712.

YEAGER, C. L., BALDES, E. J., CRAIG, W. M., & WOLTMAN, H. W. 1940. Electroencephalography as an aid in localizing intracranial lesions. *Proc. Mayo Clin., 15*, 147–149.

YEAGER, C. L., & WALSH, M. N. 1940. Changes in the electro-encephalogram from ligation of the carotid arteries: in the case of intracranial saccular aneurysm. *J. Amer. med. Assn., 114*, 1625–1626.

—— 1941. Electroencefalografía; su importancia en la clínica neurológica. *Rev. méx. Psiquiat. Neurol., 8*, 43–56.

PART VIII

THERAPY AND THE PREVENTION OF BEHAVIOR DISORDERS

Chapter 34

PSYCHIATRIC THERAPY

By Kenneth E. Appel, M.D.

A CHAPTER ON PSYCHIATRIC THERAPY may seem ironic and futile with another World War exploding with man's primitive savagery. For what is psychotherapy but the application of the principles which help us to control and to use the crude energies of the primitive instincts within us, so that we can live constructively and socially, and not destructively and madly? Yet we need not despair if we take a historical or anthropological perspective. It took hundreds of thousands of years for man to learn to walk upright. He has been using bronze and iron less than 10,000 years. The cultures on which we build, Judeo-Christian and Greco-Roman, have existed less than half that time. Our Industrial Age is in its infancy, comparatively speaking. So, from Hippocrates to Pasteur, from Socrates to Freud, or from King David to Florence Nightingale, is but a comparatively short time as one measures human progress. We may be proud, therefore, of the progress in psychiatry where new methods of treatment and of prevention (see Chapter 35 by Stevenson) have kept and will keep thousands of individuals from the suffering and ineffectiveness that nervous and mental disease entails.

A historical perspective shows us five vistas. First, the Ancients—Egyptians, Jews, and Greeks. Secondly, the Middle Ages with theological conceptions of lunacy and witchcraft. Thirdly, the astrological tradition represented by Paracelsus and later by Mesmer. Fourthly, the humanitarian period of Pinel. Finally, the modern tradition which stems from Charcot.

Ancient medicine considered that disease was caused by evil spirits or demons (Garrison, 1917). The oldest prescription in existence, one from Egypt, "calls for the exhibition of a green stone as a fumigation against hysteria." Early Assyrian tablets contain formulae for driving out evil spirits causing disease; cures and prevention were supposed to be effected by magic, charms, incantations, and rituals.

The Judeo-Christian Scriptures contain frequent references to mental disease and to various forms of healing. When the Spirit of the Lord departed from Saul and he was depressed, he called for David (1. Samuel 16:14–23). David played on his harp before Saul, the "evil spirit departed from him," and he was "refreshed" and "well." Nebuchadnezzar had a dream which was interpreted by Daniel (Daniel 4:33–34).

He became mad and was driven from men and "did eat grass like oxen," but when he lifted his eyes toward Heaven his "understanding returned."

In the New Testament are recorded many miracles of healing by Christ. The leper came asking to be healed and "Jesus put forth his hand, saying, 'I will; be thou clean,' and immediately his leprosy was cleansed" (Matthew 8:2–3). Later many "possessed with devils" were brought to Him and "He cast out spirits with his word, and healed all that were sick" (Matthew 8:28–33).

Hippocrates attempted to supplant demonological conceptions and magic with theories and practices based on observation and natural causes. The Hippocratean description of disease in many instances remains today a part of medical teaching, but the humoral conception of pathology (see Chapter 1 by McKinnon) has been displaced. Hysteria, according to Hippocrates, was due to the wanderings of the uterus through the body in search of humidity. For example, if it happened to press against the heart, the symptom was palpitation.

According to Galen, hysteria was caused by the engorgement of the uterus by the menstrual blood. He continued the path toward a merciful treatment of the insane. Celius Aurelianus in the third century continued the Hippocratean tradition that insanity was a brain disease and that treatment should be gentle and kind, which, as White (1905) says, would have saved fifteen centuries of cruel treatment of the insane had not theological teachings thrown their influence on the side of the cruder and more cruel demonological conceptions drawn from Biblical texts. Alexander of Tralles in the sixth century wrote on the treatment of melancholia. Paul of Aegina (625–690), under the protection of one of the Caliphs, stressed the cure of madness as a disease and the necessity for mild treatment.

Unfortunately, for centuries through the Middle Ages demonological conceptions and magic held practically undisputed sway. Another quieter, more kindly, self-sacrificing, and charitable tradition stemmed from the New Testament. It was submerged for the most part but it carried momentum, and here and there sporadic manifestations appeared in the form of rude hospitals and infirmaries. The most prominent of these were the Infirmary of Monte Cassino, the Hotel-Dieu at Lyons in the sixth century, and the Hotel-Dieu at Paris in the seventh. There were great charitable organizations, like the Order of St. John of Jerusalem at the time of the Crusades, which brought the spirit of charity and mercy to help the sick, wretched, and afflicted of humanity. This spirit finally blossomed in the labors of modern saints, such as Vincent de Paul, Elizabeth Fry, Florence Nightingale, and others.

But since cruelty to the lunatic was punishment for the Devil in him, it was the accepted and prescribed method of treatment for the most part. The insane were chained, beaten, scourged, and entrusted to the jailer and torturer. Almost to the seventeenth century madness was held to be due to possession by Satan.

In 1547, Henry VIII chartered a hospital in London for fifty lunatics.[1] It was called Bethlem Asylum (Bedlam) and patients from it were often allowed to beg on the streets. The colony at Gheel, Belgium, was founded in medieval times as a religious work, and continued this kindly tradition of Christianity. But it was not really until Pinel (1795) that the chains were thrown off and the modern humane treatment of the insane began.

The tradition of the royal touch and the astrological conception of disease became blended in Paracelsus (1493–1541). He believed that diseases were caused by astral influences (lunacy, from luna=moon) acting on man. This tradition with the conception of animal magnetism culminated in Mesmer (1734–1815). He believed that health and disease were due to the distribution of a kind of magnetic fluid in the body and that this could be influenced beneficially by the human hand. There is no doubt that at times good results followed his treatments, but the learned men of Paris drove him away because of his charlatanry. However, the phenomena observed in his patients and their treatment formed the starting point of modern psychopathology.

From Paris and Nancy, respectively, two or three lines of psychotherapy have developed which persist in psychiatry today. From Liébeault and Bernheim came the Suggestionists (Babinski, Baudouin, Coué) and the Persuasionists (Dubois, Déjerine). From Charcot came Janet, Freud, Bleuler, Jung, Adler, Rivers, Ross, and Hart.

Janet, a pupil of Charcot, studied especially hysteria and various automatisms. To account for these conditions Janet (1889) introduced the concepts of *dissociation*, the *subconscious*, and *psychological tension*. To account for the various manifestations of hysteria and psychasthenia, he assumed that certain mental processes go on in the subconscious independently of (dissociated from) the main stream of consciousness. The conception of psychasthenia formulated by him includes states of fear, doubt, obsession, and compulsion. The cause of the dissociation he believed to be the weakness of the (hypothetical) psychological tension. Janet's "idées fixes" became "reminiscences" in early psychoanalysis. For him the splitting was chiefly mechanical and due to lack of energy; he did not believe in repression.

Freud, born in 1856, first was associated with Breuer in Vienna, later studied with Charcot in Paris, and then returned to practice in Vienna, where he developed psychoanalysis, the influence of which has been epoch making in psychiatry.

Jung, Adler, Rank, and Stekel started with Freudian conceptions but later broke away and developed their own formulations.

No sketch of this kind would be complete without mentioning Kraepelin (1856–1924). He stands in a place alone. He cut across the confusion of psychiatric syndromes and diseases with great insight and vision, and brought order by introducing the concepts of *dementia*

---

[1] Formerly a monastic institution devoted to the care of the insane.

praecox and *manic-depressive insanity*. His great contributions were observation and classification. He stimulated organic research (Mott, Cotton, Gibbs, Dunlap, N. D. C. Lewis) which has been a continued inspiration to psychiatrists.

McDougall and Adolf Meyer do not belong to any one tradition. McDougall was interested in psychotherapy and practiced hypnosis extensively in his treatment of war neuroses. Adolf Meyer is eclectic. He is neither an organicist nor a psychogenecist. He is both. His concept of psychobiology is genetic, developmental, biographical, and individual. Treatment must necessarily be medical, psychological, educational, and sociological. He himself is an individual large enough to comprehend a great whole, and his breadth of outlook has tremendously energized American psychiatry.

Methods of Psychiatric Therapy

The Symptomatic or Direct Psychological Approaches

Hypnosis.—The method of Mesmer, who was born in 1734, which came to be known as *Mesmerism*, was really a form of hypnotism. Braid, following the work of LaFontaine, proved that no mysterious magnetic fluid passed between the operator and the subject, and originated the term *hypnosis*. (For the history of, the theory of, the techniques of producing, and the experimental work with hypnosis, see Chapter 16 by Jenness.)

As a therapeutic method, hypnosis was originally developed in work with hysteria and hysterical conditions. Charcot, Janet, Bernheim, Breuer, and Freud used it not only to remove such individual symptoms as contractions, paralyses, spasms, and anaesthesias, but also to remove amnesias. All have emphasized that sudden spectacular results should not be expected. Although hypnosis is most effective in treating conversion hysteria, and the war and occupational neuroses, it may also be helpful in treating the neurotic complications sometimes associated with organic disease. Diethelm (1936) cites, for instance, the case of an older man who was cured by hypnosis of protracted hiccough that followed a prostatectomy. Hypnosis has been used to alleviate pain in operations and in delivery. It is said to be helpful in treating dysmenorrhea, frigidity, and impotence, and it is readily applicable in psychogenic muscular disturbances. It has also been used to some extent in treating the anxiety states. However, for the obsessive-compulsive neuroses, for phobias of the psychasthenic type, and for altering neurotic characters, hypnosis is of little help. It is also ineffective for treating the perversions and the psychoses.

In using hypnosis there is a temptation to attack the individual symptom which the patient believes is the chief trouble. Diethelm (1936), Schilder (1938), and others have emphasized the inadequacy of such symptomatic treatment. Psychiatric experience has shown repeatedly that if causes are not tackled, the fundamental difficulty soon reappears in the form of another symptom. Hypnosis may, however, be employed as an aid in the attack upon causes. William Brown (1938) attributed his successful hypnotic treatment of the war neuroses to catharsis. While under hypnosis his patients acted terrified. According to Brown's theory, which harks back to the early conceptions of Breuer and Freud (1893), this emotion has been repressed, and with it the ability to speak. When the repressed emotion is worked out by the patient reliving his experience in the hypnotic trance (abreaction), the cause for the dissociation is removed. The patient's inability to speak, his memories, and his other disabilities then disappear (reassociation). Schilder (1938), however, considered cathartic hypnosis unsatisfactory. Occasionally he combined hypnosis with interviews from which he obtained an understanding of the patient's problem. During these interviews he used dream interpretation and free association, then he devoted the last 15 minutes to a hypnotic session wherein he gave an interpretation of the origin and nature of the symptoms and made suggestions that the condition would disappear as soon as the patient attained insight.

Historically, hypnosis formed a starting point for studies of psychogenesis, for psychotherapy in general, and for psychoanalysis. It is today a valuable tool for the investigation of psychosomatic relationships. Blood sugar and blood calcium levels, respiratory, heart, and basal metabolic rates, and peripheral vascular reactions (flushing and skin temperature) can be modified by hypnotic suggestions (see Chapter 16). American psychiatric practice has probably not made sufficient use of hypnosis.

Hypnosis has, however, definite limitations even beyond the temptation to attack the patient's individual complaints. It cultivates dependent and infantile attitudes. It savors of magic. The attitudes of the hypnotizer take the initiative and responsibility away from the patient. The view of the hypnotist as an omnipotent magician is not a wholesome attitude to encourage in either the patient or the physician. It is bad for the physician's relationship with his patients except in the most critical situations. Finally, hypnosis often runs counter to the best principles of psychological health, namely, the fostering of understanding, of motivation, of an evaluation of reality, and of a constructive development of personality.

Suggestion.—Probably the oldest form of psychotherapy and the one in most common use is suggestion. Whenever one human being tries to influence another, suggestion usually enters in. It is involved in the psychology of leadership, advertising, propaganda, religious faith and practice, sleep, hypnosis, and psychotherapy.

Baudouin (1920) defines suggestion as the subconscious realization of an idea. Janet (1889) follows the intellectualist tradition that suggestion is the implantation of an idea. McDougall (1926) defines suggestion as the acceptance of an idea with conviction without logically adequate goals for its acceptance. He relates it to the gregariousness of the species and the conative energy of the submissive instinct which is touched off by the prestige, authority, verbal expressions, or directions of the strong. Freudian theories are similar to those discussed under hypnosis and relate the influence of suggestion to the persistence of infantile attitudes toward the parents which are adopted or transferred to others (Jones, 1938, pp. 303–304).

When a patient comes to the doctor he is in an attitude of expecting relief not only from his physical symptoms but from his insecurities. It is important for the physician to be aware of this psychological condition even if he is treating an organic illness, and to use suggestion constructively and not destructively. It is here that the physician's manner and bearing are so important. Indefiniteness, lack of assurance, uncertainty, undue gravity, or silence may be devastating to the patient. Such behavior feeds his imagination and apprehension with all sorts of forebodings. A hasty word or an incomplete explanation may leave the patient with almost unbearable insecurity or fright.

Kraines (1941) points out that the value of suggestion is shown by its effects on a wholesome reorientation of the patient's general attitude rather than by symptom disappearance. Constructive suggestion, he believes, should help the patient direct his thoughts away from his pains and difficulties, toward outward and more pleasant possibilities. This change in attitude should relieve emotional tension so that smooth muscles relax, and should raise the threshold to pain. Suggestions made on the basis of a knowledge of the personality factors involved and of the statistical probability of cure are legitimate and helpful.

According to Diethelm (1936), treatment by suggestion is best used when the symptoms are not based on marked personality involvement. Shell shock shortly after its inception, anxiety states after accidents, conversion symptoms of recent and superficial origin are the conditions where success is most to be expected. It can be used with immature personalities or people with lowered intelligence. For obsessive and compulsive states, and psychoses, it is ineffective. It enters in part in the various forms of physical therapy such as massage, baths, ultraviolet light, etc. As Miller (1930) points out, diseased and especially nervous people are in primitive, regressive states of mind. One of the characteristics of these states is a tendency toward superstition. "They do not want a reason, they want a sign." The effectiveness of physiotherapy, of electrotherapy, and even of mild medicines is not so unreasonable as it seems, in view of the psychological state to which physicians must minister.

Many of the objections that hold for hypnosis apply also to direct suggestion. Suggestive therapy is symptomatic, not etiological. It is assertive and authoritative rather than understanding. It is superficial and dogmatic, not deep. In this sense, therefore, it is only partial and it is unrealistic. It goes against the fundamental principles of mental health because it obliterates rather than increases insight. Finally, it is impotent in severe conditions.

Coué (1929), a nonmedical practitioner, has popularized autosuggestion. For Coué, however, all suggestion is autosuggestion. When psychotherapy is effective at all through suggestion, he believes it is the result of a vivid imagination of a state of health with such conviction that pathological reactions are excluded. If imagination conflicts with the will, the imagination always wins out. Coué is undoubtedly right when he emphasizes that there are many conditions in which suggestion or imagination are effective where reason and the will are impotent. Furthermore, if his conception of imagination or suggestion be identified with the unconscious, his theory comes in line with important theoretical trends in psychiatry. In practice, the patient is taught autosuggestion by simple methods. He is simply told to repeat to himself, 20 or 30 times every day, the formula that he is "getting better and better in every way."

There are many objections to Coué's method both theoretically and practically. It is not really autosuggestion, for the suggestion comes from Coué or some other healer. The tone of command, the fixation on the root of the nose, the use of the string with knots in it as a sort of psychiatric rosary, all his auxiliary practices relate the procedure to hypnosis. From this point of view a state of dissociation is produced similar to that in hysteria and hypnosis. William Brown (1938) says that the conflict is not always between will and imagination but between a weaker and a stronger suggestion. Again the procedure and the symbolism afford no insight. The self-assurance is given, according to Schilder (1938), by the introjected father (Coué). Faith in the outcome is substituted for effort. The importance of Coué's personality in producing this faith has been underestimated. His anti-intellectualist and antivoluntarist emphasis is right, as is his emphasis on emotion and interest in determining outcomes. His emphasis on imagination, if we consider this the unconscious, his emphasis on passivity and absence of effort are important. They point out the limits of intellect and will power in life. As a routine scheme the Coué method is not used in psychiatric practice. But its main tenets have again called attention to the limits of appeals to reason and will power in psychotherapy which are, unfortunately, all too frequent in attempts at hasty therapy. The importance of optimistic representations (imaginations and suggestions) on waking up and going to sleep, and perhaps repeated during the day, has probably been minimized undeservedly by psychiatry.

Reasoning or Moral Suasion.—In 1907, Paul Dubois of Berne, Switzerland, published a book which was a landmark in the history of psychotherapy. When most physicians were emphasizing the neurological or hereditary causes of nervous diseases and treating them by physical means (see below, the Weir Mitchell treatment), he wrote that many conditions were purely or primarily psychological in origin and, therefore, required psychological treatment. Dubois quoted Charcot for the belief that psychoneuroses arise from two factors, namely, an invariable neuropathic (Dubois says it should be "psychopathic") heredity, and a "provoking agent." If a person gets a nervous disease, one can infer a latent predisposition according to Dubois. Nevertheless, we should practice "orthopedia" because we pass on not only our heredity defects to our children, but also we give them the contagious example of our faults. A man becomes psychoneurotic because of what he owes to heredity, to atavism, to education, and to his ego. Although the psychoneuroses have a physical substratum, this need not mean they have somatic causes. The weakness, fatigue, and anemia are not the causes. Psychoneuroses are afflictions of the psychic life; their source is psychic; it is ideation that causes these disorders. The stigmata of the psychoneuroses Dubois considered to be: suggestibility, fatigability, exaggerated sensibility, and exaggerated emotionalism. However, he did not consider all nervous conditions to be caused by psychological factors, so not all could be cured by psychotherapy. He pointed out that all clinical syndromes that characterize bodily illness have their counterparts in nervousness.

Dubois' therapy is often called *persuasion* in the textbooks, but his theoretical emphasis on rational and moral factors makes it more logical to refer to his therapy as *rational psychotherapy* or *moral suasion*. He contrasted his therapy with that of Bernheim who considered suggestion everything. According to Dubois, the patient should develop critical mindedness and a sense of independence as defenses against suggestibility. He anticipated the opposition to treating symptoms. One should not treat symptoms directly, but all therapy must be based on accurate diagnosis, and one should concentrate on changing the system of ideas through moral suasion. Belief in the possibility of cure must be emphasized from the beginning, for once the patient has such a conviction, he is already better. The keynotes in Dubois' method were encouraging and moralizing conversations, reasoning as to the nature of the symptoms, enlightenment concerning the false ideas and bad mental habits on which the symptoms were based, acceptance of the symptoms and ignoring their nature, and the belief and conviction of cure. Patients should be stoical, for instance, and think more of the welfare of others than of their own misfortunes.

There is no doubt that Dubois' approach heralded a new note in the history of psychiatry. His book contains numerous examples of cases, and, because of the frankness of his reports, even when he runs contrary to his own theory in the use of pure direction and assertion, they will repay reading by any interested in practical psychotherapy. Unfortunately, his reports contain too little of what was actually said and done in a particular case. From the modern point of view, moreover, we should want to know more about the personalities and their development in Dubois' cases. His studies did not compare in detail with the patient investigations that Freud was simultaneously making, but he was a great clinician, an intuitive, impressive, and successful therapist. He certainly had adumbrations of the main points emphasized in modern psychotherapy. For instance, he wrote: "The more I advance in medical experience, the more I try to make my intervention rational and avoid pure suggestion. One must not confine one's ambition to the suppression of the actual attack. One must be concerned with the connection of the (hysterical) mentality. Get your patient to confess to you, and you will detect distressing preoccupations and unhealthy mental conditions created by the circumstances of her life" (Dubois, 1907).

Clearly, however, Dubois' patients did not improve merely through his appeal to their intellect and will. His prestige, personal influence, suggestion, positive assertion, and emotional support entered into his therapy. He appealed not only to reason but to the emotions and to various unconscious factors in the personalities of his patients. Although emotions were underestimated in his theory, a sort of parent-child relationship was actually established, and faith in a sort of father confessor and director was probably quite as important in his success as appeals to reason. Dubois had remarkable success therapeutically, and his theory marked a distinct advance, but his rational and logical short-cuts to emotional problems were often superficial and inadequate both theoretically and therapeutically. He relied heavily on the old Christian teaching that, "If thou canst believe, all things are possible to him that believeth" (Mark 9:23).

Persuasion.—Dubois' theoretical reliance on reason and will power underestimated the importance both etiologically and therapeutically of emotion in the psychoneuroses. But his contemporary, Déjerine (1913), corrected this defect, called attention to and insisted on the importance of emotion, "Everything that an emotion may create in an accidental and transient way hysteria may accomplish in a lasting way" (pp. 269–270).

For Déjerine, emotions (not just wrong ideas, weakened will, and suggestibility) are causal in the development of psychoneuroses. Emotional shocks and repeated difficulties which cause marked anxiety and anguish are the starting points. The stimuli may be external, or they may be internal like a memory of a past event or an idea of future action. Conflict between our emotions and intelligence is set up, and, in the psychoneuroses, the intelligence is overwhelmed. In this process, vicious circles are established, for the patient may be emotional from lack of intellectual strength, or weakened intellectually from too strong emotions. Fatigue, overwork, and organic disease may play a role in the development of nervousness, but emotional disturbance is always basic. Sexual disturbances increase emotionalism. Functional disorders are, as it were, "crystallizations" of emotional reactions.

In Déjerine's system, each syndrome had its particular psychopathology. Hysterical conditions arose directly from strong emotional shocks. Neurasthenic conditions developed gradually from repeated emotional reactions when the patient could not free himself from the memory of and preoccupation with them. Hypochondriacal conditions might have their origin in the emotional uneasiness with regard to health caused by the overprotection of children. Psychasthenic tendencies and loss of security might arise from urging children to be too concerned with and anxious about scruples, exactness, and perfection.

In therapy, according to Déjerine, one tries to liberate (release, abreact) the personality from the harmful emotions and misrepresentations. Thorough examinations are made and no therapeutic efforts are tried at first. The patient is allowed to talk and his confidence is gained. His whole life history is gone into with sympathy. He is asked about any special emotional difficulties, sorrows, or traumatic incidents. The patient is told of the certainty of the cure. The liberating action of confession (abreaction) is stressed. Explanations of emotions and their physiological counterparts are given, but Déjerine does not try to impose his own philosophy on the patient as does Dubois. He maintains that the patient is not cured by reasoning and logic, but by the affective relationship with the therapist, which enables him to develop absolute confidence in the physician. This emotional confidence is the factor that implements persuasion. The reeducation of bad habits is employed. Encouragement is used, efforts are made to make the patient feel that he is capable.

Déjerine's persuasion is thus conceived as a more complicated process than is either the moral suasion of Dubois or suggestion. According to the theory of moral suasion, the patient gets well because he believes he can. According to the theory of suggestion, he gets well because the doctor says he should. Déjerine's formulations are broader than either of these. He takes into account the effects of emotional excitement and fatigue on intellectual function. According to the theory of persuasion, the patient gets well because it has been shown to his satisfaction that there is no reason, emotional or physiological, why he cannot recover. In the practice of persuasion, the physician tries to guide the patient in solving his difficulties, and in correcting his unwholesome habits and misinterpretations. It should not be forgotten, however, that explanations may act as suggestions.

The work of both Dubois and Déjerine shows them to have been great clinicians. Their depth of insight, and the warmth and kindliness of their therapy went beyond their theoretical formulations. They did not hesitate to use sympathy, support, kindliness, suggestion, and direction when the human situation demanded it. Modern clinical psychiatry, outside of psychoanalysis, is in practice a development and elaboration of the methods of Dubois and Déjerine.

Authority, Direction, and Will.—In the usual practice of medicine and surgery, the physician draws on his scientific knowledge and tells the patient what to do. He expects the patient to accept his pronouncements, to exert his will, and to cooperate in executing the directions. This practice of physicians in somatic disease leads them to overestimate the value of knowledge, reason, and will in the conduct of life. They project these functions onto their patients. When good results do not follow their directions in psychological disease, they are disturbed, and they protect themselves psychologically by attributing obstinacy and lack of will to their patients. The omnipotency wish of the physician is thus frustrated, and the desire to dominate and cure by sheer will power and direction is intensified. This factor is the source of many failures in psychiatric treatment.

Many physicians prepare elaborate, detailed plans according to which the patients are to live automatically and obediently. The kind of therapy advised thus depends much on the needs of the physician himself. Unquestionably, such authoritative direction of the lives of others has had its successes. But it does not develop self-reliance, independence, and the taking of responsibility, which are so important in the return to psychological health.

Payot wrote a book, *The Education of the Will* (1909), which described this type of treatment, and it had influence in psychiatry. This type of treatment finds an important place in the regimen of Austen Riggs. In this regimen the details of daily living are arranged on a schedule so that life shall be neither desultory nor impulsive, and time shall not hang heavy on the patient's hands. The routine is reminiscent of the rules of the old religious orders. At the end of the day the patient is to review the events of the day, consider his failures and his achievements, and then plan the next day so that a combination of work, reflection, and meditation is afforded. Walsh (1913) urges reflections on the significance and means of accomplishment. He also stresses the value of leisure and pleasure in life. Various other direct schemes of mind and will training have been elaborated by Pere Eymieu (1922), by Vittoz (1913), by Barrett (1915, 1925), and by Walsh (1931). In these, any combination of the following aids may be employed: nursing, occupational therapy, vocational therapy, art, social and religious therapy. Limitations of space permit no discussion of these.

The purpose of all this regimentation and activity is not merely to fill up time and to divert the patient, but also to establish certain wholesome habits. Of course, it is undeniable that having certain actions become habitual and automatic is important. Occupational therapy, one's regular vocation, and a schedule for daily living may all contribute toward this. Diverting a patient at intervals from his worries, fears, and unsolved problems may be wholesome, too. But much therapy errs in arranging so much diversion that the patient is encouraged to avoid facing his problems. It thus becomes suppressive and runs counter to the modern ideas concerning the importance of abreaction and of the resolution of conflicts. One may, for instance, be able to *make* a patient paint or photograph as a routine hobby without any reference to his feelings or his resistance. But finally, a panic of resistance and aggression may overwhelm him in an orgy in which he destroys all these accomplishments. This happened in a case we have seen. This type of therapy is based on a faulty psychology of will. In the sense of many of these writers, will turns out to be the exercise of good habits. Their therapy assumes a faculty of will. It does not recognize the importance of emotion, early training, experience, and conflict in the development of the psychoneuroses (see Chapter 29 by Malamud). It ignores the important factor of interest, both conscious and unconscious, which James long ago (1893) pointed out as the determinant of the "impulsive and inhibitive quality" of objects and of ideas that come to mind. It also ignores the "inspired purpose" and the devotion to great causes emphasized by Walsh (1931).

The Physical Methods of Treatment

Rest Treatment.—Of the physical approaches, the "rest cure" of Weir Mitchell (1893), first described in Sequin's Series of American Clinical Lectures (1875, Vol. 1), is most famous. Mitchell greatly emphasized physical factors, and especially the loss of weight, in his conception of nervous afflictions. He believed that rapid thinning was almost always accompanied by anemia. Fat was his index of health, and a gain in weight meant an increase in red blood. Weight, fat, and blood were the three great factors he tried to improve.

Mitchell's treatment consisted in the combined use of isolation, rest, diet, massage, and electricity. He made no great claim to originality because all of these methods had been used separately by other physicians. His originality consisted in the regular and systematic use of these procedures combined. The reason rest failed to cure many patients treated by other doctors was, he thought, because it was used without isolation from relatives, or without a dietary push, or without the simultaneous use of massage and electricity. Electricity, he believed, toned up the muscles and made up for the lack of exercise, increased the temperature of the body, fostered relaxation, and toned up the circulation. Cases to be so treated were: patients convalescent from fevers, those suffering from constant dyspepsia or "malarial poisonings," and cases of nervous exhaustion with spinal irritation and hysterical symptoms, with many aches and pains, and with loss of weight and anemia but without organic disease.

Although Mitchell's physiological considerations were not completely adequate, there are unquestionably sound aspects of his treatment. Rest in bed reduces tension and its harmful effects in many, but not all, cases. Adequate nutrition and frequent feedings favor absorption and assimilation. We have used insulin injections in certain cases in which severe and dangerous undernutrition was apparent (Appel, *et al.*, 1929). Massage keeps up muscle tone, favors relaxation, and aids circulation. Isolation from emotionally disturbing factors is absolutely necessary at times.

However, the most important factor in Mitchell's use of his method was the influence of his distinguished and authoritative personality. Such factors as suggestion, reassurance, support, hope, and persuasion were probably more important than his physical procedures, although they did not figure in his theory. Many other physicians using his methods mechanically have failed because these psychological factors were unrecognized. Furthermore, rest will not cure a fatigue which is the result of unconscious resentment. In such patients rest treatment is only symptomatic therapy. In a patient we saw recently, the only hope of curing the chronic fatigue was not in rest, but in discovering and making conscious the etiological factors of aggression and resentment, and in dealing with them.

Relaxation Therapy.—In his talks to teachers and students in 1892, William James (see James, 1915, pp. 54–55, 119) gave the psychological and philosophical background for many of the therapies of relaxation that were developed later. Their soundness and efficacy as valuable implements of therapy are, unfortunately, too often ignored by psychiatrists.

James quoted the observations of Hindu visitors to this country who noted the tense countenances, ungraceful and anxious expressions of so many Americans. These visitors could not comprehend our living without devoting any portion of our day to meditation and tranquillity. James thought that this overmotion (overmobilization of Riggs, 1922) was causing a "grievous national harm." In his famous theory of emotions, James (1893) emphasized the "organic stirrings" as constituting a large part of what we call emotion. Put extremely, we are sorry because we weep, or we are afraid because we run away. Although this conception is not wholly true (see Cannon's theory in Bard, 1934), it has a core of truth in it, and it provides an important therapeutic lever in psychiatry. If we pay little attention to how we feel and concentrate on what we do, and, if we think of ideas, goals, ideals, and action, the feelings will gradually be indirectly and unconsciously controlled. Regulated action will thus indirectly control feeling and its associated autonomic disturbances: palpitation, tachycardia, diarrhea, and abdominal pain. The corollary of all this is to act as if we were kindly and cheerful and courageous when we feel the opposite, and not pay too much attention to the feelings.

James (1902) argued that the cause of nervous breakdowns is not hard work but the feelings of rush, hurry, tension, dissatisfaction, solicitude, and untoward anticipations. Strong feelings about self or one's responsibilities "cramp" or inhibit the free association of our ideas and our motor responses. Relaxation, equanimity, faith, and devotion to great and extra-individual causes, he believed, should be cultivated.

In this connection, James referred to the important work of Annie Payson Call, a nurse of nervous patients who worked out an unusually successful scheme of treatment and a philosophy of practice which is summed up in a remarkable book, *Power Through Repose* (1891, 1914). Her methods were not purely physical as Weir Mitchell's were, at least theoretically. They involved relaxing exercises, and mind training for rest, repose, and "power" for effective action. She believed that we have perverted nature's laws in our rush and strain of living. She advocated that one should learn to rest throughout the day by, for instance, relaxing while sitting in a train instead of trying to help it along, that one should learn to wait without tension and impatience, and that one should avoid rapid thought and misdirecting thought. She emphasized the effect of relaxed muscles in cultivating sleep.

In her philosophy, Miss Call believed that body training was also mind training. To learn a new movement, we must forget the old one and relax. She considered worry to be "brain tension" which leads to fatigue and illness. Along with her physical exercises and mind training, she utilized moral training in which she emphasized social relationships. As axioms she used such thoughts as: "one cannot be happy without considering others"; "one must develop tolerance"; "one must train oneself to yield as well as to direct."

A little book by Rippon and Fletcher (1940), which describes a combination of training in relaxation with psychotherapy, is one of the most stimulating and helpful that has come to our attention. The relaxation exercises are very similar to those recommended by Annie Payson Call. However, just as Jacobson (1934, 1938) has extended these training techniques and supported their significance with electro-physiological investigations, Rippon and Fletcher have extended her moral or psychological therapy.

Their theory of neurosis is approximately as follows. The environment stimulates the organism both physiologically and psychologically. The primal stimulation is insecurity and inadequacy [see resemblance to Horney's (1937) theory]. Normal development so organizes the responses to this state of insecurity or inadequacy as to overcome it successfully. Inadequacy is a "natural incentive to growth, development and achievement." Health is not a static state of completeness but a succession of challenges to inadequacy and achievement. In the nervous disorders, however, misinterpretations, inadequate and overreactive responses produce anxiety which they discuss chiefly from the Adlerian point of view. For Rippon and Fletcher, anxiety is the core of neurosis, as Sidis (1916) believed long ago.

Their therapy begins by getting the patient to relax and cease all effort at definite intervals. They teach relaxation by Call's method. An attempt is then made to draw the patient out, which tends to establish the confidence that will lead him later to discuss personal matters. Encouraging him to cease all effort diminishes his desire to fight his situation and revolt against his weakness. Gradually he learns what his pattern of life has been, how it has failed, and he is thus helped to develop a new and more satisfactory pattern. In this therapy they utilize the meaning of symptoms, a tactful and unhurried elucidation of their development, the emotional relationship between patient and physician, reassurance, and imaginative exercises which are perhaps reminiscent of Coué. They also utilize inspiration and the development of a wholesome attitude toward life and reality (religion). Their discussion of the attitude with which the patient with anxiety, whether from organic disease or neurosis, comes to the physician, and of the attitude with which the physician should approach such patients could be read with profit by all physicians and psychiatrists.

The method of Rippon and Fletcher has some kinship with psychoanalysis. Processes of regression, conflict, abreaction, misinterpretation, and the development of insight are clearly implied. But free association is not used. The transference relationship and identification are obviously implied, but they are not analyzed. The development of the individual is not considered in such great detail as in psychoanalysis. Their method is essentially reeducational. Notwithstanding these criticisms, the book of Rippon and Fletcher gives an understanding insight into the nature and practice of psychotherapy that few can equal in so small a compass.[1]

Physiotherapy.—The use of physiotherapy or physical therapy in nervous and mental diseases is often a valuable procedure. Clearly, its most definite indication is the use of electro-shock in the extreme disorders of affect and motor activity, seen in the manic-depressive psychoses or involutional melancholia. The value of the continuous bath in states of psychomotor agitation and insomnia is proved. The sedative effects of massage are definitely helpful in restlessness and mild agitation. The stimulating effects of more energetic massage, of the salt glow, and of faradic current are helpful in psychophysical retardation and in asthenic states. The various douches and showers may be used for either their sedative and counter-irritative effects or their stimulating effects. Nevertheless, physiotherapy for the most part remains empirical and experimental. It is a useful adjunct in psychiatry and may often be used as a step in establishing the transference required for psychotherapy.

In all types of physiotherapy, one must bear in mind that the effects attributed to the physical agents may be due to psychological factors

------

[1] Another method with some slight kinship to these relaxation methods is that of F. M. Alexander (*Man's Supreme Inheritance*, New York: Dutton, 1918, or latest edition, 1941: *Constructive Conscious Control of the Individual*, New York: Dutton, 1923; and *The Use of the Self*, New York: Dutton, 1932). Alexander believes that most people use their bodies incorrectly in that they let movements of the extremities interfere with the major tonic patterns. This interference leads to harmful tensions which cause general and local disabilities. Alexander teaches his "pupils" (he does not profess to be a therapist) to inhibit spontaneous movements until they can be executed without disturbing the basic head-neck-trunk relationship ("primary control"). He presents several cogent arguments against specific and local exercises or attempts to obtain relaxation directly. His method seems to result in general changes (e.g., mood and outlook) as well as specific ones. Although Alexander's theory was developed independently, it is consistent with the findings of Coghill (*Anatomy and the Problem of Behavior*, New York: Macmillan, 1929) and Magnus (see either R. Magnus's elaborate monograph: *Körperstellung*, Berlin: Springer, 1924; or J. G. Dusser de Barenne's brief summary of this work in "The labyrinthine and postural mechanisms," in C. Murchison, *A Handbook of General Experimental Psychology*, Worcester, Mass.: Clark University Press, 1933). It has received considerable attention in England, but is still relatively unknown in America, despite Dewey's support. (Editor)

working unconsciously and automatically, and caution is necessary in the proper evaluation of the factors contributing to improvement or cure.

The psychological benefits of various physiotherapeutic measures may or may not be well grounded physiologically. The physical contact which the physiotherapist's procedures require diminishes the feeling of isolation in the depressed patient, and tends to interrupt the autistic reveries of the withdrawn schizophrenic. These measures help to establish social rapport and almost physiologically stimulate socially approved reaction patterns. A sedative effect is accomplished not only by the psychological accompaniments of physiotherapy but also often by the direct metabolic effects of the baths, the packs or the radiant therapy and massage.

Like most physiotherapeutic measures, massage was employed by the ancients. Weir Mitchell and Douglas Graham added to its scientific repute. Hydrotherapy began with the first bath taken by man. The solvent, stimulating, sedative, and eliminative use of water has been proclaimed throughout the history of medicine. Benjamin Rush of Philadelphia used compresses, and he introduced the use of the ice bag. In the management of the nervous and mental patient hydrotherapy plays a most important role. The use of hot or cold water under pressure combines the use of water, temperature, and pressure. The effect gained from the use of massage may be obtained from the use of water with pressure. In this combination a strong stimulative, eliminative, and, if continued, sedative effect may be obtained. Baths, as used in psychiatric therapy, are usually of the continuous type and are employed largely in treating delirium and the excitement of mania or agitation. In many cases, this sort of treatment precludes the necessity of using chemical restraints or large doses of hypnotics.

Cryotherapy or the use of cold as a physiotherapeutic measure is less well understood and consequently employed less frequently than thermotherapy. More recently, following the work of Fay, the employment of cryotherapy over longer periods of time has been recommended as an alternative procedure to the pharmacological and electric treatments. Conversely, fever therapy, following its dramatic benefits in paresis, has been used by many in the treatment of the major psychoses, but results have been almost universally unsuccessful.

Medication and Shock.—In psychiatry, pharmacological agents are employed to alter the maladaptation of the patient to his milieu both internal and external. The types of drugs from which one may choose are many, and the medication must be prescribed individually with full knowledge of the patient's specific condition, and his reaction to sedatives, and with the goal to be accomplished in view. The judicious administration of carefully selected medication is invaluable in the treatment of mental illness. It enables us to control symptoms, to interrupt the stereotypy of mental and physical functioning, to gain access into the psychology of the patient, and to render nursing care and social guidance more frictionless and effective.

Of the specific drugs, chloral is the oldest of the group. Its action is certain, prompt, and lasting, and its effects are easily graduated by the dosage. It has an unpleasant taste, and may be followed by cardiac and respiratory depression. Paraldehyde is milder in proportion to the dosage, and there are no depressive after-effects, but it is less certain in its action. It has its primary use in psychiatry in the control of withdrawal symptoms following alcoholism. The barbituric acid derivatives are the most widely used of all the hypnotics and their degree of action can be graded by appropriate dosage from a sedative effect to the production of coma. There are a great number of these derivatives, and it is preferable for the clinician to become acquainted with a few of the shorter and longer acting drugs and confine himself to these.

Besides the use of sedative drugs to produce sleep or to allay anxiety, pharmacological agents to induce prolonged narcosis were early recognized to have great psychiatric value. Such treatment interrupts the vicious cycle of psychotic thought processes by inducing a physiological state of quiescence, albeit chemically accomplished. Its greatest field of usefulness is in the management of acute illnesses in young, physically healthy people of more than average intelligence. Narcosis permits access to the patient while his resistance is lowered; it brings to light material of inestimable value in the later phases of therapy; and it makes for quicker rapport. Palmer and Braceland (1937) present a comprehensive review of this form of therapy.

Insulin treatment of schizophrenia, since Sakel (1937, 1938) first described the use of this technique at the University Clinic of Vienna about 1930, has undergone considerable variation in the actual procedures. In this method, a reduction in blood sugar that finally gives rise to prolonged coma is effected through large doses of insulin. A major need in such therapy is the adaptation of the basic technique to fit the daily needs of the individual patient (see review by Shipley and Kant, 1940). This leads to an eclectic type of treatment. The greatest indication for the use of insulin treatment is schizophrenia when a patient is not improving after the usual psychiatric therapy. Schizophrenics may have their delusional, isolated thinking interrupted for one or two hours after such treatment, and this may provide a therapeutic lever. Its use for all other psychiatric conditions is contraindicated. Neither should it be used when various organic diseases would make such therapy dangerous. Insulin treatment increases the percentage of remissions (see statistical section below), and shortens the illness in those who recover spontaneously. On the other hand, it is a long and costly therapy, and contains some danger to nerve cells and to life.

Metrazol, since its introduction by Meduna (1935), has gradually been relegated to the list of therapies used relatively infrequently, and this principally because of the advent of electric shock. In this treatment, intravenous injections of metrazol produce epileptiform convulsions in the patient (for description see Straus, Landis and Hunt, 1939). It is useful in the affective psychoses, in involutional melancholia, and in some of the acute catatonic episodes in very young people. It should not be used when electric shock is available, however, or when there is clinical cardiovascular disease, marked arteriosclerosis or hypertension, or when there is marked pathology. It has the advantage of requiring no special equipment, and it is a respiratory stimulant. However, the treatment is frightening to the patient, and there is danger of fracture. It is also capable of effecting changes in the heart musculature, and of causing damage to brain cells.

Electro-Shock.—Electricity has been used in the treatment of mental disease almost from the time of its discovery. At first, it was considered a "suggestive agency." Faradic current, however, is a valuable muscle stimulator. It can produce muscular contractions almost to the point of tetany. It is a useful vascular stimulant in sluggish, weak, or asthenic patients. The sinusoidal current has a marked trophic effect. It is an excellent stimulant for unstriated muscles where it causes very little pain.

Recently, Cerletti and Bini (1938) introduced an electrical shock treatment in which electrodes are applied to the head so that measured currents can be passed through the cerebral tissue. This produces a controllable epileptiform seizure. Like metrazol, it is used primarily in the affective psychoses, especially the depressions and involutional melancholia. It is sometimes used in schizophrenia after insulin has failed, but the results have been disappointing. Less anxiety is created by electro-shock than by metrazol. There is no anxiety over missed convulsions, and the convulsions are less severe than are those produced by metrazol. The patient does not remember the treatment. Fracture and mortality rates are also lower with electro-shock, but there is still some danger of fracture, and the danger of damage to brain cells and to memory is greater than with metrazol.

Surgical Therapy.—Various surgical treatments of nervous diseases have appeared historically, but only two modern techniques deserve mention. In the second decade of this century, Cotton (1921, 1922) tackled the problem of focal infection in these diseases. He believed that infections were more important as causes than are heredity, environment, improper training, or personality defects. He believed that emotions by way of their effect on the ductless glands could reduce resistance to infection. Thus, psychogenic factors could cause disturbances, but infection was the primary factor. Streptococci he considered the principal offenders, and they were followed by the staphylococci and the colon bacilli. He found tonsillar infection in 85% of his toxic psychoses, and he believed that the sinuses often became infected from the teeth and tonsils. Secondary foci of infection developed in the gastrointestinal tract. The cervix, tubes, ovaries, and seminal vesicles were also often infected. He believed that the disturbances in behavior resulted not from the actual infecting organisms themselves but from disturbances in the brain brought about by the toxins produced by these organisms. People were affected in different ways because the various strains of streptococci had selective affinities.

From this theory of cause Cotton turned for therapy to surgical removal of the foci of infection. Not infrequently several operations were performed on a single patient, and he reported remarkable results. In addition to removing the foci of infection, Cotton used diet, rest, and hydrotherapy, but he advised against psychotherapy.

Other psychiatrists soon turned to a controlled investigation of Cotton's theories and therapy. Kopeloff and Kirby (1923) removed the foci of infection in a group of 58 cases and left them in a control group of 62 patients. They found the recovery rates to be approximately the same in both groups. Kopeloff and Cheney (1922) carried out a similar study, and concluded that surgical removal of foci of infection produced no recovery, for no recovery took place which had not been predicted from clinical considerations before the surgery was undertaken.

Therapy by means of brain surgery was introduced by Moniz in 1936 (see Freeman and Watts, 1942). In this technique, the fibre tracts connecting the prefrontal areas with the thalamus are severed. It is most useful in chronic cases of agitated depression or involutional melancholia where other forms of therapy have failed, but it has been used to treat the whole gamut of psychiatric disorders. On the basis of over 80 successful operations, Freeman and Watts (1942) believe that this operation reduces the emotional reactions of the patient, especially the anxieties that concern himself. Tests of personal characteristics applied before and after such operations indicate a widening of the individual's horizon, reduction in preoccupation with self, and a general shift in the direction of extraversion. The depressed and obsessive become cheerful, outspoken, and often tactless. In some patients this may result in indolence and lack of tact, but Freeman and Watts report that many of their patients have attained their prepsychotic level of occupational adjustment, and some have even surpassed it (see statistical section below). Transitory disturbances of memory and other functions have been reported lasting as long as several weeks, but permanent undesirable sequelae appear to be rare.

Psychological Approaches Involving Reorganization of the Personality

Psychobiology.—Early in this century, Adolf Meyer, through the influence of Forel, became dissatisfied with Kraepelinian formulations. A study of Kraepelin's statistics showed that they varied from year to year and indicated that his disease entities were not clearly defined. Meyer (1908, 1928, 1938) concluded that Kraepelin's disease entities were really but types of reaction to difficulties or the results of difficulties in development. He therefore discarded the concept of *mental* *diseases* for that of *reaction types*. He argued that psychiatrists should study what is going on, "what is doing" in their patients, instead of searching for nerve cell changes and schemata which are largely hypothetical. Etiology should be sought in constitution, in exogenic, in organogenic, in psychogenic, and in social factors. This study of the total human being, of activities which cannot properly be considered to be the function of any part of the organism, or even merely of the brain, Meyer (1935) called *psychobiology*. These functions of the total organism he termed *ergasias*.

Therapy, according to Meyer, should endeavor to regulate and guide the patient's life after the factors favoring or hindering modification have been carefully studied and formulated. Our therapeutic goals should be to restore security, independence, and integration within the social group. Psychobiological therapy is conducted through what is called *distributive analysis and synthesis* (Diethelm, 1936; Muncie, 1939; Kanner, 1935). One first observes and analyzes the factors and situations concerned with the origin of the patient's condition. Then one synthesizes the facts which will contribute to the patient's security and to his successful biological and social adaptation. The process is one of education.

Adolf Meyer's psychobiology has exerted a highly beneficial influence and has been important in molding the whole trend of American psychiatry. It broke away from the artificial academic dichotomy of mind and body and brought psychiatry into the realm of biological science. It brought psychiatry and medicine closer together, and it contributed to the emergence of psychosomatic medicine. It has also brought psychiatry into close and important relation with sociology and education. Meyer has always emphasized optimism instead of fatalism in therapy.

Notwithstanding these positive contributions, Meyer's psychobiology is justifiably open to many criticisms. Muncie (1939, p. 146) gives some of these. There certainly is an underemphasis on unconscious processes. As does Adler, Meyer has assumed that question and answer procedures will discover and make clear to the patient the source of his difficulties. This overemphasizes the patient's capacity to reason, for there is no guarantee that once a patient has understood his difficulties, he will be able to effect the necessary changes. Meyer's form of therapy makes little or no use of free association, which itself is an *ergasia* or function which is not pathological, and which certainly favors the development of insight and new perspectives. Many patients lose intellectual interest, therapeutic enthusiasm, and become pessimistic after the exhaustive review of conscious facts and factors and the development of conscious formulations. For these cases the psychoanalytic procedure frequently offers patients something to chew on both intellectually and experimentally in living, and it tends to keep their enthusiasm and hope alive. Psychobiology has emphasized the study of patients rather than a technique of therapy. As therapy it is perhaps too simple and general to be effective in many cases. It definitely does not belong to the group of deep therapies.

Reeducation.—Austen Riggs (1922, 1929) developed an effective elaboration of psychobiology that is especially applicable to the psychoneuroses. As Adolf Meyer worked out his theories and therapy in hospitals devoted chiefly to the psychoses, Riggs developed his philosophy and his therapeutic methods in a restricted community at Stockbridge, Mass., devoted to the treatment of the psychoneuroses. Riggs' philosophy and his practices were eclectic, and various aspects of them show relationships with those of Bernheim, Dubois, Déjerine, Payot, James, Cannon, MacDougall, Meyer, and Adler. Like all these men, he emphasized psychological factors in the etiology of the psychoneuroses. In researches, he showed statistically that the causative factors for the majority of psychoneuroses cannot be found in the present environment of the individual. Nervousness, he argued, is a disorder or a conflict within the various levels of the individual: the reflex, the instinctive, the intellectual, the social, and the ethical (see relation to Meyer's formulations). Emotional strains in overreactive and overtemperamental persons produce the phenomena which are called symptoms, and these are misunderstood by the individual. The intensity of the overreactivity, or "overmobilization," may impair even the intellectual functions, thus the psychoneurotic misinterpretations, and in the more serious conditions the intellect shows only defective and distorted function.

For therapy, Riggs advised a temporary environmental change, for example, to a sanitarium such as Stockbridge. Such a change removed the patient from the strains of his usual vocational, social, and home environment. In the sanitarium, the patient saw his doctor daily for discussions. Lectures and group discussions on the psychology of human behavior and adjustment were given the whole group of patients daily. Cooperation in social living was stressed. The patient was told that he needed a process of reeducation, that he must go to school to learn the principles of personal efficiency. It was explained that the physicians and the organization would try to make him comfortable, but that comfort was purely a secondary consideration. Riggs died recently, but his eminently effective methods are being carried on by various groups throughout the country.

In the restricted community at Stockbridge, a schedule of activities is provided. This regularizes life. It removes the necessity of taking initiative and of making independent decisions. Like Payot's regimen, it distracts and diverts the patient; it develops the momentum of good habits; it affords practice in doing things because they are to be done, and allows no avoiding them because one does not like doing them. And, following James' philosophy, the regimen helps divorce feeling from action. In the regimen, a period of occupational work such as weaving, wood carving, basketry, or mental work is provided for each day. Periods are allowed for exercise, for rest, for relaxation, and for the diversions of social intercourse at meals and in the evening.

The foundation of Riggs' therapy was, thus, more than intuition and inspiration, even though these entered into Riggs' personal work. It followed definite principles. Riggs himself was a charming and imaginative person with whom people liked to be identified. This made his analyses acceptable to his patients. His procedures, furthermore, were definite, simple, and optimistic. One of Riggs' greatest influences was the effect which his conceptions and practice had in helping elimi-nate the embarrassment and stigma connected with nervous conditions. He tended to make them respectable. His writings and lecturing in col-leges helped, as did those of Beers (1908), to foster the mental hygiene and child guidance movements in this country and to make them funda-mental in education, sociology, and preventive psychiatry.

The same general objections that have been offered in connection with Adler's and Meyer's formulations and with "directive" therapy apply to Riggs' theories and procedures. Both Meyer and Riggs devel-oped their thinking and methods of treatment in connection chiefly with hospital or sanitarium practice. Both developed institutions far advanced in their approach to mental and nervous conditions with standards unsur-passed in their time. However, both have, by the nature of their organi-zations, concentrated on only part of the field, and their theory and practice reflect this situation. Their procedures of therapy have become too organized, too regimented, too directive. They have worked in environments which could be controlled. Such therapy is apt to give insufficient weight to unconscious factors. Perhaps this arose in Riggs' case because of his intense opposition to psychoanalytic formulations. But a psychology that does not recognize the importance of the concept of the unconscious is bound to be partial and in many cases ineffective.

Throughout Riggs' writings one recognizes a tremendous emphasis on the importance of social goals and on ideals for successful adjustment. Dignity, discipline, ideals, and the influence of reason—"sign up for an ideal"—permeate his writings. Certain patients have felt his standards were stern, stoical, and dogmatic and even Calvinistic. To be sure, Riggs himself counseled avoiding the New England conscience, but patients felt it implied in his recommendations. As with Adler's writings, people often feel, after having read Riggs, that they have fallen down morally in their job of living, that their pattern of life has not only been an inefficient mistake, but also a moral defalcation.

EXPLANATORY OR NOETIC THERAPY, INTERPRETATIVE THERAPY, AND BIBLIOTHERAPY.—These methods of reeducative therapy frequently over-lap. Explanatory therapy shows the patient the mechanism of his symp-toms but tends to be diagrammatic and mechanical. It is symptomatic and tends to focus on the present. Interpretative therapy tries to unravel the meaning or purpose of the condition and is more dynamic and biographical. It stresses process and teleology. Bibliotherapy uses both to enlarge the patient's knowledge and insight and is more theoretical than the others and tends to focus on human nature. Of these, explana-tory psychiatry is the easiest, interpretative is more difficult and full of pitfalls, and bibliotherapy is apt to be too general.

Explanatory therapy is an attempt to make clear to the patient his psychological machinery and how it works. Thus, it is a process of instruction. The physician teaches, explains, makes graphic the picture of the production of the symptoms as he sees it and tries to communicate this to the patient. It is an external communication to the patient of the psychiatrist's knowledge or understanding of his condition with the belief that the acquisition of this knowledge will cure it. As such, it is an attempt to implement will power with knowledge in the organization of the personality. In this type of therapy the physician may be quite active and aggressive, or more passive and suggestive. He can expound the principles of psychology and mental hygiene, or he can guide the patient to read about them and discover them in himself. After having read of a particular mechanism or having had it described by the physician, the patient explains it back, then he explains the mechanism of his own symptoms. It is easy to go from this type of therapy to interpretative psychiatry and even ultimately to free association and analysis. Sometimes it is the only possible approach some patients will accept, just as the psychiatrist is forced to start his psychotherapy with purely medical treatment in some instances.

The most satisfactory approach to explanatory therapy of which we know is in Riggs' (1922, 1929) books and pamphlets. One can, from the interim experiences and symptoms which the patient describes, use these as texts of psychology and elementary physiology. It is a simple matter to point out the relations of fear and tenseness, of worry and anorexia, of apprehension and palpitation, of excitement and flushing, of resentment and nausea, of depression and loss of weight, of insomnia, fatigue and emotion, and of emotional urgency and insecurity. The more simple psychological mechanisms can readily be explained, and the simpler displacements can be made clear and understandable. However, complicated displacements, reaction formations, substitutions, symbolisms, identifications, and projections can be explained only with difficulty. And if they can be explained they are frequently not understood, at least to the point of being serviceable in the therapeutic process.

Explanatory psychiatry forms the easiest and most ready introduction to psychology, and it is permissible to use it in any case except where one is sure that psychoanalysis is indicated and will shortly be used. One can employ it too early in treatment, however, before the patient feels that he has had an opportunity to say all that he has to say. The physician has to sense that the patient is ready for it, or that he has become discouraged with exhaustive physical and laboratory examinations and purely medical treatment, and will tolerate a consideration of some new aspect of his condition.

Interpretative therapy goes deeper than the explanatory method. It is interested in the significance of symptoms and in their function. In interpretative therapy, the psychiatrist tries to see the symptoms as part of the person in the process of adjustment. He tries to unravel the essential drives beneath the superficial manifestations, and to see the purpose of these symptom formations in the living economy of the patient.

As the psychiatrist discovers the patient's typical patterns of adjustment, he translates his reading of various situations to the patient. This type of therapy is more effective, but it requires more skill and contains more possibility of error. It has its uses and its values, but the more the physician allows the patient the opportunity of making his own interpretations and merely helps him guard against rationalizations and faulty reasoning in general, the more sure will be the ground on which he helps the patient to stand.

Even in explanatory, expository, or interpretative therapy, the inter·· view need not be formal and directed. The patient must feel free to talk of anything that comes to mind. Even if this delays the discussion of something the patient has read, it can be brought up at the end of the hour or at a later conference. It is important for patients to develop initiative and self-expression, and holding too close to something that was planned tends to dampen this self-direction.

Two of the most difficult problems in psychiatry are, when to try to explain, and when to support and help. Premature explanation falls on deaf ears, psychological blind spots, and defensive thinking. It may arouse intense resistance, evasion, and resentment. It may take away initiative, responsibility, and practice in exploration, reflection, and achievement. As such, therapy may be actually retarded, even though the goal is consciously the reverse. Much the same holds for giving advice, making decisions for the patient, and offering support and help.

Bibliotherapy is the use of books, articles, pamphlets, etc., as adjuvants in psychiatric treatment. Patients may be asked to read printed matter for a number of reasons. It serves chiefly as a means of acquiring information and knowledge about the psychology and physiology of human behavior. The references for this section (see special section in bibliography) give more information than it is here possible to consider. Menninger (1937) has an article discussing the psychological values in the use of bibliotherapy. A pamphlet by Mudd and Whitehill (1938) discusses its use in the premarital interview and sexual and marital adjustments. Ingram (1939) has many practical suggestions, not only for its use in private practice but for hospital practice as well. Twyeffort (1940) gives a general survey of the field and a most useful bibliography which will help the physician in his search for tried and practiced books. Bradley and Bosquet (1936) have published an article on the "Use of Books for Psychotherapy with Children" in which reading lists are given.

In psychiatry reading may be recommended to enable the individual to live up to the injunction "Know Thyself." Reading may be advised in an attempt to extravert the patient and arouse his interest in something outside himself. Other purposes may be to arouse interest in and acquaintance with external reality, or to effect a controlled release (abreaction) of unconscious processes, or to offer opportunities for identification and compensation. Of course, it is used to help the patient develop a clarification of his difficulties and contribute to the development of "insight" into his condition. It is also an attempt to implement the experience of others in effecting a cure. Reading supplements not only the knowledge and experience of the therapist, but it extends the period of the therapeutic conference, when the patient cannot be seeing the doctor. Its final aim is to aid the patient to live more effectively.

It is an advantage if the patient asks the physician if there is not some reading matter which will be helpful to him. Self-motivation usually means that the reading will be done more thoughtfully, conscientiously, and zestfully than if it is merely recommended by the physician. The particular book or articles recommended depend on many things. The most important are the educational and therapeutic needs of the patient, the type of person (e.g., whether a normal, healthy person seeking desired information, or a patient with a neurosis or psychosis), the educational background and intelligence of the individual, and the cultural, religious, and social background. The prescription of reading matter must be a highly individualized procedure if it is to be successful.

The order of psychiatric reading which we have found most effective follows. Osler's *Way of Life* (1932) is perhaps the most useful introduction we know. It is not written primarily for patients with nervous or mental disease, and it does not contain psychological and psychiatric terminology; nevertheless, it enables the patient to breathe an atmosphere of essential mental hygiene. It also offers a wholesome philosophy of life by an eminently successful man. The problem of living is simplified with a few plain and essential rules. This is especially helpful because patients have been thinking of so many complicated things and worries that it is a relief to get something brief, clear, authoritative, and hopeful.

Riggs' little book *Just Nerves* (1922) is an excellent one to follow Osler. It is also brief, the introduction is simple and it makes the psychology of nervousness easily understood. The last chapter on elementary rules for mental health (to which patients quickly turn) is again clear and inspiring. It contains sense which the patient recognizes. At the same time he realizes that some of these rules apply to him. He feels a sense of discovery and achievement, and that there is something definite on which to stand and build.

Discovering Ourselves (1931) appropriately comes next. This book is written in simple nontechnical language so that a person with mid-high school background can understand it. The chapters are for the most part brief and do not require prolonged periods of concentration. Technical and pathological terms are not employed but normal mental processes are described from the dynamic point of view. Extreme difficulties of thought and behavior are interpreted as intensifications and exaggerations of normal processes, rather than as morbid deviations and distortions. We have used the book not only to acquaint the patient with dynamic psychological processes, but also to stimulate in him the challenge to discover his own difficulties and take the initiative in trying to solve them.

When a patient has finished reading *Discovering Ourselves,* he is aware of the importance of childhood experiences and parental relationships. He may begin to discuss sex problems and sex education. Criti-cism of his own social and sexual education come to the fore. At this period we have found Sayles' *The Problem Child at Home* (1928) prob-ably the most satisfactory book. The chapters on mistaken ideas which influence the development of children reinforce and clarify the patient's critical faculties. They afford an outlet for resentments and aggressions.

The next transition is often made to Thom's *Normal Youth and Its Everyday Problems* (1932), or Frankwood Williams' book (1930) on adolescence. When family relationships are factors of importance in the development of nervousness, the discussion in Levy and Monroe's book, *The Happy Family* (1941), has been found most helpful. Then, if further emphasis on family education and on adolescence does not seem to be indicated, Horney's *The Neurotic Personality of Our Time* (1937) is given. This offers a clear and impressive discussion of the mechanisms of neurosis in the individual, and also emphasizes the cultural forces at work especially through the parents. A historical perspective is then added with Robinson's *Mind in the Making* (1921). This not only reviews our animal heritage but the various kinds of thinking that get not only individuals but civilizations into trouble. A note of optimism with a historical perspective may be added by Edman's *Candle in the Dark* (1939).

This reading, of course, is not a cut-and-dried and formal process. Part of the interviews has to be given over to a review of the interval history and presenting problems that have developed. Reviews of the past history of the individual are naturally discussed and they are abreacted in response to what has been read. Some interviews may scarcely get round to the consideration of reading matter at all. The procedure should be as spontaneous and flexible as possible. Some con-ditions may make it advisable to alter the order and selection of books.

Bibliotherapy, then, we believe, has a definite place in practical psy-chiatry. Its value has probably in general been underestimated. There are very few studies of its use in the literature. Its greatest advantage is time saving. We have found in many instances that therapy went ahead much faster with its use than with those patients who had not done any reading. Besides giving knowledge and information, another advantage lies in the fact that it familiarizes the patient with terminology and with the accurate use of words. This is not to be overlooked because so many people use terms so loosely, and the use of words is especially difficult in psychology and psychiatry because they deal with abstractions. Such reading introduces the patient to the conception of objectivity and helps him acquire a broader view of human nature. It can present the total picture of mental functions or mechanics much more clearly and com-pletely than one can by the question and answer technique. It also removes the personal factor. It often enables the patient to discover things for himself instead of having them pointed out by the therapist, or having to take things on his authority. It helps in relieving a sense of isolation from which so many patients with neurosis suffer. It relieves them to discover that many others have had the same (often common and even normal) difficulties.

Notwithstanding these many advantages, there are many disadvantages and limitations to bibliotherapy. Many people have not been in the habit of reading or cannot read; many others will not. Some do not have the intellectual ability to read understandingly and the majority of nervously ill patients are unable to read because of the psychological disturbances inherent in their neuroses. It is unfeasible to get the majority of patients in mental hospitals to read but there is still a large group for whom reading is advantageous and there is certainly a large proportion of patients in office practice for whom it is beneficial.

Personality Study.—In the last quarter century psychiatry has shifted its interest from detailed descriptions of nervous and mental conditions and precise classification, to an understanding of developmental and etiological conditions. Psychiatrists are not so much interested in symptoms and attempts at refined nosological demarcations; they are satisfied with general reaction types. The important things are the dynamics of the various conditions. This dynamic or developmental approach has been instigated and fostered by the great men of recent psychiatry. Among others are Freud, Adler, Kretschmer, Hoch, Meyer, and Strecker.

One of the most satisfactory ways, not only of gaining an understanding of the individual and of the condition from which he is suffering, but also of giving positive therapy is the *personality study*. Systematic study of personal development not only brings into relief the forces at work in the present personality, but, inevitably, discussing them brings to light important etiological considerations.

It may well be asked what a scheme for personality study has to do with psychotherapy, and the answer lies in the fact that therapy in psychiatry (exclusive of medical, toxic, infective, and exhaustive conditions) is different from that in medicine. Treatment, in medicine, is a separate procedure from the history taking, and the physical and laboratory examinations of the patient. In psychiatry, on the contrary, the study of the patient's personality and the exploration of its development has a distinctly beneficial therapeutic influence. The questions at once stimulate the patient to take new and wholesome attitudes towards his condition. He often comes wanting help and advice; he often is ready to submit to the authority of the physician as a child to its loved parent. His responsibility is shifted completely to the physician; he wants to be worked upon as by magic, very much according to his conception of the way the surgeon works. This is not the wholesome way in psychiatric therapy. The physician's questions show indirectly that all is not as simple and clean-cut as the patient is inclined to think. There is more to his condition that needs consideration and treatment than just the symptoms, which are not as important as he thought they were. He is thus necessarily initiated into the wholesome process of objectivity. Other relevancies than those he had considered must be gone into. Such procedure gives the patient something to do, "a bone to chew on." Instead of feeling helpless and passive, he learns there is something that he can do and is expected to do. He is challenged with the hope of a new attack on his condition of hopeless passivity and suffering. The more informal, casual, and drawn out in time (weeks or months if necessary or advisable) this process is, the more therapeutic value it will have. Casualness, equanimity, and lack of haste, exude a therapeutic strength which helps reduce the intensity of the patient's feelings. It helps to dissipate insecurity and fear, and is of inestimable value compared with formality, overseriousness, and professional terminology.

Amsden (1923) has published a satisfactory scheme of personality study, and we have worked out one that was originally published in a book on the examination of patients (Appel and Strecker, 1936). The first area investigated is physical health, with questions as to illnesses, operations, etc., and what part these have played in the life history. From this it is an easy transition to the concept of energy. Has the individual been overactive with excess of energy or is he tired much of the time? From the consideration of energy, it is an easy step to observations concerning whether the individual is usually calm or tense, and how his temper has affected him vocationally or socially. From this, one turns readily to the other emotional reactions, with social situations coming quite naturally next. Is he an outgoing, active, friendly type of person with lots of friends, or a cold, distant person whom one gets to know with difficulty? The next group of questions relates very much to self-confidence and the super-ego. Is he decisive or indecisive, is he cocky and dogmatic? Is he submissive or a fighter, etc. Is he dependent or independent? Upon what is he dependent? What are his standards? his goals? It is important to go into the patient's development, and he can be asked what he has heard about his mother's condition when she was pregnant; about his birth and early training; about his childhood fears; about his sexual training and how he felt about this; about his parental relationships (identifications and antagonisms).

Sometimes such an outline will apparently be curative, but at other times it will completely fail therapeutically. Generally, it gives the patient hope that there is something to discover that will help him out of the trouble, and this hope is one of the greatest therapeutic tools.

There are many disadvantages to such a system. It is apt to become too formal. Free association is not provided for, but practically, a certain amount can be cultivated by allowing the patient plenty of time, by letting his conversation drift where it will, and by not guiding it too much with questions. One great objection is that unless a considerable amount of free association is encouraged, the patient does not learn to know his unconscious patterns. The transference and resistance are not tackled. It cannot be used with any but the mildest psychotics, and with severe neurotics it is often therapeutically ineffective. When the patient gets talked out and the ordinary psychiatric interview is making no progress, however, the personality study can be used. When this is exhausted, one can proceed to a form of bibliotherapy, or to modified analysis. This method is a short-cut, a compromise, necessitated at times by certain inevitable exigencies.

Psychoanalysis.—HISTORY.—Charcot demonstrated the dynamics of ideas in hysteria. He showed that ideas caused such symptoms as the paralysis following emotional shock. Furthermore, ideas, or instructions, given in hypnosis can produce similar symptoms. Liébeault and Bernheim disclosed the rationalization of motives in their studies in hypnotism.

Janet, working with hysterical conditions at the Salpêtrière under Charcot, found that hidden memories were important in the development of such neuroses. They were either memories of actual traumatic incidents or of events associated with some moral perturbation. These memories dissociated themselves from the main trend of consciousness by the process of "psychological automatism" and became subconscious "idées fixes." By the discovery of these memories, a discussion of them, and by a process of moral liquidation or assimilation, of conscious reasoning, and of stimulation and direction, cure was effected in many cases (see Janet, 1889).

Freud (see 1910 and 1914) studied with Charcot in Paris and learned from him the dynamics of ideas in hysteria. He visited Bernheim at Nancy and got from him the post-hypnotic rationalization of motivation, and also the fact that by special effort the patient could discover the real motive. He was familiar with Janet's work on the effect of memories in traumatic hysterical contractures. When he returned to Vienna he collaborated with his friend Breuer who had been studying hysteria under hypnosis. In 1893 and 1895, they published their now famous report on cases of hysteria. In these they concluded that hysterical phenomena are caused by ideas to which strong affect has been attached. They believed a disturbance in associations takes place similar to that in sleepiness, in which unusual associations are formed, and the affect jumps, as it were, into abnormal physical and mental paths producing the various phenomena of hysteria. They brought about cure by bringing to consciousness these various memories or reminiscences accompanied with their usual emotion or excitements. This expression of pent-up affect along with the appropriate idea they called *abreaction,* and the process they called *catharsis.* The patient was said to suffer from reminiscences, and the essence of their cathartic therapy was to discover the traumatic events which were originally painful to the patient, and to bring them to consciousness with appropriate expression of emotion by getting the patient to talk about them during a hypnotic trance. This procedure freed the patient from symptoms.

Freud soon abandoned hypnosis as part of his procedure, however, because many patients could not be hypnotized and he was able to obtain results from his talking treatment without hypnosis. He asked the patients to speak of anything that came into their minds and did not insist on their recalling special experiences related to their symptoms. He found that finally they came of their own accord to thoughts, experiences, and phantasies, that had been important in their lives (see also Chapter 7 by French and Chapter 21 by Ribble).

Because an emphasis on sex developed in psychoanalysis, and because patients apparently fell in love with the analyst, Breuer withdrew from his collaboration with Freud. Freud persevered and began his analysis of this falling in love from which he found that the physician was a substitute for someone the patient had previously loved. This was the beginning of his studies of the mechanism of transference (see Freud, 1914).

Freud then formulated the hypothesis of the unconscious; that there are forces, inclinations, influences, impulses, attitudes, of which the individual is unaware but which modify unwittingly his conscious thinking, preferences, antipathies, and behavior. These unconscious forces he believed were especially important in the psychoneuroses and functional psychoses. In his investigations in hysteria, he found that many symptoms were apparently symbolic expressions of ideas which were once conscious but which because of their painful character had been repressed or forgotten, and remained below the threshold of awareness or consciousness (Freud, 1896). These ideas or impulses were still active, however, and they influenced consciousness and behavior even though the patient was unaware of this influence. There appeared to be a resistance against bringing these unpleasant or painful thoughts or reminiscences to consciousness. He discovered that this resistance belonged to the same set of personality factors which caused the repression. As the patient talked freely, not infrequently dreams were related. Gradually it developed that elements of the dreams appeared to be related not only to the present life and problems of the individual, but to the symptoms of the patient, and also to his past in this other "subliminal" aspect of the personality which Freud called the unconscious.

It appeared that dreams had a language of their own and a psychology that was similar to the psychology of functional symptoms. As a result of these observations and conclusions, Freud (1900) published his *Interpretation of Dreams*. Dreams are said to be the royal road to the unconscious. They represent the fulfillment of a wish. Their function is to preserve sleep. Thoughts and impulses that are hidden or rejected press forward in phantasy, disguised in symbols so that they may be more acceptable to consciousness. Free associations, letting the mind wander over the various elements of a dream, bring meaning to it usually. However, it is true that there are dreams which even the most experienced analysts cannot clarify (see also Freud, 1904, 1905).

There are great differences in the way various analysts help patients to find the meaning of their dreams. There is a contrast between active and aggressive interpretation on the part of the analyst and the technique of remaining passive, suggesting no interpretation, and allowing the patient, through his own associations to arrive at an understanding of the significance of the dream himself. This latter technique seems to me to be on much more solid ground, psychologically, than the aggressive type of interpretation. It enables the patient to assimilate his own thoughts and associations, instead of having to accept the thoughts of the analyst which may seem alien to him. The self-made interpretations, in my experience, enable the patient ultimately to see more satisfactorily the relevancy of tendencies for his own personality and problems.

THEORY OF THE DISORDERS.—That certain types of neuroses and psychoses have patterns of activity, and of associated thinking and feeling which are similar to those found in various periods of growth, is one of Freud's discoveries (see Chapter 7 by French). Stimulation, frustration, prolongation of these activities in the various stages of growth, he believed, determined the development of the various types of neuroses.

Thus Freud, Abraham, and Fenichel developed correlations between dominant fixation points in the course of development, and common clinical conditions. There is a correlation between the various disorders and the patient's effectiveness in dealing psychologically with objects. For example, in extreme schizophrenia there is no object of interest or love in the external world. In hysteria there are interests or loves but adult genital interests are excluded. In schizophrenia, particularly in the extreme degrees, the patient lives on the sucking stage of existence. In manic-depressive psychoses, the thoughts and words of the patient are shot through with oral symbols. In the compulsion neuroses, hate is expressed in anal symbols. For a brief account of these stages see Chapter 21 by Ribble, and for an extended account of clinical psychoanalysis see Fenichel (1934).

Since psychoanalysis has developed a nomenclature that is somewhat different from that of the traditional psychiatric classifications, one must be able to translate the terms of one classification into those of the other. The following are some practical translations or equivalents. Hysteria in the traditional classification is represented in psychoanalytic terminology by anxiety neurosis, conversion hysteria, and anxiety hysteria. Neurasthenia in the classical tradition is represented in psychoanalytic classification by both neurasthenia and conversion hysteria. Psychasthenia in the usual classification includes two conditions in psychoanalysis, namely, anxiety hysteria and obsessional-compulsion neurosis. If the term "anxiety states" is used, it probably includes psychoanalytically, anxiety neurosis, conversion hysteria, and anxiety hysteria. For the various psychoses psychoanalysis employs the usual terms.

It is considered practically indispensable in order to practice psychoanalysis that a physician be analyzed himself. After this, in order to be certified he must analyze a number of cases under supervision.

THE TECHNIQUE OF PSYCHOANALYSIS.—A thorough history is taken. It is important to have a report from another physician as to the physical health of the patient. Psychoanalysis classically teaches that the analyst should make no physical examination of the patient nor treat him medically. It is felt that the effect of such examination and treatment arouses emotional reactions in the patient which interfere with satisfactory therapy. Schilder disagrees with this opinion. A regular psychiatric examination, however, is made, including an examination of the patient's family history, his parent and sibling relationships, his educational history, his vocational, social, and mental history. This is important, of course, not only for diagnostic purposes, but to determine whether it is possible or wise to analyze the patient.

In psychoanalytic procedure, the patient reclines on a couch in a semi-darkened room. The analyst sits behind him. The purpose of this is to remove all external stimuli as far as possible, so that the patient may remain as relaxed as possible and concentrate on whatever comes spontaneously to his consciousness, and so that the only contact of patient and analyst is conversational. He is simply told that he is to talk of everything that comes before his mind's eye. I usually explain to the patient that he has already discussed his symptoms and life from the ordinary logical point of view, and that he has already answered questions directed to him by physicians with certain focal points of his life and illness in view. I then tell the patient that I want to observe and to help him observe his undirected thinking. We want to see what thoughts, feelings, and impulses come spontaneously to mind without direction. We want to observe his undirected, spontaneous, automatic thinking. He is told, furthermore, to let his mind wander, to talk of everything that occurs to him, to be passive, and to talk just as he would speak of things that crossed his visual path were he sitting in a railroad train. There, too, there are rapid shifts, and different things appear in no coherent order. No matter how irrelevant, how foolish, how illogical, or how unpleasant the things are which come to his mind, he is to speak of them all. Nothing is to be held back. Nothing is to be consciously rejected or selected. Of course, he may discuss and comment on anything that comes up. Religion, art, philosophy, morality, resentments, hates, fears, hopes, ideals; everything is grist for the mill. This is the method of *free association* which Schilder (1938) has called "the most important technical development in modern psychotherapy." This is clearly different from the usual conversational procedure of psychiatrist and patient. There the physician is usually very active, asking questions, directing attention, and taking the lead in reasoning and explaining. In psychoanalysis, on the contrary, the doctor remains passive and the patient is active.

The stream of consciousness relieved of social, rational, and aesthetic directions shows a definite drift in the long run. Thoughts, feelings, and desires appear and recur with a frequency and emphasis that convince the patient that there are forces at work within his personality that are important for him in his difficulties and in his life. New sequences, correlations, and relevancies emerge. These processes throw new light on his personality and its problems. By virtue of these he sees himself in a new perspective. There is scarcely any other relationship in life that allows a person continuously to speak so freely. Even the confessional does not afford this. The capacity to express even hate and resentment without being criticized and condemned helps not only to abreact (and sometimes reject) these feelings but also to obtain a mastery of them. The ability to express feelings, phantasies, impulses, and reactions which one scarcely ever has put into words is of therapeutic value. It is a first step in dealing with them and laying hold of them. And the communication of them in words to another human being is to step out of the world of privacy and isolation into a world of objectivity, that is, of reality. The fact that the analyst is there and is not shocked, not fearful and not critical, gives him an example perhaps of a capacity in another human being to meet chaos, suffering, tragedy, difficulties, fear, anger, and the more elemental and primitive sides of human nature without becoming upset. The suggestive element in merely accepting the patient for treatment, as a human relationship, is clearly present.

But psychoanalysis passively conducted is the form of psychiatric treatment in which the least suggestion enters. It is the psychoanalyst's ideal to make no suggestions, but merely to help the patient (by his questions) face his own problems, accept his own impulses, take responsibility for them, and work out gradually a more satisfactory adjustment. Of course, it is possible in one's tone of voice and by the questions asked to use suggestion. But by a neutral expression of voice and careful attention to the questions, it is possible to reduce suggestion to a minimum. No advice is given, which, of course, is against a dominant desire of the patient, unless there is an acute psychiatric or medical emergency, and, in the latter case, it is considered most desirable to turn the patient immediately over to a medical consultant.

Ferenczi and others have introduced more active methods, at times, especially in compulsive states. They force frustrations. Or if an extramarital or homosexual relationship is interfering with the progress of the analysis, it is interdicted. But in straight analysis these departures are not used. Thus the analysis can be very objective, and the contribution of the analyst can be reduced to a minimum except in giving help by asking relevant questions. The patient develops a sense of responsibility for his mental processes and sees the meaning of them in his past experiences. He is also stimulated to take an active part in dealing with them. Meaning gradually emerges from the meaningless; relevancy appears in irrelevancies; order, sequence, and correlation appear in the chaotic. Connections (associations) that have been broken up or separated (forgotten or repressed, dissociated) become reconnected (reassociated). Mental elements that had appeared isolated, insignificant or meaningless, acquire significance. In this new experience of free association and in this relationship with another human being whose chief tools are silence, questions, and help in interpretation, a new understanding and a new personality develop. And just as slips of action and speech (see Freud, 1904), dreams and phantasies take on meaning, so do symptoms, and they often disappear even when they have proved intractable with other methods of therapy.

The usual period of analysis is 50 minutes. Classically, there are six sessions a week, but for certain practical reasons this may be reduced to once a week or several times a week. Once a week, however, is usually too infrequent because too much time is taken up with the mere chronology of events. There is no time limit for an analysis. It may take from several months to several years. The latter is not surprising, however, in severe cases, when one remembers that it takes five or ten years to make a reasonably social being out of the average infant, and that patients may have gone 20 or 30 years with their habits of unsatisfactory adjustment.

TRANSFERENCE.—Emotions that the patient needs to express are projected onto the analyst. This is the process of transference. Freud writes:

> If the patient is to fight the normal conflict that on analysis is revealed against the suppressions, he requires a tremendous impetus to influence the desirable decision which will lead him back to health. Otherwise he might decide for a repetition of the former issue and allow these factors which have been admitted to consciousness to slip back into suppression. The deciding vote in this conflict is not given by his intellectual penetration—which is neither strong nor free enough for such an achievement, but only by his relation to the physician. Inasmuch as his transference carries a positive sign, it invests the physician with authority and is converted into faith for his communications and conceptions. Without transference of this sort, or without a negative transfer, he would not even listen to the physician and to his arguments. (1920)

The patient must work through his transference. A negative transference can be just as effective a tool of therapy as a positive one. Gradually he learns that he has been adopting attitudes toward the analyst which he held toward persons important in his early environment. This is inappropriate, subjective, and unrealistic. Gradually he works through this and is able to develop new and more appropriate attitudes, not only toward the analyst but toward other persons in his present environment. The control which the patient projects on the analyst through identification or rejection, he gradually learns belongs to himself.

Schilder (1938), in a chapter on the relation between physician and patient, presents one of the clearest and most illuminating discussions of which we know. It should be read by all psychiatrists. His most important points are as follows. There are three aspects to the transference, viz., winning the transference, working it through, and breaking it. The more passive the analyst remains, the less he exhibits his own opinions and ideas, the more readily the transference will develop. The transference is not made by the physician; it is developed by the patient. If a negative transference does not appear, the analysis will remain superficial. The passive, masochistic attitude of the patient may provoke an aggressive attitude on the part of the analyst, which may contain erotic components. The analyst's narcissism may be stimulated, he must watch it, for he may overrate himself as he is so accustomed to play the superior role. Perfectionist desires on the part of the physician must be watched lest they make impossible demands on the patient. The physician may react to the immature wishes of the patient, by exhibiting infantile attitudes himself, viz., the wish for absolute authority over the patient and the desire for the latter's implicit compliance. He warns against a too rigid technique. "Be human and respect the personality of the patient." He makes the further point that freedom from symptoms is no criterion of cure, it may be the result of the transference relationship.

The transference neuroses (conversion hysteria, anxiety hysteria, compulsion neuroses) are the conditions most suitable for psychoanalysis. The actual neuroses (anxiety neurosis and neurasthenia), since they are caused by defective sexual hygiene in the present, are treated with adequate sexual instruction. Psychoanalysis is indicated in the perversions, especially in homosexuality and in compulsive autoeroticism. It is helpful in marked psychoneurotic additions to certain types of somatic disease. The new emphasis on psychosomatic medicine is, of course, a fruitful field for psychoanalysis. In some cases of character disorder, and of vocational and marital failure, psychoanalysis is beneficial. Disorders of the sexual life such as impotence, premature ejaculation, and frigidity in some cases are greatly helped or cured by it. Prepsychotic personalities and prepsychotic conditions often obtain great benefit, and it is felt that sometimes a psychosis is obviated. In the remissions of manic-depressive insanity and schizophrenia, it is occasionally of benefit. A modified kind of analysis has proved distinctly helpful in a number of cases of paranoid conditions in our experience. It cannot be used, however, in the acute and chronic stages of the narcissistic neuroses. It used to be said that psychoanalysis was not to be recommended in the psychoses. This rule holds in general, but, as pointed out above, in the prepsychotic stage of a malignant psychosis, in the remissions of psychosis, and in certain mild types of malignant psychosis, in selected cases, it can accomplish a great deal.

Psychoanalysis is not successful with patients of an inferior or definitely limited intelligence. It is not applicable in conditions with organic brain disease, e.g., arteriosclerosis, syphilis, and the toxic, infective, exhaustive psychoses. Patients who do not come for treatment of their own free will are not suitable subjects. Uncooperative patients, of course, cannot be analyzed nor can those who do not desire recovery. Those lacking a certain stage of ethical development, e.g., psychopathic personalities, are not fruitful subjects, and those who cannot afford to pay something at least do not usually do well. Patients with marked pain are not satisfactory subjects, nor are faddists or dilettantes. It is usually stated that in patients over the age of fifty years psychoanalysis is contraindicated.

MODIFICATIONS OF PSYCHOANALYSIS.—Klein (1937), Anna Freud (1928), Aichorn (1936), and Susan Isaacs have applied psychoanalysis especially to behavior problems and difficulties in the development of children (p. 1149).

The Swiss physician, Jung, followed Freud for a time and was a leader in the psychoanalytic movement. Later his views diverged so much that he founded an independent school of thought called Analytic Psychology (Jung, 1916). His chief contributions have been: studies in the association experiment, the psychology of dementia praecox, a broader concept of the racial unconscious, the psychology of personality types, the concepts of the persons, the animus and the anima, studies of artistic creation, investigations into mythology, folk lore and religion and their relation to dreams, phantasies, neuroses, and the cultural strivings and conflicts of the individual. In addition he stressed a synthetic emphasis in therapy. His studies in the word-association test laid a sound foundation for the psychology of free association. He showed that there was a psychology of dementia praecox, and that earlier experiences had an influence on the development of the psychosis, and in these studies he did pioneering work in the foundation of psychopathology (see the sections on Association in Chapter 6 by White and Chapter 33 by Hunt and Cofer).

Jung emphasized the creative and prospective possibilities of man more than the erotic, infantile, egoistic impulses which Freud studied. He is more teleological, creative, and future-looking in his emphasis than was Freud. Jung has pointed to the mother as a creative symbol. Freud pointed to the father as a source of control (castration complex), a factor in social organization, and an object of hate and aggression. Libido for Jung is not merely the sexual impulse with its ramifications; for him it is life energy, allied to Bergson's *élan vital*. Part of the libido, he believes, has been dissexualized through ages of adaptation to reality.

Universal meanings and their images (archetypes) are searched for by Jung, rather than the particular experiences sought by Freud. If personal "associations" cannot be found in relation to mental images, they are held to be of archetypal origin. Man in searching for his goal relates himself to the Logos, the essential masculine principle. He is apt to ignore the recognition of the anima or feminine principle in his unconscious. Woman's principle of life is Eros and her difficulty is relating herself to the masculine Logos.

Man contains a racial unconscious which for Jung seems to be more important than the personal unconscious. As the instincts are to the organism, so are the archetypes or racial unconscious to the mind. Psychological instincts or forces of thought common to all people are inherited, as part of the experience of the race. They are ancestral interpretations of experience, i.e., primitive, primordial explanations of the forces of nature and human relations.

The therapy of Jung is directed toward an elucidation of the tendencies in the unconscious. One must learn to understand one's patterns as represented in universal symbols. The patient must learn the difference between his conscious tendencies and the unconscious urges struggling for expression.

Adler's studies and therapy have been concerned chiefly with the ego, and its fundamental strivings and mistakes (Adler, 1907, 1909, 1923). The paradigm of Adler's formulations briefly is the following. Bodily or organ inferiority ———→ will to power ———→ compensatory reactions: masculine protest = neurotic symptoms. The helplessness of the infant, the smallness of the child, and some weakness of a bodily organ produces insecurity. This stimulates his strivings to overcome this handicap. The chief striving Adler emphasizes is the will to adequacy or power. Urges to assert oneself, to excel, to be superior, and to defend oneself then develop. Aggressive or escape tendencies to win security or power are the mechanisms of this striving. These compensatory activities are subsumed under Adler's term *masculine protest*. The individual (whether masculine or feminine) wants to be a man, have power, like fathers. The various psychological processes (rationalization, phantasy, asocial behavior) developed to maintain this fiction and to deny one's weakness and inferiority are the symptoms patients complain of in neurosis. Such a paradigm, according to Adler, lies beneath every neurosis. Inadequacies and inferiorities overemphasize the drive to succeed and to excel. Suppose one's ambitions cannot be fulfilled. Unwilling to admit defeat, the individual denies his lack of success and his inadequacies, protects his self-esteem, wins substituted power and satisfaction in neurosis. He then lives as though he were ill, gets satisfaction out of his fiction, makes the demands of real illness upon his relatives and friends, emphasizing demands and rights but not duties or obligations. His strategy of life, his "life pattern," is mistaken.

Therapy consists essentially in discussing these mistakes of his life pattern and straightening them out in friendly discussion. A protracted questionnaire of the patient's life history is taken. The life pattern is crystallized early in childhood or infancy. Family relationships, thus, in addition to organ defects, are important etiological influences. The place in the family is important. The eldest child is overvalued. His parents look upon him as an extraordinary and delightful gift from heaven. He absorbs this pattern and acts it out in life. His "will to power" is exaggerated. The second child, of course, feels his inadequacy in comparison with this extraordinary first child and is very apt to compensate for this with aggressiveness. The youngest child may be spoiled, feel rejected, or very small and inadequate, and personality characteristics to compensate for this develop. The only child, of course, is spoiled with an inordinate amount of attention and concern. He becomes narcissistic and conceited. He has an exaggerated attitude of his own capacities (omnipotence) and the consideration others should show him. Achievements and rewards are desired without the necessary effort. He reacts or compensates with the fiction that people do not appreciate him and are unfair to him.

There is always an optimistic note in Adlerian teaching. The patient is told he has the capacity to learn the nature of his failures and mistaken patterns and achieve a change. Beran Wolfe has succinctly and popularly formulated Adlerian doctrines (Wolfe, 1931, 1933). Therapy is a process of education, enlightenment, discovery, and encouragement. Conscious discussion, training, and suggestion from the therapist will enable the patient to overcome his sense of inferiority and develop a normal personality.

Many criticisms of Adler's psychology and therapy can be made. The force of reason in human behavior is greatly overemphasized. Adlerian psychology seems to suffer from the rationalist's fallacy, that because reason can discover the sources of mistakes, and can unearth sequences and correlations, reason has produced them. Irrational forces are minimized and do not receive adequate consideration. Patients frequently get the impression in reading Adlerian literature that their actions have been deliberate. They feel that the interpretations in therapy are a slur on their characters, that they have been cowardly, and that they have been dangerously near fraud and malingering. It almost assumes that the patient knows his mistakes and has deliberately chosen to escape and avoid them. In Adlerian therapy there is a great tendency to force the therapist's interpretation or point of view on to the patient and to convince him.

Nevertheless, Adlerian conceptions have had a great influence in psychiatry. They are therapeutically similar in many ways to the methods of Meyer and Riggs. Adler's formulations are simple and straightforward. They are easily understood. They are reasonable and can be used beneficially when for a number of reasons it is impracticable or impossible to employ deep therapy or psychoanalysis. Adlerian conceptions are helpful to parents in considering their children's difficulties. They do not frighten parents or child as do psychoanalytic concepts at times. The terms are those of everyday speech, while Freudian terms are specialized and at times esoteric. The social and educational influence of Adler has been great and beneficial; his therapy has proved most useful in the guidance of children and in the treatment of the milder psychoneuroses and personality difficulties.

Dynamic Growth Therapy.—For want of a better name, dynamic growth therapy is the term we have given to an eclectic therapy in which, at the proper time, all of the various techniques of treatment may be employed. With tact, sympathy, kindliness, encouragement, and without crippling criticism, the psychiatrist endeavors to help the patient develop a constructive healthy personality. In the philosophy of this therapy, the importance of all functions is recognized and used: intellect, habit, action, emotion, instinct, will, social influences, and ideals. In this type of therapy, the psychiatrist establishes a constructive human relationship with the patient wherein he accepts the patient as a person and gives support, encouragement, and understanding. He may use the values of practice in action. He recognizes the value of inspiration derived from enthusiasms and social ideals, the value of abreaction, and the value of direction. General educational principles are employed, and the concept of growth is stressed. The patient becomes a new individual, with new capacities, and he is freed from the crippling attitudes and habits of his past.

Dynamic growth therapy, being eclectic, can use psychoanalysis or psychoanalytic concepts, as any therapy at the present time is bound to do. But it is not exclusively psychoanalytic. The necessity of helping the patient understand the dynamic relationships between his past experience, his training, his attitudes, his urges, on the one hand, and his difficulties and symptoms, on the other, is one of the most fundamental processes in psychotherapy. Whether this comes from a deliberate exercise of free association, or from free association in more informal conversation, in bibliotherapy, or in personality study, it is necessary for adequate psychotherapy. Dynamic growth therapy is not exclusively emotional. It is not essentially intellectual. It is minimally authoritative. It uses all the approaches to understanding and developing personality. We believe that much psychiatric therapy has fallen down because it was too one-sided. Too many therapists have been devoted too exclusively to the formulae of certain schools or leaders.

In dynamic growth therapy there is a search for causes—for the forces, urges, or needs, that push, drive or motivate individuals. One seeks to discover the dynamics of the neurosis or psychosis. This type of therapy is only partly intellectual, however. It is not a purely passive process of reflection, intellectual gymnastics and resolutions; it is a growth experience in which the patient feels and learns. This growth takes place within a relationship between two human beings, an effective relationship which is of the greatest importance in therapy. There is release of repressed, clogging and disrupting emotions, through the expression, recognition and acceptance of the patient's feelings. It is recognized that the way he feels is more fundamental than what he thinks. Therapy is not, therefore, just a process of discovery, recognition, decision and automatic implementation of new ideas and formulae for satisfactory living. It is a slow, groping process which, in addition to intellect involves feeling, and furthermore action—trial and error in the practice of living. Since most growth takes place unconsciously, the process of therapy takes time. The forces of imagination and identification (inspiration) are recognized as more important in many people than reason and will power. The patient must learn to grow out of his hindering identifications and work through to a new individuation in order to achieve a satisfying and constructive personality.

Psychiatric Treatment of Alcoholism

Alcoholism is a tremendous problem from every standpoint, social, economic, and psychiatric. Oberholzer says there are 100,000 persons suffering from alcoholism in the United States, and alcoholic psychoses represent from 10% to 15% of the total admissions to mental hospitals. In the opinion of Henderson and Gillespie (1941), however, the etiological role of alcoholism in the disorders has been exaggerated; they regard it as more commonly a symptom than a cause.

In virtue of the numerous factors considered of etiological importance in alcoholism, including, for example, such psychological factors as the release of aggressive and sexual impulses, the escape to infantile omnipotence, inferiority, immaturity, and such physiological factors as hypoglycemia and allergy, it is not surprising that therapies have been diverse and many. For the most part these treatments have been purely empirical (see comprehensive reviews by Marshall, 1940; Moore, 1941, and Voegtlin and Lemere, 1941).

Acute alcoholism has usually been treated by physiological and pharmacological methods. Goldsmith (1930) used spinal drainage to reduce intracranial pressure. Davidoff and Reifenstein (1937, 1939) have used benzedrine in 28 patients and results were favorable in 26, or 93%. In chronic alcoholics, however, they got success with benzedrine in only 10% of their patients. Benzedrine will relieve the craving for alcohol (Wilbur, 1937) as apparently will atropin, strychnine, and caffeine, which have long been used for this purpose. In his treatment of 675 alcoholics with reduction of alcohol and coincident use of bromides, or of tonics with gentian and quinine or with atropin and strychnine, 41% relapsed, 3% improved, and 55% became permanently abstinent. Lambert (1909, 1912) believed that a belladonna, xantholoxylin, and hyoscyamus mixture was almost specific for alcoholism. Emetine was used by Vivian (1929), who insisted on total abstinence and the complete cooperation of the patient. McFarland and Barach (1933) point out the relationship between oxygen want and alcoholic intoxication. Inhalation of oxygen with 7% to 10% CO_2 resulted in permanent improvement. Freeman and Watts (1942) tried prefrontal lobotomy on some cases with negligible results.

The relation of vitamin deficiency to alcoholism is an important one which is still in the process of investigation and evaluation. While it is unquestionably important in the therapy of acute conditions, its value in chronic addiction remains to be determined. Unquestionably, some of the mental disturbances formerly thought to be due to the toxic reaction of alcohol have been due to vitamin B deficiency. Bowman, Goodhart, and Jolliffe (1939) treated 51 patients with Korsakoff's syndrome with thiamin and their recovery was seven times as great as those treated with diet alone.

Metrazol has been used in treatment, but there is no evidence indicating that it has any beneficial effect on subsequent drinking habits. There has been a great deal of work on the use of insulin. Robinsin (1940) believed that insulin and carbohydrate administration are essential curative measures. Rivers (1942) worked out a technique of giving 100 cc. of 50% glucose, 30 units of insulin, and 120 mgms. of thiamin chloride intravenously with a quart of orange juice to drink. He has treated over 200 patients and has found the results efficacious especially in the psychiatric complications of acute alcoholism.

The famed Keely cure is believed to have employed apo-morphine. Fleming (1935) had 25% cures with its use with 36 patients. Purves-

Stewart used it for the purpose of establishing a conditioned avoidance-response to alcohol. Voegtlin (1940) has undertaken the most intensive study and use of the treatment by the conditioned response method. An attempt is made to establish an aversion to alcohol by the production of nausea and vomiting with the use of emetic drugs. He uses emetine instead of apo-morphine because its action is more prolonged. He reports 60% to 70% cures and this exceeds any other figure known in the literature.

Tabori (1933), Knight (1938), Chassell (quoted by Voegtlin), and Fleming and Tillotson (1939) discuss alcoholism from the psychoanalytic point of view. They generally report poor results, though Knight's figures for 1942 from the Menninger Clinic are more encouraging— 33% were apparently cured or much improved. His figures and those of Chassell are the best reported for psychoanalysis. The psychoanalysts raise the important question, whether teaching the patient to become abstinent can actually be called a cure.

The success of the various forms of religious therapy, we believe, is attributable probably to affective therapy—or the mobilization of positive affective relationships. Alcoholics Anonymous have reported striking results (1939). Voegtlin reports that of 2,000 patients they have seen in the last six years, about 1,000 are considered permanently cured.

Peabody (1930, 1935) has worked out a practical scheme of psychotherapy and reeducation which has helped many alcoholics. He emphasizes synthesis as opposed to analysis. Strecker and Chambers have developed Peabody's methods and brought them more into line with general psychiatric thinking (1939). For Strecker (1941) alcoholism is a neurosis of introversion. Alcoholism as a psychoneurotic symptom is thought of as having the function of screening unsatisfactory external and internal realities.

Psychiatric Therapy for Children

There are two general approaches to therapeutic work with children, emanating from divergent basic philosophies. One takes the view that the child has little share in the creation of his difficulties and thus minimizes his role in their resolution. The other sees him as the chief focus of the problem with a vital part to play in its solution. Many gradations exist between these two extremes out of which arise a variety of methods of therapy. There are, however, overlappings and syntheses as each psychiatrist develops an approach best for his own use and which he modifies according to the needs of the individual patient.

Therapies in Which the Child's Role Is Minimized.—*Authoritative Approaches.* These approaches depend on alteration of intellectual content or conscious desires to bring about changes in attitudes and behavior. The emphasis may lie on direction, suggestion, and advice, or it may lie on habit training, a process of reeducation by consistent repetition of appropriate habits. Thom (1937) has contributed notably to this latter method.

Environmental Manipulation aims to fit an environment to the child's needs. Healy (see 1940) first introduced a comprehensive investigation of the child and his environment in his study of delinquents (for off-shoots of this work, see Chapter 25 by Faris). The changes may consist only in getting a child into a group of children nearer his own age, changing the school, or sending him to camp; or it may consist in removing him entirely from some pernicious environment, and placing him in an institution or in a foster home selected to fit his problems and needs. An excellent description of this method is given by Rogers (1939).

Social Interpretation. By this method the child's environment is altered by interpreting his basic needs and the dynamics of his difficulties to his parents, to his teachers, and to other adults who may have him in their charge. This is a useful adjunct to any method of child therapy.

Therapies in Which the Child's Role Is Maximized.—*Release Therapy* depends mainly on abreaction for its therapeutic effect. It has been used especially by Levy (1937, 1938, 1939, 1940) who considers it especially suited for children who present a definite symptom picture of relatively short duration that has been precipitated by such a specific event as, for example, an operation. Its applicability is limited to children under ten years of age whose problems are not related to complicating family difficulties, and Levy emphasizes that in many cases it is best used in conjunction with other approaches.

Play Therapy, which includes such techniques as children's drawings (Appel, 1931; Despert, 1937; Harms, 1941), play with toys selected to fit the child's situation (Conn, 1938, 1939; Solomon, 1938, 1940), puppet shows (Bender and Woltmann, 1936), or real group activities on a children's ward (Bender, 1937), serves two purposes simultaneously. These various techniques provide a medium by which the child can reveal his strivings, his tensions, and his reactions to family influences, and thus they are methods of personality study. They also afford a situation in which the child can get catharsis by abreacting his aggressions and his anxieties in a socially acceptable way.

Relationship Therapy is best described by Allen (1942). In this approach the relationship of the child to the therapist is given major emphasis. The parent is interviewed by a case worker, while the child is spending his hour with the therapist. The time spent at the clinic is looked upon as a growth experience in which both mother and child participate. The feelings and attitudes characteristic of the child's pattern of life are from the first brought into the therapeutic hour, as the child reacts to the separation from the mother, to the necessity of entering into a relationship with the therapist, and to accepting the limitations of the situation, which include a fixed allotment of time. Play materials are available for the child to use in any way he wishes, though there are definite limitations imposed when the rights of the therapist are threatened. The content of the play and the accounts of past events and reactions are not interpreted on a historical basis, as in psychoanalysis, but as a revelation of present feelings, both negative and positive. The value of the therapy lies in the child's own experiencing of his feelings and impulses with someone who is willing to start with him as he is at the moment, and who will help him to bring all the turmoil of his changing feelings into the therapeutic hour. Essentially nonintellectual, its therapeutic influence rests on an experience of relationship to the therapist through which the child can gain a realization of himself as an individual in his own right, capable of participating in his own changes. With this realization, growth can be resumed with lessened anxiety and denial.

Psychoanalysis.—In the psychoanalysis of children, the intensity and duration of treatment is greater than in other child therapies. The patient may be seen every day for a period of from one to three years. Though the aim of child psychoanalysis is always to get at the unconscious underlying causes, and subsequently to resolve them, there are various approaches. These differ in both method and breadth of applicability. Three such variations are herewith presented.

Anna Freud (1928), who feels that psychoanalysis should be adopted only for those children suffering from a real infantile neurosis, believes that no true transference neurosis develops, as in the case of adults, because of the present existence of real and natural parents in the child's life. A negative attitude toward the analyst must be replaced by a positive attachment, however, before the child's unconscious can be reached. There is, therefore, a period of preparation in which such a connection is consciously fostered by the analyst's allying herself with her young patient, showing herself as a trustworthy, useful, or powerful adult. Play techniques are valuable chiefly in revealing the child's various reactions, attitudes, and aggressions, but they are not considered to be deeply symbolic. She regards free association as more significant. Dreams, daydreams, and drawings she finds much more profitable for direct interpretation. The analyst has also an educational role because the child's weak super-ego needs reinforcement in regulating the instinctual life. Toward the end of analysis, consequently, there is a pedagogical period to assist the child in adjusting to his outside world.

Melanie Klein (1937) feels that analysis is valuable in the treatment of every disturbance and even in assisting the development of the normal child. She believes that a true transference neurosis is produced. Play activities are considered to be on a par with adult speech and thus may be used in the same way as free association. She immediately interprets unconscious material in order rapidly to reduce anxiety and the unconscious sense of guilt. Klein thinks that the analyst should refrain from exerting any kind of educational influence.

Aichorn (1939) uses psychoanalytic principles in the treatment of delinquents, but his procedure is notable for its flexibility. A positive relationship is deliberately fostered and he achieves this quickly in a variety of ways. He may allow a child to carry out his aggressions with-out restraint until the child develops fear and feelings of guilt which make him ready to accept help from the therapist. The child is then treated on the basis of the transference. Aichorn's approach is essentially reeducation on psychoanalytic principles.

Some Statistics of Psychiatric Therapy

In view of the magnitude of the problem involved in the control of nervous and mental disease, it would be highly desirable to know which of the methods of treating each of the various reaction types is most effective. It is easier to state the importance of the problem statistically, however, than it is to measure the efficiency of the various therapies statistically. In the general hospitals of the United States there are only 375,000 beds, whereas in the mental hospitals there are 430,000 beds. There are nearly 400,000 patients in these mental hospitals, and approximately 100,000 new patients admitted annually (for a survey of these statistics in European countries as well as America, see Landis and Page, 1938). The investment in mental hospitals alone represents one billion dollars. But the problem is even broader. General medical consultants in large cities find that from 45% to 50% of their consultations concern functional conditions wherein no organic pathology can be found. More-over, psychiatric or emotional factors are estimated to cause from 50% to 65% of physical illnesses. Yet few of the 5,000 general hospitals have provided for psychiatric examinations and care of the 8,000,000 cases they admit annually. If the time each patient stayed in a hospital could be reduced by several days by attention to the emotional factors in physi-cal illness, the public could be saved millions of dollars annually.

Furthermore, in view of the problems that will arise from the Second World War, certain statistical facts from the army records of the First World War are important. Between April, 1917 and December, 1919, there were 97,657 members of the armed forces admitted for neuro-psychiatric conditions. Over 8,000 men were returned from overseas prior to June, 1919 for neuropsychiatric illness. These psychiatric dis-orders developed despite the fact that local draft boards rejected 549,099 on neuropsychiatric grounds. When it is estimated that every man who "breaks down" during military service will cost the government about $30,000 during his lifetime, the importance of extreme vigilance by the examining physicians on draft boards is clearly indicated (for a discus-sion of the unit in military service, see Chapter 27 by Stearns).

In connection with the general impression that the results of psychi-atric therapy are disappointing, Strecker and Ebaugh (1940) point out that, "It is conservatively estimated that between 60 and 75 per cent of the psychoses which are comparable to what the internist would desig-nate 'acute' are recoverable. Particularly in psychiatry do we meet con-ditions and situations which are capable of considerable modification in a favorable direction even though a complete cure may not be effected.

This is particularly true in incipient and early schizophrenia, and the failure to recognize this potentiality has made the outlook seem even gloomier than it really is."

In recent years, an increasing number of articles reporting the proportions of cures, social remissions, improvements, and unrecoverable patients for various therapies have appeared. A few summaries of these follow. Inevitably these statistics are open to misinterpretations. The standards for recovery are variable for different investigators, and it is difficult to draw lines between the various degrees of recovery. There is great need for statistical data from studies that make long-term follow-ups of the patients treated by each of the major forms of therapy.

Bond (1921, 1923, 1941) has long been interested in the problem of prognosis, and he has published results from various types of therapy at the Pennsylvania Hospital over a number of years. In 1937, Bond and Braceland reported on a five-year follow-up of 626 unselected cases of psychosis. This paper is especially interesting because it furnishes a baseline from which the results from the newer therapies can be judged. In Table I, we quote their master table for this purpose.

TABLE I

PROGNOSIS IN MENTAL DISEASE BEFORE NEWER THERAPIES BASED ON OUTCOME AFTER FIVE YEARS

	No. Cases	No. Re-covered	%	No. Im-proved	%	No. Unim-proved	%	No. Dead	No. Lost
Dementia Praecox	116	12	10.0	25	21.5	66	56.8	10	3
Manic-Depressive	171	86	50.2	19	11.1	30		24	12
Paresis	38	13		8		5		12	—
Involutional Melancholia ..	47	12	25.5	10	21.2	10		13	2
Somatic Disease	60	22		8		3		23	4
Senile	50	2		4		8		31	5
Alcoholic	10	1		—		3		2	4
Psychoneuroses	37	21	56.7	7	16.9	4	10.8	3	2
Paranoid Conditions	9	3		3		2		—	—
Unclassified	72	27		13		11		8	13
Psychopathic	8	—		4		2		1	1
Encephalitics, Adult	8	1		1		2		2	2
Total	626	200		102		146		129	48
		35%		18%		25.5%		22%	

(From Bond and Braceland, 1937)

Varying proportions of favorable results have been reported for insulin-shock therapy in schizophrenia. Sakel (1938) got his best results in cases where the symptoms had recently appeared. In a series of approximately 50 such cases, "70% showed full remission (apparently cured) and another 18% showed social remissions following treatment. . . . In other words, 88% of our recent cases showed positive results after treatment" (p. 133). These figures are higher, however, than those reported by later investigators (see review by Shipley and Kant, 1940). When the results obtained in 495 schizophrenics treated in 22 Swiss hospitals were analyzed and classified according to duration of psychosis before treatment (Müller, 1938), the proportions of full or social remissions were: for up to six months, 59%; for from six months to one year, 52%; for from one year to two years, 27%; over two years, 11%. Malzberg (1938) has compared outcome in 1,039 insulin-treated schizophrenics with outcome in 1,039 controls matched with the treated cases for institution, age, sex, and type of schizophrenia. The results showed 13% recovery and an additional 54% improvement in the treated cases, as compared with 3.5% recovery and 19% improvement in the control group. A breakdown according to duration of symptoms revealed the following proportions of recovery. *Treated group:* up to one month, 43%; one to six months, 33%; seven to twelve months, 16%; one to two years, 12%; and three to five years, 4%. *Control group:* up to one month, 8%; one to six months, 7%; seven to twelve months, 0%; one to two years, .6%; and three to five years, 0%. Not all recoveries are permanent, however. Müller (1938) reported relapses in from 6% to 13%, Malzberg (1938) in 24.5%, and Bond (1941) in 18%. In spite of these relapses, it is generally agreed that the response to insulin-shock is so favorable and so immediate that it represents a promising therapy for schizophrenia.

Striking results have also been reported for metrazol therapy in schizophrenia (Meduna, 1935). When Meduna and Friedman (1939) analyzed the combined results from 2,937 cases treated in European and American hospitals, the gross European results were 30.37% full remission, and the gross American results were 19.86% full remissions and 38.43% improvement. When these results were analyzed according to duration of symptoms before treatment, they revealed: for less than six months, 60.95% complete remission and 20% improvement; for six months to one year, 36.82% full remission and 23.13% improvement; for over one year, 8.36% full remission and 37.76% improvement. Mortality was .29% for the 2,937 cases. In spite of these statistics, it is generally agreed that metrazol therapy does not compare favorably with insulin therapy in schizophrenia (see review by Shipley and Kant, 1940). Metrazol was soon used in other disorders, however, and it has shown particularly good results in the affective psychoses. Not only has the proportion of recovery from affective psychosis been high (82% in the cases treated by Low, *et al.,* 1938) but it remains high regardless of the duration of the symptoms, and the duration of attacks was shortened from an average of one year in 8,000 untreated cases to an average of 7.5 weeks in those who received treatment. Results of metrazol therapy in severe cases of neurosis have been reported by Shapiro and Freeman (1939). Recovery occurred in five of seven of their cases of obsessive-compulsive neurosis, in three of six cases of anxiety neurosis, in two of seven cases of reactive depression with improvement in three others, and recovery in four of five cases of conversion hysteria.

The electro-shock treatment, introduced by Cerletti and Bini (1938), has developed so many advantages over metrazol that it has now almost replaced the latter. The results of electro-shock in 108 cases treated at the Pennsylvania Hospital appear in Table II. Like metrazol, this form of shock therapy is most effective (over 80% remissions) in the affective disorders. It is quite ineffective in schizophrenia, and it is of questionable value in the psychoneuroses.

TABLE II

RESULTS OF ELECTRO-SHOCK THERAPY IN 108 CASES TREATED
AT THE PENNSYLVANIA HOSPITAL

Diagnosis	Recovered %	Improved %	Unimproved %	Relapsed %	Total Treated
Involutional Melancholia	85	15	0	5	20
Manic-Depressive, Manic	70	0	30	0	10
Manic-Depressive, Depressed	72	10	18	0	49
Schizophrenia	0	7	93	0	16
Undiagnosed Psychoses	37.5	0	62.5	12.5	8
Psychoneuroses	60	0	40	0	5

Freeman and Watts (1942) have carried further Moniz's work on prefrontal leucotomy or lobotomy. The statistical side of the therapeutic aspect of their results with 80 patients appears in Table III.

TABLE III

RESULTS OF PREFRONTAL LOBOTOMY—PRESENT STATUS OF PATIENTS
WITH PREFRONTAL LOBOTOMY

Disease	No.	Regularly Employed	Studying or Partially Employed	House-keeping	At Home	Institution	Dead
Involutional Depression	38	4	3	12	11	4	4
Obsess. Tension States	18	7	—	7	2	—	2
Schizophrenias	12	3	3	1	3	1	1
Psychoneuroses	8	4	1	1	1	1	—
Undifferentiated	4	2	—	1	1	—	—
Total	80	20	7	22	18	6	7

(From Freeman & Watts, 1942)

When the female sex hormones became available for therapeutic use, it was natural that they should be tried as replacement therapy in mental conditions associated with the menopause and involutional period when the production of these substances by the body is diminished or stopped. Werner, et al. (1936) compared the progress of eight control patients with involutional melancholia and nine others whom he gave 1 cc. of theelin daily for 20 weeks, and reported enthusiastically that five patients in the treated group improved markedly, while only one in the control group improved. Schube, et al. (1937) and Bowman and Bender (1932) failed, however, to get beneficial results from estrogine administration in this psychosis. In fourteen cases of true melancholia, Roternich (1941) found that endocrine therapy failed to produce results appreciably better than those which occur spontaneously. When Palmer

(1941) treated eleven patients with stilbestrol, eight showed no change during three months, and three became increasingly agitated and depressed. He concluded, therefore, that estrogenic therapy had no favorable effect on the involutional psychoses in the female. On the other hand, when Burlingame (1941) treated 63 cases of involutional psychosis with estradiol benzoate and estrone, 9.5% recovered, 22.2% improved considerably, and 27% were improved. Thus, a total of 57% or 58% were "apparently benefited." Our own experience with estrogenic therapy has been disappointing. Not infrequently the agitation has been increased, and disturbing pelvic sensations have at times further complicated the psychological problems.

Several outstanding summaries of prognosis in the psychoneuroses have been made. Riggs (1923), reporting on the condition of 800 cases treated at Stockbridge following their discharge by an average of two years, gave the following figures: no improvement in 1.9%; improvement in 15.7%; much improvement in 49.2%; and complete recovery in 33.1%. In 1940, Coon and Raymond made an extensive follow-up of 1,060 cases treated at Stockbridge, and they gave the following summary: no improvement in 6.4%; improvement in 27.6%; much improvement in 29.9%; and no statement about 36.0%. Out of 1,186 patients treated at the Cassel Hospital, at from one to thirteen years after discharge, Ross (1936) found 31.1% well, 7.2% had improved, and 61.7% were lost sight of. Hinsie's (1935) study of 61 psychoneurotic patients treated at the New York Psychiatric Institute showed 13% recovered, 55.7% improved, and 31.2% unimproved.

By far the most searching and comprehensive surveys of the results of psychoanalytic therapy are those of Knight (1938, 1941). He presents tables using the combined categories and criteria from the Berlin Psychoanalytic Institute, from Hyman and Kessel, from the London Psychoanalytic Clinic, from the Chicago Psychoanalytic Institute, and from the Menninger Clinic. We present herewith only a composite of these tables from Knight (1941).

TABLE IV

KNIGHT's (1941) COMPOSITE TABLE ON PSYCHOANALYTIC THERAPY

	No. Cases	Broken Off	6 Mos. or Longer	Appar. Cured	Much Improv.	% AC. MI	No Change or Improv.	Worse	% I. NC
Psychoneuroses	534	151	383	125	117	63.2	110	31	36.8
Sexual Disorders	47	14	33	12	4	48.5	18	4	51.5
Character Disorders ...	111	28	83	13	34	56.6	25	11	43.4
Organ Neuroses and Organic Conditions	55	23	32	15	10	78.1	6	1	21.9
Epilepsies	10	5	5	1	1			3	
Migraine	1		1	1					
Stammering	15	3	12	3	3			3	3
Chronic Alcoholism	28	9	19	3	4		7	5	
Psychoses	151	59	92	10	13	25.0	37	32	75.0
Totals	952	292	660	183	186	55.9%	201	90	44.1%

A review of therapeutic statistics in psychiatry shows that the rate of melioration in the psychoneuroses at the time of discharge is higher (ranging from 60% to 80%) than in the psychoses (40%). On the other hand, the rates (41% to 54% continuing improved) for the psychoses in the follow-up reports for five-year periods by Bond (1921a, 1921b, 1925, and Bond and Braceland, 1937) compare favorably with follow-up rates for the psychoneuroses in Ross's (1936) reports from England (38%) and in those by the Riggs Foundation (47.2%). These figures appear to indicate that the rate of improvement among psychoneurotics who come to psychiatric institutions for treatment (and a great many remain in the community untreated, or are treated by private practitioners) is not far removed from the rates of improvement in the psychoses. Moreover, hospital reports show better results for the treatment of the psychoses than for the treatment of the psychoneuroses. The statistical results of psychoanalytic treatment (see Table IV) of the psychoneuroses differ little from those of other methods of therapy. It is possible, however, that psychoanalysis has treated more severe cases on the whole than have the other methods.

The therapeutic statistics of psychiatry appear to justify only the conclusion that the essential factors in cures are still unknown. Nevertheless, one gains the impression that therapy does something and is effective. One gains the impression that certain types of therapy are more effective in particular types of patients than in others. However, the statistics appear to indicate that any therapy is in itself more fundamental than the type employed. There is something basically effective in the process of therapy in general which is independent of the methods employed.

Conclusion

The following table shows the various methods of treatment that are available to the psychiatrist. A great deal of the success in treating a patient will depend on the psychiatrist's selection of the method or methods of treatment appropriate to the individual patient. Psychiatric therapy must be highly individualized. Every patient is an individual with his own particular and often fortuitous experiences, temperament, and goals. Mass methods, routinized procedures, and favorite (popular) generalized formulae are bound to fail in many instances.

In addition to the kinds of treatment available, something else must be considered, namely, which of the various *levels of therapy* is appropriate for the individual patient. At the level of *critical illness*, medicines, drugs, narcosis, and authoritarian therapy are the only methods an experienced doctor would consider. At the level of *vegetative convalescence*, nursing, support, and reassurance are the methods to use. Next is the level wherein routine, schedule, occupational therapy, and socialization are useful. Then there is a level where personality study, abreaction, and the description of mechanisms are useful methods. There is then the

TABLE V

METHODS OF THERAPY IN PSYCHIATRY

ENVIRONMENTAL (manipulation, change, travel, diversion)

PHYSICAL (physiotherapy, exercise, games)

MEDICAL (drugs)

PSYCHOLOGICAL

Human Relationships
Support, Encouragement, Reassurance

Directive—Authoritative
Suggestion
Hypnosis
Direction—Authoritative Guidance
Routine—Schedule
Work—Occupational Therapy
Play—Art—Literature
Rest—Exercise

Intellectual—Explanatory
Re-education
Principles of Mental Hygiene—Study
Work—Play—Rest—Socialization
Personality Study
Explanation of Mental Mechanisms

Emotional—Release
Emotional Expression—Release, Abreaction

Analytical (intellectual, abreactive, relationship)
Analytic Psychology
Psychoanalysis

PSYCHOLOGICAL (*Continued*)
Analytic, Educational
Dynamic Growth Therapy—Treatment as growth through experience, learning, and education
Relationship therapeutic (support, encouragement, acceptance, individuation)
Abreaction to make possible emotional stability, eliminate dissociation, establish reassociation, and more stable integration, open the way for clarification and insight. (Emotion)
Understanding, development of (unconscious—conscious). (Intellect)
Practice Action (development of capacities and skills, and habits of courage, persistence, endurance, and reliability)
Inspiration (identification with ways of approaching—problems by therapist through kinds of questions he asks, identification with friends and heroes in history, literature, or life; social ideals; interest; enthusiasm)
Self-Direction (development of independence, release, and freedom from ineffective bonds or fixations from the past). (Will)
Growth in Self-Realization (find satisfaction in use of abilities for needs of others—cooperation —to attain self-respect and social respect). (Socialization)

level of seeing relationships, i.e., the level for deep therapy or psychoanalysis, which leads into the realm of primitive, archaic impulses and phantasies. And finally, comes always the level where the patient must reach out and test his hypotheses and perspectives; where he must try to live a new life and practice creative living. The psychiatrist must decide, from a multitude of minor cues obtained in the clinical examination, at which level he can best approach each of his various patients, and when he should change his method.

A great deal of difference exists among psychiatrists in the ability to understand, and hence to help, patients. This capacity does not depend upon intellectual ability or on ability to classify diseases. There is much variation in rapport between doctor and patient which does not depend entirely upon the patient's transference. The doctor must make a contribution here upon which the success or the failure of treatment often depends, and the capacity for this varies widely. It may be the difference between knowledge and art, the difference between medicine as a science and medicine as an art of practice.

No therapy, however helpful and useful in itself, will be of value unless a constructive relationship is developed between patient and doctor. The therapist is not entirely responsible for the way this develops. He is not responsible for the form of the transference, for instance, but he must be aware of the various possibilities and be able, through understanding and through a sympathetic reception of the patient's expressions, to help him make constructive steps in his growth. The therapist must preserve a careful balance, however, between showing sympathetic understanding of the patient's point of view and feelings, and either agreeing with him or antagonizing him. He must also refrain from aloofness and from irritating superiority or knowingness, even while he remains intellectually objective and empirical in his approach. The therapist must not make decisions for the patient unless it is absolutely necessary, but he can frequently encourage constructive thinking by asking tactful and stimulating questions. He should enable the patient to feel that he, the therapist, has real interest in him and his problems.

Psychotherapy cannot rely on the myth of the omnipotence of the rational. In therapy as in life, the irrationals are met, and they cannot be eradicated by appeals to reason. They must be resolved by patient use of free association or semi-free association, by release through abreaction, and by the insight and the new perspectives that come through a clarification of the transference and from a breakdown of resistance.

Psychotherapy is not just talking to patients. It is not humoring them. Neither is it the giving of platitudinous suggestions. Nor is it merely the prescription of sedatives and placebos. It is more than removing an irritating, stubborn, and temperamental person from the home to give a family relief. Psychotherapy has well-defined goals. It has well-defined rules and methods (proven for the most part) of reaching these goals. New ideas, attitudes, correlations, and perspectives must be woven in the web of a patient's life according to the laws of emotional health, and it is a successful affective relationship with the therapist that helps most constructively to cultivate in a patient these dynamisms of effective living.

BIBLIOGRAPHY

Adler, A. 1907. Organ inferiority. New York: Moffat Yard.
—— 1909. The neurotic constitution. New York: Moffat Yard.
—— 1923. Practice and theory of individual psychology. New York: Harcourt, Brace.
Aichorn, A. 1936. Wayward youth. New York: Viking.
Alcoholics Anonymous. 1939. New York: Works Publ.
Allen, F. H. 1942. Psychotherapy with children. New York: Norton.
Amsden, G. S. 1923. A guide to the descriptive study of the personality with

special reference to use in psychiatric cases. N. J.: Bloomingdale Hospital Press.

APPEL, K. E. 1931. Drawings by children as aids to personality studies. *Amer. J. Orthopsychiat., 1*, 129–144.

APPEL, K. E., FARR, C. B., & MARSHALL, H. K. 1929. Insulin in undernutrition in the psychoses. *Arch. Neurol. Psychiat., Chicago, 21*, 149–164.

APPEL, K. E., & STRECKER, E. A. 1936. Practical examination of personality and behavior disorders. New York: Macmillan.

BARD, P. 1934. The neuro-humoral basis of emotional reactions. In Murchison, C., *Handbook of general experimental psychology.* Worcester, Mass.: Clark University Press.

BARRETT, E. B. 1915. Strength of will. New York: P. J. Kennedy.

—— 1925. The new psychology. New York: P. J. Kennedy.

BAUDOUIN, C. 1920. Suggestion and autosuggestion. London: Allen & Unwin.

BEERS, C. W. 1908. A mind that found itself. New York: Longmans.

BENDER, L. 1937. Group activities on a children's ward as methods of psychotherapy. *Amer. J. Psychiat., 93*, 1151–1170.

BENDER, L., & WOLTMAN, A. G. 1936. The use of puppet shows as psychotherapeutic method for behavior problems in children. *Amer. J. Orthopsychiat., 6*, 341–353.

BOND, E. D. 1921a. Results in 251 cases five years after admission to a hospital for mental disease. *Arch. Neurol. Psychiat., Chicago, 6*, 429.

—— 1921b. A review of the five-year period following admission in 111 mental patients. *Amer. J. Insan., 77*, 385–395.

—— 1923. Follow-up work in mental and surgical cases. *Amer. J. Psychiat., 11*, 445–449.

—— 1925. Underestimation of good results in mental diseases. *J. Amer. med. Assn., 85*, 503–504.

—— 1941. Continued follow-up results in insulin shock therapy and in control cases. *Amer. J. Psychiat., 97*, 1024–1029.

BOND, E. D., et al. 1939. Results and observations on the insulin shock treatment of schizophrenia. *Amer. J. Psychiat., 96*, 317–326.

BOND, E. D., & BRACELAND, F. J. 1937. Prognosis in mental disease. *Amer. J. Psychiat., 94*, 263–274.

BOND, E. D., & RIVERS, T. D. 1941. Follow-up results in insulin shock therapy after one to three years. *Amer. J. Psychiat., 98*, 382–384.

BOWMAN, K. M., & BENDER, L. 1932. Treatment of involutional melancholia with ovarian hormone. *Amer. J. Psychiat., 11*, 867–893.

BOWMAN, K. M., GOODHART, R., & JOLLIFFE, N. 1939. Observations on the role of vitamin B₁ in etiology and treatment of Korsakoff's psychoses. *J. nerv. ment. Dis., 90*, 569–575.

BRADLEY, C., & BOSQUET, S. 1936. The use of books for psychotherapy with children. *Amer. J. Orthopsychiat., 6*, 23.

BREUER, J., & FREUD, S. 1893. Über den psychischen Mechanismus hysterischer Phänomene. *Neurol. Zbl., 12.*

—— 1895. Studien über Hysteria. Vienna: Deuticke. (Trans. by A. A. Brill. *Nerv. ment. Dis. Monogr.,* 1936, No. 61.)

BROWN, W. 1938. Psychological methods of healing. London: University London Press.

BURLINGAME, C. C., & PATTERSON, M. B. 1941. Estrogen therapy in psychosis. *J nerv. ment. Dis., 94*, 265 ff.

CALL, A. P. 1891 & 1914. Power through repose. Boston: Little, Brown.

CERLETTI, V., & BINI, L. 1938. Electric shock treatment. *Bull. Acad. Med., Rome, 64*, 36.

CONN, J. H. 1938. A psychiatric study of car sickness in children. *Amer. J. Orthopsychiat., 8*, 130.

—— 1939a. The child reveals himself through play: the method of the play interview. *Ment. Hyg., N. Y., 23*, 46–49.

—— 1939b. The play interview, a method of studying children's attitudes. *Amer. J. Dis. Child., 58*, 1199–1214.

COON, G. P., & RAYMOND, A. F. 1940. A review of the psychoneuroses at Stockbridge. Stockbridge: Austen Riggs Foundation.

COTTON, H. A. 1921. The defective, delinquent and insane. Princeton, N. J.: Princeton University Press.

COTTON, H. A. 1922. The etiology and treatment of the so-called functional psychoses. *Amer. J. Psychiat., 2,* 157–210.

COUÉ, E. 1929. La maîtresse de soi-même par l'autosuggestion consciente. Paris: Oliven.

DAVIDOFF, E. A. 1936. Clinical study of the effects of benzedrine therapy on self-absorbed patients. *Psychiat. Quart., 10,* 652.

DAVIDOFF, E. A., & REIFENSTEIN, E. C. 1937. The stimulating action of benzedrine sulfate. *J. Amer. med. Assn., 108,* 1770.

—— 1939a. The results of eighteen months of benzedrine sulfate therapy. *Amer. J. Psychiat., 95,* 945.

—— 1939b. Treatment of schizophrenia with sympathominetic drugs: benzedrine sulfate. *Psychiat. Quart., 13,* 127.

DÉJERINE, J., & GAUKLER, E. 1913. Psychoneurosis and psychotherapy. Philadelphia: Lippincott.

DESPERT, J. L. 1937. Technical approaches used in the study and treatment of emotional problems in children. Part 3. Drawing. *Psychiat. Quart., 11,* 267–295.

DIETHELM, O. 1936. Treatment in psychiatry. New York: Macmillan.

DUBOIS, P. 1907. The psychic treatment of mental disorders. New York: Funk & Wagnalls.

EDMAN, I. 1939. The candle in the dark. New York: Viking.

EYMIEU, A. 1922. Le gouvernement de soi-même. Paris: Perrin.

FLEMING, R., & REYNOLDS, D. 1935. Experimental studies in alcoholism: attempt to modify concentration of alcohol in blood after intravenous administration of alcohol. *J. Pharmacol., 54,* 236.

FLEMING, R., & TILLOTSON, K. J. 1939. Further studies on personality and sociological factors in prognosis and treatment of chronic alcoholism. *New Engl. J. Med., 221,* 741.

FREEMAN, W., & WATTS, J. W. 1942. Psychosurgery. Springfield, Ill.: Thomas.

FREUD, A. 1928. The technique of child analysis. *Nerv. ment. Dis. Monogr.,* No. 48.

FREUD, S. 1896. The aetiology of hysteria. (Trans. by C. M. Baines.) In *Collected papers.* Vol. 1. London: International Psychoanalytical Press, 1924.

—— 1900. The interpretation of dreams. In *The basic writings of Sigmund Freud.* (Trans. and ed. by A. A. Brill.) New York: Modern Library, 1938.

—— 1904. On the psychopathology of everyday life. In *The basic writings of Sigmund Freud.* New York: Modern Library, 1938.

—— 1910. The origin and development of psychoanalysis. Five lectures given at the 20th anniversary of the founding of Clark University. *Amer. J. Psychol., 21,* 181–218.

—— 1914. The history of the psychoanalytic movement. In *The basic writings of Sigmund Freud.* New York: Modern Library, 1938.

FREUD, S., & BREUER, J. 1893. The psychic mechanism of hysterical phenomena. In *Collected papers.* Vol. 1. London: International Psychoanalytical Press, 1924.

—— 1895. Studien über Hysterie. In *Gesammelte Schriften, Bd. 1.* Vienna: Internationale Psychoanalytische Verlag, 1925.

GARRISON, F. H. 1917. Introduction to the history of medicine. Philadelphia: Saunders.

GOLDSMITH, H. 1930. Spinal drainage in alcoholic deliria and other acute alcoholic psychoses. *Amer. J. Psychiat., 10,* 255.

HARE, F. 1924. Treatment of alcoholism. *Practitioner, 113,* 295.

HARMS, E. 1941. Child art as an aid in the diagnosis of juvenile neuroses. *Amer. J. Orthopsychiat., 11,* 191–209.

HEALY, M. 1940. Cited in Witmer, H. L., *Psychiatric clinics for children.* New York: Commonwealth Fund. Pp. 46–48.

HENDERSON, D. K., & GILLESPIE, R. D. 1941. A text book of psychiatry. New York: Oxford University Press.

HINSIE, L. E. 1935. Determinants of adequate psychotherapy in a public mental hospital. *Psychiat. Quart., 18,* 212–213.

HORNEY, K. 1937. The neurotic personality of our time. New York: Norton.

INGRAM, M. E. 1939. Principles of psychiatric nursing. Philadelphia: Saunders.

JACOBSON, E. 1934. You must relax. New York: McGraw-Hill.

—— 1938. Progressive relaxation. Chicago: University Chicago Press.

JAMES, W. 1893. Psychology. New York: Holt.
—— 1902. The varieties of religious experience. New York: Longmans, Green.
—— 1915. Talks to teachers and students. New York: Holt.
JANET, P. 1889. L'automatisme psychologique. Paris: Alcan.
—— 1923. Principles of psychotherapy. (Trans. by H. M. Guthrie and E. R. Guthrie.) New York: Macmillan, 1924.
JONES, E. 1938. Papers on psychoanalysis. The action of suggestion in psychotherapy. The nature of autosuggestion. Baltimore: William Wood.
JUNG, C. G. 1916. Collected papers on analytical psychology. (Trans. by C. E. Long.) London: Bailliere, Tindall.
—— 1923. Psychological types. London: George Routledge.
KANNER, L. 1935. Child psychology. Springfield, Ill.: C. C. Thomas.
KLEIN, M. 1937. The psychoanalysis of children. London: Hogarth.
KNIGHT, R. P. 1938. The psychoanalytical treatment in a sanitarium of chronic addiction to alcohol. J. Amer. med. Assn., 111, 1443.
—— 1941. Evaluation of the results of psychoanalytical therapy. Amer. J. Psychiat., 98, 434–446.
KOPELOFF, N., & CHENEY, C. O. 1922. Studies in focal infection; its presence and elimination in the functional psychoses. Amer. J. Psychiat., 2, 139–156.
KOPELOFF, N., & KIRBY, G. H. 1923. Focal infection and mental disease. Amer. J. Psychiat., 3, 149.
KRAINES, S. H. 1941. The therapy of the neuroses and psychoses. Philadelphia: Lea & Febiger.
LAMBERT, A. 1909. Obliteration of the craving for narcotics. J. Amer. med. Assn., 53, 985.
—— 1912. Care and control of the alcoholic. Bost. med. surg. J., 166.
LANDIS, C., & PAGE, J. D. 1938. Modern society and mental disease. New York: Farrar & Rinehart.
LEVY, D. M. 1937. Studies in sibling rivalry. Res. Monogr. Amer. Orthopsychiat. Assn., No. 2.
—— 1938. "Release therapy" in young children. Psychiatry, 1, 387–390.
—— 1939. Trends in therapy: III. Release therapy. Amer. J. Orthopsychiat., 9, 913–936.
—— 1940. Psychotherapy and childhood. Amer. J. Orthopsychiat., 10, 905–910.
LEVY, J., & MONROE, R. 1941. The happy family. New York: Knopf.
LOW, A. A., et al. 1938. Metrazol shock treatments of "functional" psychoses. Arch. Neurol. Psychiat., Chicago, 39, 717–736.
MALZBERG, B. 1938. Outcome of insulin treatment of one thousand patients with dementia praecox. Psychiat. Quart., 12, 528–553.
MARSHALL, H. 1940. Alcohol—a critical review of the literature 1929–1940. Psychol. Bull., 38, 193–217.
McDOUGALL, W. 1926. Outline of abnormal psychology. New York: Scribner's.
McFARLAND, R. A., & BARACH, A. L. 1936. The relationship between alcoholic intoxication and oxygen want. Amer. J. med. Sci., 192, 186–198.
MEDUNA, L. V. 1935. Versuche über die biologische Beeinflussung des Ablaufes der Schizophrenie; Kampfer und Cardiozolkrämpfe. Z. ges. Neurol. Psychiat., 152, 235–262.
MEDUNA, L. V., & FRIEDMAN, E. 1939. Convulsive-irritative therapy of the psychoses. J. Amer. med. Assn., 112, 501–509.
MENNINGER, W. C. 1937. Bibliotherapy. Bull. Menninger Clin., 1, 262.
MEYER, A. 1908. The problems of mental reaction types, mental causes and diseases. Psychol. Bull., 5, 245.
—— 1928. The evolution of the dementia praecox concept. Res. Publ. Assn. Res. nerv. ment. Dis., 5, 3–15.
—— 1935. Scope and teaching of psychobiology. J. Assn. Amer. med. Coll., 10, 93–98.
—— 1938. Leading concepts of psychobiology (ergasiology) and of psychiatry (ergasiatry). Proc. 4th Conf. psychiat. Educ.
MILLER, E. 1930. Modern psychotherapy. London: Jonathan Cape.
MITCHELL, S. W. 1893. Fat and blood. Philadelphia: Lippincott.
MOORE, M. 1941. Alcoholism: some contemporary opinions. New Engl. J. Med., 224, 848–857.
MUDD, E. H., & WHITEHILL, J. L. 1938. The use and misuse of books in counselling. Parent Educ., 14, Nos. 2, 3.

MÜLLER, M. 1938. The insulin therapy of schizophrenia. *Amer. J. Psychiat., 94* (suppl.), 5–23.

MUNCIE, W. 1939. Psychobiology and psychiatry. St. Louis: Mosby.

OSLER, W. 1932. A way of life. Baltimore: Norman-Remington.

PALMER, H. D., & BRACELAND, F. J. 1937. Six years experience with narcosis therapy in psychiatry. *Amer. J. Psychiat., 94,* 35–37.

PALMER, H. D., HASTINGS, D. W., & SHERMAN, S. H. 1941. Therapy in involutional melancholia. *Amer. J. Psychiat., 97,* 1086–1115.

PAYOT, J. 1909. The education of the will. New York: Funk & Wagnalls.

PEABODY, R. A. 1930. Psychotherapeutic procedure in treatment of chronic alcoholism. *Ment. Hyg., N. Y., 14,* 109.

—— 1935. The common sense of drinking. New York: Little, Brown.

RIGGS, A. F. 1922. Just nerves. New York: Doubleday, Doran.

—— 1929. Intelligent living. New York: Doubleday, Doran.

RIPPON, T. S., & FLETCHER, P. 1940. Reassurance and relaxation. London: George Routledge.

RIVERS, T. D. 1944. The treatment of alcoholic conditions and certain toxic states. (Unpublished)

ROBINSON, G. W., JR. 1940. Treatment of delirium tremens with insulin in subshock doses. *Amer. J. Psychiat., 97,* 136–151.

ROBINSON, G. W., JR., & SHELTON, P. 1940. Treatment of uncomplicated acute alcoholism; preliminary report upon effectiveness of insulin, glucose and thiamin chloride in correcting pathological physiology. *J. Lancet, 60,* 461–464.

ROBINSON, J. H. 1921. The mind in the making. New York: Harper.

ROGERS, C. R. 1939. The clinical treatment of the problem child. Cambridge: Riverside Press.

ROSS, T. A. 1936. An enquiry into the prognosis in the neuroses. Cambridge: Cambridge University Press.

ROTHERMICH, N. O., POSTLE, B., & FOLTZ, L. M. 1941. Altered concept of involutional melancholia with estrogen and androgen. *Arch. Neurol. Psychiat., Chicago, 45,* 752–768.

SAKEL, M. 1937. The methodical use of hypoglycemia in the treatment of psychoses. *Amer. J. Psychiat., 94,* 111 ff.

—— 1938. The pharmacological shock treatment of schizophrenia. (Trans. by J. Wortis.) *Nerv. ment. Dis. Monogr. Ser.,* No. 62.

SAYLES, M. B. 1928. The problem child at home. New York: Commonwealth Fund.

SCHILDER, P. 1938. Psychotherapy. New York: Norton.

SCHUBE, P. G., *et al.* 1937. Involutional melancholia treatment with theelin. *Arch. Neurol. Psychiat., Chicago, 38,* 505–512.

SHAPIRO, H. D., & FREEMAN, W. 1939. Shock therapy (insulin and metrazol) in the neuroses. *Med. Ann. Dist. Columbia, 8,* 65–72.

SHIPLEY, W., & KANT, F. 1940. The insulin-shock and metrazol treatments of schizophrenia, with emphasis on psychological aspects. *Psychol. Bull., 37,* 259–284.

SIDIS, B. 1916. The causation and treatment of psychopathic lesions. Boston: Badger.

SOLOMON, J. C. 1938. Active play therapy. *Amer. J. Orthopsychiat., 8,* 479–497.

—— 1940. Active play therapy: further experiences. *Amer. J. Orthopsychiat., 10,* 763–781.

STRAUSS, H., LANDIS, C., & HUNT, W. A. 1939. The metrazol seizure and its significance for the pathophysiology of the epileptic attack. *J. nerv. ment. Dis., 90,* 439–452.

STRECKER, E. A. 1941. Chronic alcoholism; a psychological survey. *Quart. J. Stud. Alcohol, 2,* 12–17.

STRECKER, E. A., & APPEL, K. E. 1931. Discovering ourselves. New York: Macmillan.

STRECKER, E. A., & CHAMBERS, F. T. 1939. Alcohol—one man's meat. New York: Macmillan.

STRECKER, E. A., & EBAUGH, F. G. 1940. Practical clinical psychiatry. Philadelphia: Blakiston.

TABORI, J. 1933. Mental background of alcoholics. *Psychoanal. Prax., 3,* 10.

THOM, D. A. 1924. Habit clinics for the child of pre-school age—their organization and practical value. Washington: Government Printing Office.

THOM, D. A. 1932. Normal youth and its everyday problems. New York: Appleton-Century.
—— 1937. Habit training for children. New York: National Committee for Mental Hygiene.
TWYEFFORT, L. H. 1940. Therapy in psychoneuroses (bibliotherapy). In Piersol, G. M., & Bortz, E. L., *The encyclopedia of medicine, surgery & specialties.* Philadelphia: F. A. Davis.
VITTOZ, R. 1913. Treatment of neurasthenia by means of brain control. (Trans. by H. B. Brooks.) London: Longmans, Green.
VIVIAN, M. 1929. Management of inebriates. *Brit. J. Inebr., 26,* 223.
VOEGTLIN, W. L. 1940. Treatment of alcoholism by establishing a conditioned reflex. *American J. med. Science, 199,* 102.
VOEGTLIN, W. L., & LEMERE, F. 1941. The treatment of alcoholic addiction—a review of the literature. *Quart. J. Stud. Alcohol, 11,* 717–803.
WALSH, J. J. 1913. Psychotherapy. New York: Appleton-Century.
—— 1931. Health through will power. Boston: Stratford.
WERNER, A. A., *et al.* 1936. Treatment of involutional melancholia with theelin. *Arch. Neurol. Psychiat., Chicago, 35,* 1076.
WHITE, A. D. 1905a. History of the warfare of science with theology. New York: D. Appleton & Co.
WILBUR, D. L., *et al.* 1937. Clinical observations on the effect of benzadrine sulfate. *Proc. Mayo Clin., 12,* 97.
WILLIAMS, F. E. 1930. Adolescence—studies in mental hygiene. New York: Farrar & Rinehart.
WOLFE, W. B. 1931. How to be happy though human. New York: Farrar & Rinehart.
—— 1933. Nervous breakdown—its cause and cure. New York: Farrar & Rinehart.

ADDITIONAL REFERENCES ON BIBLIOTHERAPY

ADLER, A. 1927. Understanding human nature. New York: Greenberg Publisher.
—— 1931. What life should mean to you. New York: Little, Brown.
ALDRICH, C. A. 1932. Cultivating the child's appetite. New York: Macmillan.
AVEBURY, LORD. 1909. Peace and happiness. New York: Macmillan.
BLANCHARD, P. 1920. The adolescent girl. New York: Dodd, Mead.
BLITZSTEN, D. 1936. Psychoanalysis explained. New York: Coward-McCann.
BENNETT, A. 1938. How to live on twenty-four hours a day. New York: Doubleday, Doran.
BUTTERFIELD, O. M. 1936. Marriage and sexual harmony. New York: Emerson Books.
CADY, B. C., & CADY, V. M. 1917. The way life begins. New York: American Social Hygiene Assn.
CAMERON, H. C. 1926. The nervous child. New York: Oxford University Press.
CLARK, LeMon. 1917. Emotional adjustment in marriage. St. Louis: Mosby.
COSTER, G. 1926. Psychoanalysis for normal people. London: Oxford University Press.
DEKOK, W. 1935. Guiding your child through the formative years. New York: Emerson Books.
DENNETT, M. W. 1928. The sex side of life. New York: Author.
DE SCHWEINITZ, K. 1935. Growing up. New York: Macmillan.
ELLIOTT, G. L., & BONE, H. 1929. The sex side of youth. New York: Association Press.
ELLIS, H. 1930. Little essays of love and virtue. New York: Doubleday, Doran.
—— 1933. Psychology of sex. New York: R. Long & R. R. Smith.
FREUD, A. 1935. Psychoanalysis for teachers and parents. New York: Emerson Books.
HART, B. 1927. Psychopathology. Cambridge: Cambridge University Press.
HIMES, N. 1938. Practical birth control methods. New York: Modern Age Books.
HUTTON, I. E. 1932. The sex technique in marriage. New York: Emerson Books.

HUTTON, L. 1937. The single woman and her emotional problems. Baltimore: William Wood.

ISAACS, S. 1936. The nursery years. New York: Vanguard.

KNOPF, O. 1932. The art of being a woman. New York: Blue Ribbon Books.

LATZ, L. J. 1934. The rhythm of sterility and fertility in women. Chicago: Latz Foundation.

LOW, B. 1928. Psychoanalysis and education. New York: Harcourt, Brace.

MANNIN, E. 1932. Common sense and the child. Philadelphia: Lippincott.

MEEK, L. H. 1940. Your child's development and guidance—told in pictures. Philadelphia: Lippincott.

MENNINGER, K. A. 1938. Man against himself. New York: Harcourt, Brace.

MOWRER, H. 1932. The family: its organization and disorganization. Chicago: University Chicago Press.

NEILL, A. S. 1927. The problem child. New York: McBride.

—— 1932. The problem parent. London: Herbert Jenkins.

POPONOE, P. 1940a. Preparation for marriage. New York: Macmillan.

—— 1940b. Modern marriage. New York: Macmillan.

RHOADES, W. 1938. The self you have to live with. Philadelphia: Lippincott.

RICHARDSON, F. H. 1928. The nervous child and his parents. New York: Putnam's.

RICHMOND, W. V. 1933. The adolescent boy. New York: Farrar & Rinehart.

RIGGS, A. F. 1935. Play-recreation in a balanced life. New York: Doubleday, Doran.

RUCH, F. L., MACKENSIE, C. N., & McCLEAN, M. 1941. People are important. New York: Scott, Foresman.

STONE, H. M., & STONE, A. 1935. A marriage manual. New York: Simon & Schuster.

STRAIN, F. B. 1934. New patterns in sex teaching. New York: Appleton-Century.

—— 1936. Being born. New York: Appleton-Century.

THOM, D. A. 1929. Everyday problems of the everyday child. New York: Appleton-Century.

VOICE OF EXPERIENCE. 1932. New York: Grosset & Dunlap.

WEBB, E. T., & MORGAN, J. B. 1930. Strategy in handling people. New York: Garden City Publ.

WILE, I. S. 1934. The sex life of the unmarried adult. New York: Vanguard.

—— 1937. The man takes a wife—a study of man's problems in and through marriage. New York: Greenberg Publisher.

WILLIAMS-ELLIS, A. 1929. How you began—a child's introduction to biology. (Preface by J. B. S. Haldane.) New York: Coward-McCann.

WOLF, A. W. M. 1941. The parents' manual. New York: Simon & Schuster.

WRIGHT, H. 1931. The sex factor in marriage. New York: Vanguard.

WRIGHT, M. 1935. Getting along with people. New York: Whittlesey House.

Chapter 35

THE PREVENTION OF PERSONALITY DISORDERS

By George S. Stevenson, M.D.

THE MOST INSPIRING GOAL of our search for more knowledge of the causes and determinants of personality and of the disorders of behavior is the possibility of applying this knowledge to the refinement of human living and to the prevention of disorders of behavior, in other words to add to mental hygiene. Mental hygiene is not a hygiene through a "mental approach" as Williams (1932) implied in his *Is There a Mental Hygiene?* but a prevention of mental disorder on any basis. It has been shown (Chapters 16 to 24) that these disorders are the outgrowth of a multiplicity of factors, some more important than others, some indispensable in the production of certain forms of disorder. In other words, some burdens on the efficient behavior of the individual are general and some are quite specific. It has been shown in this book that this complexity of causative factors is very great and that the combinations are various both as to the types of factors and their sequence. The importance of the same factor may change greatly from case to case. Therefore, persons with apparently similar disorders are apt to have been influenced by very different combinations of factors. Each person is an "experiment of nature" in that nature has put each together in a new way; no one is exactly duplicated.

In most instances there are several factors that can be considered important in precipitating a certain disorder of personality or behavior, any one of which might be credited as being the last straw in breaking "the camel's back" depending on when it happened. The weight of the combination is important. In some instances, therefore, one is faced with several alternate avenues of attack in the effort to spare or unburden "the camel." Thus the preventive effort is not only individual in terms of the person to be helped, who has his own combination of causes, but is likewise individual for the person offering the help, who has his own technical strengths and opportunities for using this or that approach. In some instances the overburdening is slight, and in such cases a change in any one of many factors may suffice to lighten the load enough to remove a threat. In that case, there is wide choice in the factors to be attacked or hygienic methods to be used. By the same token, a measure undertaken to affect a community-wide factor, or one existing otherwise on a large scale, will affect many people favorably, but leave some of the more seriously disordered still overburdened. In other cases the burdening may be so heavy as to demand a change of every possible factor. Then there is little choice. This possibility of alternate choices is not always fully appreciated, with the result that one way is often considered right and all others wrong. This results in unnecessary confusion.[1]

Various Concepts of Prevention

In addition to differences in the choice of methods of prevention there are categorical differences in the very meaning of prevention. These differences cause no trouble if they are understood. They result in fruitless argument if they are not. It seems important, therefore, to sort out, label and illuminate these different categories of prevention in order that effort that is quite appropriate in striving for one may not be wasted on another.

Probably the most frequent preventive effort could be classified as "presumptive prevention." This effort is based on the knowledge that certain conditions (familial, physical, psychological, and social) antedate and appear to be etiologically related to behavior disturbances. The shut-in personality is said to precede dementia praecox. It is consequently thought to be appropriate to correct or prevent this condition in the hope of forestalling dementia praecox. It is presumed that the antecedent condition is causative or an essential intermediate step in the development of the disorder and that its correction will be preventive. If this presumption is merely slipshod "science" to avoid the trouble of further research, it is a retardant to more certain and effective prevention. If, on the other hand, it is recognized for its limitations, accepted as tentative, and accompanied by vigorous efforts to prove or disprove the presumption, it is an important step in scientific progress. If it is a way of doing the best possible, until science shows its falsity or shows a better way, it maintains activity in the field, enriches experience and gives the weight of logic to what is done for people for whom something will be done anyway. Presumptive prevention is well illustrated by the following excerpt from an article on prevention by H. L. Levin:

> Where the parents or others have been capable observers and are sufficiently cooperative to tell all they know, a history of these faulty habitual reactions in childhood can be obtained in a large proportion of the cases of adolescent or adult praecoxes who are committed to a state hospital. Four such cases are described below from the records of a state hospital, illustrating Meyer's conception that the psychotic symptoms necessitating commitment to state hospitals are but nat-

---

[1] This is in itself a behavior and personality disorder known as the "incapacity to accept difference." It is the emotional need that "my way" be the "right way" and all others "wrong ways" and results in a tendency to force others to agree with me, take my advice and follow my example. Emotional maturation has been interpreted as in part a progressive capacity to accept differences. This problem would then evidence emotional immaturity, a need for a world revolving about the self as it did in childhood.

ural outgrowths of faulty reaction habits of childhood. These are
followed by the case records of our children treated at child guidance
clinics for abnormalities in mood and conduct strikingly similar to
those of the committed adults and treated with apparent success for
two to four year periods.

Although the four problem children seemed to have been definitely
started on the praecox route, psychiatric intervention appeared to
have vitiated some of the malignant elements in the environment and
brought about for a period now of from two to four years, an apparent arrest of the praecox process. The question is raised whether
similar intervention during the childhood of the four adult praecox
cases might not have been the means of preventing chronic, if not
lifelong, psychoses. (1933, p. 806)

It is chiefly important that "presumptive prevention" be recognized
for what it is. If, for example, the shut-in child is to be dealt with on
the one hand by the chance buffets of parents, teachers or companions
or else on the other by a designed attempt to bring him into close, more
comfortable, touch with others, it is better to follow the latter course
even though it is a presumptive prevention, for at worst it is likely to
be no worse than the former, and in any case our knowledge of such
children is enriched by the attention to the problem. It would, however,
be a mistake to believe that thereby the last word in a preventive program has been said.

According to another concept of prevention, it is considered that a
disorder may be forestalled by treating a definite but simpler or earlier
disorder. This might be called "therapeutic prevention." It is only relatively preventive in that a problem has already arisen. It depends for its
rationale upon the fact that most disorders of personality and behavior
are progressive. They seldom burst forth on short notice in full form,
although there are clear-cut instances of this, but rather they are cumulative, one step in a series leading to another. By treating one step the
next is prevented. Thus the prevention of the most serious disorders—
the psychoses—leads one to give serious therapeutic attention to alcoholism, neuroses, psychosomatic disorders, antisocial behavior and distorted personality, the lazy, the moody and the overscrupulous. The
distinction from presumptive prevention is not always clear. Sometimes
both presumptive and therapeutic prevention are involved.

This form of "relative prevention" is clearly justified, but again it
must be recognized as only "half a loaf" and should be seen as an incentive to discover the way to the other half. The treatment of school failure might be considered a therapeutic preventive of truancy and delinquency and might involve a study of the causes of the failure and an
adjustment of the school program so as to bring the child again into his
social or age group. This approach to the problem leads to the discovery
and correction of the other half of the problem that would be missed if
the school failure were cured merely by removing the child from school
and putting him to work. (See radical prevention.) Kasanin and Veo

(1932) found two groups of serious mental cases who could be recognized in advance as problems by their teachers: the odd, queer, peculiar; and the shy, backward, and passive. These offer possibility of prevention and they constitute half of the prospective cases of dementia praecox. The other prospective cases seem to offer no warning to the teacher of the impending disaster. This forewarned half, however, points to the need to give to the prospective teacher some new information and experience to be included in his training, and they also tell the community to enrich its resources for dealing with these problems.

Witmer, in a careful study of the objective of prevention as a purpose of child guidance clinics, questions seriously whether there is good foundation for such an expectation. She says:

> A plan for preventing psychoses through the treatment of children who are likely to develop serious mental disorders falls down, then, for various reasons. In the first place, psychiatrists disagree as to the causes of the functional psychoses. The psychoanalytic and other dynamic theories, emphasizing as they do psychogenetic factors, offer greater hope than the others for prophylactic work in this area, but they give little support to the belief that the relative strengths and weaknesses of a child's personality can be so assessed that the likelihood of his developing a psychosis can be estimated. Then, on the factual side, there is little to substantiate the belief that the findings with respect to prepsychotic personality traits are reversible. On the one hand, there are large numbers of psychotic patients who as children appeared, according to all reports, to have been normal. On the other, even if it is granted that children with certain personality traits are more likely than others to develop mental disorders, there is nothing to indicate how much greater that likelihood is, nor does the little evidence available suggest that it is excessive. Accordingly, a mental hygiene program aimed at identifying the potential psychotics among school children would locate only a certain proportion of them at best and would expend much effort upon a group whose chance of mental disease is slight. (1940, pp. 283–284)

Similarly the clinical approach to delinquency is handicapped by the fact that in so far as delinquency is a clinical problem it is a problem of dealing with a disturbed personality, whereas delinquency is a legal label of certain symptoms that have offended society. Unlike the prevention of mental disease, however, there are other paths to the prevention of delinquency that are open beyond the clinical sphere. Meyer clarifies the preventive situation as follows:

> The habits clinics were developed, and since then The National Committee for Mental Hygiene has been enabled to establish its child-guidance clinics, nominally for the prevention of delinquency, but really as a step toward reaching the broader needs of health, happiness, efficiency, and social adaptation.
> We are at times made to believe that all our mental hygiene work and effort aims largely at the prevention of "insanity and

crime," just as the early advocates of psychopathic hospitals made it look as if, through the creation of a psychopathic hospital in each state, the existing state hospital care would then be made less expensive and perhaps in part unnecessary. To be sure, early work means a heading off of some of the disastrous depth of aberration and deviation and much unnecessary blundering. But the chief goal is much more direct; it offers prompter and more and more enlightened help both to patient and family and to the community in respect to really new problems, largely left to themselves before; it is a direct service to the positive needs and opportunities of the community in behalf of what I reemphasize as health, happiness, efficiency, and social adaptation. (1925, p. 675)

Somewhat related to therapeutic prevention is another form of relative prevention in which a problem is prevented by substituting a less serious problem in its place. This is dependent upon the fact that at certain—possibly all—stages in the development of problems there are several alternate lines of development, and that with outside help the progression can be turned into the less serious channel. Voluntary tics are especially subject to this "substitutive-prevention." A beginning tendency to nail biting may be turned into pencil-biting or some other socially less objectionable, therefore individually less burdensome, behavior disorder, and thus bring the disturbance to a lower level. In fact such substitutions take place spontaneously again and again in the course of the development of a behavior pattern. Blos has shown these shifts by detailed longitudinal case studies and also how the child reverts to older patterns when the new is unsuccessful. Again in this approach it must be kept evident that the foundation of the problem remains unchanged; the effort is palliative; and if nothing is done to improve the basic condition the achievement is apt to be temporary. It gives respite, however, for more fundamental help and is valuable where no better opportunity for prevention is offered.

A third form of relative prevention consists of circumventing a disorder by modification of general conditions that have nothing specifically to do with the determination of the problem but merely permit its occurrence. The specific conditions are unmodified. This measure of prevention may involve the change of home or the imposition of segregation and constraint. It is analogous to the prevention of cancer by removal of tissues in which cancer might occur. It is "radical prevention." Since many hazards are environmental and are a threat to many persons a modification of one person affords no protection to others. Most of our penology operates this way. Such a process has its place particularly in acute emergencies but is seldom final. It contributes little to our knowledge. It is hazardous if there is no attempt to modify these threats in the interim, but allows the return of the person or the exposing of others to the same deleterious factors.

The fact that these three forms of relative prevention—therapeutic, substitutive, and radical—are presented as a separate category does not mean that in actual practice they can be so isolated. In fact they are seldom applied in pure form, but exist in combination with each other and with presumptive and other types of prevention. In implication, however, they are somewhat different and for this reason warrant clear analysis in order that the implications of one may not be applied to the other.

The acme of prevention is of course the removal of causes or the application of scientifically validated preventive measures. This "absolute prevention" is harder to achieve in multidetermined behavior disorders than in the case of specific medical problems, and so there is a marked lag between treatment and prevention. It is, however, quite practical in the case of syphilitic and toxic behavior disorders. This "rational prevention" should not, however, be permitted to cloud the value of "empirical prevention" of which ordinary vaccination is a good example. While empirical measures may not afford the satisfaction of a good rationale, they are scientifically validated and clinically effective. In the interests of science they should be explained, but they are not presumptive. It is an established fact variously explained that religious experience, especially of the Salvation Army form, has in many persons markedly altered the course of alcoholism and some other disorders. This is a fact to be studied and understood, not one to be ignored because it is not understood.

For purposes of avoiding confusion, then, it is well to differentiate the various forms of prevention and to associate with each its values and limitations. These forms are:

Presumptive Prevention—based on the alteration of earlier or associated conditions presumed to be of causative importance.
Relative Prevention:
Therapeutic—based on the treatment of earlier less serious stages of a disorder in order to prevent more serious stages.
Substitutive—based on the substitution of a less for a more serious and progressive disorder.
Radical—based on the changing general conditions of living so as to evade factors of disorder.
Absolute Prevention:
Rational—based on the elimination of proved causes.
Empirical—based on the application of unexplained measures of proved value.

Focusing Prevention

Preventive programs, however conceived, must be pointed up strategically or else find themselves dissipated or misplaced. This effective focusing of prevention demands that it be directed at human functions that have to do with behavior disorders. Thus prevention becomes eugenical, physiological, psychological, and environmental. It needs also to respect certain general principles or facts about human behavior. Eight such principles will be considered.

Probably the most important is the fact that *human behavior is multideterined*. Entering into behavior are multitudinous factors of the past experience and current state of the four levels of human functioning listed above. As expressed by A. T. Mathers (1931, p. 486), "the causes are multiform and variable, vague and subtle, rooted widely and deeply in the very fundamentals of life and society." This means that on the one hand prevention may need to be complex, and on the other hand that many different professional groups have legitimate opportunity or obligation to participate. It means that the royal road to prevention is traversed by these professions working in unison but that lesser roads are open to them individually in connection with their daily jobs. Thus the doctor, the lawyer, minister, employer, nurse, social worker, teacher, public health functionary, all meet with opportunities as a part of their daily jobs to influence the personality and behavior of those whom they serve or those whom their clients may in turn influence. They have opportunity to influence them eugenically, physically, mentally, and through improvement in their social settings. If one studies the history of any service agency, he finds that though it started with one profession it comes to add others to its force; the schools add doctors, nurses, and social workers, and the hospitals add teachers and social workers in the effort to meet this principle as their cases reveal it. Now the coordinating council and several other patterns of community efforts in behalf of children are attempting to accomplish the same ends by effecting a functional coordination between agencies. The clinic serves the juvenile court and other agencies and so saves them the confusion of adding similar services to their own staffs; the social agency likewise renders many services to the hospitals and schools. The coordinating council consists of a council of welfare leaders in a neighborhood designed to bring the various agencies to the attention of those who need them. Through its appreciation of deficiencies of service in the community, it is in a position to strengthen existing agencies or promote the establishment of new ones. This pattern of coordination is entering more and more into the functions of individual agencies as they seek help from other agencies as a substitute for broadening their staffs.

The *second principle* grows out of the first. Since behavior disorders are determined by a multiplicity of factors, more than can be reasonably taken into account in any one program dependent upon human resources, it is necessary to be somewhat "choosy" if preventive effort is to be focused for maximum effectiveness. It is, in other words, possible to waste effort upon relatively minor factors. It is not sufficient to decide that a certain factor exists, but it must be determined that the *factor is critical,* that attacking it will likely change the resultant behavior. Furthermore, a factor must not only be critical but *accessible* and *vulnerable* to attack. A threat of disorder may be found in the death of a loved one; this may be a critical factor but not an accessible or vulnerable one. Furthermore, some factors are more specific than others in that they result more exclusively in the disorder of personality and behavior where another factor has broader influence. The removal of the latter may have bad side-effects. One at least needs to be aware of not only the desired effects of removing a factor, but also the undesired by-effects that come from its elimination.

The influence of this principle is especially evident in the way many child guidance clinics deal with cases that are referred to them. The child guidance clinic is peculiarly designed to deal with the psychopathological problems of childhood. It is, therefore, essential that it work with cases in which this factor is critical, accessible and vulnerable. The information accompanying the application on an initial diagnostic study may show that one or more of these requirements are missing: the problem may be primarily sociological; or if psychopathological it may not be accessible—for example, as often occurs in court cases, the child and his parents may oppose treatment; or it may not be subject to therapy as in the case of mental deficiency or epidemic encephalitis. The clinic then devotes a minimum of effort to such cases.

As a *third principle,* it is necessary to distinguish between the *essential characteristics* of a disorder, the aspect that makes it a disorder, and the unessentials which may merely represent human differences. There is no virtue in merely removing human differences. There is, for example, a tendency on the part of some to think of habits as disabling in themselves. There are habitual drinkers who, however, are not problem drinkers, so that the habit of drinking is not of itself a disorder. A preventive program must take this sort of distinction into account in focusing its effort if it is to avoid opposition.

Those who adhere to the regimentation of the children in a classroom think of the active classroom as disorderly because they have never separated orderly from disorderly activity. The failure to make this distinction deprives children of a spontaneous function that can contribute much to their mental growth. Similarly, child labor is not essentially bad, but is criticized because its unfortunate accompaniments are so difficult to control separately. A study of children of the dramatic stage by Zimand (1941, p. 94) has brought this out clearly. It is the pressure of the children's parents for high performance in a highly competitive field that is the real problem.

A *fourth principle* depends upon the fact that *many behavior disorders are circular.* They stand in a series of events wherein the operation of one factor leads to subsequent factors and these in turn enhance the first. To attempt to deal with the original factors in such a circular series is bewildering and often futile, because the original factors may no longer be active and better opportunity to break into the vicious circle may be found at several other points in the course. Opportunistic interruption of such circular processes at any critical point is often the best solution. One may kill the chicken or break the egg without deciding on their relative priority.

One need not go far for concrete examples of this circular effect. A simple instance is the effect of fatigue. Whatever its original cause may have been, fatigue reduces the efficiency of behavior. Mistakes and extra motions are much more abundant. To accomplish the same work when fatigued more energy is consumed and further fatigue is thereby induced than in the case when one is rested. Thus fatigue is serious when one is working on such a narrow margin of reserve that he cannot take time out to rest. Anxiety and loss of sleep may enter into this vicious circle to further complicate it. Increasing one's margin of reserve by decreasing the load of work, taking rest or getting sleep, may, any one of them, break into this vicious circle. In another case a child who is caught in the circle of a parent-teacher conflict may enjoy an interruption of the circle by transfer to another school. Camping programs, vacations, special residential schools, often without awareness, cut across such circles that include home and neighborhood problems.

A *fifth principle* depends on the fact, as emphasized by Tiebout in 1932, that the *primary causes* of a disorder are often fortuitously or otherwise solved, but the disorder lingers on by virtue of *secondary factors* that did not exist at the beginning. It may be too late to do anything about the original causes; they may be no longer accessible; they may be no longer critical; but still preventive processes may be set up to weaken the influence of these secondary factors. Stealing that was started for revenge is impossible to prevent on that basis, after the attribute of revenge is resolved. The continuance of the stealing for the secondary values derived from the use of the booty may be attacked.

The *sixth principle* emphasizes the greater promise of preventive effort applied at an *early stage* in a disorder. This assumes that habituation and secondary factors have entered less into determination in the beginning than would be the case later. This may seem somewhat contrary to the concept of disorders as being *more or less self-limiting* as Cabot (1934) conceived of delinquency. It is likely that both are valid and have to be taken into account in prevention. In other words, the alternative to early stage prevention is not necessarily progressive disorder, and this self-limiting possibility needs to be nurtured in instances in which the early treatment fails.

A great many of the programs that are designed to prevent behavior disorders are based upon the early discovery and treatment of the disorder. The visiting teacher who provides social case-work for children whose behavior or achievement is unsatisfactory provides a quick service on early cases. The special programs for mental deficiency likewise provide appropriate education at an early period of behavior deviation. Special programs for truants sometimes provide study and treatment at an early stage, but all too often they apply pressure for attendance without understanding. Professional education is more and more tending to include preparation for handling early cases as a part of the routine of social work, medicine, theology, teaching, and public health.

The *seventh principle* is based on the fact that our language by which we label causes and disorders is insufficiently rich to give the distinctions needed between the various grades of disorder. Stealing and lying cover a great diversity of very different disorders and some behavior that is not disorderly. There is a tendency to consider certain circumstances as either "good" or "bad" in themselves. What is needed is a *many-valued concept* of these factors as they relate to modifiable circumstances. Then by focusing the preventive effort on the circumstances under which it may operate, the more desirable of the values can be secured for a factor. The time (date), location, and variety of the factor have to be taken into account if preventive effort is to be focused effectively. It can then center on reducing those factors that constitute a greater threat or building up of those of greater promise. Some police programs designed to prevent delinquency aim to catch the delinquent early and give him special treatment. Unfortunately, these are too often law-centered rather than child-centered. A second appearance labels a child a second offender, and he is dealt with as such even though his record may be merely as a witness or based on unsubstantiated charges. The child who rides a bicycle on the sidewalk or plays ball in the street is equated with the more antisocial on the basis of law rather than the dynamics of behavior. These are verbal pitfalls.

As an example of the *eighth principle* it may be stated that apparently, paradoxically, in many cases one does not prevent a disorder by setting out to prevent that disorder. Rather he seeks the *positive development* of behavior in terms of its value to survival, satisfaction, and productivity. By reversing the focus from prevention to human enrichment one has by no means abandoned prevention. Accordingly, behavior disorders are prevented by focusing effort on proper educational goals in the school, by fostering an understanding of child development in the home, by health service, by good foster home placement in the case of dependent children, and by providing attractive play in the recreational facility and integrating activities of community clubs and parks.

In brief these principles are:

1. Behavior is multi-determined and involves many factors.
2. Preventive effort should be centered on the critical, accessible, vulnerable, specific factors.
3. The essentials aspects of a disorder should be separated from the nonessential.
4. Circular disorders may be attacked opportunistically rather than by historical sequence.
5. The perpetuation of disorder is often less related to its original causes than to the intervention of secondary causes.
6. Early treatment tends to be more promising, but some disorders apparently run their courses spontaneously.
7. Confusion in focusing preventive effort is reduced by a many-valued orientation.
8. Prevention is often a by-product of an effort to develop positive assets.

These eight general considerations clarify the opportunities to prevent disorders of personality and behavior and should be kept in mind in formulating any program of prevention. Prevention is necessarily directed toward the aspects of human functioning that are critically related to disorders. It cannot, however, await symptoms. It must seek to bring about optimum conditions in these spheres directly, for disorders are so various that to focus attention on prevention of various symptoms would be disconcerting and scattering. In other words, in prevention attention must be centered directly upon insuring to persons the best possible endowment at birth, upon insuring the soundest possible physiological functioning, especially in certain directions, upon the development of useful attitudes and habits, and upon affording a wholesome environment and experiences. These are the foci of preventive effort. These four foci are, of course, an academic division of the person, for actually these foci can seldom exist in isolation as a program. Nevertheless, they are useful concepts because they allow us to deal with some considerations that apply specifically to each of them.

Eugenical Prevention.—Eugenical prevention includes all efforts directed toward the best possible prenatal endowment. These include good heredity, good embryonic and fetal development, and safe passage through the processes of birth.

The application of measures designed to terminate adverse heredity influences have absorbed practically all of our interest in applied human genetics. The sort of positive breeding that is found in husbandry is almost unknown. The measures used to influence heredity include the control of marriage, sterilization, limitation of conception, and destruction of the embryo or fetus (abortion and miscarriage). Of these the control of marriage has been left largely to individual private decision, although of recent years legal statutes have been passed to obstruct precipitous marriages and to eliminate parenthood among those who have been so incompetent socially as to require guardianship. This is especially important in the case of the mental defective. Sterilization of mental defectives has been legalized in a number of states and in the case of Virginia has been declared constitutional by the Supreme Court of the United States (James E. Hughes, 1940). The chief scientific argument against sterilization, namely, uncertainty concerning a hereditary basis for mental deficiency, applies especially to the high-grade mental defective who is at the same time the most abundant and the most likely to reproduce. This approach is, therefore, very limited.

The hereditary factors in the case of the psychoses or even epilepsy are so uncertain as to cast doubt upon the desirability of any general rule, although in special cases the evidence of heredity as a major factor is very strong. The genetic factor in crime is even less evident. Problems of social inefficiency due to apparently hereditary intellectual limitations that are still above the level of mental deficiency (that is, the borderline and dull portion of the population) are not generally considered at all appropriate for eugenical prevention. In other words, the prevention of inheritance is most easily exercised in the severe cases that are in fact fewer and less likely to reproduce. The limitation of conception in so far as it is dependent upon artificial contraceptive devices is subject to legal regulations varying from state to state, some encouraging, others discouraging the practice. The Birth Control League of America is a special source of information on this subject. Induced abortion or miscarriage for eugenic purposes is quite generally prohibited and usually constitutes a serious criminal offense. It is hazardous for the woman.

It must be realized that the control of heredity involves processes about which there are deep feelings on the part of the public due to moral and religious scruples, prejudice, resistance to any encroachment upon the discretion of the individual in a vital matter, and theoretical loss of valuable persons to society. If this were not the case some doubtful questions might be answered by experimentation. These attitudes of society expressed in laws are just as real, just as demanding of respect, but also just as appropriately subjected to attempts at modification as other biological limitations.

Preventive efforts directed toward the avoidance of accidents to prenatal development and during the process of birth are generally included in good obstetric practice rather than some specific preventive program related to personality and behavior. Special attention should be called to the need to exercise special caution in irradiation of the pregnant woman with X-ray, particularly in large doses, early in pregnancy. Serious brain aplasia and idiocy have too frequently followed such irradiation.

Recent studies by Fries (1937) have shown the importance of determining the parents', particularly the mother's, attitude toward her pregnancy and the prospective child and of beginning treatment if necessary so that adverse attitudes may not become a distorting influence in the life of the child. This is really not a prenatal influence on the child, but bears mention at this point. Similarly in need of treatment is the attitude of parents and others who have adopted a fatalistic viewpoint toward the inheritance of specific behavior characteristics, who therefore expect difficulties in children born of a parent with a disorder of personality or behavior. Turning attention from the child to the parent, it might also be pointed out here that the disturbance of behavior in some women that recurs regularly with each pregnancy or delivery may be serious enough to necessitate the avoidance of pregnancy or even clinical abortion.

Physiological Prevention.—Attempts to prevent disorder through the enhancement of physiological function centers on the satisfactory development and protection of the tissues, organs, or systems of the body. Some of these physiological areas are more important than others in respect to their probable influence on behavior and personality. Some physiological functions are especially general and widespread in their effect on the body. For example, when heat regulation breaks down, delirium is apt to result. This is extreme, of course, but lesser disturbances attend lesser deviations in these general functions. Fatigue, insufficient sleep, poor nutrition, variations in atmosphere, smoldering infections, inadequate convalescence from illness, disordered metabolism and oxygenation, vitamin deficiency, endocrine imbalance, allergies, alterations of blood content, circulatory disorders, and disturbances of smooth muscle function, all have their concomitant disturbances of behavior and personality and these may at times be major considerations. Unfortunately, these physiological disorders often operate at subclinical levels that are not taken seriously by the physician because they do not involve acute or very evident incapacity. These disorders, however, presumably affect the efficient functioning of nervous tissue. It is apparent that those who deal with disorders of personality and behavior should be competent to detect and treat these physiological disturbances. The consideration of these subtle influences needs to be given more serious attention in medical education if the best preventive opportunity is to be grasped.

There are, in addition to these subtle influences, detectable disorders of nervous tissue and the sensory and motor apparatus upon whose integrity orderly behavior is dependent. It is well recognized that sensory deprivations, particularly those of hearing and sight, result in constrictions of behavior and personality sometimes resembling mental deficiency. In addition, however, these defects along with crippling act psychogenically in distorting personality, and so those who are handicapped in any way require special protective attention. Disorders of brain tissues are so frequently associated with general medical problems—syphilis, meningitis, encephalitis, accidents, poisons, pellagra—that their prevention becomes a part of good medical care. Caution in the use of drugs, encouragement of regular health examinations, the preventive and treatment programs in the field of industrial hazards, sight, hearing, venereal disease, public safety, and alcohol, therefore, are an important part of the prevention of behavior and personality disorders from both the physiological and the psychological standpoints. Disorders attendant upon arteriosclerosis and senility are only partially dependent upon organic brain changes. In part they are a response to the early handling by the family of the failures of capacity that grow directly out of the brain damage. In this respect they are to a degree preventable through wise counseling of the family by the physician and careful regular health supervision of the aging person.

It should not be forgotten that the integration of the person results not only in his behavior's being influenced by his physiological condition, but also conversely that the functioning of his tissues and organs reflects his mental state. Hence heart, gastro-intestinal and other organ symptoms are often early leads to disturbed emotional states and, if treated in relation to the person's whole life setting, will influence the disorder of personality and behavior earlier than would otherwise have been true. These functions may be, then, in a relative sense, preventive.

It is evident from studies such as Billings (1941) that general medicine stands in a highly important, potentially preventive, position if the patient as a person is taken into account along with the best that scientific medicine has to offer his body. Dr. W. A. White used to tell of the case of the pianist who broke his collarbone. His surgeon, making no distinction between men, had a set procedure for treating such fractures, a procedure that would insure a good bony union of the parts. This treatment necessitated the immobilization of the arm until healing had occurred. This immobilization so stiffened the hand of the pianist that his art was greatly impaired. No attention was given to the fact that the pianist's profession did not demand the perfect union of the collarbone that a stevedore's work would demand.

Psychological Prevention.—Attempts to prevent disorders by safeguarding the development of healthy attitudes and habits must always be executed in conjunction with physiological and social preventives if they are to be practical, since both of these react upon the person in creating his psychological composition. Fear, bigotry, suspicion, prejudice, fanaticism, moodiness, shyness, stupidity, and many other disabling personality characteristics are not disorders in themselves; nevertheless, they are legitimate starting points for preventive work, for they indicate not only the rough roads of the past that may be smoothed, but they stand as threats to the future.

Careful guidance in the formative years is a particularly important phase of psychological prevention. This does not necessitate an anxious aggressive effort to avert disaster, but rather a calm observation of the processes of growth in order to see that the inevitable problems of living are being met successfully. Cuddling a child and allowing him to suck seems to be conducive to his development in so far as they do not represent pathological needs on the part of the mother. The child or youth needs affection as a sign of his worth (Levy, 1937), particularly as he is so seldom now a financial asset to his parents. In late infancy, enuresis, eating disturbances and perhaps thumb-sucking, stuttering, confused handedness, and many other transitory behavior phenomena are certain to appear. It is not so much a matter of preventing them by prompt assault as of seeing that the usually successful handling of them by the child himself is taking place, and that the general conditions of the child are conducive to stability and calm.

Prevention of such activity may prevent some problems, but it denies the child a freedom essential to his growth and so affords greater hazards in another direction. Sometimes unusual problems emerge from unusual experiences rather than unusual make-up. There is still, as a rule, an inherent adjustability that may be given its chance through a kind consistency on the part of the parent before injecting a new constraining force into the shaping of the personality.

The handling of the anxiety and neuroses of the parent (Fries, 1937) is a major function for those who are helping the family in its guidance of the child: the doctor, the minister, nurse, and teacher especially. Such behavior deviations in a parent are the more distorting the smaller the family, and as the diluting influence of other personalities in the situation is reduced. Easing of the situation is even more important to prevention as a rule than advising some direct action aimed at modifying the behavior of the child, behavior that the resources of the child itself may be sufficient to cope with if given a chance. This is especially important when the parents' anxieties center on what they consider sex deviations, chiefly because parents are often unable to think calmly in that sphere. If the parent regards the child as a sexless creature, sex expression, such as masturbation, becomes an "abnormality," and out of it there can be no sane guidance toward satisfactory sex development. If the parent is upset about sex, the child is not helped to the kind of sex orientation that is neither too highly charged emotionally nor yet so thoroughly objective as to be unreal. Mature mental adjustments cannot be expected to grow out of an unrealistic concept of the sex function. Youth is faced with a real problem in the discrepancy between physiological and cultural maturity. Most youths handle this five- to eight-year discrepancy fairly well, but unless this discrepancy is seen as a burden on youth, other burdens may be imposed by parents and others to the point of collapse.

It is necessary to recognize that children are confronted with a continuity of extrinsic experiences, unpredictable and uncontrollable, some of which tend to contribute to adjustment and some of which tend to act otherwise. In spite of these usual tendencies, certain experiences usually regarded as destructive may under the right conditions turn out to be beneficial. Moreover, "good" experiences may prove to be the opposite. There comes about then a progressive individuation, a deviation from the rule without reference to which no "preventive" effort is assuredly good. At no time is sound behavior finally assured. At any time unhealthy reaction tendencies may be turned to advantage. In general, however, there are certain desiderata (Stevenson, 1941) conducive to good behavior and these form the basis of a practical program. One needs, however, a readiness to devise a specifically designed procedure when individual peculiarity shows the unappropriateness of the general approach. Usually it is good to insure a breadth of human and experiential contacts and satisfactions and to allow opportunity for airing one's feelings. It is a part of growth and developing strength to experience the security and the affection of family life and the assurance of this is a real preventive.

Automatization within limits is essential to the economy of behavior. Essential also to security and tranquillity is a margin of safety between capacity and the demand made on personality and behavior. This is important in school and work. Among the important automatizations, there are many essential habits such as habits of work, habits of human relations, habits of using one's talents and abilities, and habits in the use of one's hands. It is a part of growth to play, not only for the purpose of using muscles and increasing experiences, but also to soften and get perspective on and give vent to some of the inevitable disappointments of life and react to the limitations that come from a social way of life. Play is a way of redirecting and sublimating aggressions that otherwise lead to trouble. The emancipation of the child should be a gradual process, a culmination of growth beginning at birth rather than an episode of the late teens. As with play, a vocational goal is an integrating core about which to orient experience during early development, and it is useful, whether realized or not, in future work. Similarly, a philosophical construct, religious or otherwise, may act as a nucleus about which the individual can so interpret his lot in life as to achieve better personal organization.

Just as gastric or cardiac disturbances may be recognized as early evidences of mental burdening, so excess pressure may bring to evidence attitudes and habits that would otherwise remain inactive. These are signals for attention and their persistence is a signal for doing something about them and possibly the pressures that induced them. Emergencies such as war and imminent danger or threat are especially potent in magnifying such weakness and may be used to advantage in revealing the need for prevention. It is for this reason that selective service, employment and personnel systems, economic stress, school tests, examinations, and competitions often bring problems to light. These pressures augment anxieties, sensitivities, social isolations, inferiority feelings, sleep disorder, tics, conflicts with authority, evasions, aggressions against others, obsessions, indecision, temperamentality, speech disorder, and many other aspects of human discomfort.

Insight relative to these behavior tendencies is an important consideration in strengthening the person against their negative aspects. But insight itself is not altogether assuring, for it may either create new and usable perspectives or engender devastating anxiety. Insight must, in other words, be timed with the readiness of the person to use it. It is valuable to be aware of the fact that certain situations tend in certain people to precipitate serious progressive or circular behavior processes culminating in mental disorder. Insight properly timed has in such cases potentially a distinctly preventive value.

There are those (Harrington, 1938) who claim that, in the face of transient severe pressures, "playing a role," making believe that things are different from what they are, assuming postures of confidence, are sufficient to tide over the emergency and avert a break. In some cases this seems to be true, in others not. The indications for its favorable employment are not entirely clear.

Handling these potentialities for disorders that are so protean in form may demand joint action on the part of several functionaries, i.e., several community agencies. A good example of such joint action is the work of the visiting teacher in the public school who solicits joint action of home and school and insures a greater degree of individualization in the planning for certain children. In the case of the pupil whose irregular attendance constitutes a problem, the visiting teacher's first contact may be either with the attendance department or the classroom from which the case is referred to her. With these two departments she maintains collaboration throughout her study of the case. However, studies are then extended into the community aiming to elucidate the factors that may be found in the home and neighborhood. Recreational agencies are of special interest in this connection. Very frequently this brings the visiting teacher also into cooperation with relief and social case work agencies, since truancy is often associated with economic and family disorder. At other times the public health or visiting nurse organizations provide clues to her case or collaboration in its treatment. Should the problem be of long duration, it is apt also to lead to the juvenile court and probation department. Thus it is that one child becomes the nucleus of integration of agencies who are concerned with the problems behind such disorder and agencies who are occupied with its various expressions and its therapeutic attack.

Social Prevention.—It is evident from the foregoing that it is difficult to separate psychological and social efforts at prevention since, unless the person applies all psychological preventives to himself, they require someone or something in his setting to bring these about. The melioration of the setting of the individual in order to facilitate his mental and emotional growth and avoid entirely baffling situations is as broad as living itself. The home life, education, work, health forces, religious resources, play facilities, economic situation, friends, and requirements of law, all have their plus and minus values in helping or hindering in the development of personality. Completely baffling situations result in no success and no progress and are conducive to regression, whereas difficult but solvable situations have the reverse effect. The meaning or importance of the setting is, furthermore, seldom absolute, but is merely another facet of the culture whose values the individual has adopted and which has become part of his psychological structure. Thus there are very few fixed values to the setting. A divorce in a Catholic family is likely to be more disturbing than in a Protestant or Jewish family. It may be said that, in general, the mores of a group are time-tested and a fairly safe guide to what an environment should be. But this is not always the case, for mores hold on long past the conditions that created them and may be the basis of serious disturbances of personality and behavior. Furthermore, it is obvious that, while there are very likely common basic elements in the various religious formulations, the differences between them that men fight for show that they are not attuned to identical psychological needs. A certain religious formulation may become a great stabilizing force for one person, but it may become just the opposite for another. That these psychological needs are not fixed patterns is evident from the religious changes that accompany altered social conditions of certain immigrant groups. Religious conversions based on conformity to group attitudes or individual pressures must be evaluated with caution, for the formulation given up may have greater values than the one into which the convert is swept.

Home life is the keystone of emotional satisfaction and growth. At best, it affords guidance for the child in working out solutions to the situations in life that irritate him so that irrational aggressions may not burst forth from time to time to interfere with his effectiveness and spoil his happy relations. At worst, it can overbalance the fortunate effects of most other types of experience. Nagging is a frustration that aggravates either a child's anxious retardation or his hostile aggression. Parental overprotection is constricting to his experience and contributes to the impoverishment of his behavior resources. Habit training gives him useful automatizations that release his behavior resources to meet new problems. Affection and physiological satisfactions give him strength and security to move into new experiences. Neurotic parents and teachers tend to force him to adjust to their atypical patterns which are crippling. Where a member of the family is neurotic, it is well to allow for rich contacts with better patterns of personality.

Education of parents is a help in meeting some of these needs of family life, but to be effective, such education must emerge from experience with feeling instead of from words, phrases, rules, or principles. This means that parent education must help the parent benefit by home life, and out of that the child will gain. A preventive effort for the one accrues undesignedly to the other. Thus the mutual sex adjustment of a couple is a prophylactic not only for them but for the whole household.

The schoolroom is in a way a counterpart of the household. The crux of the classroom is the life adjustment of the teacher. The school is at present of value in revealing opportunities for preventive work, for the school subjects the child to two important pressures that are likely to bring out his need for strengthening his mental resources. First, the school is as a rule the first gross break from the home, and the child's capacity for progressive emancipation is reflected by this and strengthened or weakened by the way it is handled. The nursery school and kindergarten are two adjuncts to the usual school pattern that ease the child into this break and at the same time maintain a little closer touch with the home. Second, the school subjects the child to the repeated necessity of applying what he has learned either in giving him work to do that uses it or in formal testing of his knowledge. The former of these tries out his capacity to integrate his knowledge into action, the second challenges his resilience in meeting a threatening situation. Unfortunately, many schools have not the personnel such as visiting teachers or school social workers to use the leads offered by those strategic situations. It is, of course, necessary to keep the school's responsibilities within the boundaries of the school's job and not expect it to be a psychiatric clinic. Still there are certain activities the need for which is inescapable and which no other agency is situated to deal with. The child is living in the classroom. Unless his interests and ambitions are somewhat appreciated, unless he can be somewhat individualized, unless his work is somewhat related to the future through vocational guidance, unless in short his life in the classroom is both useful and satisfying, there are likely to be serious gaps in his development. Some children reveal themselves differently at different times to different teachers or different subjects or differently as between school and home. This inconsistency is a lead to be followed, a fluid state, a state that is on the one hand more vulnerable and on the other more promising. Blos (1941) has shown how these fluctuations are related to the existing or potential disturbances in personality and behavior. Leaders in the educational field have clarified these opportunities but they are blocked by many deeply rooted traditions within the school system and by public attitudes toward the school.

What the school is for the child, work is for the adult. It is the final test of emancipation, of integrating the preparatory training and experience into creative interest. At the same time, work is an instrument for gaining food and shelter and the money for essentials. Unless work life fills the needs of the person, it is permitting deficiencies in his mental life that have as serious impact as deficiencies in his diet. Monotony of work that fails to challenge the potentialities of the person has danger unless compensated outside of work life. Insecurity of work finds an important compensating preventive in unemployment insurance. Potentially industry has somewhat the same opportunities for testing the worker and instituting preventives as the school, but it is only beginning to discover that the objectives of industry are not at odds with the enhancement of personality and efficient behavior of the employee (Burling, 1939). The school may be expected to be to a degree parental, but according to a democratic way of life, employer and the employed must find a different basis for mutual helpfulness.

With growing attention to the insurance of economic security and the mechanization of industry, the deficiencies of work life need more and more compensation in play and companionship. Like religion, the different forms of play and companionship are fundamentally dependent upon common essentials, but in form they differ so from person to person that in order to satisfy the peculiarities of the individual, a wide diversity of opportunity is necessary. There is danger in the tendency to think that the form that is successful in giving satisfaction to one person reflects something inherently good that commends an avocation to all persons. Play is a deep influence exerted at an unconscious level that necessarily depends upon the peculiarities of the individual.

One cannot face the fact that a large part of the problems encountered by any doctor grow out of personal and situational disorder without accepting the importance of the medical and health fields in a preventive effort (Billings, 1941). The more serious psychiatric disorders can often be sensed and treated early by an alert general practitioner, especially if aided by psychiatric facilities in a general hospital and voluntary admission provisions for the mental hospital. The existence of psychiatric practitioners in the community (social psychiatry) not only facilitates the early use of psychiatric treatment, but brings the medical practitioner of the community into close touch with that specialty, to their own enrichment and the benefit of their patients. The physician should consider abnormal emotional states as an adjunct of the general hospital also greatly facilitates and clarifies the need for treatment of personal and situational issues before they become overburdening. The physician should consider abnormal emotional states —anxiety, resistance, lack of cooperation, etc.—as liabilities to be treated rather than obstructions to be railed against.

One of the important developments aimed at prevention of personality and behavior disorders is the child guidance clinic. This is a psychiatric clinic with associated psychological and social service. While it is impossible to say how much actual prevention of mental disease and delinquency results from the services of these clinics, there is little question that they contribute greatly to the mental health of the children they service. According to Stevenson and Smith (1934), about three-quarters of the children seen by such clinics are improved as to personality and behavior. The indications are that school failure is often averted. Whether one subscribes to Freudian concepts of causation or not, Witmer (1940) points out the common sense in beginning early with prevention. It is evident to anyone studying the records of these children that the greatest promise lies in a broad attack involving the many potential and actual community influences that bear on the child. It is also evident that every community agency dealing with children encounters opportunity for preventive work in the course of routines that would not be open to anyone else. Some of these agencies are pointed toward handling problems, others carry preventive effort by pointing their work more directly toward life well lived.

Leaders in the field of psychiatry have long envisaged plans in which those individuals and institutions in position to have a full perspective concerning the serious personality deviations and their determinants should contribute their fullest effort in providing or fostering preventive work. Our state institutions for the mentally sick are in such a position, but, unfortunately, they are so bowed down by traditions and restrictions, as are also the schools, that outside help is needed to enrich their program beyond its present confines. On this account Witmer questions the value of these institutions in sponsoring preventive work and seems inclined to look more favorably upon health departments.

Modification of laws is necessary to the realization of some preventive possibilities. Again and again, the forward movement of these established agencies toward greater preventive effort is obstructed by laws limiting the scope of their staff and their other resources. In other respects, laws that are unsuited to the situation bear upon everyone, encourage disobedience and engender disorder. There is an inevitable lag in laws, but at times the courts and the legal profession fail to take advantage even of present possibilities. Many juvenile courts continue on a criminal basis after the law allows otherwise. They suffer the same inertia as the general practitioner of medicine toward translating the glaring evidences of need for certain action into such action in the face of habit to the contrary.

These changes demand public pressure, emanating from those most seriously affected, and voluntary financial support of demonstration and education until new processes can be established.

Projects Designed to Prevent Disorders of Personality and Behavior

Professional preparation and training for work in the various fields strategically situated to prevent disorders of personality—doctors, nurses, lawyers, ministers, social workers, teachers—are essential to a widespread and effective preventive effort. Extensive projects, even without this backing, have been organized and are functioning. These projects are often motivated to prevent some specific type of behavioral difficulty—mental disease, delinquency, dependency, school failure, conduct disorders —but as a rule, if they are valid for the one type of disorder they are to a high degree valid for other types. The Gluecks (1936) have brought together a large number of descriptive statements about such activities. Undoubtedly some of these are effective for unknown reasons so one must do considerable "reading between the lines" in evaluating any project designed to prevent personality disorders. An elaborate process of dealing with a child may be successful because of some incidental change of environment or because of some change at home.

The Gluecks (1936) have laid down certain principles of crime prevention which, for the most part, are applicable to all forms of personality and behavior disorder. In brief they are:

1. Crime-prevention programs should take into account the evidence that most criminals show definite antisocial tendencies of attitude and behavior early in childhood.
2. In most instances, children should be kept away from police stations, courts, and correctional institutions until more scientific and sympathetic efforts have failed.
3. An experimental attitude should govern the establishment and conduct of crime-prevention programs.
4. It cannot be definitely concluded as yet that any one type of crime-preventive activity is necessarily superior to, or should be exclusive of, any other.
5. Existing community agencies and institutions should be used to their fullest capacity.
6. While much good can be accomplished by whatever qualified agency in a community assumes the leadership in crime prevention, the public schools can play an especially significant role.
7. Although not indispensable, a crime-prevention bureau in a police department has certain unique values.
8. Crime-preventive efforts should be discriminating in technique.
9. Crime-prevention programs should recognize that children must have ample outlets for their energies.

10. Other psychological and behavior traits of children should be taken into account in planning and carrying out crime-prevention programs.
11. Intensive work with problem children and delinquents and the attitudes and prejudices of parents should not be ignored.
12. Trained personnel should be liberally employed in crime-preventive activity.

The Gluecks (1936) also present a description of the specific projects aimed at preventing disorders. Each of these has been described by some person closely associated with the project. Some of these stories are more biased and less objective than others; many are adjusted to peculiar local situations; yet all have elements that may be worked into a program elsewhere. They give a fairly complete perspective on efforts to prevent behavior disorders. The first group of papers deals with *programs for community coordination.*

In the *Los Angeles County Coordinating Council Plan,* a program is described that provides for the counseling of the welfare leaders in a neighborhood. This program is designed to study, educate, and organize the various agencies in a neighborhood, and to bring to their attention those in need of their services. Kenyon J. Scudder, who contributes this story, might have improved it by "telling on" a few of his own delinquent progeny: those coordinating councils that try a hand at case-work, or those that tend to fall asleep on the job. In spite of these omissions, however, he is modest in his claim that the project has helped to make the community a better place in which to live.

In the *Lower West Side Crime Prevention Program,* New York City, Frederic M. Thrasher presents a modest, critical, scientific approach. It involves a great many diverse activities relating to the many causes of crime, and hence makes a less brilliant showing than some of the more intensively focused programs. Its very breadth is realistic, however, being postulated on small general gains rather than on narrow, concentrated results.

The *Foundation for Youth in Columbus,* Indiana, by Walter H. Hall and Robert K. Atkinson, discusses a program that is motivated not specifically toward crime prevention, but toward the satisfaction of the self-evident need of youth for opportunities to play. It has, consequently, no exaggerated promises to live up to. The efforts of this foundation, which are centered on a boys' club, are coordinated with all the other leisure-time services in the community through a joint director.

In the *Director-at-Large Plan of the San Francisco Recreation Commission,* a plan is outlined for giving boys individual attention, getting them to the right agencies, providing them with constructive experiences, and supplying advice. The success of this plan obviously depends upon the selection of personnel for enthusiasm, critical technical service, and full-time application. Gerald J. Linares, the author of the paper, could undoubtedly have done better in pointing out the weaknesses of his program.

The next group of papers presents *six school programs* of importance in the prevention of delinquency:

In *Character Building for Crime Prevention in Public School #181 in Brooklyn*, Dr. Nathan Peyser presents a plan based upon an educational approach so fundamental that the prevention of delinquency may be naturally expected to result. The schools have an opportunity, not only in their own sphere, but through their community relationships, to influence character development and to serve as centers of community morale. In this instance, the school became the nucleus of coordinated effort in the community. It undertook community surveys and organizations to meet community defects. It had a paid professional staff, a case-adjustment service, a Big Brother phase, and projects in the field of recreation and of adult education. Dr. Peyser expressly states that it is all experimental.

The *Bureau of Special Service in the Jersey City Public Schools,* by Thomas W. Hopkins, is the account of another plan under which the schools have assumed leadership in community coordination as well as supplying special services—clinical, visiting teacher, and the like. The point of view of the paper is promotional; no problems are described, and there is some evidence of competitive feeling with regard to the coordinating-council procedure.

The Visiting Teacher in the Cincinnati Public Schools, by Ethel Reynolds, is a clear, dispassionate presentation with no exaggerated claims. Emphasis is laid upon the fact that the visiting teacher is in essence a case-worker. She brings into the educational system a flexibility that is beyond the range of the classroom teacher. In spite of this, the requirements for the visiting teacher are primarily educational and are only secondarily those of a case-worker.

Dr. Henry J. Baker, in his paper *The Diagnosis and Treatment of Maladjusted Children in the Detroit Public Schools,* recognizes the limitations and defects of his program and faces them squarely. This work in Detroit shows how much the link—in this case the schools—needs to be strengthened before it is forged into a chain of community agencies, and how one agency, by sawing its wood all the way through, brings about coordination of effort between agencies. It also shows how the prevention of delinquency may be approached as a by-product of a job well done in some one field.

The same point is brought out by Meta L. Anderson in *The Binet Schools of Newark*. Discussing the development of a high-grade educational program for the mentally retarded, she deals with some very personal reasons for the delinquency of such children. And again one sees how a program such as this, carried through on a high level, automatically brings about cooperation between community agencies. The presentation of the program is modest and critical.

The *Montefiore Special School for Problem Boys in Chicago* presents a plan that is more distinctly pointed toward the prevention of delinquency in that it is designed for truants. The Montefiore School combines the functions of a special school with some of the services of a child-guidance clinic. Its curriculum is specially adapted to the needs of its pupils, and in that respect it is a cross between the Newark program and the regular educational program, since most of its pupils are mentally handicapped. Here, too, we see how following through the needs of a special group brings about a natural cooperation between community agencies. Edward H. Stullken, who contributes the paper, is modest in his evaluation of the program.

Two accounts of *police-department activities* are also given:

The *Crime Prevention Bureau of the New York City Police Department*, by Henrietta Additon, describes a program that has been discontinued. In its original form, it was distinctly a police program, dealing with minors in the early stages of delinquency and with such adverse community conditions as are within the reach of a police department. In addition, it exerted an unofficial influence for community betterment on the basis of the needs that came to its attention in the course of its work. Individual problems were dealt with by simple social-case-work procedures against a background of authority. Some of the bureau's activities were neglected functions of schools or other community departments. It was directed by a specially appointed police commissioner, assisted by a large corps of selected police officers and investigators.

In the *Crime Prevention Work of the Berkeley Police Department*, Elizabeth Lossing describes an evolutionary product with an attitude of critical self-appraisal and a detailed analysis of problems. The plan involved close working relationships with various community agencies, of which the first coordinating council was a natural growth. High standards for its personnel have insured the progressive development of this program. The work includes service to delinquent adult women, to girls and young boys, and to children in danger of becoming delinquent; the education of lay and professional groups; and participation in community betterment and in "upstream work antedating prevention." A host of activities along this line includes sports, reading, entertainments, and club work. In addition, the special bureaus within the police department, the personnel of the department as a whole, are expected to participate in crime-prevention work. The evaluation of this program is modest and no excessive claims are made.

Four intramural programs are presented:

Longview Farm, at Acton, Massachusetts, which is described by Leslie B. Blades as a study home for problem boys, accepts its clients chiefly from private agencies—boys who have social and personal maladjustments with which the ordinary foster home is not qualified to deal. The theory behind the work of the home is that "society itself produces problem children," and that the home must offer a more healthful social environment. While striving to be a typical home, Blades recognizes the fact that the authority of the study home is social rather than familial, but it avoids imposed study and treatment and gives the boy a chance to determine his own course, enjoying or suffering the consequences. Participation in the work of the home, whatever its nature, is regarded as worthy of respect because of its social value. The experience is designed to be educative and to develop an appreciation of social responsibility, justice, and tolerance through the natural activities of every day.

The *Children's Village at Dobbs Ferry*, New York, described by George C. Minard, is another intramural project that is experimenting with the education of delinquent children. The Village has many advantages through its long experience and its proximity to the abundant resources of New York City. Its program is fundamentally designed to give the boys an opportunity for natural self-expression, with a minimum of restrictions. The activities of the Village in the direction of the prevention of delinquency are implied rather than direct, on the principle that a satisfied consumer of our culture is its best customer.

The account of the *George Junior Republic*, by Donald T. Urquhart, while it is not promotional in the same sense as are some of the other stories, expresses an almost overwhelming conviction. The Republic is an institution of the cottage type, designed like a village, with small groupings and divisions of labor. Training for citizenship is its paramount objective. It includes self-government and an economic program of earnings designed to teach the various values of property. An attempt is made to duplicate as far as possible the functions of a normal community and to force the boy to experience the results of his own idleness and antisocial conduct. As in the case of an established society, most of the needs of this planned community have been formulated in rules and laws within which individualization may take place. This particular account of the program deals much more with the regulations than with the individualization.

The fourth intramural program is that of the summer camp for delinquent boys at *Greenwood Lake,* Delaware, Ohio. It is described by Irving A. Wagner. The camp admits boys with behavior problems and problems of adjustment. It is not restricted to delinquents. It serves as an adjunct of the court through the appointment of its director to a court office. An attempt is made to provide such adequate supervision that the spontaneous interests of the boys will find natural outlets. Both counselors and boys are carefully selected. The success of the project is estimated with relative conservatism. Experience has led those engaged in it to feel the need of a continuation of the work through an interseasonal agency.

In addition to these four intramural projects, *four extramural guidance programs* are given.

Dr. Samuel W. Hartwell contributes an account of the *Child-Guidance Clinic of Worcester,* Massachusetts. This clinic was the gradual outgrowth of a state hospital's attempt to serve its community, although at the present time the community assumes a large part of its support. It serves all the community agencies, including the court, and thus comes into contact with the antecedents of delinquency. It selects those cases that are most in need of its peculiar contribution, which is psychiatric examination and treatment. Treatment consists of personal direction of the delinquent or potential delinquent, directly by the clinic and through the court, probation staff, or home. Its program includes educational work, aimed at bringing about a better understanding of delinquency, and attacks upon community conditions that cause delinquency. Its staff is made up of psychiatrists, psychologists, and psychiatric social workers, all of whom take part in examination and treatment; their efforts are integrated through case conferences. The aim of treatment is to develop feelings of adequacy through a sense of "belongingness" and a philosophy of life. The clinic's attitude toward evaluation of its work places it among the more scientific and conservative projects.

The program of the *Alfred Willson Children's Center,* of Columbus, Ohio, is presented by Bertha Fulton. This project is a group effort which employs a psychologist, a social worker, and a physician. While it professes to be something "more than a child-guidance clinic," its staff really represents part of the usual child-guidance staff. It claims to carry on psychiatric work, but has no psychiatrist on its staff. Its understanding of the child-guidance clinic is obviously scant. It attempts child-placing, group work, parent education, and other activities usually carried on as specialized services, whereas its staff is confessedly not highly experienced.

The *Big Sister Service in Rochester,* New York, on which Elizabeth R. Mertz contributes a paper, carries on a quasi-professional case-work through volunteers under professional supervision and with professional assistance. Girls from ten to sixteen years old are referred to it by various community agencies for help with various types of personal problems of adjustment.

The *Parents School of the Domestic Relations Court* of Franklin County, Columbus, Ohio, is discussed by Erwin V. Mahaffy and Mabel I. Riebel. It is conducted by a select group of teachers who have been oriented in the various social fields, and its techniques have been developed experimentally. One of the conditions of probation for a child is that the parents shall attend this school, and everything is done to make it easy for parents to meet this requirement. The teaching is simple and to the point, in part didactic and in part carried on through group discussion.

The final section of the book deals with four instances of *boys' clubs and recreational programs*:

The *All Nations Boys Club,* in Los Angeles, discussed by Charles S. Thompson, has developed methods and techniques for leisure-time activities among underprivileged boys. Its work—a combination of group-work and case-work—is carried on in the heart of a delinquency area. It provides a gymnasium, a library, craft work, clubs, games, and other social features, and conducts a summer camp. It has a small trained staff, which is supplemented by selected college students. It tends to estimate its value in terms of a decrease in delinquency rates in its territory.

The *Boys' Club, of Worcester,* Massachusetts, is designed to deal with the neglected boy. While it does not especially advertise service to delinquents, it does make a special effort to hold the interest of this type of boy. It carries on the usual functions of a boys' club, offering a variety of facilities and supervision. It recognizes that its work is a part of a community prevention program, and its claims, as presented by David W. Armstrong, are modest.

Harold S. Keltner outlines the *crime-prevention program of the Y.M.C.A.* in St. Louis. This is a project for guiding into constructive activities the naturally organized gangs found in less privileged neighborhoods. Many minor deviations of behavior in these gangs are accepted in the effort to divert them from more markedly antisocial activities. Leadership is provided, but in the main the clubs depend upon their own resources rather than upon outside charity.

The program of the *Philadelphia Boys' Club and Settlement Project* is presented by Robert C. Taber. This project grew out of an effort to direct quasi-delinquent boys to community resources that might be of value to them. This proved to be such a large order for the one person employed that it was made a special project under a federal program, using untrained personnel. An essential part of the program has been the training and supervision of these workers. Evaluation of this program on a quite objective and critically conceived plan shows significant results.

While there are obviously great differences in the evaluations of these programs as well as in the approaches to the prevention of delinquency that they represent, they provide a useful guide for any community group that is instituting work in this field. Seldom will it be possible to copy any of the programs in its entirety, but all of them are suggestive and offer valuable leads in the organization of a program adapted to a particular community.

It is evident that these are not specifically projects to prevent delinquency, but in fact apply to all disorders of personality and behavior. As has been previously implied, prevention of disorders of personality and behavior is often the indirect result of an effort to enrich human living. Hence it depends upon the improved capacity of those regularly contributing to such enrichment. The doctor's interest in his patient as a person needs strengthening. Public health needs broadening so as to be concerned about living as well as mortality and morbidity. Education needs chiefly to follow the reality of individual differences rather than group norms, and it needs to enhance the professional feeling of the teacher. Social work needs to consider not only material lacks, but poverty of the spirit. Psychiatry needs to break away from the hospital in the direction of child guidance. Theology must be recognized as a dynamic psychological construct and a form of personal support as well as a theological revelation. Recreation must be seen as a potent and deep, but unconscious dynamic force. Industry should be seen as a social effort returning value generally in so far as it affords security and satisfaction to all involved. Since the persons served by these community forces are never related solely to any one of them, community coordination of effort is required and it becomes a mutual fortification. Education of the public is an essential part of the foundation of such community effort, and without it, such effort is likely to find itself on shifting sands. Human habits of work and adjustment change relatively slowly, and the cultural circumstances in which these habits operate may change radically and rapidly in our industrial age. No preventive effort can ever be considered permanently fixed and settled in the face of this discrepancy. Preventive efforts require continuous readjusting. The search for newer and better methods goes on. It is never ending.

BIBLIOGRAPHY

BILLINGS, E. G. 1941. The value of psychiatry to the general hospital. *Hospitals,* *15,* 30–34.

BLOS, P. 1941. The adolescent personality: a study of individual behavior. New York: Appleton-Century.

BURLING, T. 1939. Personality in the economic situation. *Amer. J. Orthopsychiat., 9,* 616–622.

CABOT, R. C. 1934. One thousand delinquent boys. *Survey, 70,* 38–40.

FRIES, M. 1937. Factors in character development, neuroses, psychoses and delinquency. *Amer. J. Orthopsychiat., 7,* 142–203.

GLUECK, S., & GLUECK, E. T. 1936. Preventing crime: a symposium. New York: McGraw-Hill.

HANKEN, A. H., & ZIMAND, G. F. 1941. Children in the theatre. New York: National Child Labor Committee.

HARRINGTON, M. 1938. A biological approach to the problems of abnormal behavior. Lancaster, Pa.: Science Press.

HUGHES, J. E. 1940. Eugenic sterilization in the United States. *Publ. Hlth Rep., Wash.,* Suppl. No. 162.

KASANIN, J., & VEO, L. 1932. A study of the school adjustment of children who later in life become psychotic. *Amer. J. Orthopsychiat., 2,* 212–227.

LEVIN, H. L. 1933. The role of child guidance in the prevention of schizophrenia (dementia praecox). *N. Y. St. J. Med., 33,* 808–812.

LEVY, D. M. 1937. Primary affect hunger. *Amer. J. Psychiat., 94,* 642–652.

MATHERS, A. T. 1931. Difficulties and problems in the programme for prevention of mental disease. *Canad. publ. Hlth J., 22,* 10.

MEYER, A. 1925. Individualism and the organization of neuropsychiatric work in the community. *Ment. Hyg., N. Y., 9,* 675–685.

STEVENSON, G. S. 1941. Mental hygiene problems of youth today. *Ment. Hyg., N. Y., 25,* 539–551.

STEVENSON, G. S., & SMITH, G. 1934. Child guidance clinics—a quarter century of development. New York: Commonwealth Fund.

TIEBOUT, H. M., & KIRKPATRICK, M. E. 1932. Psychiatric factors in stealing. *Amer. J. Orthopsychiat., 2,* 114–123.

WILLIAMS, F. E. 1932. Is there a mental hygiene? *Psychoanal. Quart., 1,* 113–120.

WITMER, H. L. 1940. Psychiatric clinics for children. New York: Commonwealth Fund.

AUTHOR INDEX

(Italicized numbers are Bibliography pages)

(*Volume I—pages 1 to 618; Volume II—pages 619 to 1191*)

A

Abadie, J., 953, *964*
Abel, T. M., 245, *246*
Abraham, K., 274, 278, 292, *299*, *303*, 624, 625, *648*, 874, 878, 900, *910*
Abt, A. F., 634, *649*
Abt, I. A., 634, *649*
Achilles, E. M., 1007, *1022*
Ackerly, S., 569, *578*, *712*, 977, *1022*
Ackerman, N. W., 242, *246*, 289, *302*, *684*
Ackerson, L., 764, 766, *788*
Adams, C. R., 189, *205*
Adams, H. F., 153, 157, *166*
Adie, W. J., 786, *788*
Adler, A., 124, *131*, 222, *246*, 768, 780, *789*, *860*, 1143, *1157*, *1162*
Adrian, E. D., 1034, 1035, 1036, 1037, 1038, 1040, 1043, 1054, 1056, *1087*
Agüero y Montoro, H., 1034, *1087*
Aichorn, A., 99, *131*, 711, *712*, 809, *819*, 1141, 1149, *1157*
Akimov, N. E., 589, *610*
Alberti, J. L., 1041, *1087*
Alcoholics Anonymous, 163, *166*, 1147, *1157*
Aldington, R., 12, 14, *43*
Aldrich, C. A., 88, *131*, 655, *684*, *1162*
Aldrich, M. M., 88, *131*
Alexander, E. J., 599, *614*
Alexander, F., 113, *131*, 217, *246*, 256, *267*, 269, 273, 274, 275, 276, 277, 278, 279, 280, 281, 282, 284, 286, 288, 289, 290, 293, 294, 295, *298*, *299*, *300*, *301*, *302*, *304*, 327, *329*, 535, *546*, 584, *610*, 809, 810, *819*, 931, *936*
Alexander, F. M., 1121
Alexander, L., *525*
Allee, W. C., 607, 608, *610*
Allen, E., 601, 607, *610*
Allen, F. H., *687*, 773, 788, *789*, 1148, *1157*
Allen, R. D., 165, *166*
Allport, F. H., 9, *43*, 192, *208*
Allport, G. W., 3, 4, 6, 7, 8, 10, 12, 15, 24, 26, 27, 28, 29, 30, 34, 35, 37, 41, 42, *43*, *44*, 49, 50, 51, 61, *66*, 70, 75, 77, *131*, 139, 146, 153, 157, 161, *166*, 170, 184, 188, 189, 195, 201, 204, *205*, 505, *523*, 796, *819*
Alper, B. S., 815, *820*
Alpert, A., *684*
Alstead, G., 722, *733*
Altenburger, H., 1036, 1038, 1076, *1091*
Altman, C. H., 898, *910*, 981, 982, 984, *1022*
Altman, M., 608, *610*
Altmann, L. L., *1099*
Alvarez, W. C., 276, *299*, 826, *832*
Alzheimer, A., 864, *918*

Amatruda, C. S., 603, *613*, 621, *650*, 664, 666, 672, *686*
Amen, E. W., 660, *684*
American Council on Education, 154, 162, *166*
Ames, L. B., 664, 666, 672, *686*
Amsden, G. S., 1134, *1157*
Anastasi, A., 34, *44*, 244, *246*, *525*, 878, 891, *910*
Anderson, C., 355, *377*
Anderson, E. E., 310, *329*, 870, *910*
Anderson, G. W., 989, *1028*
Anderson, H. H., 340, *377*, *684*
Anderson, J. E., 222, *247*, 678, *684*
Anderson, J. P., 656, *684*
Anderson, N., 161, *166*, 738, *755*
Anderson, O. D., 98, *131*, 281, *301*, 391, 392, 396, 397, 407, 408, 410, *411*, 584, *610*, 834, *860*
Anderson, V. V., 811, *819*
Andrews, E. S., 200, *205*
Andrews, H. L., 1035, 1036, 1037, 1038, 1039, 1042, 1044, 1047, 1056, 1058, 1066, 1078, *1087*, *1091*, *1094*
Angyal, A., 43, *44*, 70, *131*, 890, 896, *910*, 991, *1022*
Ansbacher, H. L., 149, *167*, 185, *205*
Anton, G., 780, *789*
Appel, K. E., 245, *246*, 778, *789*, 870, *915*, 920, *1094*, 1118, 1134, 1148, *1158*
Arakelian, P., 311, *330*
Aring, C. D., 599, *610*
Aristotle, 270, *298*
Armstrong, H. G., 586, 598, *610*
Arnheim, R., 43, *44*
Arnold-Forster, M., 218, 221, *246*
Asch, S. E., 533, *547*
Aschaffenburg, G., 999, *1022*
Asenjo, A., 1034, *1087*
Ashe, W. F., 600, *617*
Asher, E. J., 146, *167*
Asher, L., 605, *610*
Askanasy, H., 569, *579*
Atkinson, J. J., 725, *733*
Atwell, C. R., 953, *965*, 984
Auer, E. T., 415, 416, 417, 420, *428*
Ault, C. C., 608, *617*, *618*, 884, 885, *910*, *921*
Avebury, Lord, *1162*
Aveling, F., 183, *205*, 471, *498*
Axelrad, S., *820*
Ayer, J. B., *525*

B

Baar, J., 74, *131*
Babcock, H., 898, *910*, 972, 978, 979, 980, 985, 996, 1006, *1022*

1193

Blanchard, P., 222, 247, 687, 712, 766, 792, 1162
Blatz, W. D., 605, 611, 685
Blatz, W. E., 775, 789
Blaurock, M., 281, 301
Bleuler, E., 16, 44, 217, 247, 546, 868, 869, 889, 891, 897, 901, 906, 907, 908, 910, 911
Blitzsten, D., 1162
Block, H., 533, 547
Bloomfield, R., 597, 598, 612
Bloor, C., 9, 44
Blos, P., 1168, 1182, 1190
Bluemel, C. S., 783, 789
Blumer, H., 755
Boas, F., 716, 717, 733
Boelter, M. D., 598, 614
Bogardus, E. S., 191, 205
Boldrey, E., 966
Bolles, M. M., 902, 911, 987, 1013, 1015, 1016, 1019, 1023, 1061, 1102
Bond, E. D., 275, 299, 594, 611, 778, 789, 886, 911, 1151, 1155, 1158
Bone, H., 1162
Bonkáló, A., 1066, 1067, 1068, 1093
Bonner, C., 869, 870, 911
Boring, E. G., 472, 498, 1004, 1023
Bosquet, S., 1130, 1158
Bossard, J. H. S., 755
Bosselman, B., 519, 523
Bostroem, A., 571, 578
Bott, E. A., 775, 789
Boudin, M., 515, 523
Boudreau, E. N., 590, 611
Bourne, G., 285, 301
Bousfield, W. A., 205
Bowden, A. O., 5, 44
Bowen, B. D., 590, 615
Bowers, A. M., 326, 330, 1015, 1026
Bowers, P. E., 819
Bowers, R. V., 755
Bowman, K. M., 881, 911, 991, 1023, 1051, 1100, 1146, 1153, 1158
Braceland, F. J., 1123, 1151, 1155, 1158, 1161
Bradley, C., 561, 580, 681, 685, 761, 770, 787, 789, 790, 936, 1095, 1097, 1158
Bradshaw, F. F., 151, 152, 167
Bragman, L. J., 764, 789
Braid, J., 474, 478, 491, 498
Brain, R., 514, 523
Brainard, P. P., 194, 205
Bramwell, J. M., 469, 470, 472, 473, 474, 476, 478, 485, 486, 491, 498
Brander, T., 685
Brandt, H. F., 340, 377
Brandt, W., 546
Branham, V. C., 953, 964
Braun, F., 42, 44
Braun, R., 599, 617
Braune, 595, 611
Bremer, F., 1034, 1037, 1089
Brenman, M., 488, 498
Breuer, J., 216, 247, 622, 649, 888, 911, 1111, 1135, 1158, 1159
Brew, M., 869, 911
Brewer, J. M., 165, 167
Brickner, R. M., 569, 579, 958, 964, 977, 1023
Bridge, E. M., 953, 964

Brill, A., 906, 911
Brill, N. Q., 1034, 1053, 1064, 1085, 1089
Brintnall, A. K., 494, 499
Bristol, C., 165, 167
Brock, J., 629, 637, 643, 649
Brodmann, K., 566, 579
Brody, E. B., 605, 611
Brody, M. B., 972, 985, 988, 1023
Brogan, W., 143, 167
Brogden, H. E., 39, 44, 200, 205
Bromberg, W., 270, 298, 799, 805, 808, 809, 811, 813, 819
Bronner, A., 326, 330, 703, 712, 798, 811, 813, 814, 820, 1015, 1026
Bronstein, I. P., 603, 604, 605, 611, 612, 615, 616
Brooks, C. H., 473, 498
Brooks, J. J., 200, 205
Brouha, L., 597, 598, 612, 614
Brousseau, K., 778, 789
Brown, A. G., 590, 611
Brown, A. W., 594, 603, 604, 605, 611, 612, 614, 615, 616
Brown, F., 186, 205
Brown, F. W., 783, 789
Brown, G. D., 685
Brown, J. F., 64, 66, 131, 132, 853, 860, 892, 906, 908, 911, 1023
Brown, J. S., 318, 329, 434, 437, 452, 454, 464, 465
Brown, M., 952, 957, 966
Brown, S., 765, 789
Brown, W., 183, 205, 279, 299, 472, 473, 498, 1111, 1113, 1158
Brown, W. T., 1085, 1089
Browne, C. E., 652, 687
Bruch, H., 274, 299, 597, 611, 682, 685
Brunswick, R., 906, 911
Brush, A. L., 608, 611
Brush, L. A., 273, 299
Bryan, E., 894, 911
Bryan, R., 155, 156, 167
Bryant, J., 546
Bucy, P. C., 565, 575, 580, 1076, 1079, 1089
Bugelski, R., 310, 329
Bühler, C., 621, 649, 654, 685
Bull, H. B., 576, 580
Bull, H. D., 608, 610
Bumke, O., 896, 911
Bunch, M. E., 460, 464
Burchard, E. M. L., 533, 546, 863, 911, 982, 1024
Burdick, E. M., 199, 205
Burgemeister, B. B., 194, 205
Burgess, E. W., 741, 755, 756
Burgum, M., 661, 685
Burke, R. S., 200, 207
Burks, B. S., 35, 44, 201, 205, 511, 512, 523, 662, 684, 685, 687
Burling, T., 1182, 1190
Burlingame, C. C., 608, 612, 981, 1030, 1154, 1158
Burlingame, L. L., 525
Burnham, R. W., 605, 612
Buros, O. K., 204, 206
Burt, C., 30, 31, 32, 33, 34, 35, 37, 38, 43, 44, 146, 168, 685
Burtt, H. E., 142, 150, 152, 167, 183, 198, 206

Sapir, E., *735*
Sarbin, T. R., 232, *250*, 471, *499*
Sargant, W. W., *1089*
Sarkisov, S. A., 1078, *1100*
Sassaman, W. H., 1060, *1097*
Saul, L. J., 269, 272, 273, 281, 282, 283, 284, 288, 289, 290, *298*, *300*, *301*, *302*, 584, *610*, 1050, 1051, *1100*
Saunders, E. B., 993, 994, *1030*
Savitsky, N., 1078, *1098*, *1101*
Sayers, R. R., 587, *618*
Sayles, M. B., 164, *168*, 775, *792*, 1132, *1161*
Scarff, J. E., 1036, 1038, 1040, 1076, *1101*
Schachtel, E., *689*
Schäckter, M., 1034, *1101*
Schaffer, G., 473, 474, *498*, *499*
Scharf, M. P., *735*
Scheerer, M., 903, *914*
Schilder, P., 64, *68*, 469, 471, 474, 478, 486, *492*, *498*, *501*, 666, 667, *689*, *735*, *789*, *819*, 867, 890, 895, *910*, *919*, 990, 992, 1002, 1006, 1008, *1023*, *1030*, 1110, 1111, 1113, 1138, 1140, *1161*
Schiller, M., 769, *792*
Schilling, M. E., 974, 975, *1028*
Schlosberg, H., 413, 414, 416, 418, 420, *428*, *429*, 1005, *1029*
Schmelvkin, D. G., 1035, *1101*
Schmid, C. F., 747, *756*
Schmidl-Waehner, T., 661, *689*
Schmied, M., 273, *300*
Schneck, M. R., 140, *167*
Schneider, A., *919*
Schneider, C., 894, 896, 901, *919*
Schneider, K., 924, *937*
Schoen, M., 5, *47*
Scholl, R., 19, *47*
Schott, A., 875, *919*
Schott, E. L., 605, *616*, 973, 974, 975, *1030*
Schou, H. I., 588, *616*
Schreiber, F., 587, *616*
Schreiber, S. L., 604, *616*
Schrenk, H. H., 587, *618*
Schroeder, P. L., 779, *792*
Schrötter, K., 218, 221, 222, *250*
Schube, K., 244, *246*, *250*
Schube, P. G., 885, *919*, 1153, *1161*
Schulte, H., 906, *919*
Schultz, E., 590, *615*
Schulz, V. E., 281, *301*
Schwab, E. H., 281, *301*
Schwab, R. S., 1065, 1072, 1073, 1078, 1080, *1089*, *1100*, *1101*
Schwartz, A., 281, 293, *301*
Schwartz, H. G., 1036, *1101*
Schwartz, L. A., 174, *211*
Schwartz, O., 293, *304*
Schwarz, R., 898, *919*, 980, *1030*
Scott, H. D., 475, 481, *501*
Scott, R., 285, *301*
Scott, W. D., 151, *168*
Scow, R. O., 586, *617*
Scripture, E. W., 993, *1030*
Searle, O. M., 591, *616*, 863, *919*
Sears, P. S., 64, *68*, 316, *332*, 344, 345, 350, 352, *378*
Sears, R. R., 64, *66*, *68*, 152, 156, *168*, 307, 313, 315, 316, 317, 319, 321, 322, 323, 325, 326, 327, *329*, *330*, *332*, 340, *378*,

379, *388*, 443, 444, 445, *464*, *465*, 476, *501*
Seashore, C. E., 198, *209*, *211*
Sebrell, W. H., 595, 600, *616*
Secunda, L., 1085, *1101*
Sedgwick, W., 506, *525*
Segal, J., 1056, *1092*, *1101*
Segalis, M., *1092*
Segel, D., 204, *211*
Seibel, M., *690*
Seidemann, H., 1053, 1064, *1089*
Seidenari, R., 1079, *1099*, *1101*
Seidenfeld, M. A., 200, *211*
Seitz, C. P., 187, *209*, 586, *611*
Seleye, H., 385, *388*
Seligman, C. G., 720, *735*
Semeonoff, B., 198, *211*
Serota, H. M., 1035, 1043, 1082, *1093*, *1097*, *1101*
Seward, G. H., 608, *616*
Seymour, A. H., 596, *616*
Shaffer, L. F., 52, *68*, 78, *135*
Shagass, C., 1056, *1095*
Shakow, D., 226, 239, 241, *248*, *250*, 323, *330*, 482, *500*, 890, 894, 898, *910*, *914*, *919*, 972, 973, 974, 975, 976, 977, 978, 980, 981, 982, 983, 984, 985, 988, 993, 994, 996, 997, 998, 1004, 1006, *1023*, *1026*, *1029*, *1030*
Shand, A. F., 5, *47*
Shapiro, H. D., 1152, *1161*
Shapiro, L., 882, *919*
Sharp, A. A., 322, *332*
Sharp, F. C., 174, *211*
Sharp, M. L., 563, 564, *580*
Shaw, C. R., 741, 743, 745, 746, *757*, 775, *792*
Shaw, F. C., 533, *548*
Shaw, R. F., 245, *250*
Sheehan, D., 277, *300*
Sheerer, M., 1010, 1012, 1013, *1025*
Sheffield, A. E., 163, *168*
Sheldon, C. P., 510, *525*
Sheldon, J. H., 274, *300*
Sheldon, W. H., 91, *135*, 529, 537 ff, *548*, 841, *860*, 863, *919*
Shelton, P., *1161*
Sherif, M., 57, *68*
Sherman, I. C., 4, *47*, *757*
Sherman, M., 4, *47*, *689*, *757*, 1059, *1101*
Sherman, S., 885, *918*, *1161*
Sherrington, C. S., 288, 295, *302*, *305*, 400, *412*, 456, *465*, 550, *580*
Shipley, W. C., 867, 895, 902, *916*, *919*, 981, 983, 987, 1006, 1015, *1030*, 1151, 1152, *1161*
Shirley, H. F., 770, 781, *792*
Shirley, M., 655, 656, 659, 664, *689*
Shock, N. W., 584, 586, 589, 591, 592, 593, 594, 596, 598, 604, 605, *613*, *614*, *616*, *617*, 867, *919*
Shorr, E., 608, *616*, 885, *919*
Shuttleworth, F. K., 195, *211*, 678, *687*, *689*
Sidis, B., 1120, *1161*
Sigaud, C., *548*
Signori, E., 420, 426, *428*
Silberer, H., 220, *250*
Silverman, B., 774, *792*
Simmins, C., 978, 981, 1006, *1030*
Simoneit, M., 147, 149, *168*, 184, 185, *211*

V

Valentine, C. W., 242, *250*
Valentine, P. F., 4, *47*, 74, *135*
Van der Heide, C., 277, 293, 294, *300*, *304*
Van der Horst, *548*
Van der Molen, 1066, *1103*
Van Dusen, A. C., 195, *212*
Van Liere, E. J., 585, 586, *617*
Van Wagener, N. B., 187, *212*
Varendonck, J., 217, *250*
Varnum, W. H., 198, *212*
Varvel, W. A., 233, *251*
Veo, L., 1166, *1191*
Vernon, P. E., 4, 7, 8, 35, 37, 41, 42, *43*, *44*, *47*, 146, 157, *168*, 184, 185, 188, 195, *205*, *213*, 227, 229, 233, *246*
Vigotsky, I. S., 891, 892, 898, 902, *920*, 1012, 1016, 1017, 1019, *1031*
Viola, G., 528, *548*
Vittoz, R., 1117, *1162*
Vivian, M., 1146, *1162*
Voegtlin, W. L., 1146, 1147, *1162*
Voelker, P. F., 175, *213*
Vogel, F., 675, *685*
Vogt, C., *581*
Vogt, O., *581*
Voice of Experience, *1163*
Volkman, J., 341, *377*
Vollmer, H., *548*
von Monakow, 550, 566, *581*
Von Rohdev, F., *548*
Voronoff, S., 604, *617*

W

Wadsworth, G. W., 186, *208*
Waelder, R., *131*, *135*, 239, *251*
Walden, E. C., 479, *501*
Waldman, H., 415, *429*
Walker, K. F., 70, *135*
Walker, L., *43*
Wall, C., 1086, *1100*
Wall, J., 880, 884, *915*
Wallace, W. M., 1063, 1064, *1090*
Waller, J., 274, *300*
Waller, W. W., 160, *168*
Wallin, J. E. W., 953, *967*, 983, *1031*
Walsh, J. J., 1117, 1118, *1162*
Walsh, M. N., 1035, *1103*
Walter, C. W. P., *1089*, *1101*
Walter, W. G., 1033, 1034, 1035, 1036, 1041, 1050, 1076, 1078, 1082, 1086, *1089*, *1091*, *1092*, *1098*, *1103*
Wang, C. K. A., 187, *213*
Warden, A. N., 421, 425, *428*
Warkentin, J., 327, *331*
Warner, W. L., 719, *735*
Warren, H. C., 4, 8, *48*, 466, *501*
Warstadt, A., *548*
Washburn, R. W., 662, 664, *690*
Washburne, J. H., 200, *213*
Waters, R. H., 321, *332*
Waters, R. M., 593, *614*
Watson, G. B., 186, 192, 199, 204, *207*, *213*
Watson, J. B., 4, 5, *48*, 74, *135*, 768, 769, *793*
Watson, M. L., 422, *430*

Watson, R. I., 199, *213*
Watts, J. W., 277, *300*, 551, 570, 571, *579*, 864, 865, 868, *913*, *920*, 977, *1024*, *1091*, 1125, 1146, 1153, *1159*
Wauthier, M. L., 183, *206*
Webb, E., 39, *48*
Webb, E. T., *1163*
Weber, C. B., 41, *48*
Wechsler, D., 183, *213*, 582, *617*, 972, 973, 976, 978, 986, 987, 1002, 1007, *1031*
Wechsler, H., 797, *820*
Wechsler, I. S., *617*, *860*
Weech, A. A., 786, *793*
Wegner, W. R., 1076, 1078, *1092*
Wegrocki, H., 891, 903, *920*, 1013, 1015, 1016, *1031*
Weidenreich, F., *549*
Weigl, E., 1012, *1031*
Weinbach, A. P., 1053, 1054, *1103*
Weis, M. W., 608, *617*
Weisenburg, T., 978, 1008, 1009, 1010, 1011, *1031*
Weisman, S. A., *549*
Weiss, E., 281, 284, 286, 287, *301*, *302*
Welch, L., 480, *501*
Wellman, B. L., 656, *689*, *690*
Wells, F. L., 181, *213*, 215, 227, 231, 233, 235, *251*, 314, *332*, 897, 898, *920*, 973, 974, 975, 976, 983, 984, 989, 993, 994, 996, 998, 1000, 1001, 1006, *1032*
Wells, W. R., 469, 470, 473, 476, 484, 487, 488, 494, 497, *501*
Welti, J., *1087*
Wentink, E. A., 589, *617*
Wentworth, M. M., 898, 902, *921*, 974, 975, 984, 985, 1016, *1032*
Werner, A. A., 608, *617*, *618*, 884, 885, 891, *910*, *921*, 1153, *1162*
Wernicke, C., 550, *581*
Wertham, F., *549*, 560, *581*, 875, *921*
Wertham, F., 560, *581*
Wertheimer, F., 23, *48*, 533, *549*, 863, *921*
West, R., 783, *793*
Westphal, K., 276, *300*, *549*
Wexberg, E., 768, *793*
Wheeler, R. H., 51, *68*, 81, *135*
Wheeler, W. M., 98, *135*, *549*
Whelen, M., 866, *910*
Whipple, G. M., 514, *525*
Whisler, L., 199, 200, *213*
Whitaker, J. E. F., 596, *616*
White, A. D., 1108, *1162*
White, B., 273, 278, *300*
White, B. V., *860*
White, M. M., 471, *501*
White, R. C., 757
White, R. K., 317, *331*, 671, *688*
White, R. R., 183, 187, *213*
White, R. W., 472, 478, 492, 494, 495, 496, *501*
White, W. A., 1016, *1032*
Whitehead, A. N., 717, *735*
Whitehill, J. L., 1130, *1160*
Whitehorn, J. C., 270, *298*
Whiting, J. W. M., 92, 99, 100, 106, 119, 125, *135*, *735*
Whitman, R. H., 186, *213*
Whittenberger, J., 597, 598, *612*
Whitwell, J., 874, *921*
Whitwell, S. R., 270, *298*

SUBJECT INDEX

Aspiration level—*Continued*
  success and failure and, 337, 361, 373
  theoretical considerations, 356
  valences in experiment on, 356
Assessment,
  personality,
    autobiography in, 143
    case study method of, 160
    methods of German military psychol-
      ogists, 149
    objective test methods of, 214
    projective methods of, 214
    rating methods, 150
    Rorschach test in, 227
    subjective methods of, 139
Association,
  adjustment as, 52
  deterioration and, 999
  free,
    method of, 216
    personality study and, 999
    psychoanalysis and, 1138
    therapy and, 1138
  hysterical disturbances in, 1135
  introversion-extraversion and, 1000
  principle of,
    gravitation, 52
    personality traits and, 50
  tests, 181
  word, 100
    Kent-Rosanoff test of, 223, 1000
    psychotic responses in, 999
Associative learning, personality in terms
  of, 49
Associative reinforcement, 82
Asthma, psychogenic factors in, 286
Asylum, Bethlem, 1109
Atavism, criminality and, 529, 802
Atrophy, infantile, 634
Attacks,
  epileptic, 938
  grand mal, 940
  Jacksonian, 940
  petit mal, 940
  psychic equivalent, 941
Attainment level, aspiration level and, 335
Attainment score, 335
Attitudes,
  abstract or categorical,
    brain lesions and, 1012
    conception of, 903
    criticism of, 904
    schizophrenia and, 892, 895, 902
  dependency, 97
  family, generalization of, 93
  interpersonal and intergroup, 729
  measuring, interview method of, 146
  public, habit systems and, 57
  tests of, 190
Audiogenic attacks, 416 (See "Seizures")
Aura, epileptic, 940
Authority,
  balance of love and, 660
  parental, patterns of, 659
  therapy and, 1116
Autobiography, personality assessment with,
  143
Autopsychic, 550
Autosuggestion, 1112
Aviators, anoxia in, 585

B

Babcock test, 979
Baby (See "Infant")
Balinese,
  child-mother relationship among, 729
  culture of, 94, 728
Basal ganglia, 558
Behavior,
  abstract vs. concrete, 902
  antisocial, inheritance of, 518
  associative learning and, 49
  catastrophic, 1010
  catatonic, blood acidity and, 593
  changes of, gratification amount and, 671
  contextual determination of, 73
  cooperative and competitive, 105
  criminal, theories of, 798
  disorders of,
    children's, 761 (See also "Childhood,
      behavior disorders of")
    epileptic, 938
    experimental, 389, 413 (See also "Ex-
      perimental neurosis")
    functional, concept of, 552, 576, 861,
      995
    organic, 550
    psychoneurotic, 833
    psychotic, 861
  dynamics of,
    aspiration level and, 333
    clinical approach to, 255
    hormone factors in, 609
    psychoanalytic, 261, 307
  effects of,
    classification, 76
    definition, 70
  multidetermination of, 1170
  neurotic (See "Neurosis," "Psychoneu-
    rosis," "Behavior, disorders of")
    adjustment by, 59
  obsessive, harsh infantile training and,
    93
  periodic, regulation of, 603
  physiology of, research difficulties, 582
  primary group, 738
  profiles of, heredity and, 516
  schizophrenic, variability of, 886
  sexual, children's, 786
  social, hormone factors and, 609
  specificity of,
    generality and, 40
    personality and, 52
  trial-and-error, 80
  variability of, 80
    learning and, 54
Behaviorism, children's disorders and, 769
Beri-beri, 563
Bible, disorders described in, 1107
Bibliotherapy, 1130
  bibliography of, 1162
Biochemistry, functional psychoses and,
  866
Biotypes, Jaensche's, 20
Birth,
  anoxia during, 587, 636
  maternal respiration and, 588
  psychological significance of, 87
  sucking at, 637
  trauma of, 87, 700

Conflict—*Continued*
  reactions to, rat's, 413
  reward and, 80
  spread of, 462
  subculture, minority groups and, 681
  theoretical assumptions, 433
  theory of, stimulus-response, 437
  types of, 432
  typical situations of, 264
  vacillation in, 437
Conscience, 110, 111, 653, 822
Consciousness, 550, 857
Constipation, 279, 642
Constitution,
  anthropometric quantification of, 529
  children's disorders and, 776
  crime and, 534
  definitions of, 927
  differences of, childhood development, 662
  experiences of self and, 666
  functional psychoses and, 863
  Gall's work, 527
  interests and, 653
  Kretschmer's types of, 530
  morphological index and, 528
  physique and temperament, 544
  present-day problem of, 537
  psychology and,
    American and British research, 531
    Beneke's contribution, 529
    French contribution, 527
    German contribution, 529
    Italian contribution, 528
  psychopathic, criteria of, 827
  temperament and, history of, 526
  types of,
    clinical symptoms and, 534
    disease and, 530
    megalosplanchnic, 528
    microsplanchnic, 528
    psychopathologic, 842
    psychosis and, 533
Constitution Clinic, 535
Constitutional factors in personality, 526
Constitutional psychopathic inferior, 922
  interpretations of, 931
  symptoms of, 924
Context, behavioral, 73, 654
  emotional, 257
Control, constructive conscious, 1121
  primary, 1121
Convulsion,
  audiogenic, in rat, 414
  epileptic, 940
  metrazol, 588
Cooperation, 105
  migration effects on, 738
  tests of, 176
Cooperativeness,
  determinants of, 105
  intelligence testing and, 975
Coordination, community, programs for, 1185
Copulation, hormonal vs. neural factors in, 603
Correlation, heredity and, 509
Cortex,
  cerebral (See also "Brain," "Cerebrum")
    areas of, 556
    multiple sclerosis of, 778

Covariance, analysis of, heredity and, 509
Cretinism, endocrine factors in, 603
Crime,
  conflict and, 811
  definition, 795
  ecological factors in, 740
  motivation of, 805, 809
    conflict in, 814
    family factors in the, 816
    frustration in, 816
    group identification and, 816
  prevention of, 1184
  psychopathic personality and, 810
  psychosexual development and, 818
  theories of, 798
Criminal personalities, 794
Criminality,
  behavior dynamics of, 804
  ego in, 932
  heredity and, 803
  rates of,
    rural-urban, 740
    urban ecology and, 741
  stigmata of, 802
    nonexistence of, 803
  super-ego and, 813
Criminals,
  affect poverty in, 810
  anatomical characteristics of, 801
  atavism in, 529, 802
  delinquents and, definitions, 795
  epilepsy among, 809
  feeblemindedness among, 805
  intelligence of, 806
  neuroses among, 809
  personal characteristics of, 818
  psychoses among, 805
Crying,
  effort and control of, 89
  fixation of, 89
Cue, learning and, 82
Culture,
  adolescent instability and, 720
  ambivalence and, 72
  American, child training in, 98
  Appollonian vs. Dionysian, 720
  Balinese, 94
  calendar in, 730
  child treatment and, 93
  conflict and, 72
  description of, psychiatric concepts in, 721
  ecology and, 736
  emotional intensity and, 720
  habit-systems and, 57
  heterogeneity and standardization in, 723
  historical approach to, 716
  infantile learning and, 93
  interdependence of behavior patterns in, 717
  introversion-extraversion in, 720
  learning and, 732
  migration effects on, 737
  Mohave, 115
  Navaho, 95
  organismic approach to, 717
  organization within, 715
  personality and, 714
  Plains Indians', 721
  psychoanalysis and, 724
  relativity of abnormality in, 721

Development—*Continued*
  organism-environment field and, 653
  prenatal, 622
  psychosexual theory of, 622
  spurts of. sensitivities with, 665
Deviance, cultural, 722
Devil, possessed with, 1108
Diabetes, behavior effects of, 590
Diagnosis,
  brain tumor,
    EEG in, 1044, 1068
    Rorschach test in, 556
  personality,
    artistic expression in, 244
    attitude scales in, 190
    case records in, 163
    character tests in, 174
    drawing and painting in, 243
    interest-value tests in, 190
    objective tests in, 170
    play technique in, 239
    projective methods in, 214
    rating methods in, 150
    temperament tests in, 179
    thematic apperception test in, 235
    word-association in, 223
  sociometric, 158
Diet,
  behavior and vitamin, 597
  behavior effects of, 595
Dilantin, epilepsy therapy and, 949
Discipline,
  dependency and, 101
  individual reactions to, 662
  love and, 101
    balance of, 660
  punishment in, 101
Discrepancy score,
  definition, 335
  generality of, 347
  realism and, 372
  reference frames and, 371
  trait correlates of, 351
  variability of, 353
Discrepancy, vocabulary vs. mental age,
    982
Discrimination, conflict in, 452
  generalization and, 454
Disease,
  conceptions of,
    astrological, 1107, 1109
    Hippocratean, 1108
  habit-effects from, 593
  mental (See also "Disorders, mental,"
    "Disorders, neuropsychiatric," "Dis-
    orders, behavior," "Psychoneuroses,"
    "Psychoses")
    concepts of functional, 552, 576, 861,
      995
    ecology of, 738, 747
    neurological approach to, 547
    prevention of, 1164
    social organization and, 752
  Tay-Sachs, 777
  venereal disease, urban ecology and, 751
Disorders,
  affective, 873
  attack, 939
  behavior, children's, 761
    brain damage and, 777

Disorders—*Continued*
  behavior, children's—*Continued*
    classification of, 765
      dynamic, 552
    complaint factor in, 763
    EEG in, 1085
    motivation and, 767
    parent-child relationships and, 703
  chemogenic, 552
  conduct, 826
  constitutional development and, 922
  endocrine, EEG in, 1080
  genogenic, 552
  histogenic, 552
  mental (See also "Disorders, behavior,"
    and "Disease, mental")
    adolescence and, 701
    ecological factor in, 738, 747
    migration and, 738
    neurological approach to, 547
    prevention of, 1164
    rates of, ecological variations in, 739,
      740
  neuropsychiatric, vitamin deficiency and,
    563
  personality,
    multidetermination of, 1170
    prevention of, 1164
  psychogenic, 552
  sexual, children's, 785
  theory of, psychoanalytic, 1137
Disorganization, social,
  mental disorder and, 752
  mobility and, 738
Displacement, 263, 317, 461
Dissociation, 1109
  abreaction and, 1111
  Zuñi culture and, 721
"Distributive analysis and synthesis," 1126
Dobuans, paranoia in culture of, 722
Dog, conditioning in, 389
  experimental neurosis in, 390, 403
Dominance, cerebral,
  inheritance of, 514
  nature of, 572
Drawing, diagnostic uses of, 243, 992
Dreams, 218
  analysis, 588
  content of, 221
  emotional stress in, 222
  Freud's theory of, 219
  functions of, 222
  interpretation of, 1136
  summary on, 223
  symbols in, 221
Drive,
  habit adjustment and, 59
  instinctual,
    Freudian libido and, 623
    pleasure and, 623
  reduction of, reward as, 79
Drugs,
  EEG and, 1065
  psychiatric use of, 1122
Dynamics of behavior, clinical approach to,
    255
Dynamisms,
  conversion, 848
  displacement, 263, 317
  fixation, 307

Family,
attitudes from generalization of, 93
emancipation from, 127
interpersonal relations in, 656
personality formation in, 109
Fantasy,
children's, 675
schizophrenic, 890
Fatigue,
anoxia, 586
extinction and, 586
Feeblemindedness,
anoxia at birth and, 588
EEG and, 1052, 1086
inheritance of, 506
neurology and, 565
Feeding,
infancy and, 91
infantile frustration of, effects on adult,
Fetus, EEG in a, 1054
Fever, EEG and, 1054
EEG in a, 1054
learning in a, 87
Field,
child-in-total-, 654
leaving, 443
organism-environment, 653
theory, criticism of, 73
Figures,
ambiguous, manic-depressive psychosis
and, 994
Wertheimer's, 990, 992
Fixation, 264, 623
emotional reinforcement and, 60
experiments on, 308
instrumental act, 308
stimulus-response theory of, 308
Flatterer, Theophrastus', 12
Flexibility, waxy, 895
Fluency, statistical factor f, 39, 988
Food,
excessive intake and behavior, 596
selection of, homeostasis and, 602
Forgetting, unpleasantness and, 321
Formulation, symbolic, aphasia as, 1009
Friendliness, experience producing, 673
Fröhlich's syndrome, 779
Frustration,
definition of, 380
direction of reaction to, 384
ego-defensive reactions and, 383
extrapunitive reactions to, 383
impunitive reactions, 383
intrapunitive reactions, 383
need-persistive reactions to, 383
obstacles classified, 382
patterns of gratification and, 657
primary, 280
reactions to,
catastrophic, 386
childhood forms of, 670
infant differences in, 664
types of, 383
regression and, 314
secondary, 280
stress situation and, 380
symbolic processes and, 386
tension and, 380
theory of, 379
therapy and, 387

Frustration—*Continued*
tolerance, 385
complexes and, 386
early experience and, 387
symbolic processes in, 386
therapy and, 387
Function, nervous,
anoxia and, 585
lobotomy and, 551
Functional autonomy, instance illustrative
of, 55
Functional, definitions, 551, 552, 576, 861,
995
Functionalism, adjustment and, 71

G

Ganglia, basal, behavior and lesions in, 558
Gastritis,
anoxia and, 586
emotion and, 273
Gastrointestinal disturbances, 273
General paralytica, senile psychosis and,
560
Generalization,
family attitudes, 107
principle of, 452
Genes, linkage of, 511
Genetics (See "Heredity")
Genito-urinary function, emotional effects
on, 292
Genogenic, 552
Gestures, 146
Goal, defined, 56
Goat, conditioning in, 391
experimental neurosis, 391
Gonads, behavior and castration, 607
Gradients,
approach vs. avoidance, 449
conflict and, 433, 440
generalization, 452
temporal and spatial, 441
Grand mal, 940
dilantin and, 949
EEG in, 942
Gratification, frustration and, patterns of,
657
Group status, 158 (See also "Popularity")
personal preference method, 158
sociometry, 158
stability of, 159
Groups, minority, childhood experience in,
680
Growth (See also "Development")
patterns of, 666
spurts of, sensitivities created by, 665
Grundfunktion, 562
Guidance, child, 1177
Guilt, time of punishment and, 111
Gyri, malformations of, 564

H

Habit,
acquired drives as, 56
acquisition of, principle of association
and, 53

Hypnosis—*Continued*
moods induced in, 480
nature of,
early theories of, 491
goal-directed behavior, 492
psychoanalytic theory of, 491
regression, 491
suggestion and, 496
negative afterimages in, from visual hallucinations, 477
neurotic attitudes produced in, 489
phenomena of, historical, 474
psychopathology of everyday life in, 480
sleep and, 478
subject's control in, 483
suggestibility and, 475
uses of,
experimental, 479
therapeutic, 473, 490, 1110
Hypnotism, 466
definition, 466
history of, 472
technique of hypnotizing, 467
Hypnotist, definition, 466
Hypnotizability,
deference and, 472
factors which contribute to, 495
incidence of, 470
individual differences in, 470
motivation and, 472
personality traits related to, 471
Hypnotizing, 467
suggestions in, 468
Hypoglycemia, effects of, 589
Hypomania, 876
Hypothalamus, emotion and, 576
Hypothyroidism, cretinism, 603
metabolism in, 604
Hysteria, 848
brain waves in, 947
conceptions of, Galen's, 1108
conversion in, 848
dynamics of ideas in, 1135
EEG in, 1084
fumigation against, 1107
inheritance of, 519
organic pathology in, 849
pseudo-psychotic symptoms, 850

I

Iatmul, 107
mother-child relationship among, 729
Identification, 109
socialization and, 125
Idiocy,
amaurotic, 777
inheritance of, 522
Illness, physical, behavior sequels of, 777
Imagination, expanding, experience and, 675
Imaginative productions, interpretation of, 214
Imbecile, moral, 799, 824
nonexistence of, 801
Imbecility, inheritance of, 522
Imitation, socialization and, 108, 125
Immunology, 535
Impulse, *Trieb* and, 72 (note)
Incompatibility, response, types of, 456

Index,
alpha, 1044
efficiency, 896
schizophrenic and, 898
set, 994
Individual, delinquent, 812
Inertia,
dichotomous typologies and, 17
perseveration and, 17
Infancy,
anxiety in, evidences of, 628
bad habits in, 91
bladder control in, 91
brain development in, 628
constipation in, 642
crying in,
effort and, 89
fixation of, 89
dependency attitudes in, 97
discipline in, 91
early,
birth trauma and, 87
oxygen need in, 630
personality development in, 87
EEG in, 1053
experience during, personality, 622, 645
later, 91
marasmus in, 634
maternal cathexis in, 631
morality in, 93
need for contact in, 628
oral experience in, 637
patterning of behavior in, 621
pleasure strivings of,
fixation of, 623
neurosis and, 622
sex perversions and, 622
psychosexual stages of, 623
punishment in, 91
responsive treatment and learning in, 88
satisfaction in, 88
kinesthetic, 631
schedules of care in, criticism, 89
socialization in, 85
tensional states of, 628
Infant,
attachment to mother, factors in, 631
mother's relationship to, 631
newborn,
brain in, 629
characteristics of,
behavioral, 629
physiological, 629
psychological, 628
circulation in brain of, 628
feeling need in, 630
sucking in, 628
rules for handling, 86, 91, 647
Infection, focal, functional psychosis and, 865
Inferiority,
constitutional psychopathic, 826, 923
crime and, 801
inheritance of, 928
organ, children's disorders and, 770
Inflammation, brain, 558
Inheritance (See "Heredity")
Inhibition, retroactive, generalization in, 455

Initiative,
  sexual, cultural variations in, 726
  tests of, 184
Injury,
  birth,
    anoxia and, 587
    maternal respiration and, 588
  brain.
    abstract ability and, 386, 1115
    aphasia and, 1011
Ink blots, interpretation of (See "Rorschach test")
Insanity,
  constitutional, 823
  moral, 799
Instinct, *Trieb* and, 72
Institutions, social, ecology and, 741
Insulin,
  blood sugar regulation and, 601
  injections of and learning, 589
  psychiatric use of, 1123
Integration,
  adjustment and, 74
  principle of, 73
Intelligence,
  adolescent conflicts and, 699
  adopted vs. unadopted sibling, 513
  anoxia and, 586
  criminal, 806
  EEG and, 1061
  inheritance of, 511
  normal adult, 973
  parent-child resemblance in, 512
  quotient, 173, 771, 781
  tests of (See "Tests, intelligence")
  twin differences in, 512
Interests, 190; sex hormones and, 694
Interpretation, psychoanalytic, 256, 726
Interview, conference method of, 144
  framed, 147
  group, 149
  improvement of, 145
  personality appraisal in, 144
  psychoanalytic, 327
Introjection, 263
Introversion-extraversion,
  hypnotizability and, 471
  hysteria vs. psychasthenia and, 17
  morphological types and, 17
  schizophrenia vs. mania and, 17
IQ, 173, 771, 781
Irritability, anoxia and, 587

J

Jaensches biotypes, 20
Judgment, anoxia and, 585
Jurisprudence, medical, 799

K

Katzenjammer Kids, 101
Kinship, systems of, 718
Korsakoff's syndrome, memory in, 1008

L

Language,
  adjustment and, 84
  aphasic disorders of, 573, 1009

Language—*Continued*
  brain injury and, 572
  learning and, 84
Laryngitis, emotional factors in, 289
Latency period,
  imagination in, 127
  psychoanalysis and, 127
  sex-repression in, 125, 126
Latency, reflex, psychosis and, 995
Laughter, child differences in, 664
Law, criminal, habitual, 823
Leadership,
  appraisal of, 147
  assessment of, 149
Learning,
  animal experiment and, 99
  anticipatory responses in, 83
  associative,
    adjustment as, 52
    personality and, 49
    personality traits and, 50, 62
    reinforcement in, 53
  childhood experience and, 670
  cues in, 82
  discrimination in, 81
  extinction and, 81
  fatigue in, 81
  fetal, 87
  generalization in, 81
  higher order, conditioning as, 83
  language and, 84
  psychosomatic patterns and, 671
  punishment in, 80
  reinforcement in,
    association as, 53
    associative, 82
    conflict and, 80
    gradient of, 80
    reward and punishment as, 80
    stimulation reduction as, 79
    time of reward and, 80
  socialization and, 85
  theory of,
    anthropology and, 85
    reward, 78
  trial-and-error, 670
  variability of response in, 54
Lesions,
  brain,
    EEG and, 1076
    timing and effects of, 561
    types of pathology in, 554
  cerebral, factors in effects of, 554
Level of aspiration (See "Aspiration
  level")
Level, phylogenetic, cerebral localization
  and, 565
Libido, 117
  conception of, 623
Life history,
  adolescent period in, 128, 691
  critical stages in, 122, 847
  economic struggle and, 131
  infancy in,
    early months of, 86
    late, 91
  latent period in, 127
  marriage in, 130
  maturity in, 131
  parenthood period in, 130

Motivation,
  animal experimentation and, 99
  derived, theory of, 83
  emotion as, 83
  frustration as, 381
  goal, 56
  habit as, 55
  learning theory and, 79
  monopolistic theories of, 767
Movements, occular, 998
Mundugumor, 727
  sexual aggression among, 726
Music ability,
  inheritance of, 513
  tests of, 198
Mutism,
  catatonic, 895
  deaf, inheritance of, 515

N

Narcolepsy, 786
Nature, human,
  variability vs. universality of, 719
Navaho, passivity of the, 95, 96
Needs,
  classification of, 381
  growth, mother's personality and, 658
Negativism,
  catatonic, 895
  children's, 672
  infantile, mothering and, 633
Neighborhood, children's disorders and, 775
Neologisms, 894
Nervous system,
  behavioral function of, 551
  diseases of and behavior, 594
  integration of, 551
  levels of integration in, 550
  physiology and, 584
Neurasthenia, 854
Neuritis, alcoholic, 563
Neuroembryology, 622
Neurology,
  brain and mind in, 550
  clinical, EEG in, 1068
  conditioned reflexes and, 551
  lobotomy and, 551
  war injuries and, 551
Neurosis (See also "Psychoneurosis")
  adjustment in, 59
  anxiety, 853
  character, psychopathic personality and, 931
  cardiovascular, 284
  children's, 786
  conversion, 848
  crime and, 809
  esophageal disturbances in, 275
  experimental,
    activity records in, 394
    conditioned reflex method and, 389
    discovery of, 389
    etiology of, 393, 395, 402
    gastrointestinal disturbances in, 408
    human and, 405
    manifestations of, 402
    neuromuscular symptoms of, 405

Neurosis—*Continued*
  experimental—*Continued*
    Pavlov's description of, 390
    precipitating maneuvers, 402
    respiratory symptoms in, 407
    sexual disturbances, 409
    spread of conflict in, 463
  infantile pleasure strivings and, 622
  infantile, reactivation of, 124
  inheritance of, 519
  problem of choice of, 265
  psychoanalytic classes of, 1137
  skin, 289
  stomach, 275
  transference, 1141
Non-representative, test performances, 976
Normal persons,
  EEG in, 1045
  mental age in, 973
Nosology, children's behavior disorders and, 765
Nursing,
  infantile, development and, 638
  initiating, 638
Nutrition,
  behavior and, 595
  excessive, effects of, 596
  intelligence and, 596
  motivation and, 596
  vitamin, behavior and, 597

O

Obesity, nutrition vs. energy output in, 597
Occipital lobe, 572
Oedipus complex, 127, 837
  cultural variations in, 727
Opinion,
  habit systems as, 57
  public, polls of, 58
  tests of, 190
Organic, functional and, 551
Orientation, goal, cultural variations in, 731
Overeating, emotional factors in, 596
Overprotection, ecology and, 753
Ovulation,
  endocrine regulation of, 601
  progesterone and, 609
Oxygen,
  infantile deficiency in, 630
  utilization of, homeostasis and, 601

P

Paralogical, 901
Paralysis, infantile, 594
Paranoia,
  definition of, 907
  Dobuan culture and, 722
  history, 904
  homosexuality and, 326, 905
  need for punishment, 905
  obsession and, 905
  paranoid condition and, 909
  projection in, 905
  schizophrenic, 895
  symptomatology of, 907

Personality—*Continued*
  quotient, definition, 173
  rating scales of, 150
  six-year-old, 677
  sociopathic, 931
  stroke and, 553
  structure of, 3, 10
    anthropology and, 720
    anti-trait theory of, 25
    colorimetrists' analogy and, 10
    factor analysis of, 28
    habit-systems in, 57
    Kahn's theory of, 933
    phenomenal appearance and, 10
    psychoanalytic theory of, 697
    specificity of, 25, 40
    statistical factors in, 39
    stimulus-response elements in, 25
    trait theory of, 40
    type of adjustment theory of, 65
  temperament and, 8
  tests of,
    adjustment, 180
    application of, 201
    attitude, 190
    character, 174
    classification of, 171
    evaluation of, 201
    history of, 171
    intelligence tests and, 172
    interest-value, 190
    list of factors in, 199
    opinion, 190
    personal interests, 192
    temperament, 179
  theory of,
    associative learning, 49
    dynamic, 69
    trait, 40
    type, 11
  traits of,
    argument against general, 61
    aspiration level and, 351, 353
    behavioral acts as, 50
    dichotomous typologies and, 16
    habits as, 54
    habit systems as, 61
    hypnotizability and, 471
    repetitiousness of behavior and, 54
    theory of, 40
  tripartite psychology and, 10
  types of,
    anthropology and, 720
    dichotomous, 16
    psychoanalytic, 623, 642
    theory of, 11
Persönlichkeit, 3
Personnel, placement of, 148
Perspective, ambiguous, manic-depressive
    psychosis and, 994
Persuasion, 1115
Perversion,
  infantile "naughtiness" and, 116
  infantile pleasure striving and, 622
  sexual, inheritance of, 519
Petit mal, 940
  dilantin and, 949
*p*H, behavior and, 591
Phantasy (See "Fantasy")
Pharmacology, psychiatric, 1122

"Phi" phenomenon, brain injury and the,
    991
Phobias, 851
  generalization of anxiety in, 463
  stimulus-response theory of, 463
Physiology,
  adolescent changes in, 692
  functional psychoses and, 866
  mental hygiene and, 1175
  psychological factors and, 583
  social factors and, 583
Physiotherapy, 1121
Physique,
  character and, 531
  components of, 531, 537
    ectomorphy, 540
    endomorphy, 540
    mesomorphy, 540
  dimensional concept of, 531
  dysplasia of, 530
  temperament and, 544
  types of, psychosis and, 533
Pick's disease, 562
Pig,
  conditioning in, 397
  experimental neurosis in, 399
  tantrum in, 397
Pituitary,
  deficiency of, learning and, 605
  water balance and, 601
Plasmas, *p*H of body, behavior and, 591
Play, technique of in diagnosis and ther-
    apy, 241
Pleasure,
  children's motor outlets for, 784
  polymorphous, 623
  sex and, 623
  sucking and swallowing, 624
Pleasure principle, 385
Pneumoencephalogram, 558
Police, crime prevention and, 1187
Poliomyelitis, 594
Popularity (See also "Group status"), 140,
    158
  personal preference method, 159
  sociometry and, 158
  stability of, 159
Possession, demoniacal, 1108
Posture,
  cultural variations in, 731
  schizophrenic, 891
  senile posture, 554
Potentials, brain, 1033
PQ, definition, 173
Practice, schizophrenic improvement with,
    1004
Pragmatism, 862
Prefrontal lobe, 567
Prejudice, habit systems and, 57
Preliterate, psychosis in the, 722
Pressure, intracranial and symptoms, 557
Prevention,
  absolute, 1169
  crime, 1184
  eugenical, 1174
  focusing effort in, 1169
  physiological, 1175
  presumptive, 1165
  principles of, 1173
  projects of, 1184

Q

Quotient,
  conceptual, 902, 981
  intelligence, 173, 771, 781
  personality, defined, 173

R

Race, inculcating consciousness of, 681
Races,
  differences among,
    ecology and, 739
    heredity and, 517
Rat, abnormal behavior pattern, 416
  audiogenic convulsions in, 413
  experimental behavior disorders of the, 413
  factors influencing susceptibility, 419
Ratings,
  personality, 140
    heredity and, 516
  scales, 150
    halo effects in, 152
    self, 156
    semantic factor in, 152
    summary on, 157
    validity of, 157
Rationalization, aspiration level and, 375
Reaction,
  delayed, 386
    long circuiting and, 574
  leaving field as defense, 443
Reaction-formation, stimulus-response theory of, 439
Reaction-time,
  heredity and, 514
  psychotic, 993
Realism, aspiration level and, 372
Reality, distinction between fantasy and, 675
Reality principle, 385
Reasoning,
  schizophrenic, 314
  therapeutic, 1113
Recommendations, 141
  check lists vs. free expression in, 142
  improvement of, 143
  validity of, 142
Redintegration, 55
Reeducation, therapeutic, 1127
Reference scales, 337
Reflex,
  carotid sinus, 947
  conditioned,
    experimental neurosis and, 389
    method of, 392
    neurology and, 550
    thyroidectomy and, 391
  patellar,
    latency in psychosis, 995
    psychosis and, 977
Regression, 264
  behavior theory of, 311
  deterioration and, 971
  experiments on, 311
  Freud's description of, 123
  frustration and, 314
  infantile, mothering and, 633

Regression—*Continued*
  instrumental act, 311
  interpretations of, 1018
  maze-analogue of, 124
  new experience and, 673
  primitivation in, 314
  repression and, 123
  schizophrenia and, 314
  stimulus-response theory of, 462
Reinforcement,
  fixation and amount of, 308
  gradient of, 80
  reward and punishment as, 80
  time of reward and, 80
Relationships,
  child-adult, 653
  interpersonal,
    cultural variations of, 732
    interrelations among, 653
Relativity, cultural,
  abnormality and, 722
  paranoid delusions and, 721
Relaxation,
  progressive, 1120
  therapeutic, 1118
Repetition compulsion, 838
Repression, 123, 262
  anxiety and, 321
  associative (after expulsion), 321
  experimental induction of, 323
  identification with parents and, 125
  measure of existing, 321
  regression and, 123
  unconscious and, 1136
Resistance,
  childhood, 672
    anxiety in, 762
  psychoanalytic, 328
Respiration,
  alkalinity and, 592
  disturbances,
    emotional, 286
    experimental neurosis, 407
    fetal, 636
    newborn, 635
Response interference (See also "Conflict")
  anxiety and, 451
  approach-avoidance gradients in and, 435
  associative, 459
  compromises in, 461
  dynamogenesis in, 460
  spread of, 463
  stages of learning and, 459
  types of, 456
Responsibility, moral, crime and, 800
Retardation, depression and, 880
Reward,
  learning and, 79
  punishment and, 80
  stimulation reduction as, 79
Rivalry, sibling, 653
  play technique and, 772
Role, habit-adjustment, 59
Rorschach test, 227
  brain tumor and, 556
  dichotomous typologies and, 19
  epileptic responses to, 960
  extratensive, introversive types and, 19
  method of scoring, 229
  nature of, 228

(Volume I—pages 1 to 618)